Healthy Living
Quality Life

You Have What it Takes to Have Your Desired Balance
Designed to Get Results

I would love to hear from you. Please send your comments about this book to me at the address below.

Healthy Living Quality Life: You Have What it Takes to Have Your Desired Balance Designed to Get Results

Cover by Leonard Mitchell

Printed in the United States of America

ISBN #9780986137136

Library of Congress Control Number: 2015912892

Requests for information should be addressed to:

Dear & Associates
P. O. Box 293985
Sacramento, CA 95829
joedd@frontiernet.net

Healthy Living Quality Life

You Have What it Takes to Have Your Desired Balance
Designed to Get Results

Table of contents

Contents

Introduction

<u>The Good Life</u>
Life is good when…

Different people at different times will have different opinions about what constitutes "the good life." Quality living is where life is good, most of the time. Life is focused, most of the time. Most of the time life is healthy. Most of the time life is balanced and most of the time lifestyle is consistent with quality living. Most of the time, one area of your life is affected by other areas of your life. This book identified ten areas of life on which to focus: physical and mental health, financial security, family togetherness, spiritual connection, work and/or school, social connection, civic involvement, an area titled passion, purpose and vision and a final catchall area called personal initiatives, challenges and aspirations. Each of these ten areas is covered in a separate chapter.

Seldom is life the same every day. Most days, for me, life is great. Thank God! This book is about life and its various aspects, including the lifestyle you choose to follow. The lifestyle you choose to live is critical to your quality of life and ultimately, wellness or wellbeing.

Just about everything in life works together, each area of life affecting the other. Consequently a healthy, balance of the important areas of life is necessary. Lifestyle becomes critical in this discussion because it is the mechanism that can provide the consistency, maintenance and overall quality that is so important in our day-to-day existence.

I believe that you will be interested in reading this book based on three assumptions:

Assumption #1: Just about all areas of life affect the others. Everything tends to work together. I have identified 10 areas of life to be discussed in this book. Try making a list of any two of these areas that are not affected by at least one of the 10: (1) spiritual connection; (2) mental health; (3) physical health; (4) family togetherness; (5) vision, purpose, passion; (6) financial security/freedom; (7) work and/or school; (8) civic involvement; (9) social connection; (10) personal initiatives, challenges and aspirations.

Introduction

Assumption #2: A healthy balance of the areas of life that you value is important. Of the 10 areas covered in this book, I assume that a minimum of three is very important to you. Therefore, you want at least these three to be somewhat balanced, meaning that you are willing to share your time, energies and other resources on maintaining at least those three.

Assumption #3: Lifestyle plays a critical role in acquiring and in maintaining a healthy balance. Your overall lifestyle either helps or hinders the positive development of those areas that you say are important to you.

Even though the words "wellness" and "wellbeing" are mentioned sparingly, the concepts are foundational to the entire book. The words wellness and wellbeing were not commonly used back when I started gathering material for this book in 1975, soon after completing my doctoral dissertation at Northern Illinois University – Dissertation topic: *Investigating Factors of Success and Failure*. This concept of looking at all aspects of my life was bolstered in 1975 when I took a job with Success Motivation Institute (SMI) started by the late Paul Myer from Waco, Texas, now called Success Motivation International (http://www.successmotivation.co.nz). Since then, I have given workshops, presented seminars and otherwise developed materials that have evolved into what is currently being presented in *Healthy Living, Quality Life*.

My reasons for writing this book are many. One of the primary reasons, however, is to take personal responsibility for my life and my own wellness in terms of living a healthy, balanced life and lifestyle that will provide me and those around me with a quality and productive life. I also want to share what I know and what I could find through research about any possible connection between living a healthy, balanced life and lifestyle and having a quality life. As a counselor educator, I want to have for myself and provide for others a supplemental resource that is comprehensive and that covers all areas of a person's life. Usually the classes we teach cover a particular subject area related to counseling such as group, career and multicultural counseling, human development and assessment. This book will be a good supplemental resource for students to see how the subject being taught might relate to a broader context than the subject being taught, including such subjects as spirituality, mental and physical development, social, civic and other areas of life.

Another very personal reason for writing this book is because so many of my family members, friends and colleagues have lifestyles that I think are robbing them of a more quality life that I would love to have something that I can make them aware of that could be helpful. And finally, it would also be great to provide a single document that is based on the latest research and best practices that covers multiple areas of "health" concerns to everyone who is interested in having a quality life, including family, friends, students, potential clients and other professional mental health providers that can be added to their resource library.

Introduction

A Healthy, Balanced Life and Lifestyle

What I mean by a healthy, balanced life and lifestyle is to truly have an overall quality life, whereby most areas in life that are valued should be somewhat balanced much of the time. If I value physical and mental health, value financial and spiritual health and value family and work and/or school, then these areas of life should not be in complete disarray. Hopefully these and other areas of life that are valued are (or will be one day) somewhat together and those that are not are receiving at least some attention and my current lifestyle is congruent with that happening.

For example, if I spend all my time accumulating things for myself and other areas of my life, such as my physical health or family life, are getting little or no personal attention because my lifestyle is such that it does not "fit" into my day, then my lifestyle is unhealthy and out of balance. A more healthy and balanced lifestyle is one that provides attention to those areas in my life that I value. This is not to say that every area in my life that I value is okay, but it does mean that my lifestyle is such that those neglected areas that I value are at least getting some attention, or will be soon.

What I mean about a balanced lifestyle is that I have a regular system (built into my lifestyle) that allows for a regular (self) assessment of those areas in my life that I value – my spiritual health, physical, mental and financial health, family life, social and civic involvement, work and/or school life, including my personal vision, purpose and passion. As you can see, health is used broadly and not just for physical and mental well-being.

What separates the 'doer' from the 'Wannabe'?

Another reason that I wanted to write this book was to see if there is any way to differentiate the "doers" from the "wannabes" or "non-doers." Some people say they are going to get something done and they do it. Others find excuses, rationalizations, and otherwise procrastinate rather than getting done what they said they would get done.

The Third Part of this book deals with implementation. I have identified those elements that are most responsible for causing people to follow through or to act on things that they decided as goals to be accomplished. It would be great to know the difference between those people who get things done as opposed to those who don't. I wanted to know why some people get things done and why others don't. I wanted to identify the key elements or characteristics of the doers as opposed to the non-doers. In many cases, I was able to find some best practices that others have found to be helpful. For the most part, I found that life is what you make it! What you are willing to commit to, follow through on, get done and move on to the next issue.

You make it rough and it becomes rough. Make it easy, and it becomes easy. Life doesn't just "happen" by itself. Even when we are passively "letting" life go its own course, we are still in the driver's seat. It all depends on how you perceive certain situations and circumstances and your subsequent response to whatever situation is presented to you. On the one hand you have things in life to deal with that you had nothing to do with and no control over, and on the other hand, the situation is completely of your own making. In either case, the response is all yours.

Sometimes, oftentimes, we are not aware of the many and varied choices we have in just about every situation or circumstance. Some choices, at first glance might not seem to be choices at all. For example, faced with a gun-welding robber demanding your money or your life, you have a choice of handing over your money or not. Likewise, faced with your doctor's prognosis to stop smoking or die in 6 months, some smokers continue smoking. The first example is one where you had little or nothing to do with. The second example is of your own making. However, in each case, how you respond is your choice.

Take Charge of Your Life
It is my belief that the person who deliberately sets out to make things happen in his life that he wants to happen has a more fulfilling life than one who accepts what he is given. The young man who wants to become a newspaper reporter and goes through the trouble of learning about the academic requirements, internship experiences and generally, learning about the life and lifestyle of a newspaper reporter is more likely to have a fulfilling career than the person who does not put forth the effort to learn these things. Similarly, the recently laid off lawyer who finds herself in a situation with seemingly few job opportunities in the surrounding communities and little money and other resources to pay bills, can either actively work on improving her situation or face the possibility of having to lower her current standard of living.

Put up or shut up. Whether you are well off, poor, in good health or bad, you can either make your current and future situation better by actively taking charge, deliberately planning and following through with what you plan or you can make it worse by doing little or nothing. It is all up to you.

This book is about life and a way of living. I have decided to write it because I want to put on paper what I believe to be the way I try to live my life and maybe, just maybe someone else can benefit from that. I also want to share some of the "secrets" that some counselors use to advise people on strategies to a healthy, productive and rewarding life. Personally, I try to keep life as simple as possible. God is first in my life. I believe that as an active, devoted Christian, my life will be good and fulfilling if I follow what the Bible tells me about how I should live and relate with other people. I strive to treat others at least as well, if not better than I want to be treated. My ultimate goal in life is to try to imitate the life of my savior Jesus Christ.

Congruence
As you look at your life, why not be as honest as possible about what is really important. If God is important, how much time do you spend with God praying, reading His word, talking about Him, thinking about Him, and spending time with other Christians in church and at

Introduction

other times? If health is important, how much exercise do you get (in or out of the gym)? How much time do you spend paying attention to your diet? To what extent are you spending time working on keeping stress or worry out of your life? Do you "listen" to your body, get regular physical checkups and stay current on the latest health tips? How much quality time do you spend with family? Are family needs being met? The bottom line is, are you spending time on those things that you have decided are of the highest priority in your life? If not, then you need to consider making some changes and start doing more in those areas of priority.

An assessment needs to be made as to what is important in your life; where are you with your current schedule regarding your "stated" priorities. It might help to first relax and brainstorm on paper what your current priorities are, as of today, listing them in order of most important to least important. Next, estimate the amount of time you spend on each item first daily, then weekly. If the amount of time you actually spend on a certain item is vastly different from the position that item holds in your order of priorities, you need to consider going back and re-thinking your priorities or trying to figure out the mis-connect. Sometimes our "perceived" priorities are different from our "real" priorities. Our real priorities tend to be determined largely by where we spend our time.

Sometimes when we look at where we really spend our time, it becomes clear that much of the time is wasted or otherwise used in a non-productive manner. And, in most cases, that can be corrected relatively easily. Life is full of little shortcuts. One way to proceed might be to spend some time thinking about what we want to do and figuring out a way to do it. Many times we "lose" time in traffic, waiting in lines, waiting for others and performing certain activities that could wait and be done at a more opportune time. In most cases, we simply don't pay attention to the amount of time it is taking to do certain things.

Hang loose; follow your God-given spirit, first. Be yourself wherever possible as long as it is legal and ethical and no one else is harmed by it. Think positive; take the time to identify the top areas of importance and priority in your life. These things are part of your philosophy of life. I hope this book will be of assistance to you in finding the balance that works for you to have a healthy, quality life.

References
Myers, J. E., & Sweeney, T. J. (2007). *Wellness in counseling: An overview* (ACAPCD-09). Alexandria, VA: American Counseling Association.

SMI. (n.d.). *Success Motivation Institute*. Retrieved from http://www.successmotivation.co.nz

Acknowledgements

I would like to acknowledge just a few people who have been helpful through this process of getting the book published. My wife has put up with my taking time from our life to write the book in addition to the times she provided editorial suggestions and other assistance. Members of my men's support group helped with their prayers and verbal support, especially Minister Francis Moore who suggested some editorial changes. Perseus Poku, Staff Minister where I worship at St. Paul Missionary Baptist Church in Sacramento, CA was very helpful with my chapter on Spirituality. Les Holmes of Holmes Financial provided editoral support for the chapter on Finances. My professional colleagues from the American Counseling Association who have worked with me through the years and have gotten to know me provided editorial assistance.

I am especially grateful to Dr. Carol Bobby, President & CEO of CACREP and Dr. Craig Cashwell, University of North Carolina, Greensboro Professor and author of *Integrating Spirituality in Counseling* whose editorial comments and suggestions were extremely helpful. Leonard Mitchell of Artistic Graphic Design designed the book covers. Meredith Linden of Editorial Wizard provided copy editing assistance and Jerry Ward of i Street Press printed proof copies which allowed me a way of distributing hard copy proofs to colleagues and friends for feedback. Others at my church and at California State University, Sacramento provided support as well.

The concepts of "wellness" and "wellbeing" are foundational to my book. I acknowledge the work of the late Jane Myers, Thomas Sweeney, Bill Hettler, Melvin Witmer and others as revolutionary in counseling, mental health, psychology and other related fields. They are to be commended for their extensive contributions.

Just as I talk about the "ten significant areas of life," which encompass spirituality, mental and physical health, family, passion, purpose and vision, finances, work/school, civic, social and personal initiative, challenges and aspirations, they include all (or certainly most of) those areas into the concept of "wellness" and "wellbeing." Myers and Sweeney (2007) define wellness as: "a way of life oriented toward optimal health and well-being, in which body, mind, and spirit are integrated by the individual to live life more fully within the human and natural community. Ideally, it is the optimum state of health and well-being that each individual is capable of achieving" (Myers & Sweeney, 2007, p. 252).

Reference

Myers, J. E., & Sweeney, T. J. (2007). *Wellness in counseling: An overview* (ACAPCD-09). Alexandria, VA: American Counseling Association.

How to Get the Most from This Book

I recommend that you skim through the entire book first to see how Parts I, II, and III are organized. Start reading chapters one and two first, which are foundational to the entire concept of living a quality life – balance and lifestyle.

Next look over the next ten chapters to see which one would be a priority for you to work on. These chapters cover the basic areas of life: spiritual, mental, physical, financial, family, social, work or school, etc.

To have a healthy, quality life, you need your life to be balanced in reference to these ten areas. To maintain your balanced life, you must have a healthy and consistent lifestyle.

Another suggestion is if you are already in the process of working on an area in your life or have been thinking seriously about doing it, read that chapter and follow the suggestions made on how to get the most from this book. Act on what you've read!!

The next thirteen chapters are designed to help you focus on getting things done, specifically to implement any or all of the ten basic areas of your life.

Here it helps to tell the story about the difference between people who get things done and those who say they are going to but don't. Over my thirty-plus years of research, I have identified thirteen action words associated with success and getting things done. Each of these thirteen words is a chapter in this book. I suggest that you first identify which of these action words would be most helpful to you in getting done what you want to get done and read those chapters after you have identified an area in your life to work on.

Other suggestions
– Read the book as if I am speaking to you and you alone.
– Read with a goal in mind. Read it because it contains a piece of information that you need to move closer to one of your goals. Decide on what you're looking for before you read the (entire) book.
– Take Notes as you read. Write notes to yourself in the margins, at the beginning and end of chapters. Put an asterisk next to outstanding points you want to remember.
– Transfer your notes to a notepad. Don't let your ah-ha moments be left in the book to die. You'll refresh your memory by transferring them to another place and you'll have a library full of quality information and resources in no time.

According to John Michael Morgan (2013) from whom I got most of the "other suggestions" on the topic, Abraham Lincoln was an avid reader but he also devoted time for reflection to process what he learned. You'd be wise to develop this habit yourself. Try it for the next two chapters you read and notice the difference it makes. Remember that the value from this book comes from what you take and implement into your life.

Morgan, J. M. (2013). *How to get the most out of the books you read*. Retrieved from http://johnmichaelmorgan.com/how-to-get-the-most-out-of-the-books-you-read/

Chapter 1
A Balanced Life

More Balance, Less Stress

Life is in sinc; there's equilibrium; all sides are equal; working together; just right; life is good!

When life is balanced, no single area of life is in crisis. The reason for that is because each area of a balanced life is attended to, or at least looked at, on a regular, periodic basis. Balance provides peace of mind for a life of quality.

You might be one of those people whose life is pretty good, most of the time. When you look at the issues other people are having, you realize how your situation is in pretty good shape. While most areas in your life are just fine, the following are a few examples of areas worth looking at: your physical and mental health, finances, work or school, social life, civic involvement, spiritual connection and other areas of personal interest. This book has a chapter dedicated to each of these areas in addition to a chapter on passion, purpose and vision and one on personal initiatives, challenges and aspirations.

> *Have you ever thought about what a balanced life would look like?*

What would your life look like if it were completely balanced to your satisfaction in all areas? A common assumption, correct or not, is that having a balanced life is a good thing. What I mean by that is having your life in reasonably good and healthy shape (or at least working on it) in those areas that are important to you.

When's the last time you sat down and gave serious thought about what is really important to you and then looked at your schedule for the past several weeks/months to see how you have been spending your time and/or how you have dealt with the issue of balance? Oftentimes,

1

Chapter 1 – A Balanced Life

it's not until something gets out of hand, or an emergency or crisis shows up that we get a "wakeup call" and realize we should have done something differently. Why wait for the emergency or crisis situation? Why not at least look at how your life is or is not balanced such that those things that are important to you are, in fact, top priorities and are receiving the appropriate time and other resources to minimize your stress level?

A person whose life has balance is one who at least looks at or considers the various aspects of life. We will never have complete balance, but we can always strive to improve in those areas where we feel improvement would be appropriate. Most people have one, two or maybe even three areas in their lives that are well developed, or certainly more developed than other areas. In many cases, the areas of our lives that are most well developed are likely those areas we give more attention to and find easiest to spend time in or in those areas we feel we must make a high priority.

On the other hand, however, if any of the following examples remind you of your own situation, then your life is not balanced. Problems with the family budget? Spending too many hours at work or with school? Plagued with health issues? Can't seem to find time for your spiritual development, social or civic involvement and maybe you won't even consider finding time for a personal hobby or to follow up on the great idea you had months ago? These and other such circumstances are the result of an unbalanced life – too many things to do and not enough times in the day or week or month to get to them all.

According to Sirgy and Wu (2009, 2013) in their article "The Pleasant Life, the Engaged Life, and the Meaningful Life: What about the Balanced Life?," people have to be involved in multiple domains to satisfy the full spectrum of human development needs. Different life domains (health, spiritual, family, financial, work/school, etc.) tend to focus on different human developmental needs. More specifically, balance contributes to subjective well-being because subjective well-being can only be attained when both survival and growth needs are met.

The authors refer to Martin Seligman (2002), in his very popular book *Authentic Happiness* that says,

> *authentic happiness is derived from three major sets of experiences in life, namely experiencing pleasantness regularly (the pleasant life), experiencing a high level of engagement in satisfying activities (the engaged life), and experiencing a sense of connectedness to a greater whole (the meaningful life).*

These authors maintain that balance in life contributes significantly to authentic happiness, subjective well-being, or life satisfaction.

Chapter 1 – A Balanced Life

Most areas of our lives are interconnected, as was mentioned in the introduction. When your physical health is problematic, several other areas of your life are affected, similarly with your mental health, financial security and spiritual connection. Other areas of your life such as civic or social might not be affected at all at this time or possibly not as much. However, in the long run, they might be. Having balance in those areas that you see as priority is important for living a quality life.

Bhargava (1995) conducted a study in which subjects were asked to discuss life satisfaction of others. Most subjects inferred life satisfaction of others as a direct function of their satisfaction in multiple domains. They calculated happiness by summing satisfaction across several important domains—the more positive affect in multiple domains, the higher the subjective wellbeing.

Sirgy and Wu define balance as a state reflecting satisfaction or fulfillment in several important domains with little or no negative affect in other domains. They define imbalance as a state reflecting satisfaction or fulfillment in a focused domain (e.g., work, family) that ultimately leads to negative affect in other domains.

In their article Sirgy and Wu point out that research on imbalance between work and family roles has shown that work-family role conflict is associated with life dissatisfaction (e.g., Bedeian et al., 1988; Collins & Killough, 1989; Edwards & Rothbard, 2000; Fu & Shaffer, 2001; Lewis & Cooper, 1987; Parasuraman et al., 1992; Sekaran, 1986; Sturges & Guest, 2004; Wiley, 1987) as well as low marital and family satisfaction and symptoms of low mental and physical wellbeing (e.g., Bedeian et al., 1988; Parasuraman et al., 1992; Sekaran, 1986; Steffy & Ashbaugh, 1986; Wiley, 1987). The family-work conflict occurs when one domain consumes resources needed for another domain.

> *A person should not allow one life domain to overwhelm one's satisfaction or dissatisfaction with life. It is best to be invested emotionally in several domains.*

Marks and McDermid (1996) described a theory of role balance that suggests that people who have well-balanced role systems, which they conceptualize as full engagement in and enjoyment of all roles, have higher levels of wellbeing.

Doing so allows one to compensate for the dissatisfaction of some domains with satisfaction of other domains. Greenhaus, Collins, and Shaw (2003) completely agree.

Frisch (2000) addressed the issue of "putting all your eggs in one basket" by recounting the story of a patient named Carol. Carol put all her energy into caring for her children. Frisch assessed Carol's situation as putting all her emotional eggs in the one basket of family life.

Chapter 1 – A Balanced Life

> **"putting all your eggs in one basket" is a dangerous strategy**

because if things go wrong in Carol's family life, she is likely to feel depressed. And this is exactly what happened. She over-invested herself in the family domain. To overcome this problem, Frisch recommends the use of the "happiness pie." Overall happiness is the pie composed of particular slices that represent different domains of life such as family, health, finances, and the like. The entire pie represents overall happiness. Some slices are larger than others because they are more important.

A social psychologist and happiness researcher recommends:

> **"don't let your entire life hinge on one element" (Niven, 2000, p. 71).**

"Your life is made up of many different facets. Don't focus on one aspect of your life so much that you can't experience pleasure if that one area is unsettled. It can become all you think about, and it can deaden your enjoyment of everything else—things you would otherwise love" (p. 71).

In his book, *The Power of Resilience: Achieving Balance, Confidence, and Personal Strength in Your Life* (Brooks & Goldstein, 2004), co-author Robert Brooks mentions that A lot of people are having a more difficult time finding balance in their lives because there have been cutbacks or layoffs where they work. They're afraid it may happen to them, so they're putting in more hours. He says that people in this situation seem to not have much control in their lives, but they can do better by trying to focus on the things they do have control over.

> **Brooks suggests you focus your time and attention on things you can control.**

Balance is Relative
All things are not equal. Certain areas in most people's lives have higher priorities than do others. Many people put family above other areas and financial security is often in the top five.

In their book *Creating a Healthy Balanced Life* (2011), Sandra Negley and Ester Leutenberg say that living a balanced life is a process that happens moment-to-moment, day-to-day, and is filled with surprises and challenges. They insist that when we become more present in our daily thoughts and actions we can create a healthier, more harmonious balance and take personal control of our life. The book is divided into five chapters:

Chapter 1 – A Balanced Life

– The Mind Body Soul – balancing life begins and ends with the self. When an understanding of what lies within is established, a person can make choices and take action toward a healthier, more balanced way of living.

> *– Attitude – approaching life with a positive attitude allows us to be open to what each day brings and to acknowledge our many blessings. Living a healthy balanced life becomes a natural process when we approach each day with optimism and excitement.*

– Stress-less – stress is part of everyone's life. The goal to a healthy balanced life is not to eliminate stress, but to learn how to manage it by developing coping skills, simplifying, and creating an awareness of our responses to the world around us.
– Relationships – surrounding ourselves with people who help us make meaning out of our talents and strengths and who support us in sharing who we are in the world are critically important for living a healthy balanced life.
– Leisure/Recreation/Play – to stay healthy and balanced there has to be an outlet, a release for the mind and body.

> *Through recreation and play, this release can be witnessed by tears of laughter, exhaustion from physical movement or silence to focus the mind.*

Susan Smith Jones, who wrote the online article "Ten Steps to a Healthy and Balanced Life," agrees we must learn to live in the present in one of her 10 steps: Today is a new day. There is no other day like today. It is unique and special. It is also an opportunity to begin anew, to experience a clean slate, a new beginning — in this very moment.

> *Living in the moment is different from living for the moment.*

Don't compare the present with the past. Be fully present each moment – be mindful – and free yourself from the past. Take the wisdom and love you learned from all past experiences and let the rest go. What you give your attention to always expands and grows in your life. So choose to be positive, happy, and appreciative every hour of the day. Just by doing this, you become empowered. Jones's article can be found at: http://susansmithjones.com/10-steps-healthy-balanced-life.

My definition of balance might be seen as, symmetry, equally or proportionately weighted, no extremes on either side or in any area.

The proportions will shift at different times in life, which supports the need for periodic self-assessments. The proportions are determined by your priorities. For example, the following are the priority proportions I assigned to my life in November 2011 and again in July 2012 and two more times.

> ***Balance is to have (or at least strive for) optimum proportions in each area of life, that is, at any given time period of life.***

Example of my Life's Proportioned Priority (Total should be 100%)
(Proportioned November 17, 2011 and put in order of priority)
- Spiritual wellbeing –15%
- Mental wellbeing – 13%
- Physical wellbeing – 13%
- Family – 12%
- Purpose, Vision, Passion – 10%
- Financial wellbeing – 10%
- Work/school – 9%
- Personal initiatives, challenges and aspirations – 8%
- Civic responsibility – 5%
- Social – 5%

(Re-proportioned July 3, 2012 and put in order of priority)
- Spiritual wellbeing – 17%
- Mental health – 15%
- Physical health – 14%
- Family – 13%
- Personal initiatives, challenges and aspirations – 12% (complete book!!)
- Purpose, Vision, Passion – 8%
- Financial security – 8%
- Work/school – 6%
- Social – 5%
- Civic responsibility – 2%

(Re-proportioned July 1, 2014 and put in order of priority)
- Spiritual wellbeing – 17%
- Physical health – 16%
- Mental health – 15%
- Family – 13%
- Personal initiatives, challenges and aspirations – 11% (complete book!!)
- Purpose, Vision, Passion – 10%

Chapter 1 – A Balanced Life

- Financial security – 7%
- Work/school – 5%
- Social – 4%
- Civic responsibility – 2%

(Re-proportioned January 8, 2015 and put in order of priority)
- Spiritual wellbeing – 17%
- Physical health – 16%
- Mental health – 15%
- Family – 12%
- Personal initiatives, challenges and aspirations – 12% (complete book!!)
- Purpose, Vision, Passion – 9%
- Financial security – 8%
- Work/school – 5%
- Social – 4%
- Civic responsibility – 2%

1. What areas are most important to you at this time in your life?

2. How Do You Spend Your Time?
Whether we realize it or not,

> *the things that get most of our time are the things for which we have developed routines.*

Because we spend so much (consistent) time doing those things, they become a priority (deliberately, by accident or by coincidence). You might be surprised to discover how you spend your time. If you ever want to know, take any seven-day period and chart each day. You will need to make a self-assessment about every two hours or so rather than doing it only once or twice a day. Don't interrupt anything you are doing to document it, but do (the best you can) document those activities that you do mostly every day.

Chapter 1 – A Balanced Life

Consider the following example (and do the best you can):

Most of us have 4 to 6 hours of "discretionary" time to use as we please. How do you use yours? How many min./hours on each?

	Mon.	Tues.	Wed.	Thurs.	Fri.	Sat.	Sun.
Spiritual connection							
Mental health							
Physical health							
Family togetherness							
Vision, purpose, passion							
Financial security							
Work and/or school							
Civic involvement							
Social connection							
Personal initiative, etc.							

Other ways to look at balance

Balance is an ideal proportioning of your life such that you are aware of where you stand in each area, are relatively satisfied with the proportions, are aware of those areas needing work and are working on strengthening and building up the areas that are weak. Balance can be seen as a personal perspective as to where to place your priorities. It can also be seen as contentment with where you stand in those areas of your life that are important to you.

3. Balance is those proportions or configurations of priority you have allotted to the various segments of your life.

I have noted a few suggestions that others have found useful for finding balance in their lives.

Jerry Looper (2006), on the website of suite101.com, talks about balancing your life: "Five Steps to a Balanced Life:"

1) *Do a balanced life survey* (look at your life as you are currently living it, including all the areas that are important to you).

2) *Life feels in balance* and you'll feel less stress when you honor your values. To identify your most crucial values, make a list of what is important to your life. Not what's nice, but what must be in your life for you to be content? - examples might be love, fascinating work, honesty, or friends.

> *3) Passion brings balance: What do you love to do? What activities so capture your attention and energy that you lose track of time while doing them?*

4) *Strengths and balancing life*: Everyone has special strengths and talents. Your combination of special skills, interests, and inherent abilities make you unique.

> ***You have many competencies, but just a few unique strengths.***

5) *Say no and retain life balance*: Many people find it hard to say no, so they end up taking on tasks that interfere with the important aspects of their lives and then they feel resentful and guilty. Learn to say no politely and firmly.

Other Examples of Balance

Most people have enjoyed great successes in some parts of their lives, says Daniel Wood (2011) who wrote the article "How to Find Balance in Life." He went on to say:

> ***The problem is that most of us neglect some parts to succeed in others. Doing this corrodes your success and will over time start hurting your future chances.***

Wood has identified four major areas of life: Health, Family, Career and Finances. He insists that all aspects of your life work in tandem. Success in one area will spill over to another, but on the other hand neglect will destroy your success in any of the other areas of your life. Wood's answer to this issue is to set goals in each of the four areas and map out a plan to achieve them.

A strategy to deal with creating balance in your schedule is offered in an online article by Jen Uscher, WebMD Feature and reviewed by Hansa Bhargava, MD. The article is titled "5 Tips for Better Work-Life Balance," and can be found at:
http://www.webmd.com/balance/guide/5-strategies-for-life-balance

1. Build downtime into your schedule – When you plan your week, make it a point to schedule time with your family and friends and doing activities that help you recharge.
2. Drop activities that sap your time or energy. Many people waste their time on activities or people that add no value – for example, spending too much time at work with a colleague who is constantly venting and gossiping.
3. Rethink your errands. Consider whether you can outsource any of your time-consuming household chores or errands. Could you order your groceries online and have them delivered? Hire a kid down the street to mow your lawn? Have your dry cleaning picked up and dropped off at your home or office? Order your stamps online so you don't have to go to the post office? Even if you're on a tight budget, you may discover that the time you'll save will make it worth it.

4. Get moving. It's hard to make time for exercise when you have a jam-packed schedule, but it may ultimately help you get more done by boosting your energy level and ability to concentrate **Research shows exercise can help you to be more alert.** Brooks (Brooks & Goldstein 2004) said he has noticed that when he does not exercise because he's trying to squeeze in another half hour of writing, he doesn't feel as alert.

5. Remember that a little relaxation goes a long way. Don't assume that you need to make big changes to bring more balance to your life. Brooks suggest that you slowly build more activities into your schedule that are important to you, A few suggestions he makes is maybe you can start by spending an hour a week on your hobby of carpentry, or planning a weekend getaway with your spouse. Even during a hectic day, you can take 10 or 15 minutes to do something that will recharge your batteries.

> *"When your work life and personal life are out of balance, your stress level is likely to soar," is the subheading of an online article offered by the Mayo Clinic.*

The article, written by the clinic staff (July 12, 2012), is titled "Work-Life Balance: Tips to Reclaim Control," and can be found at: (http://www.mayoclinic.org/healthy-lifestyle/adult-health/in-depth/work-life-balance/art-20048134)

The Mayo Clinic article emphasizes that you start by evaluating your relationship to work and consider the consequences of poor work-life balance:

Fatigue. When you're tired, your ability to work productively and think clearly might suffer, which could take a toll on your professional reputation or lead to dangerous or costly mistakes.

Lost time with friends and loved ones. If you're working too much, you might miss important family events or milestones. This can leave you feeling left out and might harm relationships with your loved ones. It's also difficult to nurture friendships if you're always working.

Increased expectations. If you regularly work extra hours, you might be given more responsibility, which could lead to additional concerns and challenges.

Track your time. Pay attention to your daily tasks, including work-related and personal activities. Decide what's necessary and what satisfies you the most. Cut or delegate activities you don't enjoy or can't handle — or share your concerns and possible solutions with your employer or others.

Take advantage of your options. Ask your employer about flex hours, a compressed workweek, job sharing, telecommuting or other scheduling flexibility.

Learn to say no. Whether it's a co-worker asking you to spearhead an extra project or your child's teacher asking you to organize a class party, remember that it's OK to respectfully say no.

Leave work at work. With the technology to connect to anyone at any time from virtually anywhere, there might be no boundary between work and home — unless you create it.

Chapter 1 – A Balanced Life

Manage your time. Organize household tasks efficiently, such as running errands in batches or doing a load of laundry every day, rather than saving it all for your day off.

Bolster your support system. At work, join forces with co-workers who can cover for you — and vice versa — when family conflicts arise. At home, enlist trusted friends and loved ones to pitch in with child care or household responsibilities when you need to work overtime or travel.

Nurture yourself. Eat a healthy diet, include physical activity in your daily routine and get enough sleep. Set aside time each day for an activity that you enjoy.

Know when to seek professional help. Everyone needs help from time to time. If your life feels too chaotic to manage and you're spinning your wheels worrying about it, talk with a professional, such as a counselor or other mental health provider. If your employer offers an employee assistance program (EAP), take advantage of available services.

Remember, striking a healthy work-life balance isn't a one-shot deal. Creating work-life balance is a continuous process as your family, interests and work life change. Periodically examine your priorities — and make changes, if necessary — to make sure you're keeping on track.

Balance Changes Over Time

As soon as you think you have plugged up one hole in your unbalanced life, another area needing more attention becomes evident. Consequently, it becomes apparent that balance does not necessarily maintain the same proportionality throughout life. Balance is usually based on your priorities at any given time.

> *Usually there are one or two areas in your life that will play a dominant role over other areas, by design.*

In my own life, the role that spirituality plays in my life will likely always be more of a priority than any other and will therefore take more of my time. The goal of balance is to set an ideal level of proportionality and to strive to reach and maintain it until the next life focus shift is appropriate.

When I think of balance, I think of moderation, average, non-extreme and middle of the road. As I reflect on my current life and state of affairs, I might ask myself, do I have any (or many) extreme negatives or extreme positives in any of the 10 areas? To help me get a visual picture of what that might look like in each of the 10 areas, I have provided what I'm calling a continuum in each area.

On a scale of 1 to 10, where would you fall in each area of your life? Generally speaking, the positive side of the continuum might be seen as 10 and the negative side, 1. These examples are extremes.

Chapter 1 – A Balanced Life

Continuum (examples) in each area

	Positive	Negative
1. Spiritual connection	Saint	Sinner
2. Mental health development	Peaceful	Stress laden
3. Physical health development	Physically healthy	Sickly
4. Family togetherness	Well-rounded family members	Family in disarray
5. Passion, purpose, vision	Focused	Clueless about life
6. Financial security/freedom	Financially secure	In deep debt
7. Work/profession	Loves chosen career	Hates job
7. Education/school	Doing very well in school	High school dropout
8. Civic involvement	Very involved in community	Not involved at all
9. Social connection	Very healthy social life	Not socially involved
10. Personal initiatives, challenges, aspiration	Actively pursuing personal goals	Never pursues goals

These examples are from the author's point of view. You might provide your own examples once you get the idea of the point being made about positive and negative areas of your life. There is no such thing as a perfectly balanced life, and there never will be.

Another visual I have found to be helpful as I reflect on where I stand with having a well-balanced life and lifestyle has been an assessment of risk factors and protective factors that I have in each of the 10 areas of my life.

Again, if I were to give the two extremes a numerical value, generally speaking, "protective factors" would be 10 and "risk factors" would be 1. Based on those numerical values, where would your life fall in each of those areas?

(Risk factors are those traits, conditions, situations, and episodes that tend to produce negative outcomes, cause problems and exacerbate life stressors, thereby keeping individuals from maximizing their positive potential.)
(Protective factors are those traits, conditions, situations, and episodes that appear to alter – or even reverse – predictions of negative outcome and enable individuals to circumvent life stressors – Norman Garmezy.) (Source of materials: "Fostering Resiliency in Kids: Protective Factors in the Family, School, and Community" by Bonnie Benard, 1991)

Chapter 1 – A Balanced Life

Examples of Protective Factors and Risk Factors in each area (continued)

	Protective Factors	Risk Factors
1. Spiritual development	Reads Bible, goes to church, has faith in Christ	Dishonest, lies and cheats, inconsiderate
2. Mental development	Solves problems, uses mind a lot, does mental exercises	Dislikes reading, watches hours of TV, uses mind sparingly
3. Physical development	Exercises regularly, eats healthy diet, does not stress a lot	Couch potato, eats any & everything, worry a lot
4. Family togetherness	Does things together, good communication, worship together	Argues with family a lot, independent living, lack common interests
5. Passion, purpose, vision	Focused, self-directed (leader), original thinker	Dependent on others, overly cautious, seldom finishes things
6. Financial security/freedom	Good saving habits, pays bills on time, reads financial magazines	Bad credit, in deep debt, spends foolishly
7. Work/profession	Likes the job, career matches education	Work not at all satisfying, long commute to work
7. Education/school	Successful in school, enjoys school	Doing poorly in school, hates going to school
8. Civic involvement	Volunteers time, member of committees/boards, involved in community	Thinks volunteering is for suckers, spends time selfishly, not involved
9. Social connection	Spends time with friends, likes picnics, likes to talk AND listens	Self-indulgent, inconsiderate, not friendly
10. Personal initiatives, challenges, aspiration	Has hobbies, loves learning new things, positive thinker	Has no hobbies, learning is boring, worry a lot

REFERENCES
Chapter 1 – "A Balanced Life"

Bedeian, A. G., Burke, B. G., & Moffett, R. C. (1988). Outcomes of work-family conflict among male and female professionals. *Journal of Management, 14*, 475–491.

Benard, B. (1991). *Fostering resiliency in kids: Protective factors in the family, school, and community.* Washington, DC: Western Regional Center Drug-Free Schools and Communities.

Bhargava, S. (1995). An integration-theoretical analysis of life satisfaction. *Psychological Studies, 40*, 170.

Brooks, R., & Goldstein, S. (2004). *The power of resilience: Achieving balance, confidence, and personal strength in your life.* New York: McGraw-Hill.

Cheah, R. (2011). How to live a balanced lifestyle. Retrieved from http://todayhealthandfitness.blogspot.com/2011/03/how-to-live-balanced-lifestyle.html

Collins, K. M., & Killough, L. N. (1989). Managing stress in public accounting. *Journal of Accountancy, 167*(5), 92–96.

Edwards, J. R., & Rothbard, N. C. (2000). Mechanisms linking work and family: Clarifying the relationship between work and family constructs. *The Academy of Management Review, 25*, 178–199.

Frisch, M. B. (2006). *Quality of life therapy: Interventions to improve the quality of life of patients with emotional or physical problems.* New York: Wiley.

Fu, C. K., & Shaffer, M. A. (2001). The tug of work and family—direct and indirect domain-specific determinants of work-family conflict. *Personnel Review, 30*(5-6), 502–522.

Greenhaus, J. H., Collins, K. M., & Shaw, J. D. (2003). The relation between work-family balance and quality of life. *Journal of Vocational Behavior, 63*, 510-531. http://www.polyu.edu.hk/mm/jason/doc/Greenhaus-Collins-Shaw%202003%20JVB.pdf

Lewis, S. C., & Cooper, C. L. (1987). Stress in two-earner couples and stage of the life cycle. *Journal of Occupational Psychology, 60*, 289–303.

Looper, J. (2006). *Five steps to a balanced life.* Retrieved from http://suite101.com/article/five-steps-to-a-balanced-life-a6456

Marks, S. R., & McDermid, S. M. (1996). Multiple roles and the self: A theory of role balance. *Journal of Marriage and the Family, 58*, 417–432.

Mayo Clinic Staff. (n.d.). *Work-life balance: Tips to reclaim control.* Retrieved from http://www.mayoclinic.org/healthy-lifestyle/adult-health/in-depth/work-life-balance/art-20048134

Mind Tools.com (n.d.). *The wheel of life, finding balance in your life.* Retrieved from http://www.mindtools.com/pages/article/newHTE_93.htm

Negley, S. K., & Leutenbert, E. (2011). *Creating a healthy balanced life.* Duluth, MN: Whole Person Associates.

Niven, D. (2000). *The 100 simple secrets of happy people: What scientists have learned and how you can use it.* New York: Harper.

Parasuraman, S., Greenhhaus, J. H., & Granrose, C. S. (1992). Role stressors, social support, and well-being among two-career couples. *Journal of Organizational behavior, 13*(4), 339–356.

Sekaran, U. (1986). *Dual-career families.* San Francisco: Jossey-Bass.

Seligman, M. E. P. (2002). *Authentic happiness: Using the new positive psychology to realize your potential for lasting fulfillment.* New York: The Free Press.

Sirgy, M. J. & Wu, J. (2009). The pleasant life, the engaged life, and the meaningful life: What about the balanced life? *Journal of Happiness Studies, 10*, 183–196.

Chapter 1 – A Balanced Life

Sirgy, M. J. & Wu, J. (2013). The pleasant life, the engaged life, and the meaningful life: What about the balanced life? *The Exploration of Happiness* (pp. 175-191). Part of the Happiness Studies Book Series. Berlin, Germany: Springer.

Smith Jones, S. (n.d.). *10 steps to a healthy and balanced life.* Retrieved from http://susansmithjones.com/10-steps-healthy-balanced-life

Steffy, B. D., & Ashbaugh, D. (1986). Dual-career planning, marital satisfaction, and job stress among women in dual-career marriages. *Journal of Business and Psychology, 1*(2), 114–121.

Sturges, J., & Guest, D. (2004). Working to live or living to work? Work/life balance early in the career. *Human Resource Management Journal, 14*(4), 5.

Uscher, J. (n.d.). *5 tips for better work-life balance.* Reviewed by Hansa Bhargava, MD. Retrieved from http://www.webmd.com/balance/guide/5-strategies-for-life-balance

Wiley, D. L. (1987). The relationship between work/nonwork role conflict and job-related outcomes: Some unanticipated findings. *Journal of Management, 13*, 467–472.

Wood, D. (2011, March 30). *How to find balance in life.* Retrieved from: http://www.pickthebrain.com/blog/how-to-find-balance-in-life

Chapter 2
Healthy Lifestyle

Live like there is no tomorrow and there might not be a tomorrow. Your lifestyle determines the length and quality of your life.

Lifestyle

- Your lifestyle is the way you live pretty much every day, your "style" of life, the way you approach life in every aspect of your life, how you choose to live and/or can afford to live, the way of life to which you have become accustomed.

- Your lifestyle is a collection of the habits you have chosen to follow for your life – it includes how and with what you fill up your day; what foods you eat, activities you do, and habit patterns you tend to follow. In other words, lifestyle is a compilation of your living conditions, habits, rituals, customs, styles and tastes.

> *Lifestyle can change as you get older, more (or less) financially secure or as your living environment changes.*

Your lifestyle changes as the different areas in your life change. For instance, financially, it changes as your finances change; socially, it changes as your relationships change; spiritually, it changes as your spiritual commitments change; professionally, it changes as your professional involvement changes and so on. Lifestyles seldom remain (exactly) the same over a long period of time.

Generally speaking, however, for most of us, lifestyles are fairly constant and even though they do change, they do so infrequently.

Chapter 2 – Healthy Lifestyle

Lifestyle, according to the World Health Organization (WHO; 1998), is a way of living based on identifiable patterns of behavior determined by the interplay between an individual's personal characteristics, social interactions, and socioeconomic and environmental living conditions. The WHO definition suggested that patterns of behavior are continually adjusted in response to changing social and environmental conditions. It also suggested that efforts to improve health by people changing their lifestyles must be directed not only at the individual, but also at the social and living conditions that contribute to the behavior or lifestyle. There is no one "optimal" lifestyle. Many factors determine which way of living is appropriate for each individual.

In an article titled, "Including Lifestyle medicine in undergraduate medical curricula," Phillip et al. (2015) cited the World Health Organization as predicting that by 2020, two-thirds of diseases worldwide will be the result of poor lifestyle choices. Fewer than 50% of US primary care physicians routinely provide specific guidance on nutrition, physical activity, or weight control.

Importance of Lifestyle

If quality and length of life are important, then having a healthy lifestyle would be paramount. Having information about what a healthy lifestyle means to you is one of the first things to be explored with people who advise you in the various areas of your life such as your physician, nutritionist, spiritual leader, therapist, spouse, trusted friends and personal confidant.

Whether you are consciously aware of it or not, you are currently living a certain lifestyle that you have been living for a while or just recently changed. The regular routines, daily, and/or weekly activities you do can positively or negatively affect just about every area of your life including physical, mental, spiritual, financial and others.

> *Learn to develop healthy habits early that can be carried on for a lifetime, i.e., balanced diet, regular physical and mental activity, sufficient rest, stress management and regular physical checkups.*

Minimizing stress in your life is critical to a healthy lifestyle, as is developing effective coping skills. Developing good, positive relationships early in life with people who model appropriate behavior is also very important.

What is a Healthy Lifestyle

There are certain lifestyles that are more conducive to a healthy life than are others. Having a lifestyle that provides for balance is often one that is preferred, even if it is not the easiest to accomplish or maintain. A balanced lifestyle requires constant self-assessment and continuous re-evaluation of your life. Once a reasonably balanced lifestyle is in place, then your attention should go toward the maintenance of that balance at least until it becomes a part of your regular routine.

Sometimes it is helpful to write down certain elements of your current lifestyle to be compared with a preferred set of lifestyle elements.

Elements of Lifestyle

A number of elements play a part in determining lifestyle, such as:
  - the resources you have available
  - personal taste
  - living arrangements, including whether you are living alone or with others
  - your upbringing
  - financial, educational and social status
  - personal preferences
  - goals in life dictate your lifestyle
  - in addition to many other factors.

Other examples of a healthy lifestyle include
  - One where you have the capacity to enjoy close, intimate ties to other people.
  - Becoming aware of what you enjoy doing that could turn into a career goal, a hobby or an occasional social activity.
  - Knowing your temperament and in what environments you feel most comfortable working.
  - A good way of being (for me) is to get by with as little as possible. Don't "need" much to be okay. When you get more, it's a bonus.
  - Another thing that has worked for me has been the Fridays each week my wife and I take as being "our day," not to be disturbed or interrupted by anyone for anything short of an emergency.

Having a healthy lifestyle is not always about losing weight, even though maintaining a healthy weight level is important.

Maintaining a healthy diet by eating sufficient portions of fruits and vegetables, drinking plenty of water and staying away from unhealthy fatty, sweet and processed foods is more important. Incorporating some kind of regular exercise is as critical as eating a healthy diet. Fitting exercise into your daily schedule is not as difficult as you might think. It only takes some creative thinking, a positive attitude about doing it and a consistent habit pattern with the will to follow through. Maintaining a sufficient level of exercise can be accomplished without changing much with your current routine. A few obvious examples include walking whenever the opportunity presents itself, taking the stairs when possible and adding an active hobby to your regular routine.

Prevention is Key

Another obvious behavior that leads to a healthy lifestyle is getting regular annual physical checkups. Preventative measures are often the goal of regular physical checkups even though early detection of medical problems is just as important. Catching a health problem early can mean the difference between life and death. Not catching a problem early can oftentimes lead to multiple problems that could have been avoided.

> *Navigating the maze of healthy meals, physical activity and low-stress living is a life-long endeavor.*

The process of behavioral changes that will lead to the adoption of a healthy lifestyle is long and tedious. It should be undertaken with a positive attitude and a strategy to change one behavior at a time. This "race" is a long-distance run, not a sprint.

Managing Stress

According to Suzanna Smith and Joe Pergola (2006) from the University of Florida, "Stress Management: Ways to Cope," we must learn to manage stress. Stress is a normal part of living. They give three major steps to keep daily stress from becoming a problem:
- take time to relax
- talk with friends, and
- learn to keep a positive outlook.

Research shows that adults who are optimistic maintain higher levels of mental and physical health than those who are more negative. The two researchers say there seems to be a self-fulfilling prophecy at work: when a person sees a stressor as a problem or crisis it is likely to become a crisis because he or she feels unable to cope. But when a person sees an event as something that can be managed, he or she is likely to act quickly to solve a problem before it exhausts her or his energy. In other words, how people perceive the situation influences how they react.

> *Reframing a situation can sometimes help provide a different perspective. Smith and Pergola say that it is not clear because what enables some people to see a glass half full others see it half empty.*

Outlook may be affected by the person's sense of autonomy and control—feeling independent and in control of daily life. People who feel like they are in control are more likely to believe they can handle a situation and are able to prevent it from becoming stressful. People who look at a situation as something that can be handled are confident that it will be resolved and take steps to confront or solve the problem; this may prevent the situation from becoming worse. On the other hand, however, even though it is important to maintain autonomy and control, it may also be important to recognize when situations cannot be controlled. When a situation is out of reach, the most effective coping strategy may be to change your outlook by letting go rather than by forcing a solution, say the two writers. A few examples are "determined" rather than "stubborn," and "attends to detail" as opposed to "picky." Sometimes taking stock of personal and family strengths and assets helps us appreciate the positive.

> *"thrifty" as opposed to "stingy," "a leader" rather than "bossy," "quiet" rather than "shy"*

"Lifestyle" and "Health" Connection

The term "healthy lifestyle" evolved from the idea that people's daily pattern of activities can be judged as healthy or unhealthy. A healthy lifestyle is generally characterized as a "balanced life" in which you make "wise choices."

In real life, lifestyle is a product of some combination of choice, chance and resources.

In the 1974 publication, *A New Perspective on the Health of Canadians: A Working Document,* Marc LaLonde (Minister of National Health and Welfare) was among the first to identify lifestyle as a determinant of health and illness. LaLonde (1974) defined lifestyle as: "The aggregation of decisions by individuals which affect their health and over which they more or less have control…. When those risks result in illness or death, the victim's lifestyle can be said to have contributed to, or caused, his own illness or death" (p. 32). This document came to be known as the Lalonde report and was presented in the House of Commons on April 1, 1974. The paper identifies two main health-related objectives: the health care system and the prevention of health problems and promotion of good health. It proposes integrating these two aspects of health in health care policy development and details five main strategies and 74 proposals to meet this objective.

> *Personal decisions and habits that are bad, from a health point of view, create self-imposed risks.*

Healthy Lifestyle to Improve Health

Renee Lyons and Lynn Langille (2000) prepared a report for Health Canada, Population and Public Health Branch on behalf of The Atlantic Health Promotion Research Center, Dalhousie University and The Canadian Consortium of Health Promotion Research Center. The report was titled *Health Lifestyle: Strengthening the Effectiveness of Lifestyle Approaches to Improve Health.* In the report, they provided several perspectives on lifestyle choice and generated a long list of determinants of lifestyle choice and other elements to be considered.

In it, they indicated that recent perspectives on the determinants of population health have broadened their understanding of the elements that constitute a healthy lifestyle. Following are the elements they noted:

- Effective coping – now widely recognized as an important determinant of health. Coping behavior helps people deal with the challenges and stresses of life without recourse to risk behaviors.
- Lifelong learning – part of a healthy lifestyle.

> - *Social activity and volunteering – now considered important components of healthy lifestyles.*

- Safety and security precautions – in the home, school, neighborhood, and workplace are part of healthy lifestyles in recognition of the influences of social relationships on health.
- Sense of purpose and meaning, spirituality, and hope – key elements of lifestyle.

They also noted that two other factors that have been taken into account when defining a healthy lifestyle are life stage (young, middle-aged, old) and perception of risk. Research from LaLonde (1974) suggests that individuals' perceptions of a healthy lifestyle may change with life stage. For example, research in gerontology has shown that healthy aging is associated with lifestyles that include social interaction, multiple roles, leisure activities, and an internal locus of control.

A person's identity, choices, and lifestyle are defined to a very large degree by the nature of that person's interdependence. If conceived on the basis of interdependence, a healthy lifestyle is understood less as acquiring strictly personal health skills, and more as acquiring competencies and an orientation to creating a mutually supportive environment for healthy living (Lyons & Langille, 2000).

Determinants of Lifestyle Choice

(1) Personal Life Skills: Life skills are abilities for adaptive and positive behaviors that enable people to deal effectively with the demands of everyday life. Personal life skills include literacy and numeracy, decision making and problem solving, creative and critical thinking, empathy, mutual support, self-help and advocacy, communication and coping.

> *Time stress makes "health enhancing" activities such as exercise even more stressful.*

(2) Stress – Time is a big stressor. People reported cutting out things that were important to them, such as hobbies, sports or other recreational activities, in order to meet the increasing demands of careers and families (Heart and Stroke Foundation, 2000).

> *Lack of control over work contributes significantly to ill health.*

(3) The influence of norms and culture on lifestyle choice: All human behaviors (including acts of resistance to the dominant culture) reflect, to some extent, the culture and values of a given society. Meals and other eating habits are statements about society and the things considered important in culture such as social class, family relationships, life-cycle issues and aesthetics. Community norms and standards of behavior also limit personal choice. Smoking may be a widely accepted means of coping with stress in low-income and immigrant communities, but be far less acceptable behavior in middle and upper income communities.

(4) Control and coherence (Marmot et al., 1997): High levels of stress reflect a lack of control over long periods of time, leading to anxiety and insecurity. The stress response causes a wide range of physiological changes, including depression, susceptibility to infection, diabetes, high blood pressure, and increased risk of heart attack and stroke (Bruner, 1997). Lomas (1998) argues that social support and social cohesion are much stronger influences on cardiovascular disease than individual medical care.

(5) Wallerstein (1992), author of "Measuring Community Empowerment: A Fresh Look at Organizational Domains" (2001), documented the role of powerlessness as a risk factor for disease and conversely the role of empowerment as a health promoting strategy. She concludes that control over one's destiny, or lack thereof, emerges as a disease risk factor.

(6) Belonging: A healthy social environment gives people a sense of belonging and of being valued. Social relations and support from family, friends, and communities are important contributors to health and reduce premature deaths. Social support is now recognized as an important determinant of health. It is important, however, not to idealize the community as a locus of effort without substantive challenges. Community may be a major resource in health, but it also can be a major challenge.

(7) Pleasure vs. "healthy" choices: choice is further influenced by human physiology. The human body finds sweet and fatty foods tasty, becomes easily addicted to certain chemicals, and seeks opportunities to rest. These biological characteristics cannot be easily overcome. Many healthy behaviors appear to require giving up pleasure.

> *People who live in conditions of poverty and/or insecurity are more likely to engage in risk behavior, such as smoking and making unhealthy food choices.*

The pleasure provided by these activities often serves as a distraction and respite from difficult life situations.

(8) Personality traits may influence lifestyle change. Personality traits such as optimism and self-efficiency contribute to healthy living. For example, research has shown that people who are optimists live longer (Mayo Clinic, 2002). If individuals do not think well of themselves, or do not feel that their efforts will make a difference, they may wonder, why engage in a healthy lifestyle? The concept of learned helplessness demonstrates this linkage. "Learned helplessness," suggests that people can be socialized to believe that their efforts will not pay off, that they cannot have any measure of control over their environment. If people believe they cannot exercise control over various aspects of their lives, they are unlikely to attempt changes to control their health or the health of their family or community.

(9) The overabundance of choice in society: Today's society provides us with an overwhelming array of choices, and conflicting information about what are the "right" choices. People are not well equipped to sort through the many conflicting messages from the media and other sources. They can be drawn to the appeal of immediate pleasure by engaging in behaviors that may carry long-term negative consequences.

Perspectives on Lifestyle Choice
(1) Opportunities and limitations for choice vary considerably – The range of choices available is a function of education, relationships, socialization, personality, physical and mental ability, situational factors and goals, and financial and other material resources. When health is viewed as more than individual choice, clear links between lifestyle choice and life circumstances emerge.

(2) Health for most people is not an end in and of itself – Health choices and lifestyles are embedded within daily activities (work, learning, parenting, relationships) such that they may not be identified specifically as "health" choices.

> *People maintain lifestyles that they know are unhealthy because they meet certain immediate needs.*

To address "unhealthy" lifestyle choices (those that have been scientifically proven to be harmful to your health), factors in the broader context of people's lives must be understood and changed to permit healthier choices. The University of Toronto's Centre for Health Promotion model of "Quality of Life" includes the concepts of being, becoming and belonging. This model suggests that people define quality of life as a goal, and health has to make sense for your efforts toward this goal (Raeburn & Rootman, 1998; Renwick et al., 1996).

(3) There are important linkages between lifestyle choice, determinants and health – The causes of health and disease are a complex interplay between individuals, social structural factors (i.e., socioeconomic status [SES], educational attainment and occupation), cultural

factors (e.g., health beliefs of various ethnic communities and peer subcultures) and exposures to particular risk and protective factors. Overlaying these factors are persuasive pressures from the consumer marketplace and information from diverse sources that may impinge on perceptions of health and risk. Healthy lifestyles in this wider context are defined by the interaction between choices and habits of individuals with different social locations, susceptibilities and exposure risks.

Frohlich and Potvin (1999) suggest that lifestyle choices are not random behaviors unrelated to structure and context, but are choices influenced by life chances.

Which Strategies are Effective in Fostering Healthy Lifestyles?

Stroebe and Stroebe (1995) offer one of the more comprehensive analyses of efforts to promote health lifestyles. This text examines models of health behavior and strategies that have been employed to modify health behaviors. Each model is explained together with its implications for interventions. The authors suggest that the predictive success of health models have not been more powerful than general models of motivation such as the theory of planned behavior.

They also suggest that scare tactics generally are not effective, in and of themselves, for changing behavior.

Cognitive models of lifestyle that have the most predictive value tend to include components such as beliefs about the outcome of the behavior, normative and other evaluations of outcomes, the costs and benefits of engaging in a certain behavior, motivation and perceived control.

Key elements of success include mounting small, instead of large-scale, projects and developing focused objectives.

Sustainability is a key factor – Often the "gold standard" intervention that may result in the most impressive outcomes is not sustainable over time or is too costly to implement beyond the pilot stage. Interventions must parallel the resources available to sustain them.

Generally, those with the fewest resources for a healthy lifestyle require the greatest investment.

Unless and until basic living needs are ensured, persons living in low-income circumstances (or people with low self-esteem or self image, or other personal problems) will be unlikely or unable to view healthy lifestyle as a priority. It is difficult for these groups to maintain a sustained commitment, since these activities are often simply added onto existing agendas with few additional resources (or opportunities for "release or respite").

Although information can increase knowledge, such interventions rarely have a strong impact on behavior. Information competes against a barrage of real-life experiences that promote conflicting messages. Efforts to provide information should be accompanied by (strong support) public policies and services that alter people's experiences (Stroebe & Stroebe, 1995).

The February 22, 2010 edition of *Time Magazine* featured "The Science of Living Longer" on their cover page. In that issue was a story entitled "How to Live 100 Years" (Alice Parker, 2010). In the article, it was reported that most people fall prey to chronic diseases that strike in mid- to late-life—conditions such as cancer, heart disease, stroke and dementia—and end up nursing disabilities stemming from these illnesses for the remainder of their lives. Centenarians, on the other hand, appear to be remarkably resilient when it comes to shrugging off such ailments; they seem to draw on some reserve that allows them to bounce back from health problems and remain relatively healthy until their final days.

According to the article, dozens of studies have investigated such individuals, with the goal of picking out the secrets to their salubrious seniority. Those analyses, however, have generally followed two separate, if parallel, tracks. The traditional approach has been to study the lifestyle and behavioral components of vigorous aging—the good habits, such as a healthy diet, regular physical activity and mental exercises that might keep the elderly vibrant through their golden years.

> *The New England Centenarian Study (Boston University, School of Medicine, 2010), which included 850 people entering their 100s, for example, has identified several behavioral and personality traits that seem to be critical to longevity, including not smoking, being extroverted and easygoing and staying lean.*

Another promising piece of the article was reported that only about 30% of aging is genetically based, which means that the majority of other variables are in our hands. Not only can getting such factors under control help slow the aging process before it starts, it can also help those who are already in their golden years improve their fitness and strength. Recent studies have shown, for example, that when seniors from ages 65 to 75 exercise with resistance weights, they can improve their scores on cognitive tests as well as their memory and decision-making. Other research in Germany found that regular physical activity lowers the risk of developing cognitive impairment in people over age 55.

The article concluded by stating that none of this means centenarian studies will produce a youth pill for the rest of us anytime soon—or ever, despite all the overblown claims made by hawkers of anti-aging compounds such as human growth hormone or resveratrol, an ingredient found in red wine. The goal, at least at first, will be merely to give us back some of what we lose from living a modern—which is to say, overfed, overstressed and underactive—lifestyle. "One misconception of aging research is that we are looking to prevent aging, says David Sinclair, a professor of pathology at Harvard Medical School. "What we are hoping to do is to come up with something that will give us a lifestyle that now only centenarians enjoy." More information on centenarians can be found at: http://www.bumc.bu.edu/centenarian. The *Time Magazine* article can be found at: http://content.time.com/time/covers/0,16641,20100222,00.html

Unhealthy Lifestyle

> *People with a lifestyle that is unhealthy tend to have more health problems, more incidences of not feeling well, longer periods of illnesses and a quality of life usually less positive than that of a person with a healthy lifestyle.*

Lifestyle and its elements are also to be within your means. When you try to live beyond the lifestyle you can afford (have time, money, capability or other resources for), problems are likely to follow.

Getting "stuck" in one job, especially one you think might be "just for a little while," can cause you to have what might be called a lifestyle dilemma. Some people look back after 10 years on a job (just for a little while) and find themselves "stuck" and cannot afford to leave. The lifestyle dilemma exists because they would have to make drastic changes to their current lifestyle in order to correct a situation that should never have gotten started in the first place.

A story about getting "stuck"

An example of this is a story about a physical therapy intern who followed his dream of doing the work he loves, helping people work through their physical ailments. With one more year to go on an internship working with other physical therapists in a very prestigious hospital, he runs into a few financial problems. Even though things look pretty good for his future employment there at the hospital, he leaves this position for one with the county office of research as a clerical assistant which pays quite a bit more than his internship stipend, but he does not like the work. This person plans to make these personal sacrifices and suffer in this position just for a little while until he can pay off a few pressing bills.

Three years later, he has moved into an assistant secretary position, which pays a little more than the clerical assistant, but he still does not like the work and hates going into the office five days a week. After another five years at the county position, he has built up an impressive resume with numerous clerical-type positions; he has moved up the support staff pay scale and now cannot afford to leave the county position because of a number of other bills he has accumulated. In other words, he is now "stuck" in a position he does not like, and his lifestyle would have to change dramatically for him to get back into his original area of interest of physical therapy. Too many people give up on their dream positions for just-for-a-little-while jobs that they get stuck in and cannot (or feel that they cannot) afford to leave. This is called a lifestyle dilemma.

A few of the other well known results of a bad lifestyle would include irregular visits to the dentist; not getting sufficient sleep; uncontrolled high stress levels; misuse and abuse of tobacco; alcohol and other drugs; and a lack of regular social and intimate interactions with friends, family and others.

> *The tragedy of life is not that it ends so soon, but that we wait so long to begin living* **(Mason, 1993).**

Lifestyle Diseases

"Make Positive Health Choices to Avoid Lifestyle Diseases" by Branda Polk (January 27, 2010) says, Lifestyle disease is defined as a disease linked to the way a person or group of people live and the choices they make every day. Unlike a bacteria or virus that make you sick over a short time or even overnight, the choices that lead to lifestyle diseases are made every time a person chooses what to eat, whether or not to be physically active, to drink alcohol, to smoke cigarettes or to take drugs. And, while the occasional "treat" food or a day on the couch won't lead to dire disease, a pattern of unhealthy choices day in and day out lead a person down this deadly path that severely limits and even kills the ability to live an abundant life.

Find other activities to get strong including running, weight training, fitness classes and swimming. Manage stress through prayer, journaling, and sharing your thoughts and feelings with trusted people.

> *Remember, just as you didn't wake up one day unhealthy, the solution will not be instant.*

But the solution and reversal begins one choice at a time. As you begin making positive health choices, you will begin to experience better health and have the opportunity to live abundantly in better health.

http://www.lifeway.com/Article/make-positive-health-choices-to-avoid-lifestyle-diseases

According to *Obesity* (2008), a research journal, if current trends continue, 86% of the adult American population will be overweight or obese by 2030. In Europe today, it's 35%. But many consumers are heeding medical advice and paying closer attention to their diets. Health and wellness will be a significant driver of consumer behavior for the next decade. The most sought-after packaging health claims are whole grains, high fiber, low-fat, low sodium, absence of trans fats, and low sugar. Consumers also want products with antioxidants, dietary fiber, omega-3 and probiotics.

Change or Suffer the Consequences

According to an article taken from the Healthy Lifestyle website (2007) – http://healthy-lifestyle.most-effective-solution.com/2007/11/24/americans-in-unhealthy-lifestyle-crisis/) – "Americans in Unhealthy Lifestyle Crisis" by David Robinson, being grossly overweight to obese and living an unhealthy lifestyle has become status quo in today's society.

> *It's almost acceptable, with most people generally feeling apathetic about being overweight.*

But if people don't change their unhealthy lifestyles, the consequences will cause them to pay dearly for it in more ways than they ever imagined.

They start out by asking a very serious question: If all these popular weight loss diets, books and programs being marketed over the years have really been effective, why has the number of people engaged in unhealthy lifestyles and becoming overweight to obese exploded to over 65% of the total population?"

That spells disaster, because that's a recipe for wasting your money, ruining your life and dying early!

Back in 1998, the author of the aforementioned article, Dr. David Robinson anticipated that the unhealthy lifestyles and growing numbers of obese Americans would result in the health insurance industry and legislators taking action soon.

The concept of "mandatory minimum health insurance," which was brought up in 2000 while on a speaking circuit locally in Boston's North Shore, received laughs and snickers, he states. In 2006, it became law in Massachusetts. In 2010, the Patient Protection and Affordable Care Act (PPACA), became law, commonly referred to as Obama care, health care reform or the Affordable Care act (ACA).

Not so shocking when you think about it. The majority of people value, have the time, money and desire for the new styles, new vehicle, movies, sports games, entertainment, new furniture, manicures, hair styles, new gadgets, vacations, lottery tickets, casinos, lunches and dinners out all week, and on and on. But when it comes to valuing, spending time, effort and money on regular exercise, proper nutrition, nutritional supplements, relaxation and meditation time, preventive health practices, and maintaining healthy lifestyles, the only things people always seem to have are excuses for why they can't or don't.

Chapter 2 – Healthy Lifestyle

A Crisis is Brewing

Such chronic conditions are preventable for the most part and are primarily resulting from unhealthy practices.

> *To say there is an urgent need for a brutally direct approach to the serious unhealthy lifestyle issues that most Americans need to address is an understatement.*

More than ever before, it is an absolute necessity that we wake up to the fact that if we do not change our unhealthy lifestyles, health insurers and legislators will institute more dramatic and costly changes to health insurance and care. This will be the brutally direct approach. The changes will be things such as using "Colossus" – the health insurance industry's well-kept secret – to track lifestyles and issue "Lifestyle Grades" to "Merit-Rate" health insurance premiums and impose "Lifestyle-Contributed Surcharges on Care."

It should already be obvious that this has begun, with the legislating of "mandatory minimum health insurance," and that a "New Order" of health insurance/care has dawned.

A study by a Michigan State University epidemiologist (Mathew Reeves) finds that very few Americans are doing all they can to maintain a healthy life, a situation he said could have dire consequences if it doesn't change.

> *A study: "Americans' Unhealthy Lifestyle is the Leading Cause of Death" (2005)*

The research of Mathew Reeves, which used nationally representative data from 153,000 adults and was published in the April 25, 2005 issue of the journal *Archives of Internal Medicine,* found that only 3% of the sample undertook four basic steps that define a healthy lifestyle:
- not smoking
- holding weight down
- eating right and
- exercising.

Reeves was surprised at how low that number was. However he feels that these results illustrate the extraordinarily low prevalence of healthy lifestyles in the U.S. adult population.

Few People Display Healthy Lifestyle Characteristics

Mathew Reeves (2005), an epidemiologist with the Michigan Department of Community Health, analyzed data obtained from the Behavioral Risk Factor Surveillance System (BRFSS), a national survey conducted in 2000 that looked at Americans' health habits.

Chapter 2 – Healthy Lifestyle

Of the 153,000 respondents, only 3% participated in all four of what are termed healthy lifestyle characteristics, or HLCs.

Looking at these HLCs individually:
75% of participants didn't smoke.
23% ate five or more fruits and vegetables everyday.
22% exercised regularly.
40% maintained a healthy weight, which is defined as a body mass index (BMI) of 25 or less.

Reeves said that women tended to follow more of the HLCs than men, as did whites compared with minority populations. But no one group, he said, came even close to what is necessary to lead a healthy life.

> *"It's important to note that the effect of following these (HEALTHY) lifestyles is greater than anything else medicine has to offer." (p. 856)*

> *"I don't know anything a doctor's office can do that would reduce your risk of diabetes or cardiovascular disease by 80 to 90 percent, which is what other studies have now shown if you: don't smoke, hold your weight down, eat right and exercise," says Mathew Reeves, a Michigan State University epidemiologist. "Before it was just common sense. But now we know from epidemiologic studies that if you do this there are huge benefits in terms of increased life expectancy, reduced disease risk, reduced medical costs and improved quality of life." (p. 856)*

The consequences of continuing down this path are evident in many ways, far beyond the issues of quality of life and life expectancy. One example, said Reeves, is the challenge to the nation's healthcare system.

"We have millions of people now going through adult life leading unhealthy lifestyles and a medical system that can treat illnesses and keep you alive longer than ever before," he said. "If we don't turn this around, the costs to society are going to be crippling."

A need for societal change?

According to Reeves, all the Healthy Lifestyle Characteristics (HLCs) defined in the study are controllable, so the million dollar question is, why are only a tiny minority of adults able to follow a healthy lifestyle?

He said that to get a large segment of the population to change its ways of living, it will be up to society as a whole to shift the cultural norms in terms of how it views healthy lifestyles.

Chapter 2 – Healthy Lifestyle

> *"We are not proactive enough in challenging people to incorporate physical activity and other aspects of healthy lifestyles into their everyday lives." (p. 856)*

We need a societal change so that leading a healthy lifestyle is seen as a necessary expectation, and not something only followed by some tiny minority – everyone needs to understand what we are giving up by not doing this."

The literature is replete with research showing the profound effect lifestyle has on a number of areas in our life, including longevity.

What research says about the impact lifestyle has on a person's life

A group of scientists and researchers from Harvard, other universities and government agencies completed a study that sheds light on preventable diseases and deaths in the U.S. The published article describing their research was titled "The Preventable Causes of Death in the United States: Comparative Risk Assessment of Dietary, Lifestyle, and Metabolic Risk Factors" by G. Danaei et al. (2009).

Highlights of the study findings are here noted

A number of modifiable factors are responsible for many premature or preventable deaths. For example, being overweight or obese shortens life expectancy, while half of all long-term tobacco smokers in Western populations will die prematurely from a disease directly related to smoking. Modifiable risk factors fall into three main groups. First, there are lifestyle risk factors. These include tobacco smoking, physical inactivity, and excessive alcohol use. Second, there are dietary risk factors such as a high salt intake and a low intake of fruits and vegetables. Finally, there are "metabolic risk factors," which shorten life expectancy by increasing a person's chances of developing cardiovascular disease (in particular, heart problems and strokes) and diabetes. Metabolic risk factors include having high blood pressure or blood cholesterol and being overweight or obese.

Also, they noted that the hazardous effects of some risk factors accumulate gradually after exposure begins and decline slowly after exposure is reduced. This is illustrated by results from trials that have lowered blood pressure and cholesterol and from studies in which some people quit smoking (Doll et al., 2004; Law, Ward, & Thompson, 1994).

The researchers (Danaei et al., 2009) extracted data on exposures to 12 selected risk factors from US national health surveys, and they obtained information on deaths from different diseases for 2005 from the US National Center for Health Statistics. Of the 2.5 million US deaths in 2005, they estimate that nearly half a million were associated with tobacco smoking and about 400,000 were associated with high blood pressure. These two risk factors, therefore, each accounted for about 1 in 5 deaths in US adults. Overweight–obesity and physical inactivity were each responsible for nearly 1 in 10 deaths.

Chapter 2 – Healthy Lifestyle

> ***Among the dietary factors examined, high dietary salt intake had the largest effect, being responsible for 4% of deaths in adults.***

Finally, while alcohol use prevented 26,000 deaths from ischemic heart disease, ischemic stroke, and diabetes, the researchers estimate it caused 90,000 deaths from other types of cardiovascular diseases, other medical conditions, and road traffic accidents and violence.

King, Mainous, and Geesey (2007) found that a midlife switch to a healthy lifestyle that includes a diet of at least five daily fruits and vegetables, exercise, maintaining a healthy weight, and not smoking results in a substantial reduction in mortality and cardiovascular disease over the subsequent four years. This benefit was independent of age, race, gender, socioeconomic status, a history of hypertension, hypercholesterolemia, diabetes, or previous cardiovascular disease.

The study adds three new features to the current literature: first, that the benefit of switching to a healthy lifestyle past age 45 was evident in short-term follow up of four years; second, that the beneficial impact of the changes occurred despite the relatively modest changes in health habits; and third, the healthy lifestyle was beneficial when compared to all persons with less than three healthy habits, not just in comparison to people with none or one habit. People adopting only three healthy habits experienced lower mortality but not fewer cardiovascular disease events over the same period.

The study's findings are consistent with recent research conducted in the Health Professionals Follow-up Study (Chiuve et al., 2006) and the Women's Health Study (Kurth et al., 2006).

The principal aim of this next study was to test associations between lifestyle behaviors in early midlife and cognitive decline over a 20-year period. Key findings were that a consistently healthy dietary choice was associated with slower memory decline, and consistently high or increasing physical activity from early midlife to midlife was associated with slower visual search speed decline, independently of each other lifestyle behavior and of social class of origin, childhood cognition, educational attainment, adult social class, or symptoms of anxiety and depression.

> ***Risk and protective factors for health can exert their most critical influences at different ages (Fratiglioni, Paillard-Borg, & Winblad, 2004).***

This is acknowledged by the life course approach and the hypothesis that positive lifestyle behaviors such as nonsmoking, being physically active, and choosing healthier diets may protect cognitive functioning and slow cognitive decline in later life. Fratiglioni, Paillard-

Borg, and Winblad (2004) identified key periods for potential risk and protective factors. Early life seems to be most critical for the development of cognitive reserve (learning and education) (Stern, 2009), when distal adverse influences (such as poor childhood social circumstances) contribute to the risk of adult disease or later life risk of dementia.

Lifestyle behaviors, including those that influence cardiovascular and metabolic risk, become more influential in midlife, although some, such as diet and physical activity, track back into childhood (Kuh & Cooper, 1992; Mikkila et al., 2004), whereas mental and physical activity patterns may continue to moderate these risks into later life (Iwasa et al., 2012; Menec, 2003). The fact that the lifestyle behaviors are modifiable implies that encouraging a healthy lifestyle may prevent or ameliorate cognitive decline and underlying cerebrovascular and cardiovascular risk factors (Esiri et al., 1999). Such interventions should take into account the relative beneficial effect of each independent behavior as well as their combined and cumulative effects.

> *There are several plausible biological mechanisms underlying associations between physical activity and cognitive decline.*

Physical activity reduces cardiovascular risk (Colcombe et al., 2003), increases cerebral perfusion, and facilitates neurogenesis (Cotman & Engesser-Cesar, 2002; Neeper et al., 1996; Prickaerts et al., 2004). In contrast, impaired blood flow in the midbrain (Edman et al., 2011; Zlokovic, 2011) is a risk factor for subsequent cognitive impairment and dementia. Of interest, physical activity was specifically associated with a slower decline in psychomotor speed, which is consistent with evidence that especially fit individuals respond faster to stimuli (Spirduso, 1980).

Our finding that maintained healthy dietary choice was associated with a slower rate of memory decline is consistent with the results of a recent systematic review, which highlighted that a diet high in saturated fat represents an increased risk of cognitive decline and subsequent dementia (Lee et al., 2010). The emphasis on identifying specific nutrients associated with cognitive ability in later life, such as antioxidants (vitamin C, E, carotenoids, and polyphenols), minerals, and dietary lipids (total, trans, and saturated mono- and polyunsaturated fats) (Shatenstein et al., 2012) is now giving way to studies of global diet quality indices for guidance in modeling dietary risk in relation to cognitive performance (Kesse-Guyot et al., 2011; Scarmeas et al., 2006).

Earl Ford (2011) wrote an article with the assistance of colleagues titled "Low Risk Lifestyle Behaviors and All-Cause Mortality: Findings from the National Health and Nutrition Examination Survey III Mortality Study" that highlights the significance of lifestyle on the health of an individual.

Chapter 2 – Healthy Lifestyle

> ***The main focus of the study emphasizes that lifestyle behaviors lie at the root of many chronic diseases (Danaei et al., 2009; McGinnis & Foege, 1993; Mokdad et al., 2004).***

Smoking, unhealthy diets, and sedentary behavior predispose numerous people to diseases that rank among the leading causes of death such as heart disease, cancer, stroke, and diabetes. The costs associated with these behaviors are enormous (Centers for Disease Prevention and Control, 2010; Colditz, 1999; Dall, 2009; Frazao, 1999).

The author points out that previous studies have generally examined the independent isolated effect of these lifestyle behaviors on a variety of adverse health outcomes.

> ***Yet, optimal health is only achieved by maximizing the number of healthy behaviors.***

Therefore, examining the joint effect of multiple lifestyle behaviors on health outcomes yields valuable insights into the improvements in health that are potentially achievable in populations.

Ford et al. (2009) show that starting around 2000, research appeared that examined the impact of multiple low-risk lifestyle behaviors on various health outcomes including cardiovascular disease (Akesson et al., 2007; Chiuve et al., 2006; Chiuve et al., 2008; Djousse, Driver, & Gaziano, 2009; Forman, Stampfer, & Curban, 2009; Kurth et al., 2006; Myint et al., 2009; Stampfer et al., 2000), diabetes (Ford et al., 2009; Hu et al., 2001; Mozaffarian et al., 2009), all-cause mortality (Hayeman-Nies et al., 2002; Khaw et al., 2008; King, Mainous, & Geesey 2007; Knoops et al., 2004; Kvaavik et al., 2010; Spencer et al., 2005; Van Dam et al., 2008), and mortality from cancer (Khaw et al., 2008; Kvaavik et al., 2010; Van Dam et al., 2008).

Few studies relating multiple low-risk life-style factors to all-cause mortality have been conducted in the United States or have included substantial samples of racial/ethnic minorities (Khaw et al., 2008; King et al., 2007; Van Dam et al., 2008).

In the United States, adherence to a healthy behavior in relation to the above factors decreased between 1988 and 2006: obesity in adults has increased from 28% to 36%, smoking rates have not changed, the consumption of five or more portions of fruit and vegetables a day has dropped from 42% to 26%, and the adherence to all five healthy habits decreased from15% to 8% (King et al., 2009). The societal and monetary costs of the negative effects of these modifiable behaviors are huge (Scarborough et al., 2011).

Chapter 2 – Healthy Lifestyle

While many studies have investigated the effects of single lifestyle behaviors on health (Adams et al., 2006; Doll et al., 2000; Hung et al., 2004; Warburton et al., 2006), the minimization of the individual risk of disease might only be achieved by a combination of these behaviors. In the last decade, several cohorts have been examined for the combined effects of lifestyle factors on various outcomes.

Therefore, we conducted a systematic review and a meta-analysis of prospective studies in order to quantitatively assess the association between the number of lifestyle habits (smoking, diet, physical activity, alcohol consumption, BMI) and all-cause mortality.

The present study is robust due to the very large sample sizes and long follow-ups of the underlying investigations. The multiple sensitivity analyses showed that effect sizes remained equal in subgroups of studies that were more homogenous in their definition of a healthy lifestyle or methodological aspects. All studies consistently found that the number of lifestyle behaviors adopted is associated with a decreased risk of mortality. A meta-analysis of prospective studies might represent the most accurate source of evidence currently available because randomized controlled trials, in which multiple lifestyle factor are modified, are limited by low adherence (Ebrahim et al., 2011) and prohibitive costs.

An interesting article appears in the *Journal of School Health* that talks about the article titled "Promoting health lifestyle behaviors: The heart smart discussion activity."

> *Judith McCalla et al. (2012) provides documented information about students health habits, encouraging students to discuss health-related information and set achievable behavioral goals to improve heart health.*

The health habits of high school students affect not only their current health but also their future risk for obesity and cardiovascular disease (Daniels et al., 2005; Kavey et al., 2003). National surveys revealed that the majority of US high school students do not consume the recommended daily amounts of fruits and vegetables or meet recommended aerobic physical activity requirements (Eaton, Kann, Kinchen et al., 2011; Kimmons et al., 2009).

Almost one third of high school students engage in three or more hours per day of sedentary activity (i.e., using computers for nonacademic purposes or watching television) (Eaton, Kann, Kinchen et al., 2011). The probability of students engaging in unhealthy lifestyle behaviors and failing to follow healthy behavior guidelines is increased when they are stressed, a common occurrence during high school (American Psychological Association, 2011). Because unhealthy lifestyle behaviors contribute to cardiovascular disease risk, prevention efforts for high school students are vital (Daniels et al., 2005; Gidding, 2006). Many cardiovascular risk factors, such as obesity, poor eating habits, and inactivity, are modifiable through behavior change.

Chapter 2 – Healthy Lifestyle

Two important aspects of encouraging behavior change are (1) creating awareness of the connection between lifestyle habits and health outcomes and (2) increasing self-efficacy for behavior change by setting achievable goals (Budd & Volpe, 2006; Schwarzer, 2008). Health education can improve students' wellbeing and reduce their cardiovascular risk (Kann, Telljohann, & Wooley, 2006).

This may be accomplished by engaging them in activities that promote healthy habits and helping them attain personal goals consistent with recommended healthy lifestyle guidelines (U.S. Department of Health & Human Services, 2011). The Heart Smart Discussion Activity was developed to provide information about heart health, good nutrition, physical activity, and stress management. It encourages students to discuss health-related information and set achievable behavioral goals to improve heart health.

On a more positive note, OptumHealth commissioned GfK Roper Public Affairs and Corporate Communications to conduct research that resulted in a white paper report titled "Motivating Factors for Healthy Lifestyles" (Karkula & Rosen, 2011). The survey included a base sample of over 1,000 respondents. Key findings were titled *Living a Healthy Lifestyle Is a High Priority for Most Americans*. Seven out of 10 respondents say that living a healthy lifestyle is important to them. They give Americans in general only a C or D grade for the healthfulness of their current lifestyles, but most graded themselves a bit higher. The same fraction of respondents (70%) believes that their health is mainly determined by their lifestyle choices, not just heredity.

REFERENCES
Chapter 2 – "Healthy Lifestyle"

Adams, K. F., Schatzkin, A., Harris, T. B. et al. (2006). Overweight, obesity, and mortality in a large prospective cohort of persons 50 to 71 years old. *New England Journal of Medicine, 355*, 763–778.

Akesson, A., Weismayer, C., Newby, P. K., & Wolk, A. (2007). Combined effect of low-risk dietary and lifestyle behaviors in primary prevention of myocardial infarction in women. *Archival of Internal Medicine, 167*(19), 2122–2127.

American Psychological Association. (2010). *Stress in America 2010*. Retrieved from https://www.apa.org/news/press/releases/stress/2010/national-report.pdf

Ardisson Korat, A. V., Willett, W. C., & Hu, F. B. (2014). Diet, lifestyle, and genetic risk factors for type 2 diabetes: A review from the nurses' health study, nurses' health study 2, and health professionals' follow-up study. *Current Nutrition Reports, 3*, 345–354.

Boston University, School of Medicine. (n.d.). *The New England centenarian study*. Retrieved from http://www.bumc.bu.edu/centenarian/

Bruner, E. J. (1997). Stress and the biology of inequality. *British Medical Journal, 314*, 1472–1476.

Budd, G. M., & Volpe, S. L. (2006). School-based obesity prevention: Research, challenges, and recommendations. *Journal of School Health, 76*(10), 485–495.

Centers for Disease Control and Prevention. (1999). *An ounce of prevention: What are the returns?* (2nd ed.). Atlanta, GA: Author.

Centers for Disease Control and Prevention. (2010). *Smoking and tobacco use*. Retrieved from http://www. http://www.ncbi.nlm.nih.gov/pubmed/21900875

Chiuve, S. E., McCullough, M. L., Sacks, F. M., & Rimm, E. B. (2006). Healthy lifestyle factors in the primary prevention of coronary heart disease among men: Benefits among users and nonusers of lipid-lowering and antihypertensive medications. *Circulation, 114*(2), 160-167.

Chiuve, S. E., Rexrode, K. M., Spiegelman, D., Logroscino, G., Manson, J. E., & Rimm, E. B. (2008). Primary prevention of stroke by healthy lifestyle. *Circulation, 118*(9), 947-954.

Colcombe, S. J., Erickson, K. I., Raz, N. et al. (2003). Aerobic fitness reduces brain tissue loss in aging humans. *Journals of Gerontology A, 58*(2), 176–180.

Colditz, G. A. (1999). Economic costs of obesity and inactivity. *Medical Science Sports Exercise, 31*(11 suppl), S663–S667.

Cotman, C. W., & Engesser-Cesar, C. (2002). Exercise enhances and protects brain function. *Exercise and Sport Sciences Reviews, 30*(2), 75–79.

Culture of Health Institute. (n.d.). *Motivating factors for healthy lifestyles: An OptumHealth research study*. Retrieved from https://www.optum.com/content/dam/optum/resources/articles/Motivating-Factors-in-Healthy-Lifestyles-02152011.pdf

Dall, T. M., Fulgoni, V. L., III, Zhang, Y., Reimers, K. J., Packard, P. T., & Astwood, J. D. (2009). Potential health benefits and medical cost savings from calorie, sodium, and saturated fat reductions in the American diet. *American Journal of Health Promotion, 23*, 412–422.

Danaei, G., Ding, E. L., Mozaffarian, D. et al. (2009). The preventable causes of death in the United States: Comparative risk assessment of dietary, lifestyle, and metabolic risk factors. *PLoS Medicine, 6*(4):e1000058.

Danaei, G., Ding, E. L., Mozaffarian, D., Taylor, B., Rehm, J., Murray, C. J….Geesey, M. E. (2007). Turning back the clock: Adopting a healthy lifestyle in middle age. *American Journal of Medicine, 120*, 598–603.

Daniels, S. R., Arnett, D. K., Eckel, R. H. et al. (2005). Overweight in children and adolescents: Pathophysiology, consequences, prevention, and treatment. *Circulation, 111*(15), 1999–2012.

Chapter 2 – Healthy Lifestyle

Djousse, L., Driver, J. A., & Gaziano, J. M. (2009). Relation between modifiable lifestyle factors and lifetime risk of heart failure. *Journal of the American Medical Association, 302*, 394–400.

Doll, R., Peto, R., Boreham, J., & Sutherland, I. (2004). Mortality in relation to smoking: 50 years' observations on male British doctors. *British Medical Journal, 328*, 1519. doi: 10.1136/bmj.38142.554479.AE

Eaton, D. K., Kann, L., Kinchen, S. et al. (2012). Youth risk behavior surveillance — United States, 2011. *Morbidity and Mortality Weekly Report Surveillance Summaries, 61*(4), 1–162.

Ebrahim, S., Taylor, F., Ward, K., Beswick, A., Burke, M., & Davey Smith, G. (2011). Multiple risk factor interventions for primary prevention of coronary heart disease. *Cochrane Database Systemic Review, 19*, CD001561.

Edman, A., Edenbrandt, L., Freden-Lindqvist, J., Nilsson, M., & Wallin, A. (2011). Asymmetric cerebral blood flow in patients with mild cognitive impairment: Possible relationship to further cognitive deterioration. *Dementia and Geriatric Cognitive Disorders Extra, 1*(1), 228–236.

Esiri, M. M., Nagy, Z., Smith, M. Z., Barnetson, L., Smith, A. D., & Joachim, C. (1999). Cerebrovascular disease and threshold for dementia in the early stages of Alzheimer's disease. *The Lancet, 354*(9182), 919–920.

Ford, E. S., Bergmann, M. M., Kroger, J., Schienkiewitz, A., Weikert, C., & Boeing, H. (2009). Healthy living is the best revenge: Findings from the European Prospective Investigation Into Cancer and Nutrition---Potsdam study. *Archives of Internal Medicine,169*(15), 1355–1362.

Ford, E. S., Zhao, G., Tsai, j., & Li, C. (2011). Low risk lifestyle behaviors and all-cause mortality: Findings from the national health and nutrition examination survey III mortality study. *American Journal of Public Health, 101*(10).

Forman, J. P., Stampfer, M. J., & Curhan, G. C. (2009). Diet and lifestyle risk factors associated with incident hypertension in women. *Journal of the American Medical Association, 302*, 401-411.

Fratiglioni, L., Paillard-Borg, S., & Winblad, B. (2004). An active and socially integrated lifestyle in late life might protect against dementia. *The Lancet Neurology, 3*, 343–353.

Frazao, E. (1999). High costs of poor eating patterns in the United States. In E. Frazao (Ed.), *America's eating habits: Changes and consequences*. Washington, DC: U.S. Department of Agriculture, Economic Research Service, Food and Rural Economics Division.

Frohlich, K. L., & Potvin, L. (1999). Collective lifestyles as the target for health promotion. *Canadian Journal of Public Health*, (90), 11–14.

Gidding, S. S. (2006), Cardiovascular risk factors in adolescents. *Current Treatment Options Cardiovascular Medicine, 8*(4), 269–275.

Haveman-Nies, A., de Groot, L. P., Burema, J., Cruz, J. A., Osler, M., & van Staveren, W. A. (2002). Dietary quality and lifestyle factors in relation to 10-year mortality in older Europeans: The SENECA study. *American Journal of Epidemiology, 156*(10), 962–968.

Heart and Stroke Foundation. (2000). *Annual report on Canadians' health*. Toronto: Author.

Hu, F. B., Manson, J. E., Stampfer, M. J. et al. (2001). Diet, lifestyle, and the risk of type 2 diabetes mellitus in women. *New England Journal of Medicine, 345*(11), 790–797.

Hung, H.-C., Joshipura, K. J., Jiang, R. et al. (2004). Fruit and vegetable intake and risk of major chronic disease. *Journal of the National Cancer Institute, 96*, 1577–1584.

Hyndman, B. (1998). *Health promotion in action: What works? What needs to be changed?* Unpublished manuscript, University of Toronto at Toronto.

International Union for Health Promotion and Education. (1999). *Lessons from Canada. In International Union for Health Promotion and Education, The evidence of health promotion effectiveness: Shaping public health in a new Europe* (Part 2, pp. 134-144). Brussels, Luxembourg: Author.

Iwasa, H., Yoshida, Y., Kai, I., Suzuki, T., Kim, H., & Yoshida, H. (2012). Leisure activities and cognitive function in elderly community-dwelling individuals in Japan: A 5-year prospective cohort study. *Journal of Psychosomatic Research, 72*(2), 159–164.

Johns Hopkins Bloomberg School of Public Health. (2008*). Study suggests 86 percent of Americans could be overweight or obese by 2030.* Retrieved from http://www.jhsph.edu/publichealthnews/press_releases/2008/wang_obesity_projections

Chapter 2 – Healthy Lifestyle

Johns Hopkins. (March 2010). *Medical letter: Health after 50: Diabetes and exercise—Keeping your blood glucose levels in check*. Johns Hopkins: Author.

Kann, L., Telljohann, S. K., & Wooley S. F. (2007). Health education: Results from the school health policies and programs study 2006. *Journal of School Health, 77*(8), 408-434.

Karkula, L., & Rosen, M. W. (2011). *Motivating factors for healthy lifestyles*. [White paper]. Retrieved from http://www.optumhealth.com/~/media/OptumHealth/Podcast/Pdfs/Publications/Motivating-Factors-in-Healthy%20Lifestyles-02152011.PDF

Kavey, R. W., Daniels, S. R., Lauer, R. M., Atkins, D. L., Hayman, L. L., & Taubert, K. (2003). American Heart Association guidelines for primary prevention of atherosclerotic cardiovascular disease beginning in childhood. *Circulation, 107*(11), 1562–1566.

Kesse-Guyot, E., Amieva, H., Castetbon, K. et al. (2011). Adherence to nutritional recommendations and subsequent cognitive performance: Findings from the prospective Supplementation with Antioxidant Vitamins and Minerals 2 (SU.VI.MAX 2) study. *American Journal of Clinical Nutrition, 93*(1), 200–210.

Khaw, K. T., Wareham, N., Bingham, S., Welch, A., Luben, R., & Day, N. (2008). Combined impact of health behaviours and mortality in men and women: The EPIC--Norfolk prospective population study. *PLoS Medicine, 5*(1), e12.

Kimmons, J., Gillespie, C., Seymour, J., Serdula, M., & Blanck, H. M. (2009). Fruit and vegetable intake among adolescents and adults in the United States: Percentage meeting individualized recommendations. *Medscape Journal of Medicine, 11*(1), 26. Retrieved from http://www.ncbi.nlm.nih.gov/pmc/articles/PMC2654704/? tool=pmcentrez

King, D. E., Mainous, A. G., III, & Geesey, M. E. (2007). Turning back the clock: Adopting a healthy lifestyle in middle age. *American Journal of Medicine, 120*(7), 598-603.

King, D. E., Mainous, A. G., III, Carnemolla, M., & Everett, C. J. (2009). Adherence to healthy lifestyle habits in US adults, 1988–2006. *American Journal of Medicine, 122*, 528–534.

Knoops, K. T., de Groot, L. C., Kromhout, D. et al. (2004). Mediterranean diet, lifestyle factors, and 10-year mortality in elderly European men and women: The HALE project. *Journal of the American Medical Association, 292*(12), 1433–1439.

Kuh, D. J. L., & Cooper, C. (1992). Physical activity at 36 years: Patterns and childhood predictors in a longitudinal study. *Journal of Epidemiology and Community Health, 46*(2), 114–119.

Kurth, T., Moore, S. C., Gaziano, J. M. et al. (2006). Healthy lifestyle and the risk of stroke in women. *Archives of Internal Medicine, 166*(13), 1403–1409.

Kvaavik, E., Batty, G. D., Ursin, G., Huxley, R., & Gale, C. R. (2010). Influence of individual and combined health behaviors on total and cause-specific mortality in men and women: The United Kingdom health and lifestyle survey. *Archives of Internal Medicine, 170*, 711–718.

LaLonde, M. (1974). *A new perspective on the health of Canadians: A working document*. Retrieved from http://www.phac-aspc.gc.ca/ph-sp/pdf/perspect-eng.pdf

Larsson, S., Akesson, A., & Wolk, A. (2014). Healthy diet and lifestyle and risk of stroke in a prospective cohort of women. *Neurology, 83*, 1699–1704.

Law, M. R., Wald, N. J., & Thompson, S. G. (1994). By how much and how quickly does reduction in serum cholesterol concentration lower risk of ischaemic heart disease? *British Medical Journal, 308*, 367–372. doi: 10.1136/bmj.308.6925.367

Lee, J., Back, H., Kim, J. et al. (2010). Systematic review of health behavioral risks and cognitive health in older adults. International *Psychogeriatrics, 22*(2), 174–187.

Loef, M., & Walach, H. (2012). A review: The combined effects of healthy lifestyle behaviors on all cause mortality: A systematic review and meta-analysis. *Preventive Medicine, 55*, 163–170.

Lomas, J. (1998). Social capital and health: Implications for public health and epidemiology. *Social Science and Medicine, 49*, 1181–1188.

Lopez, A. D., Mathers, C D., Ezzati, M., Jamison, D. T., & Murray, C. J. L. (2006). Global and regional burden of disease and risk factors, 2001: Systematic analysis of population health data. *Lancet, 367*, 1747–1757.

Lyons, R., & Langille, L. (2000). *Healthy lifestyle: Strengthening the effectiveness of lifestyle approaches to improve health*. Ottawa: Public Health Agency of Canada.

Chapter 2 – Healthy Lifestyle

Marmot, M. G., Bosma, H., Hemingway, H., Brunner, E., & Stansfeld, S. (1997). Contribution of job control and other risk factors to social variations in coronary heart disease incidence. *The Lancet, 350*, 231-235.

Mason, J. L. (1993). *You're born an original don't die a copy.* Tulsa, OK: Insight International.

Mayo Clinic. (2002, August 13). Mayo Clinic study finds optimists report a higher quality of life than pessimists. *Science Daily.* Retrieved from http://www.sciencedaily.com-/releases/2002/08/020813071621.htm

McCalla, J. R., Juarez, C. L. Williams, L. E., Brown, J., Chipungu, K., & Saab, P. G. (2012). Promoting healthy lifestyle behaviors: The heart smart discussion activity. *Journal of School Health, 82*(12).

McGinnis, J. M., & Foege, W. H. (1993). Actual causes of death in the United States. *Journal of the American Medical Association, 270*(18), 2207-2212.

Menec, V. H. (2003). The relation between everyday activities and successful aging: A 6-year longitudinal study. *Journals of Gerontology Series B, 58*(2), S74–S82.

Mikkilä, V., Räsänen, L., Raitakari, O. T., Pietinen, P., & Viikari, J. (2004). Longitudinal changes in diet from childhood into adulthood with respect to risk of cardiovascular diseases: The Cardiovascular Risk in Young Finns study. *European Journal of Clinical Nutrition, 58*, 1038–1045.

Mokdad, A. H., Marks, J. S., Stroup, D. F., & Gerberding, J. L. (2000). Actual causes of death in the United States. *Journal of the American Medical Association, 291*(10), 1238-1245.

Mozaffarian, D., Kamineni, A., Carnethon, M., Djousse, L., Mukamal, K. J., & Siscovick, D. (2009). Lifestyle risk factors and new-onset diabetes mellitus in older adults: The cardiovascular health study. *Archives of Internal Medicine, 169*, 798-807.

Myint, P. K., Luben, R. N., Wareham, N. J., Bingham, S. A., & Khaw, K. T. (2009). Combined effect of health behaviours and risk of first ever stroke in 20,040 men and women over 11 years' follow-up in Norfolk cohort of European Prospective Investigation of Cancer (EPIC Norfolk): Prospective population study. *British Medical Journal, 338*, b349.

Neeper, S. A., Gómez-Pinilla, F., Choi, J., & Cotman, C. W. (1996). Physical activity increases my RNA for brain-derived neurotrophic factor and nerve growth factor in rat brain. *Brain Research, 726*(1-2), 49–56.

Parker, A. (2010, February 22). The science of living longer. *Time Magazine.* Retrieved from http://content.time.com/time/covers/0,16641,20100222,00.html

Phillips, E., Pojednic, R., Oolak, R., Bush, J., & Trilk, J. (2015). Including Lifestyle medicine in undergraduate medical curricula. *Medic Education Online, 20.* 10.3402/meo.v20.26150. http://www.ncbi.nlm.nih.gov/pmc/articles/PMC4317469/

Polk, B. (n.d.). *Lifestyle diseases kill abundant life.* Retrieved from http://www.lifeway.com/Article/make-positive-health-choices-to-avoid-lifestyle-diseases

Prickaerts, J., Koopmans, G., Blokland, A., & Scheepens, A. (2004). Learning and adult neurogenesis: Survival with or without proliferation? *Neurobiology of Learning and Memory, 81*(1), 1–11.

Raeburn, J., & Rottman, I. (1998). *People-centered health promotion.* West Sussex, England: John Wiley & Sons.

Reeves, M. J., & Rafferty, A. P. (2005). Healthy lifestyle characteristics among adults in the United States, 2000. *Journal of Archives of Internal Medicine, 165*, 854-857. Retrieved from http://archinte.ama-assn.org/cgi/reprint/165/8/854

Renwick, R., Brown, I., & Nagler, M. (Eds.). (1996). *Quality of life in health promotion and rehabilitation.* Thousand Oaks, CA: Sage.

Robinson, D. (2007). *Americans in unhealthy lifestyle crisis.* Retrieved from http://healthy-lifestyle.most-effective-solution.com/2007/11/24/americans-in-unhealthy-lifestyle-crisis/

Scarborough, P., Bhatnagar, P., Wickramasinghe, K. K., Allender, S., Foster, C., Rayner, M. (2011). The economic burden of ill health due to diet, physical inactivity, smoking, alcohol and obesity in the UK: An update to 2006–07 NHS costs. *Journal of Public Health, 33*, 527–535.

Scarmeas, N., Stern, M., Tang, X., Mayeux, R., & Luchsinger, J. A. (2006). Mediterranean diet (MeDi) and risk of Alzheimer's disease (AD). *Neurology, 66*(5), 309.

Schwarzer, R. (2008). Modeling health behavior change: How to predict and modify the adoption and maintenance of health behaviors. *Applied Psychology, 57*(1), 1–29.

Chapter 2 – Healthy Lifestyle

Shatenstein, B., Ferland, G., Belleville, S. et al. (2012). Diet quality and cognition among older adults from the NuAge study. *Experimental Gerontology, 47*(5), 353–360.

Smith, S., & Pergola, J. (2006). *Stress management: Ways to cope EDIS*. Florida Cooperative Extension Service, University of Florida. FCS2078. Retrieved from http://edis.ifas.ufl.edu/FY517

Spencer, C. A., Jamrozik, K., Norman, P. E., & Lawrence-Brown, M. A. (2005). Simple lifestyle score predicts survival in healthy elderly men. *Preventative Medicine, 40*, 712-717.

Spirduso, W. W. (1980). Physical fitness, aging, and psychomotor speed: A review. *Journals of Gerontology, 35*(6), 850–865.

Stampfer, M. J., Hu, F. B., Manson, J. E., Rimm, E. B., & Willett, W. C. (2000). Primary prevention of coronary heart disease in women through diet and lifestyle. *New England Journal of Medicine, 343*(1), 16–22.

Stern, Y. (2009). Cognitive reserve. *Neuropsychologia, 47*(10), 2015–2028.

Stroebe, W., & Stroebe, M. S. (1995). *Social psychology and health*. Pacific Grove, CA: Brooks/Cole Publishing.

U.S. Department of Health and Human Services. (2011). *Healthy people 2020: Topics and objectives*. Office of Disease Prevention and Health Promotion. Retrieved from http://www.healthypeople.gov/2020/topicsobjectives2020/default.aspx

van Dam, R. M., Li, T., Spiegelman, D., Franco, O. H., & Hu, F. B. (2008). Combined impact of lifestyle factors on mortality: Prospective cohort study in US women. *British Medical Journal, 337*, a1440.

Wallerstein, N. (1992). Powerlessness, empowerment and health. Implications for health promotion programs. *American Journal of Health Promotion, 6*, 197–205.

Warburton, D. E. R., Nicol, C. W., & Bredin, S. S. D. (2006). Health benefits of physical activity: The evidence. *Canadian Medical Association Journal, 174*, 801–809.

World Health Organization (WHO). (1998). *Health promotion glossary* (p. 16). Geneva [WHO/HPR/HEP/98.1 Distr.: Limited]. Retrieved from http://whqlibdoc.who.int/hq/1998/WHO_HPR_HEP_98.1.pdf

World Health Organization (WHO). (1998a). *Health promotion glossary*. Geneva, Switzerland: Author. [WHO/HPR/HEP/98.1 Distr.: Limited]. Retrieved from http://whqlibdoc.who.int/hq/1998/WHO_HPR_HEP_98.1.pdf

World Health Organization (WHO). (2011a). *Data and statistics*. Retrieved from http://www.who.int/research/en/

World Health Organization (WHO). (2011b). *Risk factors*. Retrieved from http://www.who.int/gho/ncd/risk_factors/en/index.html

Zlokovic, B. V. (2011). Neurovascular pathways to neurodegeneration in Alzheimer's disease and other disorders. *Nature Reviews Neuroscience, 12*(12), X723–X738.

Part II
Ten Significant Areas of Life

Now that we have a foundation that talked about balance and lifestyle, it is time to discuss the different areas in life that need to be balanced. The next questions to be answered include the different areas of your life – areas to be further developed, given more or less attention and/or focus. Since every human being only has 24 hours, 7 days a week to work with in life, one question might be how can this time be most effectively and efficiently used in order to have a healthy, balanced lifestyle that is likely to provide a quality life.

This author has chosen 10 different areas of life on which to focus:
Chapter 4 – spiritual connection
Chapter 5 – mental health development
Chapter 6 – physical health development
Chapter 7 – family togetherness
Chapter 8 – passion, purpose, vision identified & clearly focused
Chapter 9 – financial security/freedom
Chapter 10 – work and/or school
Chapter 11 – civic involvement
Chapter 12 – social connection
Chapter 13 – personal initiatives, challenges and aspirations

Chapter 3
Spiritual Connection

Bottom Line, This is Where it ALL Begins and Ends!

Does the Spirit of God rule your life? Believing there is a power greater than you and any other human being is paramount! The most important aspect of life that encompasses all others is the spiritual connection. The quality living you enjoy is largely because of your spirit-filled life.

Whether you see spirituality and religion as being the same, similar, overlapping and/or completely different, the connection is still an extremely powerful force in most people's lives.

Spirituality provides you with what you need from the divine elements of life. It does not matter whether its simple or complex, internal or external, for yourself or for someone else, spiritual knowledge can get you where you want or need to be.

> *Your spirituality will help get you through life's crazy, impossible situations and anything else that life can bring.*

You can find peace in the middle of your storms and provide strength when most would have given up.

I believe it is commonly accepted that spirituality is broader than religion, that spirituality is personally and specifically relevant for the individual whereas religion is more of an institution or organization relevant to a group of people. Nevertheless, individual or group, one's spirituality or religion plays a very significant role in a person's and/or group's life.

Chapter 3 – Spiritual Connection

Spirituality is about the spirit or the soul of a person, a representation or expression of or a search for your inner most being.

Religion is a set of stated beliefs a group or organization has accepted, a provided structure by which a group with like beliefs can come together and share a common belief system; a system provided by which a group can worship or praise a common deity.

The main benefit or advantage of having a spiritual connection is the provision for a Divine resource during times of need, especially at those times when your human sources are either not available or ineffective.

My personal experience with the spiritual connection include such times as when I am seeking direction for decisions needing to be made or when things seem to be hopeless and I don't have a clue what to do next. The spiritual connection also comes in handy when I find myself acting in ways contrary to my spiritual or moral beliefs.

> *My spiritual connection alerts me that I need to act differently.*

For example, during times when I am really angry with my wife or a friend or even a stranger, I will often want to tell them off by saying something inappropriate that I will regret later. It is during these times that I will often catch myself, meaning the Holy Spirit, my spiritual connection, will somehow connect with me and calm me down in such a way that I act differently, usually in a more pleasant or reasonable manner.

My Personal Belief on the Topic

Before I get too far into the topics of spirituality and religion, I feel a personal obligation to make note that I am a devout Christian. As has been noted in other parts of this book, I am also a counselor educator. Many of my students, clients and other individuals and groups with whom I work are not. And, many of the readers of this book might not be. Consequently, as I approach this subject, I will first talk a little about my own perspective on the subject.

> *I believe that Jesus Christ is the one and only God whom I serve and strive to emulate.*

At a young age, I accepted the Lord Jesus Christ as my Savior who died on the cross for my sins and He rose again. I believe that the Bible is the ultimate source of truth and I believe that when I die, I am going to Heaven and that privilege was given to me by the grace of God. It was not something I had to earn.

Chapter 3 – Spiritual Connection

I am by no means a scholar on the subject and consequently, as I have done in all the other chapters in this book, I rely on other credible and reliable sources to expound on the subjects covered in my book.

Since the title of this chapter is Spiritual Connection, I have chosen sources I found that come closest to stating my position on the subject. They both talk about the differences between spirituality and religion from a Christian's perspective. This is the extent I have chosen to talk about my beliefs on the subject. I also do not expect to have all Christians and non-Christians agree with my position on the subject. Nor do I completely agree with everything said by all the sources cited in this book.

The Difference Between Spirituality and Religion

This article was found on the website:
http://christianity.net.au/questions/what_is_the_difference_between_spirituality_and_religion with the title "What is the Difference Between Spirituality and Religion?" Author, anonymous.

When speaking about the differences between religion and spirituality, it is important to remember that there are different perspectives when looking at this question. This answer will focus on a Christian perspective.

From a Christian understanding, there is a difference between religion and spirituality. However, this does not mean that the two are incompatible.

> *From a Christian perspective, to be spiritual is to know that Jesus Christ came in the flesh and is King and Savior (1 John 4:2).*

But spirituality is not based on what people feel or experience. From a Christian perspective, spirituality is determined by knowing God because God is Spirit and the only way to worship Him is through His Spirit (John 4:4). And knowing the truth about God can only come from God (1 Corinthians 2:11).

This makes sense when we think about it in that we can never know what a person is thinking unless they tell us what they are thinking. In the same way, no one can know God unless God tells us about Himself.

In terms of religion, it is an organized matter of worship. It is humans following rules and regulations in the worship of God.

But following a religion was not as important to God as the people being committed to him (Isaiah 1:13-14). That is not to say that religion is not important to God. But if a person's heart is not in it, then being religious will not impress God. For as God says, a Christian is saved by grace (a free gift given by God because of Jesus) and not by works so no one can boast (Ephesians 2:8).

A final point on religion: in Christianity, it is essential to have organized religion because what God is doing in the world is building His church, which is to say that God is bringing His people together to serve him (1 Peter 2:5). The Bible uses the analogy of a body being like the church (1 Corinthians 12:15-20) because people are different but we need to come together to serve God. That takes organization, and religion provides Christians with an organization they need to serve God.

Another source I found was a little redundant but I still thought it was worthy to be shared. It came from the website: http://www.gotquestions.org/religion-spirituality.html with a very similar title: "Question: What is the Difference Between Religion and Spirituality?"

Answer: Before we explore the difference between religion and spirituality, we must first define the two terms. Religion can be defined as belief in God or gods to be worshipped, usually expressed in conduct and ritual or any specific system of belief, worship, etc., often involving a code of ethics. Spirituality can be defined as the quality or fact of being spiritual, non-physical or predominantly spiritual character as shown in thought, life, etc.; spiritual tendency or tone. To put it briefly, religion is a set of beliefs and rituals that claim to get a person in a right relationship with God, and spirituality is a focus on spiritual things and the spiritual world instead of physical/earthly things.

> **The most common misconception about religion is that Christianity is just another religion like Islam, Judaism, Hinduism, etc.**

Sadly, many who claim to be adherents of Christianity do practice Christianity as if it were a religion. To many, Christianity is nothing more than a set of rules and rituals that a person has to observe in order to go to Heaven after death. That is not true Christianity. True Christianity is not a religion; rather, it is having a right relationship with God by receiving Jesus Christ as the Savior-Messiah, by grace through faith. Yes, Christianity does have "rituals" to observe (e.g., baptism and communion). Yes, Christianity does have "rules" to follow (e.g., do not murder, love one another, etc.). However, these rituals and rules are not the essence of Christianity. The rituals and rules of Christianity are the result of salvation. When we receive salvation through Jesus Christ, we are baptized as a proclamation of that faith. We observe communion in remembrance of Christ's sacrifice. We follow a list of dos and don'ts out of love for God and gratitude for what He has done.

The most common misconception about spirituality is that there are many forms of spirituality, and all are equally valid. Meditating in unusual physical positions, communing with nature, seeking conversation with the spirit world, etc., may seem to be "spiritual," but they are in fact false spirituality, according to the Christian. True spirituality is possessing the Holy Spirit of God as a result of receiving salvation through Jesus Christ. True spirituality is the fruit that the Holy Spirit produces in a person's life: love, joy, peace, patience, kindness, goodness, faithfulness, gentleness, and self-control (Galatians 5:22-23). Spirituality is all about becoming more like God, who is spirit (John 4:24) and having our character conformed to His image (Romans 12:1-2).

> *What religion and spirituality have in common is that they can both be false methods of having a relationship with God.*

Religion tends to substitute the heartless observance of rituals for a genuine relationship with God. Spirituality tends to substitute connection with the spirit world for a genuine relationship with God. Both can be, and often are, false paths to God. At the same time, religion can be valuable in the sense that it points to the fact that there is a God and that we are somehow accountable to Him. The only true value of religion is its ability to point out that we have fallen short and are in need of a Savior. Spirituality can be valuable in that it points out that the physical world is not all there is. Human beings are not only material, but also possess a soul-spirit. There is a spiritual world around us of which we should be aware. The true value of spirituality is that it points to the fact that there is something and someone beyond this physical world to which we need to connect.

> *Jesus Christ is the fulfillment of both religion and spirituality.*

Jesus is the One to whom we are accountable and to whom true religion points. Jesus is the One to whom we need to connect and the One to whom true spirituality points.

As I end my personal beliefs on the subject, I quote a friend and colleague Perseus Poku (personal communication, March 4, 2015) who stated: "Spirituality denotes the existence of a non-physical realm. Topics dealing with the non-physical fall under the term "metaphysics." Metaphysics deal with things that are not physical such as beingness (human beings, angelic beings, God...etc.), it also deals with things such as prayer, angels, souls, etc. Finally, spirituality may get you on the road to knowing that God may exist but Jesus will get you through the door to an everlasting relationship to the authentic God."

Spirituality: The True Wealth
Sharon Janis (2008), in *Spirituality for Dummies,* illustrates the great wealth found in spirituality with the analogy of dollar signs and a simple smile. Wealth is often used to denote monetary success, but riches come in many different forms. People say that "health is the greatest wealth," "a good mind is paramount," or "having loving relationships is what's really important." However, there is a prosperity that only a small percentage of people are likely to attain. Their wealth is the experience of expanded consciousness, inner peace, and serenity that comes from spiritual awareness.

Chapter 3 – Spiritual Connection

Here is an analogy that can give a sense of how spirituality gives enhanced meaning to all the good things you have achieved thus far. Imagine that all the enjoyments and achievements of your life are like a string of zeros: 000,000,000,000,000,000,000,000. Only when you put the number one before them, will each zero add more value, like this:
1,000,000,000,000,000,000,000,000

It's a big difference in value, right? Adding a spiritual perspective of life is like adding that number one. Spiritual wisdom gives greater value to all the elements of your life. When you enter the dawning of spiritual understanding, you may outwardly seem nearly the same as before–with all the same set of accomplishment zeros. However, inwardly you will have gained a greater wealth of peacefulness, faith, love, and spiritual vision.

The spiritual connection is responsible for the purpose and passion we find in our work, play, family and social life and all the other areas of our life. The Bible tells us we are more than conquerors, we have a direct connection to the ultimate source and when we take full advantage of our spiritual resources, we are truly awesome. "I can do everything through Him who gives me strength" (Philippians 4:13). The Creator who created us loves us. We operate under God's power, when we turn our will over to Him.

> *We turn our will over to Him when we admit that we cannot deal with an issue and give it to someone who can and will.*

More on the Difference Between Spirituality and Religion

As has been said before, spirituality and religion really indicate two different aspects of the human experience. Janis, in *Spirituality for Dummies,* describes spirituality as the wellspring of divinity that pulsates, dances, and flows as the source and essence of every soul. Spirituality relates more to your personal search, to finding greater meaning and purpose in your existence. Some elements of spirituality include:

- Looking beyond outer appearances to the deeper significance and soul of everything
- Love and respect for God, for yourself and for everybody. Spirituality is so much more than religion. Spirituality is the essence of the person, according to Janis.

Religion is most often used to describe an organized group or culture that has generally been sparked by the fire of a spiritual or divine soul, Janis continues. Religions usually act with a mission and intention of presenting specific teachings and doctrines while nurturing and propagating a particular way of life. Religion and spirituality can blend together beautifully. Different religions have different areas of focus.

"In order for an individual to get real help, they must be pointed in the right direction. Perseus Poku commented:

> Religion alone will not get you the help that you need. Rites are not necessarily the same as relationships. Many are religious but to have an authentic view of life a

person must accept Jesus Christ. As was stated earlier, many religious exercises mirror those of Christianity. However, outside of Jesus no other group has access to the Holy Spirit. He alone can give us the strength to live in accordance to the will of the true God. (personal communication, March 4, 2015)

Spirituality intersects with all areas of our lives. Our physical and mental health, family and social relationships and interactions with colleagues and others with whom we work; our spirituality will affect the nature of the connection in each area of our lives.

Spirituality is Internal, Religion is External

According to Cashwell and Young (2011), spirituality is the universal human capacity to experience self-transcendence and awareness of sacred immanence, with resulting increases in greater self-other compassion and love. In other words, the psychospiritual development involves an increased capacity for compassion for others and self to experience and accept more fully one's own pain and suffering and the pain and suffering of others, resulting in a transformation of that suffering into compassion as one becomes fully awake.

They go on to say that although spirituality is considered universal, ecumenical, internal, affective, spontaneous, and private, religion is denominational, external, cognitive, behavioral, ritualistic, and public (Richards & Bergin, 1997).

> *In other words, religion provides a social context within which a set of beliefs, practices, and experiences occur.*

Religion provides a structure for human spirituality, including narratives, symbols, beliefs, and practices that are embedded in ancestral traditions, cultural traditions, or both. Religion can provide a valuable service such as a place for youth and others new to the experience to begin; a place to meet and interact with other like-minded believers; a place to ask questions, get clarifications and validation; and in many cases a place to see how other areas of life intersect with that particular religion. Human support can also be found among the different religious groups.

Examples of Confusion

Cashwell and Young (2011) call these examples ambiguous. It's confusing to me. Spirituality and religion often get confused. For example, some people participate in organized religion out of obligation and have virtually no spiritual experience and little disciplined spiritual practice outside of formal religious meetings. In this case, it is more like anxiety management than anything else.

Another example is the person who becomes deeply interested in religion and studies a lot about religion. This person can quote the Bible and knows all the right sayings but does nothing about infusing what they are learning into their life experiences.

Still another example is the person who engages in spiritual materialism (Trungpa & Mipham, 2008) by frequently exchanging one spiritual practice for another—window shopping for the "mountaintop experience" of a spiritual high. Such a practice is often grounded in neither a set of spiritual beliefs nor a disciplined and sustained spiritual practice. In many cases these experiences have nothing to do with the persons day to day life and the lifestyle they live. Some of us call these practices "playing church."

Spirituality, Religion and Belief

When people are asked, "Are you a spiritual person?", the answer is often given with information about the person's belief system. The core of spirituality, however, is more than belief. To more fully understand a person's spiritual reality, we must consider their day-to-day activities that tell the real story.

> *"By taking into account the interplay of the person's beliefs, practices and experiences, we are able to get a better picture of their spiritual life" (Cashwell & Young, 2011, p. 8).*

Beliefs, Practices and Experiences

In addition to distinguishing among spiritual beliefs, practices and experiences, it is important to differentiate the translative and transformative purposes of religion and spirituality (Wilber, 2008). The translative aim of spirituality is to assist with the meaning-making and purpose-seeking aspects of life. This is frequently connected to the formation of beliefs. Conversely, the transformative aspects of spirituality entail those practices and experiences that enable a person to be transformed or "born again." This is where they are acting on what they believe, what some call authentic religious-spiritual practices. Our beliefs come from the values we hold starting with what we were taught as children including those experiences that helped us develop a belief system that we live by and eventually follow in most of our day-to-day life.

People's beliefs about spirituality and/or religion are central to their worldview and can be an influence on other areas of their lives including their family life, physical and mental health.

What Research Says About the Spiritual and Religious Connection

For a number of years now, there has been a growing literature base of diverse scientific disciplines (gerontology, medicine, psychology, sociology) exploring the role of religion and spirituality in mental and physical health. Koenig (2009), in his research presented in "Religion, Spirituality, and Mental Health: A Review," is a prime example.

Various spiritual and/or religious practices help to balance out some of the more challenging aspects of life. Those individuals who never or seldom get such positive and rejuvenating experiences tend to have more difficulty dealing with life's challenges.

Chapter 3 – Spiritual Connection

- An article in the *Medical Journal of Australia* by Williams and Sternthal (2007) indicates that levels of religious belief and behavior are remarkably high in the United States.

> **Most Americans believe their spiritual beliefs and behaviors influence their health.**

- Over 90% of American adults say they pray and believe in God or a higher being, two-thirds are members of churches or synagogues, 40% attend religious services regularly, and a majority of patients would like medical providers to discuss the spiritual aspects of their illness. Moreover, 79% of US adults believe that spiritual faith can help people recover from illness, injury, or disease.

- Considerable work has focused on behavioral measures, such as church attendance, linked to health outcomes. Jeff Levin and Harold Koenig (2005) editors of *Faith, Medicine and Science,* found that people who attended church weekly (or more often) were significantly less likely to be admitted to a hospital in the previous year and had fewer hospital admissions and fewer days in the hospital than did those who attended less often. Spiritual connection requires faith and unconditional commitment to one's belief system. Life becomes so much more manageable when we can call on a higher power greater than our own human limitations.

- "There is a popular saying in Christian apologetics, 'What one believes matters because ideas have consequences'" (Perseus Poku, personal communication, March 4, 2015).

- A review of 35 studies of the relationship between religiosity and health-related physiological processes found that both Judeo-Christian and Eastern religious practices were associated with reduced blood pressure and improved immune function (Seeman, Dubin, & Seeman as cited in Williams & Sternthal, 2007).

- Because addressing spiritual issues can make such a difference in an individual's experience of illness—and often in health outcomes as well—weaving spirituality into medical education has become a priority among integrative medicine leaders. Today two-thirds of the nation's 125 medical schools now include courses on spirituality and faith, up from just three total in 1992 (Williams & Sternthal, 2007).

- A study from the University of Missouri-Columbia (2007) shows that religion helps many individuals with disabilities adjust to their impairments and gives new meaning to their lives. According to the study, persons facing impending death may use religion to help them accept their condition, come to terms with unresolved life issues, and prepare for death. However, the study suggests that religion may be an equally, if not more important, coping mechanism for persons with chronic disabilities such as traumatic brain injury, spinal cord injury, stroke and arthritis.

Chapter 3 – Spiritual Connection

> *People who are connected with a church (… tend to live more stable lives).*
> *(University of Missouri, 2007, Religion and Health Care Should Mix, MO:MU*
> *News Bureau)*

- People who are connected with a church are provided things that are good for health and wellbeing, including social support, a sense of purpose, a coherent belief system and a clear moral code.

- A study of prayer use by patients showed that 47% of study subjects prayed for their health, and 90% of these believed prayer improved their health. Those who prayed had significantly less smoking and alcohol use and more preventive care visits, influenza immunizations, vegetable intake, satisfaction with care, and social support, and were more likely to have a regular primary care provider. The study concluded that those who pray had more favorable health-related behaviors, preventive service use, and satisfaction with care (O'Connor, Pronk, Tan, & Whitebird, 2005).

Love and Talbot's (1999) definition seem to be among the first, and often quoted, definition of spirituality in student affairs literature. It is also comprehensive. Their definition is based upon three assumptions. The first assumption is that "the quest for spiritual development is an innate aspect of human development," the second is "spiritual development and spirituality are interchangeable concepts," and the third is "openness is a prerequisite to spiritual development" (p. 364).

Based upon these assumptions Love and Talbot (1999) offer five propositions that form their definition:
- Spiritual development involves an internal process of seeking personal authenticity, genuineness, and wholeness as an aspect of identity development.
- Spiritual development involves the process of continually transcending one's current locus of centricity.
- Spiritual development involves developing a greater connectedness to self and others through relationships and union with community.
- Spiritual development involves an increasing openness to exploring a relationship with an intangible and pervasive power or essence that exists beyond human knowing (pp. 364-367).

> - *Spiritual development involves deriving meaning, purpose, and direction in one's life.*

54

Chapter 3 – Spiritual Connection

Tisdell's (2003) understanding of spirituality is similar to that of Love and Talbot (1999). Her seven-part definition is based upon several qualitative research studies. Her definition of spirituality is:

- Spirituality and religion are not the same, but for many people they are interrelated.
- Spirituality is about an awareness and honoring of wholeness and the interconnectedness of all things through the mystery of what many I interviewed referred to as the Life-force, God, higher power, higher self, cosmic energy, Buddha nature, or Great Spirit.
- Spirituality is fundamentally about meaning-making.
- Spirituality is always present (though often unacknowledged) in the learning environment.
- Spiritual development constitutes moving toward greater authenticity or to a more authentic self.
- Spirituality is about how people construct knowledge through largely unconscious and symbolic processes, often made more concrete in art forms such as music, art, image, symbol, and ritual, which are manifested culturally.
- Spiritual experiences most often happen by surprise (pp. 28-29).

Several general themes are common to both Love and Talbot (1999) and Tisdell (2003). They are that spirituality is both deeply individual and communal, there is some sort of power beyond human existence, and humans develop by trying to make sense (meaning-making) of their existence in light of this power.

Spirituality in Clinical Practice

In an article written by Carolyn Jacobs (2010) titled "Exploring Religion and Spirituality in Clinical Practice," religious problems have become important content for clinical practice (Lukoff, 1998). More specifically, these are religious problems involving a person's conflicts over the beliefs, practices, rituals, and experiences related to a religious institution and spiritual problems involving distress associated with a person's relationship to a higher power or transcendent force that is not related to a religious organization.

> *Therefore, attention to spiritual and religious assessment is important in diagnosis and in the ongoing clinical relationship.*

The Diagnostic and Statistical Manual of Mental Disorders (*DSM-IV*; American Psychiatric Association, 1994) (and now the new *DSM V*, 2013) provide diagnostic categories on the frequent occurrence of religious and spiritual issues in clinical practice: "This category can be used when the focus of clinical attention is a religious or spiritual problem. Examples include distressing experiences that involve loss or questioning of faith, problems associated with conversion to a new faith, or questioning of spiritual values that may not necessarily be related to an organized church or religious institution" (p. 685).

Chapter 3 – Spiritual Connection

Canda and Furman (2010) provided a summary of 12 *commonly mentioned attributes of the concept of spirituality* from the helping professions and religious studies:

1. An essential quality of a person that is inherently valuable, sacred, or immaterial. This is sometimes associated with beliefs about soul, spirit, vital energy, life force, consciousness, true self, or core nature.
2. An innate drive of persons to search for meaning.
3. A developmental process of searching and moving toward a sense of wholeness and connectedness in oneself and with others.
4. The contents of beliefs, values, moral frameworks, practices, and relationship with self and others, including ultimate reality, involved in this process.
5. Transpersonal levels of consciousness.
6. Particular experiences and states of consciousness of a profound, transpersonal, or sacred nature, such as out of body experiences, revelatory visions, sense of connection with spirits, communing with God, or cosmic consciousness.
7. Participation in spiritual support groups that may or may not be religious.
8. Engagement in particular beliefs and behaviors that support growth toward wholeness or contact with the sacred, such as prayer or meditation, in a religious or nonreligious context.
9. Central priorities that orient life toward what is considered ultimate, sacred, or transcendent.
10. Virtues that may arise from development of spirituality, such as compassion, love, sense of justice, forgiveness, and humility.
11. Qualities of well-being that may arise from spiritual development, and as resilience, joy, peace, contentment, and clear life purpose.
12. A holistic quality of the entire person in relationship, not reducible to parts, that includes yet transcends all the parts. Holistic awareness may emerge as one becomes aware of all one's aspects and relationships and works out a sense of integration and connectedness (p. 74).

They concluded that religion is "an institutionalized (i.e., systematic and organized) pattern of values, belief, symbols, behaviors, and experiences that involves spirituality, a community of adherents, transmission of traditions over time, and community support functions (e.g., organizational structure, material assistance, emotional support, or political advocacy) that are directly or indirectly related to spirituality" (p. 76).

> *They also argued that spirituality is a process of human life and development focusing on the search for a sense of meaning, purpose, morality, and well-being (Canda & Furman, 2010).*

Chapter 3 – Spiritual Connection

This process holds in context the relationship with oneself, other people, other beings, the universe, and ultimate reality however understood (e.g., in animistic, atheistic, nontheistic, polytheistic, theistic, or other way).

Griffith and Griffith (2002) provided definitions of religion and spirituality that are most applicable to a study involving the exploration of spirituality and religion in clinical practice. According to them, "Religion represents a cultural codification of important spiritual metaphors, narratives, belief, rituals, social practices and forms of community among a particular people that provides methods for attaining spirituality, most often expressed in terms of a relationship with the God of that religion" (p. 17).

On the other hand, spirituality is a commitment to choose, as the primary context for understanding and acting one's relatedness with all that is. With this commitment, one attempts to stay focused on relationships between oneself and other people, one's physical environment, one's heritage and traditions, one's body, one's ancestors, and a Higher Power, or God. Spirituality places relationships at the center of awareness, whether they are relationships with the world or other people, or relationships with God or other nonmaterial beings (pp. 15-16).

Perseus Poku commented, "The ability to choose stems from the "will." The "will" is defined in philosophy as the inclination by a rational agent towards a desired goal. For Christians, they choose or will to love God. Conversely non-Christians will to love other things or individuals" (personal communication, March 4, 2015).

Lee et al. (2009) defined spirituality as multidimensional. It entails cognitive, philosophical, experiential, emotional, and behavioral aspects.

The findings of the Jacobs (2010) study support the belief that attending to religious and spiritual practices in clinical work is an important contribution that experienced clinicians bring to furthering our knowledge and appreciation of this dynamic of practice (Canda & Furman, 2010; Epstein, 1995; Lee et al., 2009; Lukoff, 1998; Northcut, 2000; Sheridan, 2004).

Self Assessment

It does not matter whether you are a new believer or one who has believed for years, we all need to do a self-assessment on a regular basis. The value of a self-assessment is to help us stay connected and to reflect on where we think we should be in our spiritual walk. Because it is difficult, if not impossible, to get a real good and accurate assessment from our own perspective alone, we need to recruit others who know us well to help. One way to get started is to be asked the following questions:

> *How satisfied are you with your spiritual development?*

Do you feel you are on the "right" track, headed in the "right" direction with this area of your life? Or, do you feel that you need to spend a lot more time developing yourself in this area? On a scale of 1 to 10, where would you place this area of your life in terms of being satisfied with this area? Ten (10) meaning you are completely satisfied and 1 means you are very much dissatisfied.

One way to keep in touch with where we are spiritually is to do periodic self-assessments that are based on the "here and now" and that are brutally honest and as truthful and as straight forward as we can possibly make it. It is a good idea to make a written assessment of where you think you are and where you want to be in the area of spirituality. This activity might take place over a period of several days, weeks, or maybe even months. The important thing is to begin to document (with dates) as complete and as accurate an assessment as you can. It is worth mentioning again that it would be a good idea to get feedback from friends, relatives, colleagues and others who know you well and whose opinions you trust and respect. Their opinions are often helpful to either confirm or refute your own assessment.

Once you have made that self-assessment and have identified that you are in a place different from where you want to be, your next step might be to begin a strategy of getting to that desired next level. For most of us, that involves some aspect of change in our behavior.

Next Steps

A number of different strategies can be used to get to and through that next step. This is simply one of many. This is also from a Christian perspective. Be reminded that for this author, there is a need to differentiate the general revelation from the specific revelation. In other words, make clear the Biblical principles found in the sources of those cited.

The desire to take that next step needs to come from the heart.
- Pray to God to help you through these next steps and to give you the desire to do whatever it takes to get to where He wants to take you. 1 Peter 2:2 says, "Desire the pure milk of the word, that you may grow thereby."

> - *For the beginning believer, hang in there when things get tough and you want to quit.*

For the more mature person, don't think that you only need to grow a little because you have been there before. 1 Corinthians 10:12 says, "Therefore let him that thinks he stands take heed lest he fall." People who are saved might think they don't need to grow anymore, but that is simply not true. On the other hand, however, the very next verse, 1 Corinthians 10:13, promises that things in life will not get so bad that you will not be able to handle it.

- Read first, then study the Bible, attend worship services, fellowship with fellow believers and pray often and find a way to "live" what you are studying from the Bible. Acts 17:11 says, "Now the Bereans were of more noble character than the Thessalonians, for they received the message with great eagerness and examined the Scriptures every day to see if what Paul said was true. Psalm 1:2 says, "But his delight is in the law of the Lord, and on his law he meditates day and night."

Let Your Light Shine

As you read the Scriptures and learn more of His Word. Find a way to use what you are reading. Practice what's in the Word and infuse it into your daily life and make it a part of your lifestyle. I Timothy 4:7 says, "…train yourself to be godly." Be an example for others who see you. When people see you, they should see God in your behavior and the way you respond to crisis situations.

Once again, it does not matter where you are in your level of maturity.

> *We all need to do our best to be the best role model we can be.*

When people see us, they know automatically that you are a believer. The best time for them to see you is when trouble hits and they still see that you are a true believer and your witness shows.

I look at my relationship with my (heavenly) Father similar to the way a son would relate to his (earthly) father. Even though I know my father is going to protect me regardless of what I do, he goes that extra mile for me when I keep my end of the bargain: surrender my will, (show) love unconditionally, and maintain a spirit to serve others. Surrendering my will should be relatively easy to understand since I'm surrendering it to the all mighty God who created everything and who knows all and especially who knows what is best for me, certainly better than I know what is good for me.

D'Souza and Rodrgo (2004) used spiritually augmented cognitive behavior therapy in a mental health study. The study demonstrated that spiritually augmented cognitive behavior therapy helped reduce hopelessness and despair, improved treatment collaboration, reduced relapse, and enhanced functional recovery.

It's All About Love

If we can get this one area of our lives together, all the other areas will not only be easier, they are likely to lead to a truly quality life. Your spiritual base is the foundation from which to build all the other areas of your life. Because God loves us, we were created in His image.

It takes a writer of the caliber of Jeff Levin (2010) to describe the awesomeness of God's love which he calls "Divine Love," when he talks about "the ultimate aim for many of the world's major faith traditions is to love and be loved by God—to live in connection with the Divine, in union with the Beloved, in reconciliation with the Ultimate." He goes on to say:

> To be loved by God, to enter into a mutual and covenantal relationship with the Divine, may well offer solutions to many of the current crises around the world. Only a loving relationship with the Source of being within the context of the great faith and wisdom traditions of the world can fully inform and motivate the acts of love, unity, justice, compassion, kindness, and mercy for all beings that are so desperately required to counter the toxic influences in the world. (Levin & Post, 2010).

God is love!!

Two of my favorite scripture verses come to mind when I think I need some spiritual help:

Galatians (5) 22-23 – Fruits of the Spirit
22 But the fruit of the Spirit is love, joy, peace, forbearance, kindness, goodness, faithfulness. 23 gentleness and self-control. Against such things there is no law.

Philippians (4) 8
Finally, brothers, whatever is true, whatever is noble, whatever is right, whatever is pure, whatever is lovely, whatever is admirable – if anything is excellent or praiseworthy – think about such things.

A Personal Note: The Survival of the Christian Church
In recent years, there seem to be a diminishing number of church members.

In a *Christian Post* news article dated August 23, 2013, Thom Rainer confirmed what most of us believe and few people will argue that church attendance in many churches in America is declining. Our own research indicates that the majority of churches in our country are not growing. Rainer also believes that most of us have our own ideas why attendance is declining. Many have suggested that our nation is shifting away from its Christian roots, and thus the churches are declining as a smaller proportion of our country are believers in Christ.

I agree wholeheartedly with the part that most of us have our own ideas why attendance is declining. My idea is that we are losing our youth and young people in churches. The number of youth and young adult church attendance in many churches has been going down for several years and the trend is likely to continue unless something drastically different from current practices is done.

Chapter 3 – Spiritual Connection

Spirituality and Youth

> *50 years ago, Berger and Luckman (1967) talked about "plausible structures" as being necessary for churches to make Christianity believable for youth and young people to want to participate and be involved. That same concept applies today.*

Importance of Plausibility Structure for Youth

In Richard Rymarz's (2009) article, he points out how Berger and Luckman (1967) argue that for religious beliefs to be sustained, they must be supported by plausibility structures. These structures are essentially a social base whereby the beliefs of the group are made subjectively real. Key plausibility structures are family, schools, workplaces and community groups. It is within these structures that religion becomes plausible (Berger & Luckman, 1965, p. 34). If a religious community is to survive, then it must be able to provide an ongoing explanation of the world, not just on a cognitive level, to those who are within the faith community. In other words, the plausibility structures need to be maintained.

There are three elements that are of pivotal importance. Firstly, plausibility structures must be able to provide mechanisms for socializing the next generation. This includes a wide range of social practices both within the family and in the wider social network.

Secondly, there must be many opportunities for conversation within the community. Conversation here means occasions when the members of the community can rehearse over and over again what it means to be a member of that community. This involves a range of actions over a prolonged period of time. For an evangelical community, for example, this could involve attending Bible study, giving witnesses, taking part in regular prayer evenings and going away together to summer camp.

Finally, the plausibility structure must be able to provide a clear and cogent explanation of the faith to those within the community, especially at times when individuals are challenged.

> *Religious traditions have an obvious strong stake in how religious commitment is passed on to the younger generations.*

At the very least, this ensures the continuing vitality of the tradition and also has implications for the wellbeing of children and youth associated with that tradition. The importance of inter-generational transfer of religious beliefs and practices has been commented on in a variety of studies spanning numerous faith traditions (Bendroth, 2002; Goa, 1989; Keysar, Kosmin, & Scheckner, 2000).

Rymarz concludes by stating that the era when the Christian community could rely on passive socialization and a supportive general culture to form its members has receded if not disappeared. In the immediate future, the mainstream churches are faced with a number of significant challenges if they are to engage young people on an ongoing basis. They need, above all else, to think more in terms of how they can most effectively present themselves to people who have a wide range of choices and no compelling reason to choose a particular one.

In my opinion, the churches might focus more on things that attract youth and young adults. I must admit that my own church is doing a number of things to keep youth and young adults involved by engaging them in ministries and setting up small accountability groups so they can socialize with other youth and young adults. Our church also has youth involved in programs designed specifically for their age groups such as our Manhood Development Program and Alert Girls program among others. Our church also has periodic youth services specifically designed for youth in the church.

REFERENCES
Chapter 3 – "Spiritual Connection"

American Psychiatric Association. (1994). *Diagnostic and statistical manual of mental disorders* (4th ed.). Washington, DC: Author.

Bendroth, M. (2002). *Growing up Protestant.* New Brunswick, NJ: Rutgers University Press.

Berger, P. (1967). *The sacred canopy: Elements of a sociological theory of religion.* Garden City, NY: Anchor.

Berger, P. L., & Luckmann, T. (1966). *The social construction of reality: A treatise in the sociology of knowledge.* New York: Doubleday.

Berger, P., & T. Luckman. (1967). *The social construction of reality: A treatise in the sociology of knowledge.* Garden City, NY: Anchor Books

Canda, E. R., & Furman, L. D. (2010). *Spiritual diversity in social work practice: The heart of helping* (2nd ed.). New York: Oxford University Press.

Cashwell, C. S., & Young, J. S. (2011). *Integrating spirituality and religion into counseling: A guide to competent practice* (pp. 7-9). Alexandria, VA: American Counseling Association.

D'Souza, R. F., & Rodrigo, A. (2004). Spiritually augmented cognitive behavioural therapy. *Australasian Psychiatry 12*, 148–152.

de Souza, M. (2009). Editorial, Spirituality and wellbeing. *International Journal of Children's Spirituality, 14*(3), 181–184.

Epstein, M. (1995). *Thoughts without a thinker.* New York: Basic Books.

Estanek, S. M. (2006). Spirituality, self-efficacy, and quality of life among adults. *College Student Journal, 40*(2), 270–281.

Goa, D. (1989). *The Ukrainian religious experience.* Edmonton, Canada: Canadian Institute of Ukrainian Studies.

Griffith, J. L., & Griffith, M. E. (2002). *Encountering the sacred in psychotherapy.* New York: Guilford Press.

Ho, D. Y. F., & Ho, R. T. H. (2007). Measuring spirituality and spiritual emptiness: Toward ecumenicity and transcultural applicability. *Review of General Psychology, 11*(1), 62–74.

Holt, L. B. (2006, June 21). *Exploring common themes in world religions and the role of nature in the spiritual quest.* Retrieved from http://www.religiousscholar.com/religion-vs-spirituality-terms/

Jacobs, C. (2010). Exploring religion and spirituality in clinical practice. *Smith College Studies in Social Work, 80*(2-3), 98–120.

Jacobs, C. (2010). Spiritual development. In J. G. Lesser & D. S. Pope (Eds.), *Human behavior and the social environment: Theory and practice* (2nd ed., pp. 226–242). New York: Pearson Education.

Janis, S. (2008). *Spirituality for dummies.* Hoboken, NJ: Wiley Publishing, Inc.

Keysar, A., Kosmin, B., & Scheckner, J. (2000). *The next generation: Jewish children and adolescents.* New York: SUNY Press.

Koenig, H. G. (2009). Research on religion, spirituality, and mental health: A review. *Canadian Journal of Psychiatry, 54*, 283–291.

Lee, M. Y., Ng, S., Leung, P. P. Y., & Chan, C. L. W. (2009). *Integrative body-mind-spirit social work: An empirically based approach to assessment and treatment.* New York: Oxford University Press.

Levin, J., & Koenig, H. (Eds.). (2005). *Faith, medicine and science: A Festschrift in honor of Dr. David B. Larson.* New York: Haworth.

Levin, J., & Post, S. (Eds.). (2010). *Divine love: Perspectives from the world's religious traditions.* Philadelphia: Templeton Press.

Love, P., & Talbot, D. (1999). Defining spiritual development: A missing consideration for student affairs. *NASPA Journal, 37*(1), 361–375.

Chapter 3 – Spiritual Connection

Lukoff, D. (1998). From spiritual emergency to spiritual problem: The transpersonal roots of the new DSM-IV category. *Journal of Humanistic Psychology, 38*(2), 21–50.

Merriam, S. B. (2002). *Qualitative research in practice: Examples for discussion and analysis.* San Francisco: Jossey-Bass.

Northcut, T. B. (2000). Constructing a place for religion and spirituality in psychodynamic practice. *Clinical Social Work Journal, 28*(2), 155–170.

O'Connor, P. J., Pronk, N. P., Tan, A., & Whitebird, R. P. (2005). Characteristics of adults who use prayer as an alternative therapy. *American Journal of Health Promotion, 19*, 369–375.

Oxford Dictionaries. (2012). *Definition of spiritual.* London: Oxford University Press.

Richards, P. S., & Bergin, A. E. (1997). *A spiritual strategy for counseling and psychotherapy.* Washington, DC: American Psychological Association.

Rymarz, R. (2009). Nurturing well-being through religious commitment: Challenges for mainstream Christian churches. *International Journal of Children's Spirituality, 14*(3), 249–260.

Seeman, T. E., Dubin, L. F., & Seeman, M. (2003). Religiosity/spirituality and health: A critical review of the evidence for biological pathways. *American Psychologist, 58*(1), 53–63.

Sheridan, M. J. (2004). Predicting the use of spiritually-derived interventions in social work practice: A survey of practitioners. *Journal of Religion and Spirituality in Social Work, 23*(4), 5–25.

Tisdell, E. J. (2003). *Exploring spirituality and culture in adult and higher education.* San Francisco: Jossey-Bass.

Trungpa, C., & Mipham, S. (2008). *Cutting through spiritual materialism.* Boston, MA: Shambhala.

University of Missouri. (2007). *Religion and health care should mix.* Columbia, MO: MU News Bureau.

Wilber, K. (2008). *The pocket Ken Wilber.* Boston, MA: Shambhala.

Williams, D. R., & Sternthal, M. J. (2007). Spirituality, religion and health: Evidence and research directions. *The Medical Journal of Australia, 186*(10), 47.

Chapter 4
Mental Health Development

Your mind controls your behavior, consciously or subconsciously. A developed mind is precious.

Since our mind is usually the initiator of our actions, if we are mentally healthy, strong and capable of warding off many of life's stressors and challenges, we can control our behavior in such a way as to become successful in most of the endeavors we undertake. Our mental capacity has the potential of doing great things. It is said, "whatever the mind can conceive, we can achieve." By the same token, with a strong mental capacity we are able to learn new things, initiate positive thoughts, construct useful ideas and, for the most part, control our behavior for our own benefit. A mentally healthy person knows that he can choose to think on things that are positive or negative; they realize that when someone does something to them, they control how they respond. In other words, they realize that the other person's action did not make them do anything or cause them to do anything; they realize they are in control of how they choose to respond. A person who is mentally healthy is usually quite resilient, with a healthy self-concept and copes well in dangerous and stressful situations.

Mental toughness, mental fitness, mental health. What do they mean? How mentally fit are you? How much do you think about your mental health? Unless we are having issues related to your mental faculties, we tend to not think about our mental condition. We tend to take our mental capacity for granted while we are young but our mental development becomes more important as we get older. However, when it is all said and done, for most of us, our mind is the most precious part of our body.

Mental health is the gateway to a pleasant and wonderful life.

Chapter 4 – Mental Health Development

What is Mental Health?

"Mental health does not exist on its own," is the way an article by Bhugra, Till and Sartorius (2013, p. 3) starts off. The article is titled, "What is Mental Health?" "It is an integral and essential part of overall health, which can be defined in at least three ways – as the absence of disease, as a state of the organism that allows the full performance of all its functions or as a state of balance within oneself and between oneself and one's physical and social environment (Sartorius, 2002). Which of these three definitions is used depends on the level at which the basic health needs are satisfied. These needs include food, shelter, survival, protection, society, social support, and freedom from pain, environmental hazards, unnecessary stress or any part of exploitation (Maslow, 1968).

The Mental Health Foundation (MHF; 2008) notes that mental health is defined by how individuals think and feel about themselves and their life and that it affects how an individual copes and manages in times of adversity. Mental health is seen as affecting one's abilities to function, making the most of the opportunities that are available, and participating fully with family, workplace, community and peers. There is a close link between physical and mental health, as they affect each other directly and indirectly.

The Society for Health Education and Promotion Specialists (SHEPS; 1997) suggests that mental health also involves feeling positive about oneself and others, feeling glad and feeling joyful and loving. Mental health, like mental illness, is also affected by biological, social, psychological and environmental factors. The individual at the core of functioning is surrounded by the social world—in the proximal world it will include family, kinship, employers, peers, colleagues, friends and, in the distal context, society and culture.

According to a web page that was last updated from the U.S. Center for Disease Control (October 4, 2013) (found at: http://www.cdc.gov/mentalhealth/basics.htm). Researchers (Keyes, 1998; Ryff, 1989; Ryff & Keyes, 1995) suggest there are indicators of mental health, representing three domains. These include the following:
- Emotional wellbeing
    such as perceived life satisfaction, happiness, cheerfulness, peacefulness
- Psychological wellbeing
    such as self-acceptance, personal growth including openness to new experiences, optimism, hopefulness, purpose in life, control of one's environment, spirituality, self-direction, and positive relationships
- Social wellbeing
    social acceptance, beliefs in the potential of people and society as a whole, personal self-worth and usefulness to society, sense of community

The former surgeon general notes that there are social determinants of mental health as there are social determinants of general health that need to be in place to support mental health. These include adequate housing, safe neighborhoods, equitable jobs and wages, quality education, and equity in access to quality health care.

Chapter 4 – Mental Health Development

Self Control

Our mental health and stability is what keeps us from going crazy. It's different from illness because the focus is our ability to adapt, cope, think and keep the perception of control, being grounded, having high self-esteem and otherwise being prepared to build up positive reserves.

Much of a person's mental wellbeing is self-controlled.

How people respond to their environment affects their mental wellbeing. The average person with normal mental capabilities can usually enjoy a reasonable level of mental well being if they learn to control their levels of stress, control how they respond to problem situations and provide their mind with regular (and moderate amounts of) stimulation and rest. Most research has equated subjective wellbeing with emotional wellbeing, which consists of avowed happiness and satisfaction with life as well as the balance of positive to negative affect (Diener et al., 1999). The model of psychological wellbeing proposed by Ryff (1989), however, expanded the scope of wellbeing to include self-acceptance, personal growth, positive relations with others, environmental mastery, purpose in life, and autonomy.

A person's attitude about life, emotional stability and personal self-confidence plays an important part in mental health and wellbeing. Our mental wellbeing plays a significant role in what we think about life, our perception of our overall wellbeing and what we think of ourselves—our self-efficacy and self-worth. According to the Surgeon General (U.S. Department of Health and Human Services, 1999), mental health is a state of successful performances of mental function, resulting in productive activities, fulfilling relationships with people, and the ability to adapt to change and to cope with adversity.

An interesting observation can be made if you are asked: which would you rather have, a problem that is physical or one that is mental in nature?

Of course you would rather have neither, but if you had to choose, most people would likely say physical since most people are more familiar with managing with a physical rather than a mental problem. As I see it, if I absolutely had to choose, I would rather have my mind intact rather than trying to deal with a mental problem, even if my (physical) body were not in the best of shape.

Resiliency and Empowerment

Health professionals have a variety of definitions for mental and emotional wellbeing, but the consensus is that mental fitness is more than just the absence of illness. According to Sarah Newth (2004), the two qualities that appear most often in definitions of wellbeing are resiliency—the ability to rebound from life's setbacks—and empowerment, which means having a sense of control over your life whether you live in an institution or in the community.

An important aspect of resiliency is learning how to cope with different situations. It is especially valuable to model good coping skills for children so they are better equipped to meet life's mental and physical demands. If you've had a tough day or are experiencing some extra stress, do something that will take your mind off your problems and allow you to relax: take a bath, get outdoors, do some yoga, listen to your favorite music, or otherwise do something relaxing.

Aaron Antonovsky (1987), in "Unraveling the Mystery of Health," explored the relationship between positive mental health and overall health in detail: How people manage stress and stay well. He studied survivors of Nazi concentration camps and noticed that some of them were in remarkably good health and had coped relatively well with their horrific experiences. To explain this, he theorized that people with a healthy outlook on life are more able to cope successfully with trauma and stress. He defined a healthy outlook (or a sense of coherence) as the extent to which people feel that life is meaningful, manageable and comprehensible. In fact, feelings of wellbeing can be protective in various ways.

> *For example: people who are sick but have happier dispositions tend to have decreased hospital visits, calls to the doctor, medication use and work absences.*

Emotional wellbeing also affects physical health through social relationships, behavior, stress, accidents, suicide, coping strategies, and immune system functioning.

Starting with 9-11, and especially since the economic meltdown that began in the fall of 2008, we've been living in a world that's rapidly transforming beneath our feet. Today's world is an interconnected, interdependent, diverse, unpredictable and unstable global community. And that's created new psychological challenges for everyone, challenges that require a highly proactive mentality (LaBier, 2010).

Assessment

Most people might equate mental development with IQ or mental acuity. The mental health and wellbeing covered here is much more concerned with your mental state of being as you might define where you stand in this area of your life. Would you consider yourself to be "mentally healthy" at this stage in your life? How clearly do you think? Do you find yourself stressed out a lot?

> *How well do you deal with stressful situations?*

Are you satisfied with where you are? How much are you satisfied on a scale of 0 to 10 (0 being not at all and 10 being extremely satisfied)?

Chapter 4 – Mental Health Development

A Healthy Mind Beats Stress

There is a lot more literature on mental illness than there is on mental health. Yet the health of your mind is so very important to the total wellbeing of the person. If your mental capacity is weak, you are not likely to function well in other aspects of your life. For example, if you are worried about something or you are stressed out, you are likely not functioning at full capacity and it is difficult to carry out many of life's regular functions.

The mental health concerns for the average, healthy individual might include such things as stress, anxiety, worry, forgetfulness and fear. Any one of these things can cause you to seek professional help if it gets out of hand or try finding a way to reduce the intensity of the issue if it is not so serious. Stress is likely to be among the highest concerns.

Humans continually face situations requiring actions to achieve valued goals with meaningful consequences at stake (Seery, 2011). Although the pursuit of such goals can be a negatively "stressful" experience, it is not necessarily so. According to the biopsychosocial model of challenge and threat, evaluations of personal resources and situational demands determine to what extent individuals experience a relatively positive (challenge) versus negative (threat) psychological state in this context.

Challenge occurs when evaluated resources meet or exceed demands, whereas threat occurs when demands exceed resources.

The challenge response thus reflects resilience in the face of potential stress.

Suggestions are offered by Smith, Segal and Segal (2009) at Helpguide.org on things that influence your tolerance level for stress:

Your support network – A strong network of supportive friends and family members is an enormous buffer against life's stressors. (Another way of saying the same thing is "The love of family and friends is what keeps us alive and healthy.")

On the flip side, the more lonely and isolated you are, the greater your vulnerability to stress.

A caution for the retiree who does not find appropriate activity to be involved in to replace the rigor of the work schedule: oftentimes, people who work build up support systems at work that are lost when they retire. There is also the physical and mental activity that might have been going on for decades that sometimes ends at retirement. Comparable activity or at least something needs to be put in its place to maintain a healthy lifestyle.

Your sense of control – If you have confidence in yourself and your ability to influence events and persevere through challenges, it's easier to take stress in stride. People who are vulnerable to stress tend to feel like things are out of their control.

Your attitude and outlook – Stress-hardy people have an optimistic attitude. They tend to embrace challenges, have a strong sense of humor, accept that change is a part of life, and believe in a higher power or purpose.

Your ability to deal with your emotions – You're extremely vulnerable to stress if you don't know how to calm and soothe yourself when you're feeling sad, angry, or afraid. The ability to bring your emotions into balance helps you bounce back from adversity (and helps keep you from doing something stupid. Think first).

Your knowledge and preparation – The more you know about a stressful situation, including how long it will last and what to expect, the easier it is to cope. For example, if you go into surgery with a realistic picture of what to expect post-op, a painful recovery will be less traumatic than if you were expecting to bounce back immediately.

Mental Workout

The Neurological Foundation of New Zealand offered a number of suggestions as it relates to the brain and overall mental health under the overall heading of Mental Workout. Among the subheadings were "Exercise Your Mind," "Cognitive Training," "Engaging your brain," Social interactions," and "Keeping your memory sharp." This information was retrieved from: http://www.neurological.org.nz/brain-health/mental-workout

> *The old adage, "use it or lose it" is true not only when exercising muscles of the body, but also the brain.*

Neuroscience research is continually revealing that building cognitive reserve is beneficial to maintaining mental alertness and to decreasing one's risk of developing Alzheimer's.

Staying mentally active doesn't mean we have to master 5-star Sudoku every day, but it does mean turning off the television, a notoriously passive activity. The key is to actively engage the brain in novel ways. This could mean breaking out of old routines and learning something new, or simply doing something old in a new way. Activities that stimulate and challenge us intellectually seem to be best.

Exercise your mind

A lifestyle that includes stimulating mental activity, especially in the context of social interaction, is clearly correlated with healthy brain aging and has been a consistent finding from large, well-designed studies of older adults. The largest controlled clinical trial to date,

70

funded by the National Institutes of Health and reported in the prestigious *Journal of the American Medical Association* (*JAMA*), found that cognitive training sessions improved the memory, concentration and problem-solving skills of healthy adults 65 and older.

The effects were powerful and long lasting, effectively erasing 7-14 years of normal cognitive decline and persisting for at least two years.

The NIH trial follows numerous smaller studies that have shown varying degrees of benefits from specific types of training. A common theme that has emerged is that cognitive training can improve older (and younger) adults' ability to maintain day-to-day activities, and the skills learned can enhance functioning on similar-minded tasks but may not transfer to other aspects of cognition.

> *For example, memory training might improve recall, but may not help with problem-solving.*

Cognitive training
In the largest clinical trial ever conducted to test the usefulness of cognitive training interventions (dubbed the "ACTIVE" trial), study subjects engaged in three types of training exercises.

Memory training included strategies for remembering word lists and sequences of items, text material and main ideas and details of stories.

Reasoning skills involved training in how to solve problems that follow patterns and strategies that can be used in tasks such as reading a bus schedule or filling out an order sheet.

Speed-of-processing training focused on the ability to identify and locate visual information quickly, which can be applied to tasks such as looking up a phone number, finding information on medicine bottles and responding appropriately to traffic signs.

Immediately following the five-week training period, 87% of participants in speed training, 74% of participants in reasoning training and 26% of participants in memory training demonstrated reliable improvement on the respective cognitive ability. The training effects continued through a two-year follow-up period, particularly for the participants who received "booster" training.

Engaging your brain
Though more research is needed on which types of activities are best, most brain experts are convinced that staying mentally active throughout life is good advice.

> *"We can make the brain work better by simply accumulating more knowledge, which builds more networks of connections in the brain," says James McGaugh, PhD, at University of California, Irvine.*

Above quote retrieved from: (http://www.neurological.org.nz/brain-health/mental-workout), 11th paragraph.

Acquiring more knowledge—and therefore building more nerve connections—may enable our brain to essentially compensate for, or at least forestall, any age-associated loss of synaptic connections that may occur. In other words, our brain would be better equipped to forge alternate pathways of nerve connections to accomplish mental tasks. There is evidence from brain imaging studies that older (and not-so-old) people who maintain mental sharpness do in fact harness alternate brain pathways to accomplish the same tasks as younger people.

> *The brain is a learning machine.*

The brain craves novelty and challenge. Acquiring new skills and seeking out new experiences—rather than simply repeating the same old routines—will help ensure the machine continues to perform at its best.

Social interactions

Maintaining social ties is another factor that has been consistently correlated with healthy brain aging. For example, Claudia Kawas has been following a second group of 1,100 adults age 90 and above since 1981. One clear finding, she says, is that people seem to do better if they get out of their houses and interact with other individuals, even if that interaction is not particularly sophisticated. You don't necessarily have to take French classes. The more contact people have with others, the better they seem to do cognitively, she says.

Activities that not only use your senses but also have you engaging with other human beings can be a great form of brain exercise. Social activities such as dancing, attending parties or other social events, playing cards, travelling with friends, golfing or taking yoga classes are some examples experts give that could fit the bill. A large study reported in the *New England Journal of Medicine* that people who engaged in leisure activities such as learning to play a musical instrument or dancing were less likely to develop dementia. Dancing may be especially beneficial to the brain because it combines physical activity with social interaction and often involves a cognitive challenge in learning dance steps.

Chapter 4 – Mental Health Development

Keep your memory sharp

> *What may seem like a faltering memory may in fact be a decline in the rate at which we learn and store new information.*

Practice these memory skills to enhance learning and make remembering easier.

RELAX: Tension and stress are associated with memory lapses and managing stress improves memory.

CONCENTRATE: Your teachers were right: if you want to recall something later, pay attention.

FOCUS: Try to reduce distractions and minimize interferences.

SLOW DOWN: If you are rushing, you may not be focused or paying full attention.

ORGANIZE: Keep important items in a designated place that is visible and easily accessed.

WRITE IT DOWN: Carry a notepad and calendar and write down important things.

REPEAT IT: Repetition improves recall; use it when meeting new people and learning new things.

VISUALIZE IT: Associating a visual image with something you want to remember can improve recall.

The material "Brain Health – Mental Workout" has been used with the kind permission from the Dana Alliance for Brain Initiatives. www.dana.org/stayingsharp

Leisure Helps

Focusing on work-specific stress, Trenberth et al. (1999) examined the role of leisure activities in stress coping among 695 secondary school principals in New Zealand.

> *They found that while active and challenging forms of leisure were useful, "the more strain the individual was experiencing, the more important passive leisure became as a means of coping" (p. 99).*

In a subsequent paper, Trenberth and Dewe (2002) offered a compensatory framework to elaborate on this finding.

> *Within this framework, it is suggested that passive, recuperative leisure counteracts stress by serving a "balancing" function (e.g., 'to relax'), 'choice' (e.g., 'to be free to do what I like'), or 'mood-feelings' (e.g., 'to feel better mentally')" (p. 69).*

In their study "Building on Strengths and Resilience: Leisure as a Stress Survival Strategy," Iwasaki, Mactavish, and Mackay (2005) indicate that their project on stress and coping provided some important insights into the ways in which leisure can contribute to coping with or counteracting stress from diverse perspectives, including marginalized groups. First, their findings suggested that leisure acts as a palliative coping strategy. Not only does leisure involve taking a time-out from one's stressful life and providing a positive, alternative focus, but it also helps individuals feel rejuvenated and gain a sense of renewal. Furthermore, leisure can provide an opportunity to facilitate balance in life as a stress-coping strategy, for example, by "stopping the world from spinning around" or counter-acting "a vicious circle."

Elements affecting mental health

Roger Walsh, in his article titled "Lifestyle and Mental Health" (2011), talks about a number of elements that affect mental health, including involvement in enjoyable activities, nutrition, nature and good relations. Involvement in enjoyable activities is central to healthy lifestyles, and the word recreation ("re-creation") summarizes some of the many benefits (Fredrickson, 2002). In behavioral terms, many people in psychological distress suffer from low reinforcement rates, and recreation increases reinforcement. Recreation may overlap with, and therefore confer the benefits of, other TLCs such as exercise, time in nature, and social interaction. Recreation can involve play and playfulness, which appear to reduce defensiveness, enhance wellbeing, and foster social skills and maturation in children (Lester & Russell, 2008), and perhaps also in adults (Gordon & Esbjorn-Hargens, 2007). Recreation can also involve humor, which appears to mitigate stress, enhance mood, support immune function and healing and serve as a mature defense mechanism (Lefcourt, 2002). Many studies suggest that enjoyable recreational activities, and the positive emotions that ensue, foster multiple psychological and physical benefits (Gordon & Esbjorn-Hargens, 2007; Ho et al., 2003; Lester & Russell, 2008).

There is now considerable evidence of the importance of nutrition for mental health, and an extensive review of over 160 studies suggests that dietary factors are so important that the mental health of nations may be linked to them (Gómez-Pinilla, 2008). Given the enormous literature on this topic, it is easy to feel overwhelmed. Therefore, the following sections review this complex literature but also distill easily communicable principles, because such ease of communication strongly influences whether therapists recommend and patients adopt such treatments (Duncan, Miller, Wampold, & Hubble, 2009). Two major dietary components must be considered: food selection and supplements.

Imagine a therapy that had no known side effects, was readily available and could improve your cognitive functioning at zero cost. Such a therapy has been known to philosophers, writers, and laypeople alike: interacting with nature. "Many have suspected that nature can promote improved cognitive functioning and overall wellbeing, and these effects have recently been documented" (Berman, Jonides, & Kaplan, 2008, p. 1207).

For thousands of years, wise people have recommended nature as a source of healing and wisdom. Shamans seek wilderness, yogis enter the forest, Christian Fathers retreat to the desert, and American Indians go on nature vision quests. Their experience is that nature heals and calms, removes mental trivia, and reminds one of what really matters (Walsh, 1999).

Chapter 4 – Mental Health Development

The idea that good relationships are central to both physical and mental wellbeing is an ancient theme, now supported by considerable research.

> ***Rich relationships reduce health risks, ranging from the common cold to stroke, mortality, and multiple psychopathologies.***

On the positive side, good relationships are associated with enhanced happiness, quality of life, resilience, cognitive capacity, and perhaps even wisdom (Fowler & Christakis, 2008; Jetten, Haslam, Haslam, & Branscombe, 2009).

Other mental health issues might include just about any behavior or mental function that is extreme and/or out of the normal range for an unreasonable length of time. Extreme behaviors such as antisocial, compulsive or obsessive behaviors can cause problems. Similarly emotional outbursts and feelings of sorrow or depression can get out of hand when you experience these things for an extended period of time. The important thing is to be aware of your mental state of being as much as possible so if you find yourself experiencing any of these issues, you might want to seek a healthy balance toward a more normal level of mental security.

> ***A much preferred state of being is to have as much peace of mind in your life as possible.***

Peace of Mind

Peace of mind is a state of inner calmness and tranquility, together with a sense of freedom, when thoughts and worries cease, and there is no stress, strain or fear. Peace of mind may be experienced while being engaged in some kind of an absorbing or interesting activity, such as while watching an interesting movie or TV program, while being with someone you love, while reading a book or while lying on the sand at the beach. Most of us have experienced peace of mind from time to time.

According to successconsciousness.com's "Peace of Mind Tips and Advice" by Remez Sasson, there are a few things that just about anyone can do to increase their peace of mind:

> – ***Stay away from negative conversations and from negative people.***

- Don't hold grudges. Learn to forget and forgive. Nurturing ill feelings and grievances hurts you and causes lack of sleep.
- Don't be jealous of others. Being jealous means that you have low self-esteem and consider yourself inferior to others. This again, causes lack of inner peace.
- Accept what cannot be changed.

- Everyday we face numerous inconveniences, irritations and situations that are beyond our control. We must learn to put up with such things and accept them cheerfully (at least until we can do something that is under our control).
- Learn to be more patient and tolerant with people and events.
- Don't take everything too personally. Some emotional and mental detachment is desirable. Try to view your life and other people with a little detachment and less involvement. Detachment is not indifference, lack of interest or coldness. It is the ability to think and judge impartially and logically. Don't worry if again and again you fail to manifest detachment. Just keep trying.

Let bygones be gone.

Forget the past and concentrate on the present moment. There is no need to evoke unpleasant memories and immerse yourself in them.

- Practice some concentration exercises.
- Learn to practice meditation. Even a few minutes a day will make a change in your life.
- Inner peace ultimately leads to external peace. By creating peace in our inner world, we bring it into the external world, affecting other people too.

(This author would add taking regular "you time" [at least a day, or part of a day, a week] to do whatever you want.)

Retrieved from: http://www.successconsciousness.com/peace_mind.htm

Another very important component of mental wellbeing is sleep. People who get adequate sleep are much more likely to feel mentally alert.

Sleep

People who don't get sufficient sleep may become more irritable than usual, and find they are having frequent mood swings. You may find it difficult to concentrate or make decisions or become more easily disoriented. You may find yourself questioning the uncertain and unpredictable nature of the situation. Sleep and eating patterns may be disrupted. Some individuals may become withdrawn and isolated and want to avoid their usual activities.

Sleep is an essential component of healthy mental wellbeing.

WASHINGTON, DC, (February 2, 2015)–The National Sleep Foundation (NSF), along with a multi-disciplinary expert panel, issued its new recommendations for appropriate sleep durations. The report recommends wider appropriate sleep ranges for most age groups. The results are published in *Sleep Health: The Journal of the National Sleep Foundation.*

The National Sleep Foundation convened experts from sleep, anatomy and physiology as well as from pediatrics, neurology, gerontology and gynecology to reach a consensus from the broadest range of scientific disciplines. The panel revised the recommended sleep ranges for all six children and teen age groups. A summary of the new recommendations includes:

- Newborns (0-3 months): Sleep range narrowed to 14-17 hours each day (previously it was 12-18)
- Infants (4-11 months): Sleep range widened two hours to 12-15 hours (previously it was 14-15)
- Toddlers (1-2 years): Sleep range widened by one hour to 11-14 hours (previously it was 12-14)
- Preschoolers (3-5): Sleep range widened by one hour to 10-13 hours (previously it was 11-13)
- School age children (6-13): Sleep range widened by one hour to 9-11 hours (previously it was 10-11)
- Teenagers (14-17): Sleep range widened by one hour to 8-10 hours (previously it was 8.5-9.5)
- Younger adults (18-25): Sleep range is 7-9 hours (new age category)
- Adults (26-64): Sleep range did not change and remains 7-9 hours
- Older adults (65+): Sleep range is 7-8 hours (new age category)

Retrieved from: https://sleepfoundation.org/media-center/press-release/national-sleep-foundation-recommends-new-sleep-times

According to Brandon Peters, M.D.'s (2010) "How Much Sleep Do I Need," one simple way to determine how much sleep you need is to set aside a week or two that you can focus on your sleep and not allow disruptions or changes to your sleep schedule. Select a typical bedtime and stick with it, night after night.

Allow yourself to sleep in as long as you want, awakening without an alarm clock in the morning. After a few days, you will have paid off your sleep debt, and you will begin to approach the average amount of sleep you need. Once you determine your need, try to set your bedtime at an hour that will allow you the sleep you need, while still waking up in time to start your day.

Concentration

Improving your concentration and ability to focus can be a benefit for your mental health.

According to Jeff Cohen of solveyourproblem.com, poor concentration is one common reason for a scattered mind-set. If your mind isn't as strong and alert as it could be, you won't be able to focus clearly for extended periods of time. Mental exercises can help because they strengthen your ability to concentrate and will improve your focus over time. Cohen wrote an article titled "3 Mental Exercises to Improve Your Focus:"
Retrieved from: http://www.solveyourproblem.com/time-management/improve-focus.shtml

Chapter 4 – Mental Health Development

Strengthen concentration

> ***Twice a day, practice holding a specific object in mind steadily for 5 to 10 minutes.***

The item should have some detail that you can imagine, but it should also be simple to "see" it in your mind. Some good examples: an apple, a pencil, the face of your child or pet, your house as it looks from the outside, and so on. Choose something you won't have trouble picturing, but something that requires you to focus in order to see it clearly. Call up a strong mental image of it, and then try to keep your focus on the object for a full 5 or 10 minutes without losing your focus.

This is hard to do at the beginning because your mind is probably untrained. Random thoughts and pictures may keep popping in and you'll have to keep pulling your attention back to the object again. As you keep working at it daily, you'll notice that you find it easier and easier to concentrate. The stronger your ability to concentrate during your focus sessions, the more you'll notice you're not having trouble concentrating at other times either.

Empty your mind

Another focus-killer is a head full of scattered thoughts. You know those days when you've got a million things going on and you're trying to remember them all at once and you keep forgetting things anyway? Emptying your mind can do wonders for scattered thoughts! Before you do this exercise, first make a list of everything you can think of that you need to remember. This will help you feel more comfortable about releasing your scattered thoughts.

Then, set aside 5 or 10 minutes to focus on quieting your thoughts. Though this exercise is called "empty your mind," you really can't completely empty your mind of thoughts. Your thoughts will keep on flowing through your mind the whole time. However, you can detach and simply let them pass by. You become an observer of sorts, watching your thoughts flow by. You're aware that you're having thoughts, but you don't latch on to them and start actively "thinking" about them. You simply sit in a space of peace and being while your thoughts flow calmly past. This experience is hard to describe, but once you master it you'll have discovered a powerful technique for releasing stress and improving your focus in a very short period of time!

Visualize for practice

If you've got an important goal or task coming up and you're feeling unsure about your ability to do it, visualize it first! Many studies have been done on the power of visualization, and the general consensus is that performing tasks and activities mentally over and over again is equally as effective as performing them physically! That means that visualization can serve as a powerful practice session that helps you master anything—including better time management!

Try visualizing yourself staying balanced, calm and focused throughout the course of your day, easily handling any surprises and interruptions, and feeling happy and proud of yourself at the end of the day.

> *Visualize yourself giving a successful speech, getting better at sports activities, or anything else you want to master.*

The trick is to go through it completely in your own mind, seeing and feeling what you would see and feel while it's really happening. The more you do this, the more proficient you will become at it and the more you'll start seeing results in your physical activities.

Less Frustration

Be willing to not have things your way—it holds down frustration.

One way that I stay even tempered is through avoiding frustrating situations. I tend to not forget a lot of things because I carry pen and paper with me all the time and write things down that I need to remember. It also helps to write things down in your own words to help you learn it better and remember it. I also tend to not put off things that need to be done until later. I try to do things as soon as I remember they need to be done so I don't forget to do them.

Some people need to grow to a point of satisfaction.

> *When things get really busy, try very hard to maintain your regular routine.*

That keeps you consistent in your life and helps with your becoming less frustrated.

It is said that something controls our behavior other than our intellect—have you ever done something stupid, knew it was stupid at the time you did it and did it anyway; then you said that you would not do it again and find yourself doing it again? and again? and again? Why? There is no answer because we sometimes do stupid things.

What's the difference between being smart and being brilliant? What about those who are insightful and the truly gifted?

> *The principles by which we live and behave determine what we get from life.*

Overall, when you eat healthy, exercise and stay away from stress you will enjoy a more healthy life; if you work hard, you will likely have "stuff."

Chapter 4 – Mental Health Development

Struggle is Not All Bad

This author believes everyone should have some struggle or challenge in their life on a regular (daily?) basis, overcoming and succeeding in most of them, we grow from those and the others that we do not succeed in. That might be why long suffering in the Bible is a fruit because long suffering helps us increase our faith. Those people who have not experienced long suffering or difficult times are "deprived." We as human beings need to "stretch" our perspective on life and get creative with solutions.

> *If we did not have challenges, we would not get a chance to stretch, nor would we get a chance to do something beyond our comfort zone.*

> *Another thing that is good for our mental health and wellbeing: "Forgiveness is a way of protecting yourself."*

Mental Health development through improved brain power: "Cognitive Fitness"
Roderick Gilkey and Clint Kilts wrote an article in the *Harvard Business Review* (2007) titled "Cognitive Fitness." In the article, they point out that the more cognitively fit you are, the better you will be able to make decisions, solve problems, and deal with stress and change. They say that surprisingly, it was once believed that the brain necessarily diminishes with age. It turns out, however, that neurons, the basic cells that allow information transfer to support the brain's computing power, do not have to die off as we get older. In fact, a number of regions of the brain important to functions such as motor behavior and memory can actually expand their complement of neurons as we age. This process, called neurogenesis, used to be unthinkable in mainstream neuroscience. The process of neurogenesis is profoundly affected by the way you live your life. The brain's anatomy, neural networks, and cognitive abilities can all be strengthened and improved through your experiences and interactions with your environment.

Steps to Improve Brain Power

Drawing selectively from the rapidly expanding body of neuroscience research as well as from well-established research in psychology and other mental health fields, the two college professors from Emory University in Atlanta, GA have identified four steps you can take to greatly improve your brain power. They emphasize that these steps are by no means exhaustive. They overlap and reinforce one another. "Together they capture, we believe, some of the key opportunities for maintaining an engaged, creative brain."

Step 1 – Understand how experience makes the brain grow

> *The experience-dependent nature of cognitive health has long been appreciated by psychologists.*

Chapter 4 – Mental Health Development

As early as the middle of the twentieth century, they noted that rich experience helped very young children interact with their environment. We've also known for some time that experience has a physiological impact on the brain.

Step 2 – Work hard at play

Another one of the most effective ways you can promote your cognitive health is to engage in the serious business of play. As the philosopher Henri Bergson wrote, "To exist is to change, to change is to mature, to mature is to go on creating oneself endlessly." To do this well requires consciously drawing on one of the great legacies of childhood—our ability to play, which lies at the heart of our capacity to imagine and invent.

The origin of the word "play" is telling: It is derived from the Old English word "plegian," which means to exercise. As a verb, "play" is often defined in terms of individual or group imaginative activity that promotes discovery and learning, or social activity that promotes what psychologist Daniel Goleman would call emotional and social intelligence. Jaak Panksepp's neuroscientific research on mammals identified play as a primary human drive and the brain's source of joy, which is linked to the release of a specific neurochemical that modulates gene expression critical to the development of a child's social brain. Joy provides what has been described as "emotional fuel," which helps the brain develop and expand its synaptic networks.

Some organizations go out of their way to let people experiment and play. A host of hard-driving Silicon Valley companies, such as Google and Apple, provide environments that encourage some kind of play, referred to variously as Zen dens, play spaces, and chat chambers.

Step 3 – Search for patterns

As most people know, the brain is composed of two hemispheres that have interconnected but very different functions. Neuroscience technology and research have provided us with a more complete picture of the left and right hemispheres' specialized roles. The left hemisphere contains the primary source of neural information a person uses to carry out routine tasks. The right deals with novelty, including experience and data that are less linear and less structured linguistically or mathematically. The right hemisphere operates in metaphorical, image-based, imaginative ways.

Although it's important to stimulate creative, divergent thinking, you'll derive just as much benefit, and perhaps more, from stimulating the analytic neural networks that are often viewed as left hemispheric. The Nobel laureate Herbert Simon considers pattern recognition to be the most powerful cognitive tool we have at our disposal.

> *Pattern recognition is the brain's ability to scan the environment; discern order and create meaning from huge amounts of data; and thereby quickly assess a situation so that appropriate action can be taken right away and with a high degree of accuracy.*

It is a complex chain reaction that uses the highest-level capacities for abstraction and reflection that are based on the deepest repositories of stored experience. The power of pattern recognition can be seen in the capacity to simplify without being simplistic.

Step 4 – Seek Novelty and Innovation

We have looked at the role of the left hemisphere in achieving the highest levels of cognitive fitness; now let's turn to the right hemisphere's contribution. The importance of expanding the brain's capacity to deal with novelty, a capacity typically associated with right-hemisphere functioning, becomes particularly obvious when we consider the fact that

> *the right brain hemisphere deteriorates faster with age than the left.*

For many years, it wasn't clear how critical a role the right hemisphere played in obtaining the knowledge and wisdom later encoded in the left side. Research is now revealing that the right hemisphere is the exploratory part of the brain, dedicated to discovery and learning. When a child studies a language or an adult takes up painting—any time people look at and experience the world in a novel way—the right hemisphere is exercised. Later, the new knowledge (language, for instance) migrates to the left, exploitative hemisphere, where it is organized, encoded, and made available for day-to-day retrieval and use.

> *If the left brain hemisphere is about language expression, then the right is about language acquisition.*

The more new things you learn, the better you become at learning. Actively engaging in novel, challenging activities capitalizes on your capacity for neuroplasticity—the ability of your brain to reorganize itself adaptively and enhance its performance.

In addition to the four steps to improve your brain power, Gilkey and Kilts provide a few other pointers on cognitive fitness. (Intermingled among the other pointers on cognitive fitness is information from another article titled, "Cognitive Fitness" by Sandra Dias published in the *Healthcare Ledger*, March 9, 2010, which can also be obtained from http://today.uchc.edu/headlines/2010/mar10/cognitive_fitness.html

Chapter 4 – Mental Health Development

Exercising Your Brain: A Personal Program

Because the brain is an interactive system, any activities that stimulate one part of it can easily stimulate other parts. Although some stimuli may initially create greater activations in, say, the right hemisphere, both hemispheres will ultimately be involved in the process of mastering new challenges.

There is a lot of evidence that keeping one's mind active later in life, even once cognitive deficiency has begun, appears to be very beneficial, according to George Kuchel, M.D., professor of medicine at the University of Connecticut School of Medicine and director of the UConn Center on Aging. Interestingly, we are also seeing that physical activity not only helps to prevent physical decline, it also helps to preserve cognitive functioning.

"Some amount of cognitive decline is a normal part of aging," Kuchel said. Scientific research shows that certain parts of the brain actually shrink with age. As a result, critical metabolic processes are disrupted and nerve cells in the brain stop working, lose connections with other nerve cells, and ultimately die, leading to memory failure, personality changes, and problems conducting basic activities of daily life. Parts of the brain most affected are the prefrontal cortex and the hippocampus. Both areas are important to learning, memory and planning, according to the National Institute on Aging (Dias 2010).

> *One of the greatest boosters of cognitive reserve is lifetime education, Kuchel said.*

Intellectual stimulation throughout life is now believed to build brain cells and improve connections between them. It appears that education acts as a buffer against normal cognitive declines associated with aging as well as pathological changes. Kuchel said there is substantial evidence that higher education offers "major" protection against the development of dementia. But whether one has a Ph.D. or merely a high school education, it is never too late to challenge the brain; in fact, it is critical. The key is to learn how to slow stages of cognitive decline when the signs are still minimal. Kuchel said there are two ways to preserve mental function early on: maintain a healthy lifestyle and perform brain workouts (Dias, 2010).

Manage by walking about

> *The very act of walking and moving about invigorates your brain.*

That's why when you have a mental block on some problem you are solving, getting up and changing your environment can lead to an "aha" moment.

Read funny books

Humor promotes insight and enhances our health—even the immune system seems to love a good joke, as it is strengthened by the use of humor and the perspective it offers.

Play games

Activities like bridge, chess, Sudoku, and the *New York Times* crossword puzzle all provide good neural workouts. Try new games that challenge your left hemisphere, such as pool.

Brian K. Dessureau, Ph.D., a clinical neuropsychologist and assistant professor at UMass Memorial Health Care in Worcester, MA, said it is important for people to continue to explore their areas of interest...it has less to do with a specific activity and more to do with finding things that keep the older person engaged and challenged, especially after retirement. When someone retires or loses a spouse, Dessureau said there is a "risk of losing an established way of remaining active" in life.

But just finding something to keep busy is not good enough. It's important for any cognitive activity to challenge the participant, said Patti Celori Said, B.A., M.A., executive director of the New England Cognitive Center (NECC), a non-profit organization that develops and disseminates innovative research-based cognitive fitness programs in Hartford, CT. Someone who does a lot of crossword puzzles may enjoy them and be good at them, for instance, but they may not sufficiently stimulate the brain if they are not hard enough (Dias, 2010).

Act out

At its best, play is discovery, and what you discover through improvisation is your inner actor, who can try on many roles. Trying out different ways of interacting with colleagues, for example, increases cognitive fitness.

Get the most out of business trips

Travel provides excellent opportunities for jolting your brain. Visit a museum, read a novel set in the city you are visiting, devote a couple of hours to talking with locals around town. These activities not only increase your cultural IQ, they are also a good form of cognitive exercise.

> *Take notes - and then go back and read them.*

One of the world's greatest entrepreneurs, Richard Branson, carries a bound book with blank pages wherever he goes. Every time he sees or hears something interesting and new, he jots it down. He says that many of these ideas have become new businesses.

Try new technologies

Playing with that new touch screen and downloading that goofy video from YouTube on your iGadget to display on your megascreen TV activates innumerable brain channels linking your auditory, visual, and tactile networks with your limbic system and your prefrontal cortex. Talking about it and sharing your emotional energy with your friends will extend the activity throughout the brain.

> ***One of the most consistently identified defenses against developing Alzheimer's disease is a good exercise regimen.***

Learn a new language or instrument

Studying a new language puts you at the pinnacle of mental athleticism. Learning a musical instrument or really playing that old clarinet in the closet gives your brain a big boost, too. Take lessons.

Exercise, exercise, exercise

Your brain is not an island; it is part of a system that benefits from cardiovascular exercise, good diet, and proper sleep habits.

Very specific beneficial biochemical changes, such as increases in endorphins and cortisol, result from both cardiovascular and strength training. Those benefits literally flow through your blood vessels and reach your muscles, your joints, your bones, and, yes, your brain.

What Research Has to Say About Mental Health and Wellbeing

Historically, mental health has been viewed as the absence of mental disorder, despite conceptions that health in general is something positive and consists of wellbeing and not merely the absence of illness (Sigerist, 1941). Mental wellbeing—i.e., positive mental health—is now a focus of national policy and science. The World Health Organization's report on mental health defined it as a state of wellbeing in which the individual realizes his or her own abilities, can cope with the normal stresses of life, can work productively and fruitfully, and is able to make a contribution to his or her community (World Health Organization, 2004).

In an article titled, "To Flourish or Not: Positive Mental Health and All-Cause Mortality," Corey Keys and Eduardo Simones (2012) shared some of the findings of their many years of research on the topic of mental health. They begin by explaining that mental health has been operationalized under the rubric of subjective wellbeing, or individuals' evaluations of the quality of their lives. The nature of subjective wellbeing has been divided into two streams of research. The first approach equates wellbeing with feeling good and the second with functioning well in life. These two streams of subjective wellbeing research grew from two distinct philosophical viewpoints on happiness—one reflecting the hedonic tradition, which champions pleasure (i.e., positive feelings), and the other following the eudaimonic tradition, which emphasizes striving toward excellence or a good life as an individual and a citizen.

A few studies have investigated constructs reflecting psychological or social wellbeing (Boyle, Barnes, Buckman, & Bennett; Gruenewald, Karlamangla, Greendale et al., 2007; Krause, 2009; Sone, Nakaya, Ohmori et al., 2008; Surtees, Wainwright, Luben, Khaw, & Day, 2003; Wainwright, Surtees, Welch et al., 2008).

These reports suggest that the dimensions of psychological wellbeing (e.g., purpose in life) and social wellbeing (e.g., social coherence—the belief that life makes sense and is predictable—and a sense of contribution to society) are also predictive of mortality.

> *Adults with higher levels of purpose in life; who find life more meaningful, manageable, and predictable; and who feel more useful to other people have a lower adjusted risk of all-cause mortality*

(Boyle, Barnes, Buckman, & Bennett; Gruenewald, Karlamangla, Greendale et al., 2007; Krause, 2009; Sone, Nakaya, Ohmori et al., 2008; Wainwright, Surtees, Welch et al., 2008).

Looking Ahead – Future Trends

In a blog titled *Transforming Diagnosis* and dated April 29, 2013 by Thomas Insel, Director of the National Institute of Mental Health, he wrote that when the American Psychiatric Association released its new edition of the *Diagnostic and Statistical Manual of Mental Disorders* (*DSM-5*) in May 2013, this volume tweaked several existing diagnostic categories, from autism spectrum disorders to mood disorders. While many of these changes have been contentious, the final product involves mostly modest alterations of the previous edition, based on new insights emerging from research since 1990 when *DSM-IV* was published. Sometimes this research recommended new categories (e.g., mood dysregulation disorder) or that previous categories could be dropped (e.g., Asperger's syndrome) (Nature, 2013).

The goal of this new manual, as with all previous editions, is to provide a common language for describing psychopathology.

> *While the DSM has been described as a "Bible" for the field, it is, at best, a dictionary, creating a set of labels and defining each.*

> *The strength of each of the editions of DSM has been "reliability" – each edition has ensured that clinicians use the same terms in the same ways. The weakness is its lack of validity.*

Unlike our definitions of ischemic heart disease, lymphoma or AIDS, the DSM diagnoses are based on a consensus about clusters of clinical symptoms, not any objective laboratory measure. In the rest of medicine, this would be equivalent to creating diagnostic systems based on the nature of chest pain or the quality of fever. Indeed, symptom-based diagnosis, once common in other areas of medicine, has been largely replaced in the past half-century as we have understood that symptoms alone rarely indicate the best choice of treatment.

NIMH has launched the Research Domain Criteria (RDoC) project to transform diagnosis by incorporating genetics, imaging, cognitive science, and other levels of information to lay the foundation for a new classification system. Through a series of workshops over the past 18 months, we have tried to define several major categories for a new nosology (see below). This approach began with several assumptions:

- A diagnostic approach based on the biology as well as the symptoms must not be constrained by the current DSM categories,
- Mental disorders are biological disorders involving brain circuits that implicate specific domains of cognition, emotion, or behavior,
- Each level of analysis needs to be understood across a dimension of function,

> - *Mapping the cognitive, circuit, and genetic aspects of mental disorders will yield new and better targets for treatment.*

It became immediately clear that we cannot design a system based on biomarkers or cognitive performance because we lack the data. In this sense, RDoC is a framework for collecting the data needed for a new nosology. But it is critical to realize that we cannot succeed if we use DSM data, not on the current symptom-based categories. Imagine deciding that EKGs were not useful because many patients with chest pain did not have EKG changes. That is what we have been doing for decades when we reject a biomarker because it does not detect a DSM category. We need to begin collecting the genetic, imaging, physiologic, and cognitive data to see how all the data—not just the symptoms—cluster and how these clusters relate to treatment response.

That is why NIMH will be re-orienting its research away from DSM categories. Going forward, we will be supporting research projects that look across current categories—or sub-divide current categories—to begin to develop a better system. What does this mean for applicants? Clinical trials might study all patients in a mood clinic rather than those meeting strict major depressive disorder criteria. Studies of biomarkers for "depression" might begin by looking across many disorders with anhedonia or emotional appraisal bias or psychomotor retardation to understand the circuitry underlying these symptoms. What does this mean for patients? We are committed to new and better treatments, but we feel this will only happen by developing a more precise diagnostic system. The best reason to develop RDoC is to seek better outcomes." NIMN Director Tom Insel's Blog was retrieved from http://www.nimh.nih.gov/about/director/2013/transforming-diagnosis.shtml

> *RDoC, for now, is a research framework, not a clinical tool. This is a decade-long project that is just beginning (May 2013).*

A Partnership of Sorts Between NIMH and APA

The Director of the National Institute of Mental Health NIMH, Thomas Insel, and Leffrey Lieberman, President-elect of the American Psychiatric Association issued a press release dated May 13, 2013 concerning the two organization's shared agendas: http://www.nimh.nih.gov/news/science-news/2013/dsm-5-and-rdoc-shared-interests.shtml The entire post is excerpted here.

"NIMH and APA have a shared interest in ensuring that patients and health providers have the best available tools and information today to identify and treat mental health issues, while we continue to invest in improving and advancing mental disorder diagnostics for the future.

"Today, the American Psychiatric Association's (APA) Diagnostic and Statistical Manual of Mental Disorders (DSM), along with the International Classification of Diseases (ICD) represents the best information currently available for clinical diagnosis of mental disorders. Patients, families, and insurers can be confident that effective treatments are available and that the DSM is the key resource for delivering the best available care. The National Institute of Mental Health (NIMH) has not changed its position on DSM-5. As NIMH's Research Domain Criteria (RDoC) project website states, 'The diagnostic categories represented in the *DSM-IV* and the International Classification of Diseases-10 (ICD-10, containing virtually identical disorder codes) remain the contemporary consensus standard for how mental disorders are diagnosed and treated.'"

> *"Yet, what may be realistically feasible today for practitioners is no longer sufficient for researchers."*

"Looking forward, laying the groundwork for a future diagnostic system that more directly reflects modern brain science will require openness to rethinking traditional categories. It is increasingly evident that mental illness will be best understood as disorders of brain structure and function that implicate specific domains of cognition, emotion, and behavior. This is the focus of the NIMH's Research Domain Criteria (RDoC) project. RDoC is an attempt to create a new kind of taxonomy for mental disorders by bringing the power of modern research approaches in genetics, neuroscience and behavioral science to the problem of mental illness.

"The evolution of diagnosis does not mean that mental disorders are any less real and serious than other illnesses. Indeed, the science of diagnosis has been evolving throughout medicine. For example, subtypes of cancers once defined by where they occurred in the body are now classified on the basis of their underlying genetic and molecular causes.

"All medical disciplines advance through research progress in characterizing diseases and disorders. *DSM-5* and RDoC represent complementary, not competing, frameworks for this goal." Press release retrieved from http://www.nimh.nih.gov/news/science-news/2013/dsm-5-and-rdoc-shared-interests.shtml

American Counseling Association Comment on the Proposed RDoC
"The National Institute of Mental Health is to be applauded for taking on the monolith that the DSM has become," says American Counseling Association Chief Professional Officer David Kaplan, "as we have needed a more developmental, systemic and ecological alternative for a long time. However, we need to have a healthy skepticism as NIMH has traditionally focused on the biological causes of mental health issues and so the Research Domain Criteria project may just be replacing one problem for another. ACA will monitor this and provide input to NIMH as the project develops."

ACA President-Elect Cirecie West-Olatunji (2013) has mixed reactions to news of NIMH's proposed RDoC and what it could mean for the counseling profession.

"The new statement by NIMH regarding use of the DSM is promising and laudable while also posing challenges for clinicians," she says. "The positive side of their position is that a major entity in mental health is providing a critical analysis of the usefulness of the DSM, particularly within a contemporary context. Further, NIMH is offering a viable alternative. And, while other scholars and organizations have previously offered alternative nosologies for diagnosing clients, having a major organization such as NIMH take a critical stance is significant and encouraging."
However, West-Olatunji has her reservations regarding the RDoC.

"The danger lies in focusing exclusively or primarily on biological factors," she continues. "Other concerns, those that are humanistic and environmental in nature, can also provide valuable information about clients' presenting problems. Moreover, there is just as much danger of over-pathologizing clients, particularly those who are marginalized, within the approach offered by the NIMH." The American Counseling Association comments were from the May 6, 2013 Issue of *Counseling Today*, written by Heather Rudow, A publication of ACA and can be found at http://ct.counseling.org/page/20/?s=May+2013+issue

About the National Institutes of Health (NIH): NIH, the nation's medical research agency, includes 27 Institutes and Centers and is a component of the U.S. Department of Health and Human Services. NIH is the primary federal agency conducting and supporting basic, clinical, and translational medical research, and is investigating the causes, treatments, and cures for both common and rare diseases. For more information about NIH and its programs, visit the NIH website.

REFERENCES
Chapter 4 – "Mental Health Development"

American Psychiatric Association. (2000). *Diagnostic and statistical manual of mental disorders* (4th ed., TR). Washington, DC: Author.

Antonovsky, A. (1987). *Unraveling the mystery of health.* San Francisco: Jossey-Bass.

Berman, M. G., Jonides, J., & Kaplan, S. (2008). The cognitive benefits of interacting with nature. *Psychological Science, 19,* 1207–1212. doi: 10.1111/j.1467-9280.2008.02225.x

Bhugra, D., Till, A., & Sartorius, N. (2013). What is mental health? *International Journal of Social Psychiatry, 59,* 3. Retrieved from http://isp.sagepub.com/content/59/1/3

Boyle, P. A., Barnes, L. L., Buchman, A. S., & Bennett, D. A. (2009). Purpose in life is associated with mortality among community-dwelling older persons. *Psychosomatic Medicine, 71*(5), 574–579.

Brandon, P. (2010). *How much sleep do I need?* Retrieved from http://sleepdisorders.about.com/od/howmuchsleepdoineed/a/how_much_sleep.htm

Brim, O. G., Ryff, C. D., & Kessler, R. C. (2004). *How healthy are we? A national study of well-being at midlife.* Chicago, IL: University of Chicago Press.

Centers for Disease Control and Prevention. (2009 October 1). *National death index.* Retrieved from http://www.cdc.gov/ nchs/ndi.htm

Chida, Y., & Steptoe, A. (2008). Positive psychological well-being and mortality: A quantitative review of prospective observational studies. *Psychosomatic Medicine, 70*(7), 741–756.

Cohen, J. (2009). *3 Mental exercises to improve your focus.* Retrieved from http://www.solveyourproblem.com/time-management/improve-focus.shtml

Diener, E., & Chan, M. Y. (2011). Happy people live longer: Subjective well-being contributes to health and longevity. *Applied Psychological Health and Well Being, 3*(1), 1–43.

Diener, E., Suh, E. M., Lucus, R. E., & Smith, Heidi L. (1999). Subjective well-being: Three decades of progress. *Psychological Bulletin, 125,* 276–302.

Duncan, B. L., Miller, S. D., Wampold, B. E., & Hubble, M. A. (Eds.). (2009). *The heart and soul of change: Delivering what works in therapy* (2nd ed.) Washington, DC: American Psychological Association.

Fowler, J. H., & Christakis, N. A. (2008). Dynamic spread of happiness in a large social network: Longitudinal analysis over 20 years in the Framingham Heart Study. *British Medical Journal.* Advance online publication. doi: 10.1136/bmj.a2338

Fredrickson, B. (2002). Positive emotions. In C. Snyder & S. Lopez (Eds.), *Handbook of positive psychology* (pp. 120–134). New York: Oxford University Press.

Gallagher, M. W., Lopez, S. J., & Preacher, K. J. (2009). The hierarchical structure of well-being. *Journal of Personality, 77*(4), 1025–1050.

Gilkey, R., & Kilts, C. (2007). Cognitive fitness. *Harvard Business Review, 85*(11), 53–66.

Gómez-Pinilla, F. (2008). Brainfoods: The effect of nutrients on brain function. *Nature Reviews Neuroscience, 9,* 568–578. doi: 10.1038/nrn2421

Gordon, G., & Esbjorn-Hargens, S. (2007). Integral play. *Journal of Integral Theory and Practice, 2,* 62–104.

Grant, N., Wardle, J., & Steptoe, A. (2009). The relationship between life satisfaction and health behavior: A cross-cultural analysis of young adults. *International Journal of Behavioral Medicine, 16*(3), 259–268.

Gruenewald, T. L., Karlamangla, A. S., Greendale, G. A., Singer, B. H., & Seeman, T. E. (2007). Feelings of usefulness to others, disability, and mortality in older adults: The MacArthur Study of Successful Aging. *Journals of Gerontology Series B: Psychological Sciences and Social Sciences, 62*(1), P28–P37.

Ho, C.-H., Payne, L., Orsega-Smith, E., & Godby, G. (2003). Parks, recreation, and public health. *Parks & Recreation, 38*(4), 18, 20–27.

Hosmer, D. W., Taber, S., & Lemeshow, S. (1991). The importance of assessing the fit of logistic regression models: A case study. *American Journal of Public Health, 81*, 1630–1635.

Howell, R. T., Kern, M. L., & Lyubomirsky, S. (2007). Health benefits: Meta-analytically determining the impact of well-being on objective health outcomes. *Health Psychology Review, 1*(1), 83–136.

Insel, T. G. (2013, April 29). *Transforming diagnosis*. Retrieved from http://www.nimh.nih.gov/about/director/2013/transforming-diagnosis.shtml

Iwasaki, Y., Mactavish, J., & Mackay, K. (2005). Building on strengths and resilience: Leisure as a stress survival strategy. *British Journal of Guidance & Counseling, 33*(1), 82–100.

Jetten, J., Haslam, C., Haslam, S. A., & Branscombe, N. R. (2009). The social cure. *Scientific American Mind, 20*, 26–33. doi: 10.1038/scientificamericanmind0909-26

Kaczynski, A. T., Manske, S. R., Mannell, R. C., & Grewal, K. (2008). Smoking and physical activity: A systematic review. *American Journal of Health Behavior, 32*(1), 93–110.

Kahneman, D., Diener, E., & Schwarz, N. (Eds.). (1999). *Well-Being: The foundations of hedonic psychology*. New York: Russell Sage Foundation.

Katzman, R., Terry, R., DeTeresa, R., Brown, T., Davies, P., Fuld, P. et al. (1988). Clinical, pathological, and neurochemical changes in dementia: A subgroup with preserved mental status and numerous neocortical plaques. *Annals of Neurology, 23*(2), 138–144.

Kessler, R. C., Andrews, G., Mroczek, D., Ustun, B., & Wittchen, H.-U. (1998). The World Health Organization Composite International Diagnostic Interview short form (CIDI-SF). *International Journal of Methods in Psychiatric Research, 7*(4), 171–185.

Keyes, C. L. M. (1998). Social well-being. *Social Psychology Quarterly, 61*(2), 121–140.

Keyes, C. L. M. (2002). The mental health continuum: From languishing to flourishing in life. *Journal of Health and Social Behavior, 43*(2), 207–222.

Keyes, C. L. M. (2005). Mental illness and/or mental health? Investigating axioms of the complete state model of health. *Journal of Consulting in Clinical Psychology, 73*(3), 539–548.

Keyes, C. L. M. (2006). The subjective well-being of America's youth: Toward a comprehensive assessment. *Adolescent Family Health, 4*(1), 3–11.

Keyes, C. L. M. (2007). Promoting and protecting mental health as flourishing: A complementary strategy for improving national mental health. *American Psychology, 62*(2), 95–108.

Keyes, C. L. M. (2009). The Black-White paradox in health: Flourishing in the face of social inequality and discrimination. *Journal of Personality, 77*(6), 1677-1706.

Keyes, C. L. M., & Grzywacz, J. G. (2002). Complete health: Prevalence and predictors among U.S. adults in 1995. *American Journal of Health Promotion, 17*(2), 122-131.

Keyes, C. L. M., & Simones, E. J. (2012). To flourish or not: Positive mental health and all-cause mortality. *American Journal of Public Health, 102*(11), 2164.

Keyes, C. L. M., Dhingra, S. S., & Simoes, E. J. (2010). Change in level of positive mental health as a predictor of future risk of mental illness. *American Journal of Public Health, 100*, 2366–2371.

Kleinbaum, D. G., Kupper, L. L., & Muller, K. E. (1987). *Applied regression analysis and other multivariable methods*. Boston, MA: PWS-KENT Publishing Company.

Krause, N. (2009). Meaning in life and mortality. *Journal of Gerontology Series B: Psychological Sciences and Social Sciences, 64*, 517–527.

LaBier, D. (2010). The new resilience. *Psychology Today*. Retrieved from https://www.psychologytoday.com/blog/the-new-resilience

Lamers, S. M. A., Westerhof, G. J., Bohlmeijer, E. T., & ten Klooster, P. M. (In press.). Longitudinal evaluation of the Mental Health Continuum-Short Form (MHC-SF): Measurement invariance across demographics, physical illness and mental illness. *European Journal of Psychological Assessment, 28*(4), 290-296.

Lamers, S. M., Westerhof, G. J., Bohlmeijer, E. T., ten Klooster, P. M., Keyes, C. L. M. (2011). Evaluating the psychometric properties of the Mental Health Continuum-Short Form (MHC-SF). *Journal of Clinical Psychology, 67*(1), 99–110.

Lefcourt, H. (2002). Humor. In C. Snyder & S. Lopez (Eds.), *Handbook of positive psychology* (pp. 619–631). New York: Oxford University Press.

Chapter 4 – Mental Health Development

Lester, S., & Russell, W. (2008). *Play for a change: Play, policy and practice: A review of contemporary perspectives*. London: National Children's Bureau.

Lipowski, Z. (1967). Delirium, clouding of consciousness and confusion. *The Journal of Nervous and Mental Disease, 145*, 227–255.

Maslow, A. (1968). *Towards a psychology of being*. New York: Van Nostrand.

Mental Health Foundation. (2008). *What works for you?* London: MHF.

Mokdad, A. H., Marks, J. S., Stroup, D. F., & Gerberding, J. L. (2000). Actual causes of death in the United States. *Journal of American Medical Association, 291*(10), 1238–1245.

Mokdad, A. H., Marks, J. S., Stroup, D. F., & Gerberding, J. L. (2000). Correction: Actual causes of death in the United States. *Journal of American Medical Association, 293*(3), 293–294.

National Institute of Mental Health. (2013). *DSM-5 and RDoC: Shared interests*. Retrieved from http://www.nimh.nih.gov/news/science-news/2013/dsm-5-and-rdoc-shared-interests.shtml

Newth, S. (2004). *Wellness Module 1: Mental health matters*. BC Partners for Mental Health and Addictions Information. Retrieved from http://www.heretohelp.bc.ca/wellness-module/wellness-module-1-mental-health-matters

Pressman, S. D., & Cohen, S. (2005). Does positive affect influence health? *Psychology Bulletin, 131*(6), 925–971.

Remez, S. (n.d.). *Peace of mind – Tips and advice: What is peace of mind?* Retrieved from http://www.successconsciousness.com/peace_mind.htm

Robitschek, C., & Keyes, C. L. M. (2009). Keyes's model of mental health with personal growth initiative as a parsimonious predictor. *Journal of Counseling Psychology, 56*(2), 321-329.

Rubin, D. B., & Schenker, N. (1991). Multiple imputation in health-care databases: An overview and some applications. *Statistical Medicine, 10*, 585–598.

Rudow, H. (2013). NIMH announces project to replace DSM. *Counseling Today,* Monthly archives: May 2013. A Publication of the American Counseling Association.

Ryff, C. D. (1989). Happiness is everything, or is it? Explorations on the meaning of psychological well-being. *Journal of Personality and Social Psychology, 57*, 1069–1081.

Ryff, C. D., & Keyes, C. L. M. (1995). The structure of psychological well-being revisited. *Journal of Personality and Social Psychology, 69*, 719-727.

Sartorius, N. (2002). *Fighting for mental health*. Cambridge: Cambridge University Press.

Scarmeas, N., & Stern, Y. (2003). Cognitive reserve and lifestyle. *Journal of Clinical and Experimental Neuropsychology, 25*, 625–633.

Seery, M. D. (2011). Challenge or threat? Cardiovascular indexes of resilience and vulnerability to potential stress in humans. *Neuroscience Biobehavioral Review Journal, 35*, 1603–1610.

Siahpush, M., English, D., & Powles, J. (2006). The contribution of smoking to socioeconomic differentials in mortality: Results from the Melbourne Collaborative Cohort Study, Australia. *Journal of Epidemiology Community Health, 60*, 1077–1079.

Sigerist, H. E. (1941). *Medicine and human welfare*. New Haven, CT: Yale University Press.

Smith, M., Segal, R., & Segal, J. (2009). *Understanding stress: Symptoms, signs, causes and effects*. Retrieved from http://www.helpguide.org/mental/stress_signs.htm

Society for Health Education and Promotion Specialists. (1997). *Ten elements of mental health, its promotion and demotion: Implications for practice*. London: SHEPS.

Sone, T., Nakaya, N., Ohmori, K. et al. (2008). Sense of life worth living (ikigai) and mortality in Japan: Ohsaki Study. *Psychosomatic Medicine, 70*, 709–715.

Steptoe, A., Dockray, S., & Wardle, J. (2009). Positive affect and psychobiological processes relevant to health. *Journal of Personality, 77*, 1747–1776.

Stern, Y. (2002). What is cognitive reserve? Theory and research application of the reserve concept. *Journal of the International Neuropsychological Society, 8*, 448–460.

Surtees, P., Wainwright, N., Luben, R., Khaw, K. T., & Day, N. (2003). Sense of coherence and mortality in men and women in the EPIC-Norfolk United Kingdom prospective cohort study. *American Journal of Epidemiology, 158*, 1202–1209.

Chapter 4 – Mental Health Development

The Neurogical Foundation of New Zealand. (n.d.). *Brain health: Mental workout.* Retrieved from http://www.neurological.org.nz/brain-health/mental-workout

Trenberth, L., & Dewe, P. (2002). The importance of leisure as a means of coping with work related stress: An exploratory study. *Counseling Psychology Quarterly, 15*(1), 59–72.

Trenberth, L., & Dewe, P. (2005). An exploration of the role of leisure in coping with work related stress using sequential tree analysis. *British Journal of Guidance & Counseling, 33*(1), 101–116.

Trenberth, L., Dewe, P., & Walkey, F. (1999). Leisure and its role as a strategy for coping with work stress. *International Journal of Stress Management, 6*, 89–103.

U. S. Department of Health and Human Services. (2012). *Behavioral health United States 2012.* Retrieved from http://media.samhsa.gov/data/2012BehavioralHealthUS/2012-BHUS.pdf

U.S. Department of Health and Human Services. (1999). *Executive summary: A report of the Surgeon General on Mental Health.* Rockville, MD.

Valenzuela, M. J., & Sachdev, P. (2006). Brain reserve and dementia: A systematic review. *Psychological Medicine, 36*, 441–454.

van Praag, H., Kempermann, G., & Gage, F. H. (2000). Neural consequences of environmental enrichment. Nature reviews. *Neuroscience, 1*(3), 191–198.

Wainwright, N. W., Surtees, P. G., Welch, A. A., Luben, R. N., Khaw, K. T., & Bingham, S. A. (2008). Sense of coherence, lifestyle choices and mortality. *Journal of Epidemiology and Community Health, 62*, 829-831.

Walsh, R. (1999). *Essential spirituality: The seven central practices.* New York: Wiley.

Walsh, R. (October 2011). Lifestyle and mental health. *American Psychologist, 66*, 579–592.

World Health Organization. (2004). *Promoting mental health: Concepts, emerging evidence, practice.* Geneva, Switzerland.

Chapter 5
Physical Health
Development

How Healthy Are You, Physically?

> *Eat right, sleep well, exercise and don't stress and have regular physical checkups is the formula for a physically healthy body.*

People whose lifestyle consistently fit that description are likely to be physically healthy.

Do you consider yourself to be physically healthy? Have you been physically healthy continuously for a long time? Many people who are physically healthy and have been physically healthy for a long time do not get sick very often and when they do, they don't stay sick for very long, largely because they have what might be called "preventive reserves." Many of their vital health signs are well above the "healthy" range. When your vital health signs are above the healthy range, those "reserves" serve a preventative function that comes in handy when your body needs that extra source of protection.

Can you climb a few flights of stairs without being winded? Can you lift a reasonable amount of weight and not strain yourself? How's your eyesight or hearing? Do you suffer from high blood pressure, high cholesterol? diabetes or some other disease? Do you have heart problems? The answers to these and similar questions are posed to help determine your physical wellbeing. Professionals in the medical field suggest to us that we need to have regular checkups, eat a healthy diet, exercise regularly, get six to eight hours of sleep every night and work at maintaining a stress-free lifestyle as much as possible.

> ### *In other words, "listen" to what your body might be "telling" you –*

People who follow these suggestions tend to enjoy a relatively high quality of (physically healthy) life. They are also the people who have the preventive reserves. Those who don't eventually suffer the consequences. Other suggestions might include such things as taking as few medications as possible and paying close attention to body indicators.

if you notice a slight pain in your side that doesn't go away within a reasonable time, check it out with a professional. Physical health also includes your energy level and general overall physical health and access to quality health care.

It should be noted here that NO recommendations are being made. Every individual is different and has different needs. It is always wise to check with your doctor to make an assessment of what is best for you.

ASSESSMENT
Making an honest, current, and personal observation of where you are with your physical health might be something you want to check out. Self-assessments are only as good as you are honest, objective and as open as you can be.

> ### *Self-assessments serve as barometers for later assessments or comparisons.*

When we make a self-assessment, we are looking at where we are with any and all aspects of our physical health as we see it, at this point in time. Self-assessments can help us see if we are on the right "track" and moving in the right direction as far as our physical health is concerned. This might mean taking a look at where I am physically, today in relation to where I want to be next week, next month, next year or even five years from now.

> ### *One of the primary components of physical fitness is habit patterns and lifestyle.*

Do you currently have good healthy habits and are you living a healthy lifestyle that is likely to keep you physically fit? If not, then now is a good time to start making changes

EDUCATION
Obesity and the Problems it Causes
Obesity is more serious than most people want to become aware of. An obese person is prey to certain critical health disorders. These disorders include cardiovascular problems like stroke, diabetes milletus type 2, sleep apnea, depression, osteoarthritis, cancer, hormone deficiency, an especially sharp fall in testosterone level in men, fast aging and Obesity Hypoventilation Syndrome (OHS) (Obesity Therapy, 2007).

Obesity raises cholesterol and triglyceride levels and lowers HDL good cholesterol leading to stroke. It also raises the levels of blood pressure and blood sugar. This combination increases the risk of heart attack.

Obesity also causes osteoarthritis in the hand, hip, back and knee. Obesity issues affect post-menopausal women by increasing their chances of having breast cancer. Obese men may also suffer from breast cancer. Increased BMI may cause cancer of the esophagus. A person with super weight may have endometrial and renal cell cancer, particularly for women.

Obesity increases the risk of cardiovascular diseases, carpal tunnel syndrome, chronic venous insufficiency, gallbladder problems, daytime sleeping, fatigue, gout, hypertension, pancreatic problems, infertility and low back pain. Obstetric and gynecological complications in women are also reported.

The University of Delaware Extension (n.d.) provided a program called Childhood Obesity Prevention and an Early Learning Center that included an active parent team that published an excellent list of suggestions for parents and their families. The focus was on instituting lifestyle changes for the family, especially involving the children.

The Increasing Value of Education to Health
In an article titled "The Increasing Value of Education to Health,"

> *Dana Goldman and James Smith (2011) wrote that richer and better-educated people are healthier is a robust empirical finding in health.*

They also noted that socioeconomic status affects mortality and morbidity in many studies (Marmot, 2000) and particularly for education—the relationship is quantitatively large (Case et al., 2002; Currie & Stabile, 2003; Marmot, 2000, Pappas et al., 1993; Preston & Taubman, 1994; Smith, 1999). Less clear is how this relationship changed over the last three decades, as health care has advanced and education levels have risen.

Trends in disease prevalence by education
Of key interest is not just the overall trend in disease prevalence, but how it differentially impacts people with different education. For all five chronic conditions—arthritis, heart, lung, hypertension and diabetes—disease prevalence for the least educated is rising and the gap in prevalence between the least and most educated is increasing over time. This growing gap by education is particularly dramatic for arthritis, heart disease, and diabetes (Waidmann, Bound, & Schoenbaum, 1995).

There is little doubt that across these decades (from 1978 to 2005) the likelihood of having each of these chronic diseases during middle age has increased for the less educated compared to the more educated.

Chapter 5 – Physical Health Development

Health among those with disease

The presence of specific diseases is not the only factor influencing health status.

> ***Disease severity and duration, complications of medication, and co-morbidities are also relevant.***

Even without controlling for disease, on average there is a 30 percentage point higher fraction in fair or poor health in the low education group compared to the high one. Within disease, differentials in health status are even larger—typically over 40 percentage points, indicating that impacts of disease are much more severe on the less educated. This could reflect several factors including more rapid disease progression among the less educated due partly to earlier onset and a lower ability to effectively manage disease trajectory.

Trends in Risk Factors by Education Group

Since there is no strong overall or within education group trend, average height, often used as a simple summary marker for childhood nutrition, is not a plausible reason for growing disparities in disease prevalence or health status by education. Disparities between the highest and lowest education group in all other risk factors by education increased significantly over time and all these growing education disparities are statistically significant. These expanding differences in health behaviors by education are particularly large for smoking, exercise, and the lack of health insurance.

Obesity is well established as a strong contributor to the increase in diabetes over time (Smith, 2007a). While obesity rates rose rapidly for all education groups (all trends are statistically significant), rates of increase were somewhat larger among the least educated.

Not having health insurance is strongly graded by schooling. In 2006, the fraction of uninsured is 25.7% among those with less than a high school education compared to 7.7% for those beyond high school. While the fraction of all uninsured rose over time, this problem is growing much faster among the less educated.

These risk factors combine to explain a significant part but not all of the education gradient in disease. Comparing the two models for each disease, about half the education difference between the low and high education groups is explained for diabetes and arthritis, about a third for heart and lung disease and about a fifth for hypertension.

Goldman and Smith (2011) conclude that we need a better understanding of what the barriers are that make it more difficult for the less educated to invest in their health and benefit equally from the health enhancing improvements. Without waiting for that understanding, we need to find remedies that compensate for deteriorating relative health outcomes of the most disadvantaged.

Chapter 5 – Physical Health Development

Start Early

> ***The best time for a person to learn good healthy habit patterns is as early in life as possible.***

You can raise a child to enjoy healthy eating and to be selective about food choices. Habits developed in childhood will hopefully last throughout their lives, according to Linda Van Horn, Ph.D., R.D., professor of preventive medicine at Northwestern University and lead author of the Dietary Intervention Study in Children (DISC) Study (USHHS, 2005). The main DISC trial is the first long-term clinical trial of the effects of a fat-reduced dietary intervention on growing children. With the right guidance and nutrition education, children learn to prefer healthy foods such as carrots and raisins or cereal as snacks, for example. We could really help improve both the nutritional quality and energy balance of our children's diets by teaching them to make healthy food choices at an early age.

Prevention is Key

According to the American Dietetic Association,

> ***A strong immune system is one of your best defenses against infections from bacteria and viruses.***

A healthy immune system also helps protect against other health problems such as arthritis and certain types of cancer. Eat a variety of nutrient-rich foods to give your body the nutrition it needs every day to help protect against illness and reduce your risk of chronic disease.

By choosing nutrient-rich foods that provide the most nutrients per calorie, you can build a healthier life and start down a path of health and wellness. Small steps can help you create healthy habits that will benefit your health now and for the rest of your life:

- Start each day with a healthy breakfast that includes whole grains and calcium-, vitamin D- and vitamin C-rich foods.
- Replace refined grains with whole grains like whole-grain breads and cereals and brown rice.
- Pre-washed salad greens and pre-cut vegetables make great quick meals or snacks.
- Choose fresh, whole fruit for snacks and desserts.
- Don't forget beans, which are rich in fiber, foliates and flavanoids.

> ***You should enjoy your diet because nutrient-rich foods are familiar, easy to find and represent the five basic food groups***.

Chapter 5 – Physical Health Development

Achieving balance and building a healthier diet can be simple and stress-free. Selecting nutrient-rich foods and beverages first is a way to make better choices within your daily eating plan. Choose first among the basic food groups:

- Brightly colored fruits and 100% fruit juice
- Vibrantly colored vegetables and potatoes
- Whole, fortified and fiber-rich grain foods
- Low-fat and fat-free milk, cheese and yogurt
- Lean meats, poultry, fish, eggs, beans and nuts.

Healthy Habits are a Family Affair

"Making Healthy Habits a Family Affair: Finding Balance for You and Your Family" is the title of a PowerPoint presentation by project personnel at the University of Delaware Extension. They offer the following suggestions for families
http://childcareaware.org/sites/childcareaware.org/files/news_room/naccrra_in_the_news/2012/volume_24.pdf

- We could "graze" all day—low-cost, highly energy-dense foods are everywhere.
- We eat more meals away from home. Fast foods are very popular! Portion sizes have increased.

Our environment puts us at risk of eating more than we need.

- It may be hard to find the time and place for physical activity.

What's a Parent to Do? Overview

- Be as healthy as possible – evolve toward a healthy weight by focusing on healthy habits, not diets.
- Set goals you can reach.
- Your child learns by watching and imitating you.
- Love your body – your child will pick up on your cues and learn to like or dislike his/her body.
- Turn off TV and phones.
- Have kids help choose and prepare foods
- Use this time to talk with your child. Share experiences. Accent the positive.
- Enjoy each other's company. Avoid complaining and criticizing.
- Set regular times for family meals, snacks, naps and bedtimes – Don't let children snack all day.
- Help everyone find physical activity they can enjoy every day.
- Build activity into your routines with family chores and family walks.

- *Think up ways to have active family fun.*

- Limit screen time for everyone in the family to less than 2 hours a day – avoid screen time for children under 2!
- No TVs or computers in bedrooms – Make it "hard" to turn on the TV and easy and fun to move.
- Limit children's exposure to advertising – children will want what is advertised whether it is healthy or not.

Provide Healthy Food Choices

- If you keep little or no "junk food" at home, it will be easier to make healthy choices.
- Limit foods that are low in nutrients and high in fats and calories.
- Avoid sweetened drinks and limit fruit juice.
- Serve milk at meals and water between meals.
- Let children choose what and how much to eat – Parents provide, children decide.
- Let children serve themselves.
- Use routines and limits to help children feel safe, secure.
- Provide healthy food – then let children choose what and how much to eat.
- Help children learn to like foods that are good for them – by offering foods time and again.
- Pay attention to when they are hungry and when they are starting to feel full.
- After your child is 2, accent low-fat dairy products.
- Let children leave the table when they are ready.
- Avoid restricting – it nearly always backfires – and makes the problem worse.
- Most of the food advertised is high in fat, sugar, and calories.
- Don't have any food groups that are "off limits."
- Don't overly restrict sweets or treats.
- Children naturally like sweet and salty tastes. They have to learn to like other flavors.
- Breastfeed if you can.
- It may take 8-15 times to learn to like some veggies and whole grains.
- Offer new foods when children are most hungry. Serve a new food with a familiar one.
- Try this family rule: Everyone tries at least one bite.
- Be a great role model by eating (and enjoying!) a variety of healthful foods.

MyPyramid.gov Key Concepts (*updated to myplate.gov*)

- Make half your grains whole • Vary your veggies • Focus on fruit • Get your calcium rich foods • Go lean with protein.
- Find your balance between food and physical activity.
- Never put a child on a diet to lose weight – unless under a doctor's close supervision.
- Help children grow into healthy weights by accenting healthy habits – not diets.
- Some children are born to be large, some small. Every child can be healthy.
- If your child is overweight, it's especially important to nurture the 5 C's.
- competence, • confidence, • connections (with family & friends), • character and • caring.

Chapter 5 – Physical Health Development

Eva Obarzanek, PhD., RD, NHLBI nutritionist and Dietary Intervention Study in Children (DISC) project officer, (USHHS, 2005) agrees that most children could benefit from healthier eating patterns like those followed by DISC participants. "DISC has shown that following a diet low in saturated fat and cholesterol is safe for young children in this age group—and a heart-healthy diet can lower blood cholesterol levels," she noted. Studies have shown that atherosclerosis, or hardening of the arteries—the leading cause of heart disease—begins in childhood.

> *The National Cholesterol Education Program recommends that children over the age of about 2 years, as well as all adults, adopt a heart-healthy eating pattern*

to reduce their risk of developing heart disease as adults. Children and adults can also lower their risk by maintaining a healthy weight and by being physically active.

Diet – elements in food that contribute to good nutrition, individual nutritional requirements.

You are What You Eat

National Restaurant Association (2010)

(1200 17th St., NW • Washington, DC 20036 • (202) 331-5900) online at: http://www.restaurant.org/Downloads/PDFs/Industry-Impact/eatingtips_brochure_201102 and at: http://www.restaurant.org/foodhealthyliving/

A few healthy eating suggestions by the National Restaurant Association include:

- Learn how many calories your body needs per day when taking into account your lifestyle and activity level, and plan your meals for the day—if you have a big breakfast, have a lighter lunch, for example.
- Watch the amount of salad dressings and other sauces; try starting out with a small amount. Or, ask for the dressing on the side. This way, you can control how much you add and you can always add more to taste.
- Use mustard or herbs and spices on sandwiches instead of mayonnaise or oils.
- Foods that are baked, grilled, broiled, poached or steamed generally use less fat in food preparation and usually have fewer calories.
- Prepare or choose meals with vegetables and fruits as key ingredients. Fruits and vegetables are naturally low in calories and fat, and can provide dietary fiber as well as many vitamins and minerals.
- Variety, moderation and balancing your food choices are the keys to healthy eating. Even though many healthy people do not completely deprive themselves of the foods they enjoy occasionally, you might consider working on acquiring a taste and love for more healthy foods. Most foods can fit into a healthy well-balanced diet. Unhealthy foods should be held to a bare minimum.
- Variety means eating foods from all five food groups: (1) breads (whole grains when possible), cereal, rice, and pasta; (2) fruits; (3) vegetables; (4) dairy (low fat when

possible) milk, yogurt and cheese; and (5) (low-fat) meats, poultry, fish, dry beans, eggs, and nuts. Also drink plenty of water.

- Moderation (realistically) means that you can enjoy most foods as part of a healthy diet as long as your food choices are very light on fat (especially saturated fat), sugars, salt, and alcohol. It doesn't mean that you (absolutely have to) give up (forever) certain foods, it means setting (strict) limits to how much and how often. One meal or one food (eaten occasionally) will not create or destroy a healthy diet. It is your overall pattern of food choices over time that is important for health.

- Shop at the right time. Ask people at your supermarket when their produce is delivered, and shop then. Your vegetables will have a longer "shelf life."

> - *Add spices to make plain dishes zippier. "Curry, ginger, garlic, chili powder have tremendous anti-oxidant effects."*

In other words, the spices can help fight certain kinds of cancer. She also suggests you buy your spices in small quantities (since they usually keep their flavor for just 6 to 12 months) and that you go to a store where there's a frequent turnover of spices so they'll be fresher.

Suggestions on Controlling Hunger

Take a walk, drink water, eat a rice cake or raw vegetables.

Know the difference between "mouth hunger" (urge to use food to soothe feelings of boredom, nervousness, anger, sadness or stress) and "stomach hunger" (your body's way of telling you it really does need food).

Sense of control has also commonly been associated with positive physical health outcomes in *How Happy are We?* (Brim, Ryff, Carol, & Kessler, 2004). Diet appears to be a primary cause of weight gain. Exercise helps mentally as well as physically and psychological benefits such as a greater sense of wellbeing, increased self-esteem and decreased anxiety or depression have all been linked to exercise.

Fat Replacers

Moderate use of low-calorie, reduced-fat foods, combined with low total energy intake, could potentially promote dietary intake consistent with the objectives of healthy eating.

> *Evidence suggests that lowering total energy intake along with a reduction in total fat intake can have a substantial impact on body weight and risk of chronic diseases.*

Fat replacers are used to provide some or all of the functional properties of fat while providing fewer calories than the fat being replaced and are used in a variety of products, from baked goods to frozen desserts. Fat replacers can be effective only if they lower the total caloric content of the food and if the consumer uses these foods as part of a balanced meal plan. Consumers should not be led to believe that fat- and calorie-reduced products can be consumed in unlimited amounts. Fat replacers are most useful when they help with calorie control and when their use encourages the consumption of foods delivering important nutrients (American Dietetic Association, 1998).

Other Dietary Tips (John Hopkins Health Letter, n.d.)

At any age, improving your diet gives you a powerful weapon against chronic disease. What you eat—and what you don't eat—may determine whether and when you develop a disorder that reduces the quality of your life, or threatens to shorten it.

Limit your daily sodium to 1,300 mg daily (1,200 mg after age 70). Eight daily servings of fruits and vegetables to get enough potassium (4,700 mg of potassium is recommended—or double the old amount). Two to four servings of fat-free or low-fat dairy products for calcium and protein.

Prostate cancer preventative measure, not prevention: Limit fat from animal sources, especially meats and dairy products. Eat a diet rich in whole grains, have at least five servings daily of fruits and vegetables, and include plenty of cruciferous vegetables such as broccoli, cauliflower and cabbage. Eat several servings of cooked tomato products (such as tomato sauce) per week. A high intake of lycopene, an antioxidant found in tomatoes can be good for you.

> *According to the Center for Reintegration (2003), the importance of water in the diet cannot be overstated.*

Healthy lifestyles that include exercise and a high fiber diet require plenty of water intake. Experts suggest eight 8-ounce glasses of water daily. For anyone participating in a regular exercise program, 9-13 glasses of water are recommended.

Getting Fit

Taken from *Time Magazine* – June 6, 2005 Issue – www.time.com
Lose that spare tire – special report on "how to get fitter, faster."

100 years ago, staying in shape just wasn't an issue. The old energy-balance equation—calories in should equal calories out is seriously out of whack…. We (Americans) are not burning enough calories or moving our bodies enough to maintain good health.

As bad as it is to be overweight, it may be just as bad to be inactive. In fact, some health authorities believe it's worse. Being overweight is a more conspicuous problem. You can see it with your eyes, you can measure it on a scale. Fitness isn't so easy to size up. ," According to Carlos Crespo, professor of social and preventive medicine at the University of Buffalo in New York, fitness is not a matter of being skinny; it's a matter of being healthy. Experts like

Chapter 5 – Physical Health Development

Crespo talk about seven components of fitness, a list that varies a bit from study to study but typically goes something like this: (1) body composition, (2) cardio-respiratory function, (3) flexibility and range of motion, (4) muscle strength, (5) endurance, (6) balance and (7) agility and coordination.

This year, the Federal Dietary Guidelines for Americans (http://health.gov/dietaryguidelines/2015.asp), which have been issued every five years since 1980, included its most explicit recommendations to date on exercise. Dr. Tim Church, medical director of the Cooper Institute, a fitness research center in Dallas, Texas suggests:

> **The rock-bottom message should be (a minimum) 30 minutes (of exercise) a day, five days a week.**

And while 30 uninterrupted minutes are preferable, three 10-minute bursts also do the trick. Church and many others believe there's a simple way for more Americans to get the activity their bodies need, and it doesn't require gym memberships or fancy equipment. The answer, they say, is walking.

PHYSICAL ACTIVITY

Increasing physical activity and improving health-related fitness (HRF) in children have emerged as important health priorities. Research has shown that multi-component school-based interventions that involve a collaborative approach to improving physical activity and fitness (involving the school curriculum, the school environment and families) are the most efficacious (Kriemler et al., 2011). The positive results from this study will add to the growing body of evidence supporting the value of school-based interventions that target improvements in physical fitness in children and youth and will help inform future intervention design and implementation. Given the program was based on the subject matter of the school curriculum, the program has great potential for future large scale dissemination and/or translation into mandatory primary school Health and Physical Education (HPE) programs (Eather, Morgan, & Lubans, 2013).

Physical fitness in young people

Increasing physical activity for young people is a major initiative of First Lady Michelle Obama. Thivel et al. (2011) did a study titled "Effect of a 6-Month School-Based Physical Activity Program on Body Composition and Physical Fitness in Lean and Obese School Children." In their study, they referenced a number of other interesting studies. Some of their findings are shared here. The alarming worldwide progression of obesity has been associated with low levels of physical activity (PA) (Maffeis, Zaffanello, & Schutz, 1997) presented as a leading cause in both aerobic and anaerobic fitness decline (Lafortuna, Fumagalli, Vangeli, & Sartorio, 2002; Tomkinson, Léger, Olds, & Cazorla, 2003). Decreased physical fitness is a contributing factor in the development of obesity complications from a very young age.

Chapter 5 – Physical Health Development

> **Most studies present aerobic fitness as the primary factor supporting good health (including a healthy diet),**

yet anaerobic fitness may be just as important in maintaining overall health and fitness (Armstrong & Welsman, 1997). Physical activity is a behavior, while physical fitness (PF) represents a physical trait determining the ability to carry out physical work. Consequently, it would seem necessary to assess their effects independently (Andersen et al., 2008). PA, PF and the presence of fat have been independently associated with clustering of cardiovascular risk factors as part of the European Youth Heart Study (Andersen et al., 2006; Anderssen et al., 2007) independent of country, age and sex (Andersen et al., 2008).

Blair et al. (1995) underlined the relationship between both low levels of PA and decreased PF and a marked increase in all causes of mortality rates (Blair et al., 1995), with subjects who are not physically fit being at higher risk compared to fit subjects even when matched for BMI (Lee, Jackson, & Blair, 1998; Léger, Lambert, & Mercier, 1983; Wong et al., 2008).

It is now clearly established that obesity often results in a gradual decrease in exercise capacity and aerobic fitness due to the vicious cycle of inactivity and deconditioning (Bouchard & Shephard, 1994; Knöpfli et al., 2008). Shang and collaborators recently presented research showing inferior performance during physical fitness tests in overweight and obese 6- to 12-year-old children when compared to their healthy schoolmates (Shang et al., 2010; Slentz et al., 2007).

Narelle Eather, Phillip Morgan and David Lubans (2013) did a study to evaluate the impact of a multi-component school-based physical activity intervention (Fit-4-Fun) on health-related fitness and objectively measured physical activity in primary school children. In an article in *Preventative Medicine*, they noted a number of other studies on the subject.

> **Physical fitness is an important predictor of physical and psychological health in young people (Ortega et al., 2008; Parfitt et al., 2009).**

Recent studies demonstrate that children who display high levels of health-related fitness (HRF) (e.g., cardiorespiratory fitness, muscular fitness, flexibility and body composition) have a decreased risk of developing cardiovascular disease and other chronic illnesses (McMurray & Anderson, 2010), are less likely to suffer from anxiety and depression (Parfitt et al., 2009), and are more likely to perform better academically (Grissom, 2005; Van Dusen et al., 2011). Evidence also confirms that a large proportion of children are unfit (Ortega et al., 2011; Tomkinson et al., 2003), that children's fitness levels decline with age and fatness levels increase with age (Stratton et al., 2007), and that children do not participate in physical activity of sufficient volume and intensity to accrue the associated health benefits (Booth et al., 2005; Currie et al., 2008; Ortega et al., 2011). Considering the low levels of physical activity typically observed among youth (AHKC, 2012; Ekelund et al., 2011; Hardy et al., 2010) and secular declines in youth fitness levels (Boddy et al., 2012; Tomkinson & Olds, 2007; Tremblay et al., 2010), there is an urgent need to develop and evaluate interventions that promote high intensity activity but that are also appealing to young people. Indeed, the latest national physical activity guidelines include physical fitness parameters (USDHHS, 2009).

Exercise, Exercise, Exercise (The Center for Reintegration, 2003)

Exercise is fundamental in maintaining a healthy body and an active lifestyle. Exercise can help you mentally as well as physically. Regular exercise helps to:
- Prevent heart disease (aerobic)
- Normalize blood pressure (aerobic)
- Regulate blood sugar
- Prevent bone mineral loss
- Support body structure
- Promote weight loss
- Promote flexibility

Tips for Getting Started (The Center for Reintegration, 2003)

If you have not been exercising, it is important not to start off too fast or too hard. If you overdo it, you are likely to end up feeling discouraged or causing strain, pain, or injury to yourself. Keep the following points in mind as you get started with your exercise program:
- Talk to your doctor before beginning a new program.
- Begin gradually
- Give yourself a one-month trial period
- Expect some initial discomfort
- Try to focus on the process of exercise (rather than competing with others or yourself)
- Remember to warm up before you exercise, and cool down afterwards
- Coordinate your eating and exercise (avoid exercising less than 90 minutes before a meal, and don't eat until 1 hour after exercising)
- Don't exercise when you feel sick.

> *My recommendation is to make exercise as independent as possible and free of things you need in order to exercise.*

Set it up such that you can exercise <u>anywhere</u> and just about <u>anytime</u>. Do not be dependent on certain equipment or other requirements to get a recommended 3 to 4 days—every other day—of exercise every week. Also don't be dependent on other people to exercise with.

What is exercise? According to Proactol (2006), many people walk from their desk to the fax machine a few times a day and qualify that as their weekly exercise routine. Some do 10 or 15 sit-ups a couple of days a week and feel that they have done enough. Still others, wanting to lose weight, only stick to a diet. They think that simply cutting back on calories is sufficient enough without exercise. While all of these things are good, they are not enough to keep the body healthy.

Exercise is hard to beat

Exercise is about much more than simply losing weight or getting into good shape. Studies have shown that a healthy amount of exercise daily or weekly can actually help prevent heart diseases and certain types of cancer, such as colon and breast cancer. It also decreases your chances of getting a stroke or diabetes. Other serious diseases and disorders such as bone and joint disorders can also be prevented by an exercise routine. Regular exercise also helps prevent premature death, giving you a long and healthy life.

While the previously mentioned benefits of exercise are good, a lot of people prefer to see noticeable benefits as a motivation to help them keep going with a regular routine. Obviously, exercise helps the body lose weight, but there are some other benefits that are noticeable soon after you start exercising. Some of these benefits include a higher amount of energy and stamina throughout the day, leaner, toned muscles and more mental alertness. It will also greatly improve your sleep. Many people these days complain that they are not getting enough sleep, or that they cannot fall asleep at night. Exercise will likely bring the sandman as soon as your head hits that pillow!

Depression, chemical imbalances, and mood swings are more prevalent today as well. Could it be a coincidence that these things are occurring as more and more people aren't getting enough exercise? Studies show that it is not a coincidence! Exercise will greatly improve your mood and your general attitude about yourself, causing your self-esteem to improve as well. Still not convinced? Consider this fact: Sometimes people find that nothing gives them quite the same feeling as a really good piece of decadent chocolate. Well, get ready for this: Exercise actually releases the same endorphins in your brain that come from eating chocolate! If that isn't incentive enough to get off of the couch and start working out, then I don't know what is!

> **When planning your exercise routine, be careful not to overdo it.**

Extremes are never good in any situation, and the same goes for exercise. The belief that the more you push your body, the faster you'll be in shape is definitely not true. Your body needs time to adjust to your workout. It is much healthier and safer to start off slow, and gradually build up from there. Remember, it doesn't matter how much you do; it is consistency that is important.

When to stop exercising

If you experience any of the following symptoms during exercise – STOP and REST and call your doctor if your symptoms persist:

- Dizziness or lightheadedness

- Abnormal heart rhythm
- Pain in the chest under the breastbone, and/or down the arm
- Pain in the knees, feet, or ankles

<u>Keep up your motivation</u>

> *Exercise and eating a proper diet are lifetime endeavors.*

The most difficult part about this process is getting started. Once you have started and have a regular routine started, try very, very hard to not lose it. If you stop, all your hard work will be lost within weeks after you stop.

Some people like to find exercises that can be fun or that can fit into their regular routine of work or home activity. My way of looking at exercise is that it is one of those things in life that must be done whether I like it or not. I call it "paying dues is the price I pay for a healthy life is 1-3 hours a day, 3-4 days a week. The way I see it is, "feel like it" or "want to do it," has nothing to do with whether I do it or not. Not doing it is not an option.

MORE ON PHYSICAL FITNESS

In the beginning of this chapter I asked whether you consider yourself to be both physically healthy and physically fit. If you are physically healthy, that's very good. If you happen to also be physically fit, that would be fantastic. I would guess that most of us might be physically healthy but few are also physically fit.

Mark Perry (2012) wrote an article titled "Physical Fitness: What is Physical Fitness?" that gave a very thorough definition of physical fitness that can be distinguished from simply being physically healthy.

*"**Physical Fitness (D/F)** – A measure of the body's ability to function efficiently and effectively in work and leisure activities, resist hypokinetic diseases (diseases from sedentary lifestyles), and to meet emergency situations."*

While this is the short answer for "What is Physical Fitness?", there is a longer and more interesting answer when you dig deeper. By looking at the individual components of physical fitness, we can get a better picture of what physically fit means in terms of how to identify it, measure it, and assert its significance.

The following are the top 10 facets of physical fitness adapted from sources that include President's Council on Fitness, Sports & Nutrition, CrossFit, and the National Strength & Conditioning Association. The first five facets are health-related and can be improved through proper training and the last five are skill related, which can be improved through practice of motor skills—aside from power #9 and speed #10, which require both. The following photos were retrieved from http://www.builtlean.com/2012/02/21/physical-fitness/

Physical Fitness #1 | Body Composition

Definition: The relative amount of fat, muscle, bone, and other vital parts of the body.

Significance: While it is possible for an individual to have a high degree of fitness and still have excess body fat, losing body fat while retaining lean muscle will improve all other physical fitness metrics given that strength/power to weight ratio will be improved, along with other general health markers.

Physical Fitness #2 | Strength

Definition: The ability of a muscle group to exert force

Significance: Strength is required to perform basic functional movements in our life; squatting, lunging, pushing, pulling, and bending are important in our everyday life. In addition, as we age, muscle size and strength tend to decrease along with bone mass, a decrease that can be reversed with strength training.

Physical Fitness #3 | Cardiovascular Fitness

Definition: Ability of the circulatory systems and respiratory systems to supply oxygen during sustained physical activity.

Significance: Improved cardiovascular fitness increases lung capacity so the heart does not have to work as hard to pump blood to the muscles. It is also important for overall heart health and prevention of lifestyle diseases.

Physical Fitness #4 | Flexibility

Definition: The range of motion at a joint

Significance: The optimal range of motion about various joints has a direct effect on almost all other facets of physical fitness. For example, if one's hip flexors are tight, that can affect the ability to reach maximum speed, or perform agility drills to maximum effect.

Physical Fitness #5 | Muscular Endurance

Definition: The ability of muscles to continue to perform repeated contractions against submaximal resistance.

Significance: Performing repetitious physical activity such as gardening, raking leaves and washing your car will become less fatiguing.

Skill-Related physical fitness:
Physical Fitness #6 | Agility

Definition: The ability to rapidly change the position of the entire body in time and space with speed and accuracy.

Significance: Changing directions is a common cause of injury, so proper movement control from high levels of agility is essential.

Physical Fitness #7 | Balance

Definition: The ability to maintain equilibrium while moving or stationary.

Significance: Especially as we age, balance becomes increasingly important to prevent falls, which can result in serious injury. Balance is one of the most overlooked areas of fitness.

Physical Fitness #8 | Coordination

Definition: The ability to use the senses, such as sight and hearing, together with body parts, in performing motor tasks smoothly and accurately.

Significance: Whether you want to play a musical instrument like the drums, or just get into your car while balancing your morning coffee, coordination is involved in many daily activities.

Physical Fitness #9 | Power

Definition: The ability of a muscular unit or a combination of muscular units to apply maximum force in minimum time

Significance: The ability to move a body quickly through space is very important in all sports and is also required in daily living such as getting out of a chair, which requires not just strength, but power.

Physical Fitness #10 | Speed

Definition: The ability to perform a movement within a short period of time

Significance: Some sports are based purely on speed, and most sports require speed. Speed is also helpful in everyday life, especially when you leave your wallet in a cab and need to run after it.

Whether you are physically healthy and/or physically fit, you will want to know about and be on a consistent regimen of taking your essential nutrients.

MORE ON ESSENTIAL NUTRIENTS

Water

> ***The body needs the following six essential nutrients, every day: Water, Carbohydrates, Proteins, Fats, Vitamins and Minerals.***

Water is the most essential nutrient the body needs. Forty to sixty percent of your body weight is water. Muscle composition is approximately 70% water.

Why is being hydrated so important?
- To answer this question, consider the following functions of water in our bodies:
- in saliva and stomach secretions it helps to digest food
- in blood, it helps transport nutrients and oxygen to all the cells of the body
- in body fluids, it helps lubricate joints and cushions organs and tissues · in urine, it carries waste products out of the body
- in sweat, it removes body heat generated during exercise

(from Physician and Sports Medicine, Nancy Clark MS, RD - May 1995).

Drinking plenty of water is also important for healthy skin. Another interesting fact: sometimes our body confuses a thirst signal for a hunger signal, which is why drinking a glass of water before a meal or snack is a common weight management tip.

Why is it so hard to stay hydrated?
For one, our bodies are constantly losing water. The most obvious way is through daily urine output. If you exercise, you sweat. Studies of athletes have shown sweat losses of 2 quarts per hour while exercising! Most of us will lose less than that on our daily walk/run, but sweating is still a large source of water loss. Even when not exercising we are losing water through our skin - this is called 'insensible losses'. Other insensible losses are through respiration and feces.

Another reason we have a hard time staying hydrated is that our thirst mechanism has a sort of lag time. Once we are thirsty, our bodies have already reached the point of moderate dehydration, and it becomes more difficult to replenish the fluids to the point of hydration.

.,
How do you know if you're hydrated or dehydrated?
The best way to tell if you're hydrated is to monitor your urine. You should be urinating a significant amount regularly (3-4 times) throughout the day. If your urine is pale yellow or clear in color you are drinking enough. If it is dark yellow and odorous, get a big glass of water and start guzzling! Keep in mind that a vitamin pill will also make your urine dark - so it is possible to have dark urine and still be hydrated.

The first sign of dehydration is thirst. Other signs of moderate dehydration are low grade headache and fatigue. Severe dehydration is accompanied by nausea, chills, increased heart

rate, inability to sweat, and lightheadedness. At this point, medical attention is warranted.
How much water do I need?
Again, it depends on who you are. A rule of thumb that you may have heard is no less than 64 oz. per day. That's about 8 glasses of water per day if you prefer to think of it that way. This amount would probably be adequate for someone who lived in a temperate climate and was totally sedentary. Hopefully, no one out there is totally sedentary and Arizona is definitely not a temperate climate in August! When you add exercise and hot weather, your fluid needs increase significantly. It would be a good idea to add at least two more cups if you live in an intemperate climate.
Information about water was written by Paige Holm, R.D. retrieved from:
https://www.health.arizona.edu/health_topics/nutrition/general/waterhydration.htm

Carbohydrates
Carbohydrates: quality matters
What's most important is the *type of carbohydrate* you choose to eat because some sources are healthier than others. The *amount of carbohydrate* in the diet – high or low – is less important than the *type of carbohydrate* in the diet. For example, healthy, whole grains such as whole wheat bread, rye, barley and quinoa are better choices than highly refined white bread or French fries. (1)
Many people are confused about carbohydrates, but keep in mind that it's more important to eat carbohydrates from healthy foods than to follow a strict diet limiting or counting the number of grams of carbohydrates consumed.

What are carbohydrates?
Carbohydrates are found in a wide array of both healthy and unhealthy foods—bread, beans, milk, popcorn, potatoes, cookies, spaghetti, soft drinks, corn, and cherry pie. They also come in a variety of forms. The most common and abundant forms are sugars, fibers, and starches. Foods high in carbohydrates are an important part of a healthy diet. Carbohydrates provide the body with glucose, which is converted to energy used to support bodily functions and physical activity. But carbohydrate quality is important; some types of carbohydrate-rich foods are better than others:
- The healthiest sources of carbohydrates—unprocessed or minimally processed whole grains, vegetables, fruits and beans—promote good health by delivering vitamins, minerals, fiber, and a host of important phytonutrients.

Unhealthier sources of carbohydrates include white bread, pastries, sodas, and other highly processed or refined foods. These items contain easily digested carbohydrates that may contribute to weight gain, interfere with weight loss, and promote diabetes and heart disease.
Information about carbohydrates was retrieved from:
http://www.hsph.harvard.edu/nutritionsource/carbohydrates/

Cautionary note about sugar
According to the August 2015 University of California *Wellness Letter* we might not know all we need to know about the effects of sugar in our diet. "Sugar: the bitter truth: it's not just

making us fat, it may be making us sick," is the title of the article based on the latest research on the subject. This front-page article states that in the past, worries were confined to its increasing the risk of diabetes and obesity and its causing cavities, but now research has also linked sugar to heart disease, hypertension, strokes, gout, periodontal disease, fatty liver disease, and a host of other health problems.

The new proposed Dietary Guidelines for Americans recommend a limit on sugar for the first time: no more than 10 percent of a person's daily calories should come from added sugar. That amounts to about 12 teaspoons (50 grams) for someone consuming 2,000 calories a day (1 teaspoon contains about 4 grams of sugar). The article recommend that you eat mostly whole foods (as opposed to processed foods) and rarely consume sugary drinks.

Protein

According to Amanda Hernandez protein is the major structural component of cells and is responsible for the building and repair of body tissues. Protein is broken down into amino acids, which are building blocks of protein. Nine of the 20 amino acids, known as essential amino acids, must be provided in the diet as they cannot be synthesized in the body. Ten to 35 percent of your daily calories should come from lean protein sources such as low-fat meat, dairy, beans or eggs.

Retrieved from: http://healthyeating.sfgate.com/6-essential-nutrients-functions-4877.html

Another source concerning protein provided additional information. This information was retrieved from: "Proteins are essential to life!"
http://www.eufic.org/article/en/nutrition/protein/artid/proteins/

Proteins are essential to life!

Proteins are found in different foods. Animal sources of protein, such as meat, poultry, fish, eggs, milk, cheese and yogurt, provide high biological value proteins. Plants, legumes, grains, nuts, seeds and vegetables provide low biological value proteins.

However, as the limiting amino acid tends to be different in different vegetable proteins, combination of vegetable sources of proteins in the same meal (e.g. legumes or pulses with cereals), results often in a mix of higher biological value. These combinations are generally found in traditional culinary recipes from the different continents (e.g. beans with rice, pasta or manioc, chick-peas with bread, lentils with potatoes, etc).

Fat

Fat is another term for lipid. Too much fat in your diet can lead to obesity, heart disease, heart attacks, and strokes. Fat does have its uses though.

> *The body needs some fat to process vitamins and minerals and to insulate its inner systems.*

Chapter 5 – Physical Health Development

Fats are essential for good health. They aid in energy production, cell building, oxygen transport, blood clotting, and the production of extremely active hormone-like substances called prostaglandins.

Fats can be saturated, polyunsaturated, or monounsaturated. Our bodies can produce both monounsaturated and saturated fats. Polyunsaturated fats, or essential fatty acids, cannot be produced in the body and must come from the diet.

Key Functions

- Fat is mostly stored in the body's adipose (fat) cells but is also found in blood plasma and other body cells.
- Fat insulates your body, cushions vital organs, and can be converted into energy.
- Fat is used to build new cells and is critical for normal brain development and nerve function.
- Fat is also needed to carry and help absorb fat-soluble vitamins, such as vitamins A, D, E, and K, and carotenoids.

Food Sources

Fat is twice as calorie-dense (1 gram = 9 calories) as carbohydrates or protein (1 gram = 4 calories). Although there are health benefits associated with olive and canola oils, they are still high in calories (1 tbsp = 120 calories). In addition, many processed foods and fast foods are high in fat, especially saturated fat.

- Mono-unsaturated fats are found in olive and canola oils.
- Saturated fats are found in animal products such as butter, cheese, whole milk, ice cream, cream, and fatty meats, as well as some vegetable oils – coconut, palm, and palm kernel oils.
- Polyunsaturated fats are found in safflower, sunflower, corn, and soybean oils.

Information about fats was retrieved from: "Role of Fats in Good Nutrition" http://www.nutrilite.com/en-us/Nature/Nutrients/fats.aspx?

11 Essential Vitamins and Minerals Your Body Needs

Experts recommend fueling your body with healthy food before you turn to supplements. The best bet is to make sure you eat a balanced diet with as many wholefoods as possible –if you need a boost, here's the low-down on what letter does what, from A (that is, vitamin A) to Z (or - zinc).

This information on vitamins and minerals was retrieved from: http://www.goodnet.org/articles/11-essential-vitamins-minerals-your-body-needs

1. VITAMIN A GOOD FOR: Healthy eyes and general growth and development, including healthy teeth and skin.
NATURAL SOURCE: Carrots and other orange foods including sweet potato and cantaloupe melons – all of which get their hue from the carotene pigment.

2. B VITAMINS GOOD FOR: Energy production, immune function and iron absorption.

NATURAL SOURCE: This crucial group of nutrients can be found in whole unprocessed foods, specifically whole grains, potatoes, bananas, lentils, chili peppers, beans, yeast and molasses.

3. VITAMIN C
GOOD FOR: Strengthening blood vessels and giving skin its elasticity, anti-oxidant function and iron absorption.
NATURAL SOURCE: Everyone knows this one – oranges! But they're not the only source – other fruits and veggies packed with Vitamin C include guava, red and green peppers, kiwi, grapefruits, strawberries, Brussels sprouts and cantaloupe.

4. VITAMIN D GOOD FOR: Strong healthy bones.
NATURAL SOURCE: Apart from spending a few minutes out in the sun
, which stimulates Vitamin D production, you can get this nutritional must from eggs, fish and mushrooms.

5. VITAMIN E GOOD FOR: Blood circulation, and protection from free radicals.
NATURAL SOURCE: Our favorite Vitamin E-rich food is the mighty almond. You can also fill up on other nuts, sunflower seeds and tomatoes to reap the benefits.

6. VITAMIN K GOOD FOR: Blood coagulation – that is, the process by which your blood clots.
NATURAL SOURCE: Leafy greens are the best natural sources of Vitamin K – so make sure you're eating lots of kale, spinach, Brussels sprouts and broccoli.

7. FOLIC ACID GOOD FOR: Cell renewal and preventing birth defects in pregnancy.
NATURAL SOURCE: There are plenty of scrumptious natural sources of folic acid, including dark leafy greens, asparagus, broccoli, citrus fruits, beans, peas, lentils, seeds, nuts, cauliflower, beets and corn.

8. CALCIUM GOOD FOR: Healthy teeth and bones.
NATURAL SOURCE: This mineral is another one that most of us already know - the best sources are dairy products like yogurt, cheese and milk, along with tofu and black molasses.

9. IRON GOOD FOR: Building muscles naturally and maintaining healthy blood.
NATURAL SOURCE: You might be surprised to know that clams take the top spot for iron content, followed by oysters and organ meats like liver. For the vegetarians among us, soybeans, cereal, pumpkin seeds, beans, lentils and spinach are great sources of iron.

10. ZINC GOOD FOR: Immunity, growth and fertility.
NATURAL SOURCE: Seafoods like oysters are also zinc-rich, along with spinach, cashews, beans and – wait for it – dark chocolate.

11. CHROMIUM GOOD FOR: Glucose function – making sure every cell in your body gets energy as and when needed.

NATURAL SOURCE: As long as your diet contains servings of whole grains, fresh vegetables and herbs, you should be getting enough chromium.

STRESS
Stress and Your Physical Health

> *Stress kills thousands of people each year yet this is one health risk factor that can be controlled.*

According to a fact sheet put out by the United States Department of Health and Human Services (n.d.) (retrieved from: http://www.nimh.nih.gov/health/publications/stress/index.shtml), stress can be defined as the brain's response to any demand. Many things can trigger this response, including change.

How does stress affect the body?

Not all stress is bad. All animals have a stress response, which can be life-saving in some situations. The nerve chemicals and hormones released during such stressful times, prepares the animal to face a threat or flee to safety. When you face a dangerous situation, your pulse quickens, you breathe faster, your muscles tense and your brain uses more oxygen and increases activity—all functions aimed at survival. In the short term, it can even boost the immune system.

However, with chronic stress, those same nerve chemicals that are life-saving in short bursts can suppress functions that aren't needed for immediate survival. Your immunity is lowered and your digestive, excretory, and reproductive systems stop working normally. Once the threat has passed, other body systems act to restore normal functioning. Problems occur if the stress response goes on too long, such as when the source of stress is constant, or if the response continues after the danger has subsided.

How does stress affect your overall health?

There are at least three different types of stress, all of which carry physical and mental health risks:

- Routine stress related to the pressures of work, family and other daily responsibilities
- Stress brought about by a sudden negative change, such as losing a job, divorce or illness
- Traumatic stress experienced in an event like a major accident, war, assault, or a natural disaster where one may be seriously hurt or in danger of being killed

The body responds to each type of stress in similar ways. Different people may feel it in different ways. For example, some people experience mainly digestive symptoms, while others may have headaches, sleeplessness, depressed mood, anger and irritability. People under chronic stress are prone to more frequent and severe viral infections, such as the flu or common cold, and vaccines, such as the flu shot, are less effective for them.

Of all the types of stress, changes in health from routine stress may be hardest to notice at first. Because the source of stress tends to be more constant than in cases of acute or traumatic stress, the body gets no clear signal to return to normal functioning.

> *Over time, continued strain on your body from routine stress may lead to serious health problems, such as heart disease, high blood pressure, diabetes, depression, anxiety disorder, and other illnesses.*

How can I cope with stress?

The effects of stress tend to build up over time. Taking practical steps to maintain your health and outlook can reduce or prevent these effects. The following are some tips that may help you cope with stress:

- Seek help from a qualified mental health care provider if you are overwhelmed, feel you cannot cope, have suicidal thoughts, or are using drugs or alcohol to cope.
- Get proper health care for existing or new health problems.
- Stay in touch with people who can provide emotional and other support. Ask for help from friends, family, and community or religious organizations to reduce stress due to work burdens or family issues, such as caring for a loved one.

> *Recognize signs of your body's response to stress, such as difficulty sleeping, increased alcohol and other substance use, being easily angered, feeling depressed, and having low energy.*

- Set priorities – decide what must get done and what can wait, and learn to say no to new tasks if they are putting you into overload.
- Note what you have accomplished at the end of the day, not what you have been unable to do.
- Avoid dwelling on problems. If you can't do this on your own, seek help from a qualified mental health professional who can guide you.
- Exercise regularly – just 30 minutes per day of gentle walking can help boost mood and reduce stress.
- Schedule regular times for healthy and relaxing activities.
- Explore stress coping programs, which may incorporate meditation, yoga, tai chi, or other gentle exercises.

The above information on stress was retrieved from the National Institute of Health at: http://www.nimh.nih.gov/health/publications/stress/index.shtml

Chapter 5 – Physical Health Development

I read an interesting article in my May 2015 Health Newsletter from the University of Berkeley about BPA (bisphenol A). For years, concerns were raised about BPA, a chemical used in the production of plastics and resins, such as some water bottles and the coatings of some food cans. The concern was raised because of potential problems related to the fact that it mimics estrogen and is thus classified as an endocrine disruptor—that is, a chemical that can interfere with hormone functions. The question is whether the levels of BPA to which we are typically exposed have adverse health effects.

The interesting part of this front-page article is a sub-titled article about thermal paper. This thin smooth paper is coated with heat-activated printing developers, usually either BPA or the related chemical BPS (bisphenol S). Such paper is used for many kinds of receipts (notably from cash registers, ATM machines, gas pumps and credit card terminals) and tickets (for airlines, movies, lotteries, for instance). You can tell it's thermal paper if scratching the printed side produces a dark mark.

The BPA on the surface of thermal paper is in the free form so it easily rubs off on your hands and can then get on food you handle. It can also be absorbed through the skin, which may be more dangerous than oral absorption because the BPA would enter the circulatory system and go directly to tissues before being metabolized in the liver.

A small study in the *Journal of the American Medical Association* (2014) found that

> ***when people handled thermal receipts for two hours, urinary PBA increased three- to five-fold over 24 hours.***

This is obviously a concern for cashiers and others who handle the paper frequently at work.

But even briefly handling thermal paper may be a problem under circumstances. This was seen in a series of small experiments done at the University of Missouri and published in *PLOS ONE* (in 2014), which got lots of press. In one test, participants held thermal paper for up to four minutes either with dry hands or with hands wet with an alcohol-based sanitizer. About 100 times more BPA was transferred to the wet hands (almost none to the dry hands).

Then in what might be a worst-case scenario—though one that may occur in a fast food restaurant—some participants used hand sanitizer, immediately handled thermal receipts with wet hands, and then ate French fries. This led to a dramatic increase in skin and oral absorption of BPA in most of them (especially the women), as seen in urine and blood tests over the next 90 days. Why did hand sanitizer worsen matters? Like some other skin care products, such as moisturizers and sunscreens, it contains chemicals that enhance penetration of accompanying ingredients through the skin. Thus, the sanitizer, especially because it was still wet, greatly increased the transfer and absorption of BPA.

Some experts criticize the study for not testing what would have happened if the sanitizer had been allowed to dry (as instructions on the product advise). Clearly, less BPA would have been transferred from the receipts and then absorbed.

I included this article because it was interesting. That said, I have found no credible research or other evidence that shows BPA to be harmful. The U.S. Food and Drug Administration's (FDA) current perspective, based on its most recent safety assessment (June 2014), is that BPA is safe at the current levels occurring in foods. Based on FDA's ongoing safety review of scientific evidence, the available information continues to support the safety of BPA for the currently approved uses in food containers and packaging.

REFERENCES
Chapter 5 – "Physical Health Development"

Active Healthy Kids Canada. (2012). *Is active play extinct? The Active Healthy Kids Canada 2012 Report Card of physical activity for children and youth.* Toronto, Canada: Active Healthy Kids Canada.

American Dietetic Association, Academy of Nutrition and Dietetics. (n.d.). *It's about eating right: Vitamins and nutrients.* Retrieved from http://www.eatright.org/public/content.aspx?id=5554

American Dietetic Association, Academy of Nutrition and Dietetics. (n.d.). *It's about eating right: Choosing a nutrient-rich diet.* Retrieved from http://www.eatright.org/Public/content.aspx?id=6791

American Dietetic Association. (2005). Position of the American Dietetic Association: Fat replacers. *Journal of American Dietetic Association, 105*(2), 266–275.

Andersen, L. B., Harro, M., Sardinha, L. B., Froberg, K., Ekelund, U., Brage, S., & Andersen, S. A. (2006). Physical activity and clustered cardiovascular risk in children: A cross-sectional study (The European Youth Heart Study). *Lancet, 368,* 299–304.

Andersen, L. B., Sardinha, L. B., Froberg, K., Riddoch, C. J., Page, A. S., & Andersen, S. A. (2008). Fitness, fatness and clustering of cardiovascular risk factors in children from Denmark, Estonia and Portugal: The European Youth Heart Study. *International Journal of Pediatric Obesity, 3,* 58–66.

Anderssen, S. A., Cooper, A. R., Riddoch, C., Sardinha, L. B., Harro, M., Brage, S., & Andersen, L. B. (2007). Low cardiorespiratory fitness is a strong predictor for clustering of cardiovascular disease risk factors in children independent of country, age and sex. *European Journal of Cardiovascular Preventative Rehabilitation, 14,* 526–531.

Armstrong, N., & Welsman, J. R. (1997). *Young people and physical activity.* Oxford University Press, Oxford.

Blair, S. N., Kohl, H. W., Barlow, C. E., Paffenbarger, R. S. J. R., Gibbons, L. W., & Macera, C. A. (1995). Changes in physical fitness and all-cause mortality. A prospective study of healthy and unhealthy men. *The Journal of the American Medical Association, 273,* 1093–1098.

Boddy, L. M., Fairclough, S. J., Atkinson, G., & Stratton, G. (2012). Changes in cardiorespiratory fitness in 9- to 10.9-year-old children: SportsLinx 1998–2010. *Medicine and Science in Sports & Exercise,* 4481–4486.

Booth, M. L., Denney-Wilson., Okely, A. D., & Hardy, L. L. (2005). Methods of the NSW Schools Physical Activity and Nutrition Survey (SPANS). *Journal of Science and Medicine in Sport, 8,* 284–293.

Bouchard, C., & Shephard, R. J. (1994). Physical activity, fitness and health: The model and key concepts. In C. Bouchard, R. J. Shephard, & T. Stephens (Eds.), *Physical activity, fitness, and health: International proceedings and consensus statement* (pp 77–88). Champaign, IL: Human Kinetics.

Brim, O. G., Ryff, Kessler, C. D., & Kessler, R. C. (Eds.) (2004). *How Healthy are we? A national study of well-being at midlife.* London: University of Chicago Press.

Cale, L., & Harris, J. (2009). Fitness testing in physical education — A misdirected effort in promoting healthy lifestyles and physical activity? *Physical Education and Sports Pedagogy, 14*(1), 149–108.

Case, A., Lubotsky, D., & Paxson, C. (2002). Economic status and health in childhood: The origins of the gradient American. *Economic Review, 92,* 1308–1334.

The Center for Reintegration. (2003). *"Exercise" and "Tips on getting started."* Retrieved from http://www.reintegration.com/resources/lifestyle/

The Center for Reintegration. (2003). *The role of water in good nutrition.* Retrieved from http://www.reintegration.com/resources/lifestyle/

Chapter 5 – Physical Health Development

Currie, C., Nic Gabhainn, S., Godeau, E., Roberts, C., Smith, R., Currie, D.,...Barnekow, V. (2008). *Inequalities in young people's Health: HBSC international report from the 2005/6 survey.* Health policy for children and adolescents (No. 5). Copenhagen, Denmark: WHO Regional Office, Europe.

Currie, J., & Stabile, M. (2003). Socioeconomic status and child health: Why is the relationship stronger for older children? *American Economic Review, 93,* 1813–1823.

Eather, N., Morgan, P. J., & Lubans, D. R. (2013). Improving the fitness and physical activity levels of primary school children: Results of the Fit-4-Fun group randomized controlled trial. *Preventive Medicine, 56,* 12–19.

Ehrlich, S., Calafat, A., Humblet, O., Smith, T., & Hauser, R. (2014). Handling of thermal receipts as a source of exposure to Bisphenol A. *Journal of the American Medical Association, 311,* 859–860.

Ekelund, U., Tomkinson, G., Armstrong, N. (2011). What proportion of youth are physically active? Measurement issues, levels and recent time trends. *British Journal of Sports Medicine, 45,* 859–865.

European Food Information Council (EUFIC). (2005). *Proteins are essential to life!* Retrieved from http://www.eufic.org/article/en/nutrition/protein/artid/proteins/

Goldman, D., & Smith, J. P. (2011). The increasing value of education to health. *Social Science & Medicine, 72*(10), 1728–1737.

Goodnet.com. (2013). *11 essential vitamins and minerals your body needs.* Retrievd from http://www.goodnet.org/articles/11-essential-vitamins-minerals-your-body-needs

Grissom, J. B. (2005). Physical fitness and academic achievement. *Journal of Exercise Physiology Online, 8,* 11–25.

Hardy, L., King., L., Espinel Diaz, P., Cosgrove, C., & Bauman, A. (2010). *NSW Schools Physical Activity and Nutrition Survey (SPANS) 2010: Full rep*ort. Sydney, Australia: NSW Ministry of Health.

Harvard.edu. (n.d.). *Carbohydrates: quality matters.* Retrieved from http://www.hsph.harvard.edu/nutritionsource/carbohydrates/

Health.gov. (2015). *Physical activity guidelines.* United States Department of Health and Human Services. Retrieved from http://www.health.gov/paguidelines/

Hernandez, A. (n.d.). *6 essential nutrients and their functions.* Retrieved from http://healthyeating.sfgate.com/6-essential-nutrients-functions-4877.html

Holm, P. (n.d.). *Water and hydration.* Retrieved from https://www.health.arizona.edu/health_topics/nutrition/general/waterhydration.htm

Hormann, A., vom Saal, F., Nagel, S., Stahlhut, R., Moyer, C. et al. (2014). Holding thermal receipt paper and eating food after using hand sanitizer results in high serum bioactive and urine total levels of Bisphenol A (BPA). *PLoS ONE 9*(10): e110509. doi:10.1371/journal.pone.0110509

John Hopkins Health Letter. (n. d.). *Life stories*: Health. Retrieved from http://oldie-newbie.com/health.html

Knöpfli, B. H., Radtke, T., Lehmann, M., Schätzle, B., Eisenblätter, J., Gachnang, A.,...Brooks-Wildhaber, J. (2008). Effects of a multidisciplinary inpatient intervention on body composition, aerobic fitness, and quality of life in severely obese girls and boys. *Journal of Adolescent Health, 42,* 119–127.

Kriemler, S., Meyer, U., Martin, E., Van Sluijs, M. F., Andersen, L. B., & Martin, B. W. (2011). Effects of school-based interventions on physical activity and fitness in children and adolescents: A review of reviews and systematic update. *British Journal of Sports Medicine, 45,* 923–930.

Lafortuna, C. L., Fumagalli, E., Vangeli, V., & Sartorio, A. (2002). Lower limb alactic anaerobic power output assessed with different techniques in morbid obesity. *Journal of Endocrinological Investigation, 25,* 134–141.

Lee, C. D., Jackson, A. S., & Blair, S. N. (1998). US weight guidelines: Is it also important to consider cardiorespiratory fitness? *International Journal of Obesity and Related Metabolic Disorders, 22*(Suppl 2), S2–S7.

Léger, L., Lambert, J., & Mercier, D. (1983). Predicted VO2 max and maximal speed for a multistage 20-rn shuttle run in 7000 Quebec children aged 6–17. *Medicine & Science in Sports & Exercise, 15,* 142–143.

Maffeis, C., Zaffanello, M., & Schutz, Y. (1997). Relationship between physical inactivity and adiposity in prepubertal boys. *Journal of Pediatrics, 131,* 288–292.

Marmot, M. (2000). Multilevel approaches to understanding social determinants (pp. 349-367). In L. Berkman, I. Kawachi (Eds.), *Social epidemiology.* New York: Oxford University Press.

Chapter 5 – Physical Health Development

McMurray, R. G., & Anderson, L. B. (2010). The influence of exercise oetabolic syndrome in youth: A review. *American Journal of Lifesytyle Medicine*, 476–186.

National Restaurant Association. (n.d.). *Tips on eating smart.* Retrieved from http://www.restaurant.org/Downloads/PDFs/Industry-Impact/eatingtips_brochure_201102

nutrilite.com. (n.d.). *Role of fats in good nutrition.* Retrieved from http://www.nutrilite.com/en-us/Nature/Nutrients/fats.aspx?

Obesity Therapy. (2007). *Effects on health.* Retrieved from http://obesity-therapy.most-effective-solution.com/effects-on-health/

Ortega, F. B., Labayen, I., Ruiz, R., Kurvinen, E., Loit, H. M., Harro, J.,… Sjostrom, M. (2011). Improvements in fitness reduce the risk of becoming overweight across puberty. *Medicine & Science in Sports & Exercise, 43*, 1891–1897.

Ortega, F. B., Ruiz, R. J., Castillo, M. J., & Sjostrom, M. (2008). Pediatric review: Physical fitness in childhood and adolescence: A powerful marker of health. *International Journal of Obesity, 32*, 111.

Pappas, G., Queen, S., Hadden, W., & Fisher, G. (1993). The increasing disparity in mortality between socioeconomic groups in the United States, 1960 and 1986. *New England Journal of Medicine, 329*, 103–109.

Parfitt, G., Pavey, T., & Rowlands, A. V. (2009). Children's physical activity and psychological health: The relevance of intensity. *Acta Paediatrica, 98*, 1037–1043.

Perry, M. (2012). *Physical fitness: What is physical fitness?* Retrieved from http://www.builtlean.com/2012/02/21/physical-fitness/

Proactal. (2006). *Benefits of exercise.* Retrieved from http://proven-fat-binders.com/benefits%20of%20exercise.html

Shang, X., Ailing, L., Yanping, L., Xiaoqi, H., Lin, D., Jun, M., … Guangsheg, M. (2010). The association of weight status with physical fitness among Chinese children. *International Journal of Pediatrics, 2010*, 515–414.

Slentz, C. A., Houmard, J. A., Johnson, J. L., Bateman, L. A., Tanner, C. J., McCartney, J. S., Duscha, B. D., & Kraus, W. E. (2007). Inactivity, exercise training and detraining, and plasma lipoproteins. STRRIDE: a randomized, controlled study of exercise intensity and amount. *Journal of Applied Physiology, 103*, 432–442.

Smith, J. P. (1999). Healthy bodies and thick wallets: the dual relation between health and economic status. *Journal of Economic Perspectives, 13*, 145–167.

Smith, J. P. (2007). Nature and causes of trends in male diabetes prevalence, undiagnosed diabetes, and the socioeconomic status health gradient. *Proceedings of the National Academy of Sciences, 104*, 13225-13231.

Stratton, G., & Mullan, E. (2005). The effect of multicolor playground markings on children's physical activity level during recess. *Preventive Medicine, 41*, 828–833.

Stratton, G., Canoy, D., Boddy, L. M., Taylor, S. R., Hackett, A. F., & Buchan, I. E. (2007). Cardio-respiratory fitness and body mass index of 9–11-year-old English children: A serial cross-sectional study from 1998 to 2004. *International Obesity*, 1172–1178.

Thivel, D., Isacco, L., Lazaar, N., Aucouturier, J., Ratel, S., Doré, E., Meyer, M., & Duché, P. (2011). Effect of a 6-month school-based physical activity program on body composition and physical fitness in lean and obese schoolchildren. *European Journal of Pediatrics, 170*, 1435–1443.

Tiersky, E. (2015, April 30). *FAQs on BPA: The attacks continue, but are they justified?* Retrieved from http://shelflifeadvice.com/content/faqs-bpa-attacks-continue-are-they-justified

Time Magazine. (2005, June 6). Lose that spare tire! Special report on how to get fitter, faster. Retrieved from http://www.amazon.com/Magazine-Special-Report-Fitter-Faster/dp/B000LF3A9C

Time Magazine. (2005). *Get moving.* Retrieved from http://www.time.com/time/magazine/article/0,9171,1066943,00.html

Tomkinson, G. R., & Olds, T. S. (2007). Secular changes in aerobic fitness test performance of Australasian children and adolescents. *Medicine in Sports & Science, 50*, 168–182.

Tomkinson, G. R., Léger, L. A., Olds, T. S., & Cazorla, G. (2003). Secular trends in the performance of children and adolescents (1980–2000): An analysis of 55 studies of the 20 m shuttle run test in 11 countries. *Sports Medicine, 33*, 285–300.

Chapter 5 – Physical Health Development

Tremblay, M. S., Shields, M., Laviolette, M., Craig, C. L., Janssen, I., & Gorber, S. C. (2010). Fitness of Canadian children and youth: Results from the 2007–2009 Canadian Health Measures Survey. *Health Report*, 21–20.

United States Department of Health and Human Services (2009), Physical activity guidelines, retrieved from: http://health.gov/paguidelines/

U.S. Department of Health and Human Services, National Institute of Health. (2005). *New NHLBI-sponsored study shows programs can teach children to eat healthier.* Retrieved from http://www.nih.gov/news/pr/jun2005/nhlbi-01.htm

United State Department of Health and Human Services. (n.d.). *Fact sheet on stress.* Retrieved from http://www.nimh.nih.gov/health/publications/stress/index.shtml

United State Department of Health and Human Services. (n. d.). *Q&A on stress for adults: How it affects your health and what you can do about it.* Retrieved from http://www.nimh.nih.gov/health/publications/stress/index.shtml

University of California, Berkeley. (2015). Sugar: The bitter truth: It's not just making us fat, it may be making us sick, *Wellness Letter, 31*, (13).

University of Delaware Extension. (n. d.). *How can parents help prevent childhood obesity?* Retrieved from http://ag.udel.edu/extension/fam/obesity/powerpoint/KeysPar.pdf

University of Delaware Extension. (n.d.). *Making healthy habits a family affair: Finding the balance for you and your family.* Retrieved from http://ag.udel.edu/extension/fam/obesity/powerpoint/KeysPar.pdf

Van Dusen, D. P., Kelder, S. H., Kohl, H. W., III, Ranjit, N., & Perry, C. L. (2011). Associations of physical fitness and academic performance among schoolchildren. *Journal of School Health, 81*, 733–740.

Waidmann, T., Bound, J., & Schoenbaum, M. (1995). The illusion of failure: Trends in the self-reported health of the U.S. elderly. *Milbank Quarterly, 73*, 253–287.

Wong, P. C. H., Chia, M. Y. H., Tsou, I. Y. Y., Wansaicheong, G. K. L., Tan, B., Wang, J. C. K., …Lim, D. (2008). Effects of a 12-week exercise training programme on aerobic fitness, body composition, blood lipids and C-reactive protein in adolescents with obesity. *Annals Academy of Medicine Singapore, 37*, 286–293.

Chapter 6
Family Togetherness

Family is First

> *Family ties are forever. Just as blood is thicker than water, family is closer than friends!*

Whether you are married or single, the only child or have several siblings, family is likely to be the closest ties you have with other human beings. In most cases, family members (at one time or another) lived together, share a common set of values and are around one another for long periods of time. Consequently, family members become close and in most cases want the best for one another.

The love I have for members of my family is different from the love I have for others. Family togetherness or wellbeing here is not meant to mean how content or well each member of your family happens to be at any given time, but it is more about the relationship you have with members of your family. Are you on good terms with members of your family? Do you spend time with them that is not confrontational most of the time? Do you enjoy one another's company? Family members "fuss" and "fight" with one another because they are together so much and, in many cases, they know where those "soft" spots" or "hot buttons" are. At the same time, however, most family members love one another and would do just about anything, one for the other. Family togetherness is certainly not having a perfect relationship with each family member, but it does involve some sharing, caring and genuine love.

Communication Helps Bind Relationships
Usually, communication is critical to family togetherness. Family members who communicate one with the other tend to enjoy one another's company more than those who

do not communicate. It stands to reason that a person's environment plays a very important role in the "happiness" and contentment of the family living in that environment.

William Fleeson (1968, 2004), in a study reported in "The Quality of American Life at the End of the Century," observed that marriage, or a marriage-like close relationship, was the most important domain for a life of good quality.

> *There are very few bonds that are as strong as the bonds of a close family.*

If a person evaluated himself as doing well or poorly in an area, Fleeson then looked to see what connection—positive or negative—that had to do with overall life satisfaction. For example, he says, some individuals can easily experience a high-quality life despite an unsuccessful career, so the connection between career and life satisfaction is not as significant. But few indicate they are happy with the overall quality of their life if they have an unhappy marriage. "We often have to make decisions in our lives about where to invest our energy, be it family, career or health," Fleeson says. "The study suggests that individuals' investment in maintaining their relationships and their financial stability are more richly rewarded than are efforts in other domains."

The renowned author of the book *7 Habits of Highly Effective Families* Stephen Covey (1997) said that the mission of his family is to create a nurturing place of faith, order, truth, love, happiness, and relaxation and to provide opportunity for each individual to become responsibly independent and effectively interdependent in order to serve worthy purposes in society through understanding and living the gospel of Jesus Christ.

Environment within the family system is viewed as an open system and a component of the larger community and society, with the assumption that families benefit from and contribute to the network of relationships and resources in the community (McCubbin & McCubbin, 1989). Harmony is necessary for balance within the individual, family, and community (Sobralske, 1985). Achieving and maintaining harmony with oneself, family and community are important social goals.

Family Connection
McCubbin and McCubbin (1989) define (family) health as: "family resiliency or the ability of the family to respond to and eventually adapt to the situations and crises encountered over the family life cycle." Resilience is seen as a characteristic families use to achieve that balance and harmony.

Chapter 6 – Family Togetherness

> *Finding ways for family to stay connected is one of the most important elements of a healthy family.*

Tracy Togliatti (2007), who wrote "Stay Connected to Loved Ones," makes several suggestions on how that might be done. She lists such things as tradition, family meetings and spending quality time with each family member as being critical. Togliatti says that family traditions play an important role in family togetherness and staying connected. Whether it's a holiday gathering or a regular vacation, make sure there is something in place for the entire family to look forward to on a regular basis.

> *She also says to make it a point to give each family member at least fifteen minutes of undivided attention each day.*

This does not need to be an official event, just something for you to make it a point to do every day. This is especially important if you are all going in different directions and rarely even get to spend supper together. How you spend these fifteen minutes is up to you. It might (even) be divided up throughout the day.

Benefits of Family Togetherness

Christine Mann (2008) suggests that having family dinners together can go a long way to help families to stay together. Children who take part in family dinners at least five times a week do better than other children in at least six important ways:

- They Eat More Healthy Foods, Fewer Junk Foods and Sodas. Children in families that eat dinner together eat more fruits, vegetables, grains and calcium-rich foods. They also drink fewer soft drinks, which have been connected with obesity and documented in numerous studies.
- They Create Stronger Connections with Their Parents
- They Build Larger Vocabularies
- They Get Better Grades in School
- They Develop Fewer Eating Disorders
- They Engage in Fewer Risky Behaviors
- Even a Few Family Dinner Nights a Week Pay Off

The University of Delaware Extension offered suggestions for families:
1) Be the best "healthy habits" role model you can be.
2) Use routines and limits to help children feel safe, secure.
3) Make it easy to make healthy choices.
4) Provide healthy food – then let children choose what and how much to eat.
5) Help children learn to like foods that are good for them – by offering foods time and again.

6) Family meals are "family glue" that makes kids feel loved and connected.
7) Being active helps everyone feel good – and it makes our brains work better!
8) Avoid restricting – it backfires!

> *Others have espoused praying together, playing together and even working on mutually interesting projects together can serve as healthy activities that families can do to become closer.*

Families play important roles in supporting children's learning not just in school but also in the many out-of-school contexts in which they learn. Harvard Family Research Project's Helen Westmoreland (2009) talks about how families and non-school learning settings, such as out-of-school time programs, museums, and libraries, can work together to promote student achievement.

> *Whatever the process you use, it all boils down to spending quality time together.*

Frankly, good things can come from all the suggestions. Traditions have a way of strengthening the foundation of a family by setting up long-lasting habits and trends that can be carried on from one generation to the next. One tradition my family did that many families do is get together during holidays, birthdays, graduations and weddings. These are special times that allow family members to catch up with what is going on one with the other. It is also a time to share stories about what certain family members used to do or how things were in the family in the past. Many times, we find out things about family that were forgotten or in some cases things that were never known. Family gatherings, regardless of the form or reason, are always times for family to break bread together and to talk.

Some families have instituted family meetings (family reunions) as a way to stay in touch with what is going on in the family. Oftentimes, family meetings have a specific purpose or goal such as using the meeting to let everyone in the family know at the same time good news or bad news or to share something that everyone in the household needs to know (a sibling is joining the military, a parent will be away from home for an extended period of time or family members will need to start thinking about what they want to do for summer vacation, for example). Family meetings are also good times to consider discussing things that are becoming a problem or to discuss certain family practices that need to be changed. Oftentimes, concerns or minor problems can be avoided and "nipped in the bud" before they become major problems by having a family meeting for discussing and working on them.

There is also merit in families praying together and working together. In each case, family members get to do things together as a unit. There is something (positive) to be said about family members each playing their part in a family activity. When family members pray together, they are each sharing their part of the family message to God. When they are working together, they are each doing their part in the total project or task, whatever it is. In both cases, family members should be encouraged to become full participants in the joint, family activities.

In her Masters Degree Thesis, Alexandrea Shanea Ellington (2011) expounds on the significance of family time. In it, she references researchers on why time is important, the benefits of family time and reasons families don't spend time together.

> *Family scholars have a growing concern about the time demands and hectic pace of parents' jobs, which are causing families to have less time together (DeGenova, Stinnett, & Stinnett, 2010).*

Data from national research on approximately 2,000 parents indicated that about 50% of the parents reported too little time with the children (Milkie et al., 2004). Similarly, research examining family time among parents and adolescent children found that family time was rare. Higher level of family time was related to more affectionate, loving and intimate relationships (Crouter et al., 2004).

Why is family time important?

Family strengths research over the past four decades has consistently identified spending time together as one of the major qualities that characterize strong families. Conversely, lack of time together has been reported to be a critical problem of American families (Defrain, 2007; DeGenova et al., 2010). Family time is a very important part of the human developmental process and the family bonding system. Family time is also important because the ecological perspective on human development emphasizes the importance of joint activities as building blocks of individual competence and close relationships, which in turn underlie psychological adjustment (Crouter, Head, McHale, & Tucker, 2004).

Although research has shown the importance of family time, the exact nature of family time has yet to be understood. Some may argue that family time alone is enough to make an impact on an individual. In contrast, others feel it is the "what" that is taking place during the family time that makes a difference.

> *What happens during that shared time is also important (Larson & Richards, 1994).*

For example, in order for families to be healthy, its members must have daily interactions in which their emotional worlds come into meaningful contact, times when their minds meet, when closeness is shared (Larson & Richards, 1994). Eating meals and spending other time together is thought to provide the opportunity for a family to replenish themselves and affirm their experience of wellness (Larson & Richards, 1994).

Research has a variety of meanings for the term family time; however, most would conclude that just because you spend time together doesn't mean it is considered quality. In a study conducted by Daly (2001), one response to an interview question states, family time is togetherness, more than everyone being around and busy with the household operation. Rather it was when we do things together as a family as opposed to just the time after 5:00, like cooking supper and doing homework. Family time should not be running errands or going to the kids' recreational activities, for these events would require the family's attention to be focused elsewhere. Family time should be when everyone can focus their attention only on one another, relax and enjoy themselves.

The family is the child's first and longest-lasting context for development; families are pervasive, parenting is universally important to children's lives, and children who lack a satisfying, supportive family life are likely to crave it (Berk, 2012).

Benefits of family time

Core family leisure activities are significantly related to family cohesion, and balanced family leisure activities are related to family flexibility (Smith, Freeman, Zabriskie, & Ramon, 2009). The higher the family leisure involvement, the higher the level of communication the family has with one another. As a result, these individuals learn to communicate with others better. Communication between family members in a leisure setting is often less threatening and demanding, and more open and relaxing than in any other family settings (Zabriskie & McCormick, 2001).

Research has shown that couples who participate in family time report having higher marital satisfaction. recreational activities are more satisfied with their marriages than those who do not (Zabriskie & McCormick, 2001). Spending quality family time also has great benefits for the children involved. Research shows some relation between family time and adolescents' and children's behavior.

> *Husbands and wives who share leisure time together and participate in joint family time is related to lower levels of risky behaviors in adolescents (Crouter, Head, McHale, & Tucker, 2004).*

Benefits of family time on child development

Spending family time together has great benefits on children's learning development. Most parents who practice family time view this as an opportunity for family communication, bonding, child development, and learning (Zabriskie & McCormick, 2001). When parents' perceptions of family leisure were examined, findings showed that shared recreation was especially helpful in developing social skills, such as learning to problem solve, to compromise and to negotiate (Mactavish & Schleien, 1998). These are the qualities that naturally build great pro-social skills. Family time is the perfect setting in which to naturally teach children how to do the right thing. Parents should model positive behaviors, especially in a relaxing family time setting that should naturally motivate the children to do the same.

134

Chapter 6 – Family Togetherness

The time parents devote to their children is a major form of investment linked with children's wellbeing and development (Gauthier, Smeeding, & Furstenberg, 2004).

Research shows that playing together is very beneficial for children's development.

> ***Play has been described as the purest, most spiritual activity of man (Froebel, 1907).***

It gives joy, freedom, contentment, inner and outer rest, and peace with the world.

Reasons families don't spend time together
Many factors are to blame for the lack of quality time families spend together.

> ***The major factor in the lack of time for quality family time is families being able to balance work and family.***

Research shows not being able to properly balance work and family can put a significant amount of stress on a family. Work and family domains have the ability to influence each other (Perrewe & Hochwarter, 2001). For example, the line of demarcation separating work and family domains is blurred by the fact that situations that occur at work spill over into the family, and vice versa. Research has substantiated dysfunctional outcomes associated with work-family conflict (Perrewe & Hochwarter, 2001). These outcomes include decreased family and occupational wellbeing and job and life dissatisfaction.

The most well-documented pressures family members experience in balancing work and family are overload and conflict due to multiple roles (Hansen, 1991). These families have too much to do and too little time to do it. Research shows not being able to balance work and family is one cause of families not having time to spend quality family time together. In a study conducted by Daly (2001), interviews were conducted with family members about their family time together and the results showed three themes in the responses: there was never enough family time because of paid work, housework, and other competing activities; much of their time together was characterized by obligation, demand, and conflict; and most of their family time was in service of the children.

Every family has very different reasons for issues that get in the way of spending quality family time together.

> ***Research shows that each family member has to have their own personal meaning of family time and place their own values upon it to see that it is carried out.***

The meaning of family time involves an exploration of how beliefs, desires, expectations and ideals are part of, and shape, the everyday experience of family time (Daly, 2001). Whereas the pressures on family time have changed in response to changing patterns of work and family structure, beliefs about time appear to be resistant to radical change. Families have to want to spend quality family time together and value it dearly. Families who do not value spending quality time together will allow it to be shadowed by other demands and obligations. Knowing the benefits of spending quality family time together should make it very high on every family's priority list. Research has explained the importance of spending family time together and the issues that get in the way of families spending quality time together. Research has also explained how not having time to spend family time together can cause stress in the family.

When families find themselves developing a pattern of not spending time together, the consequences are often tragic: family members' needs are not met and the family culture turns negative. Eventually if things don't change, negative family traits begin to develop and sometimes last for generations. At that point, problems become so entrenched that they are next to impossible to change.

Beating the Odds – A Transitional Character

ForeverFamilies.net published an article written by Kristi Tanner (n.d.) entitled "Becoming a Transitional Character: Changing Your Family Culture" that cites other research showing that passing on negative family traits from generation to generation isn't a foregone conclusion.

> *Even if you grew up in a damaging home environment, you can choose different behaviors than those you experienced there.*

You can stop the negative patterns from flowing downstream to future generations. With education, focused effort, and help from others, you can choose to be a transitional character.

The late Carlfred Broderick (1932-1999), a renowned marriage and family scholar at the University of Southern California, coined the term transitional character and described it this way (Broderick 1992): A transitional character is one who, in a single generation, changes the entire course of a lineage. Their contribution to humanity is to filter the destructiveness out of their own lineage so the generations downstream will have a supportive foundation upon which to build productive lives.

Following is a snapshot of suggestions provided:
- Develop a vision of yourself as a transitional character. Seeing yourself successfully changing negative family patterns can help keep you focused on your goal to be a transitional character rather than a simple transmitter of damaging behavior.
- Build supportive relationships with strong adults.
- Be deliberate about making changes.
- Celebrate (positive) family rituals.

- Create a healthy emotional distance. The people we spend time with influence all of us. If your family of origin is particularly negative, consider distancing yourself so their impact on your own family is minimized.
- Marry at a later age.
- Read good books about family life.
- Join organizations that can help.
- Get an education. A good education teaches you to think clearly and make wise choices. It doesn't matter what you study as long as you're using your mind and developing your intellect.

The Tanner article was retrieved from:
https://foreverfamilies.byu.edu/Pages/challenges/Becoming-a-Transitional-Character-Changing-Your-Family-Culture.aspx

Also the article can be found at: http://thefamily.com/2011/02/25/becoming-a-transitional-character-changing-your-family-culture/

Family Resiliency

According to Lin and Chen (1994), many words have been used to describe the characteristics of a healthy family. "Family strengths" has been used to describe the family resource of adaptability and integration, which denotes a happy, successful and stable family.

> *"Happy family" refers to a healthy, comfortable, intimate, harmonious, warm and well-balanced family life.*

These two labels may be used interchangeably.

"Healthy" is not limited to the narrow medical definition. Instead it encompasses a much broader meaning regarding the harmonious relations and successful functioning so both the individual's and the family's needs can be met. Every family, including healthy families, has problems.

> *Those families who are able to cope and adjust well with daily life demands are termed "healthy families."*

Therefore, the definition of a healthy family is not based solely on the structure of the family; even a single-parent family can be considered a healthy family as long as that family's needs are met and stresses are managed through positive mechanisms. A healthy family is a stress-effective family in that such a family is able to cope with daily life demands.

"Seven Strategies for Building Your Family's Resilience" is the title of an article written by Paula Davis-Laack that is worth noting. The article was dated November 1, 2011 and can be found at: http://www.psychologytoday.com/blog/pressure-proof/201111/7-strategies-building-your-familys-resilience

1. <u>Shut down catastrophic thinking</u>. It's a downward spiral style of thinking that leaves you unable to take purposeful action. Try not to panic in emergency situations.
2. <u>Create a strengths family tree</u>. Identifying your family's strengths is a great self-awareness tool and a wonderful opportunity to talk to your kids about leveraging what they do well. If you or your kids are facing a challenge, have a discussion about how you can leverage your strengths to figure out solutions.
3. <u>Grab the good stuff</u>. Thanks to the negativity bias, human beings are predisposed to notice and remember the bad stuff that happens during the day. Positive interactions abound, but you often fail to remember them.

> *At the end of each day, ask each other to name several good things that happened during the day, and why that good thing was important.*

This exercise only takes a few minutes, but studies show that those who make this activity a regular habit experience increased levels of happiness and optimism (Seligman et al., 2005).

4. <u>Encourage positive risks and discuss the lessons learned from failing</u>. Sometimes children need to be given the opportunity to experience failure. By giving every kid an "A," and saying every kid makes the team, we're robbing our kids of the ability to figure out how to get out of a challenge by studying harder, preparing differently, or by practicing more. A hallmark of resilience is being able to pick yourself up and course correct when the going gets tough.
5. <u>Rejuvenate regularly</u>. Positive emotion is a key component of resilience (Cohn et al., 2009). Being able to generate positive emotion through laughing together, doing physical activities, going to the spa, playing board games and more will build your resilience as a family. Even though time is in short supply for many busy parents and kids, model the importance of taking time out to rejuvenate. You can't be there for your family if your tank is always on empty.
6. <u>Be there for each other when things go right</u>. Study after study shows that building strong social connections builds not only resilience but happiness. Shelly Gable's research shows that how you respond to a person's good news actually does more for building a relationship than how you respond to bad news. This applies across the board from personal relationships to business interactions. Responding in an active and constructive way, that is, helping the bearer of good news savor it is the only response that builds good relationships. Killing the conversation by offering a terse response or hijacking the conversation by making it about you are quick ways to weaken a relationship (Gable, Gonzaga, & Strachman, 2006). Encourage your kids to start practicing active constructive responding not only with family members, but also with their friends.
7. <u>Allow family members to replicate successes</u>. Dr. Carol Dweck has researched for decades what she calls fixed and growth mindsets. Oftentimes, when things go well, you

tell your kids "great job," or "you must be really smart." While nice, it doesn't help your kids replicate their success.

> *According to Dweck, when you notice someone doing something well, name the specific strategy, skill, and effort that led to the good outcome.*

Notice the difference between, "Wow, the way you sprinted down the middle of the field, blocked the defender, and kicked the ball to the right side of goal was amazing," and "You're such a great athlete" (Dweck, 2008).

"Family Strengths" is the title of an article written by Saralee Jamieson and Lisa Wallace (2010) that can be found at (http://extension.missouri.edu/bsf/strengths/). In it, the University of Missouri Extension colleagues talk about traits that make families strong. They explain that families are crucial in the development of human competence and character. Recent research tells us that the family's influence is even greater than we have imagined. Families play a major role in how well children do in school, how well they perform on the job as adults and how well they contribute to society in general. Families have the first and foremost influence on our development. The two colleagues share some of their research findings.

Research findings
Research indicates that many problems of individuals and society are related to dysfunctional family relationships. For instance, early teen sexual acting out, youth suicide, teen pregnancy, runaways, substance abuse, childhood and adolescent depression, child abuse and neglect, family violence, and civil unrest are known to be aggravated by problems in the family.

What makes families strong? Researchers have worked hard to answer this question and agree that strong, healthy families have nine traits in common (Krysan, Moore, & Zill, 1990). These traits have been found in families of different types, races, social backgrounds, nationalities, and religious beliefs.

The nine traits are:
1. caring and appreciation
2. time together
3. encouragement
4. commitment
5. communication
6. cope with change
7. spirituality
8. community and family ties
9. clear roles

Chapter 6 – Family Togetherness

Mindfulness and Work/Family Balance

Results from a study by Allen and Kiburz (2012) indicate that those with greater mindfulness report greater work-family balance, better sleep quality, and greater vitality. In their article, the two writers indicate that the concept of mindfulness is centuries old. Originally stemming from Buddhist tradition, it has only more recently come into prominence within Western society (Kabat-Zinn, 1990). Mindfulness has been defined as, "intentionally paying attention to present-moment experience (physical sensations, perceptions, affective states, thoughts, and imagery) in a nonjudgmental way, thereby cultivating a stable and nonreactive awareness" (Carmody, Reed, Kristeller, & Merriam, 2008, p. 394). Mindfulness is a state of consciousness unique from that of typical cognitive processing because a person allows sensory input and simply notices it rather than comparing, evaluating, or ruminating about it (Brown, Ryan, & Creswell, 2007).

Mindfulness can be honed and therefore become a part of an individual's life, incorporated into daily chores, activities, and role performance (Dane, 2011; Kostanski & Hassed, 2008).

Although varying uses and definitions of the work-family balance term exist, we define work-family balance as an overall appraisal regarding one's effectiveness and satisfaction with work and family life (Greenhaus & Allen, 2010). Unique from constructs such as work-family conflict and work-family enrichment, balance is not a linking mechanism between work and family because it does not specify how conditions or experiences in one role are causally related to conditions or experiences in the other role (Greenhaus et al., 2003). Rather, balance represents an overall inter-role phenomenon. Several studies provide psychometric evidence that supports viewing conflict, enrichment, and balance as three distinct constructs (Allen et al., 2010).

As a relatively new construct in the work-family literature, there has been limited research investigating the predictors and outcomes of balance. Time spent in various activities is one predictor. Specifically, longer work hours have been associated with less satisfaction with work-family balance and more quality time spent with children positively associated with perceived balance (Milkie et al., 2010; Valcour, 2007). Another predictor is job characteristics.

> *Specifically, job complexity and control over work time have been positively associated with satisfaction with work-family balance (Valcour, 2007).*

Outcomes associated with work-family balance include job satisfaction, organizational commitment, family satisfaction, family functioning, and life satisfaction (Allen et al., 2010; August & Carlson et al., 2009).

Based on self-regulation and role balance theories, there are several reasons to hypothesize that mindfulness relates to work-family balance. In their theory of role balance, Marks and MacDermid (1996) note that positive role balance is the tendency to approach every typical

140

role and role partner with an attitude of attentiveness and care. The present moment alertness that is a part of mindfulness should enable individuals to fully immerse themselves with care and attentiveness while engaged in each role. This practice should facilitate perceived balance across roles.

As noted by Marks and MacDermid (1996), the habit of bringing full attentiveness to each role helps dissipate the perceived problem of role management, facilitating effective personal resource allocation.

> *Moreover, with focused attention on the role at hand, individuals may perform more effectively (Dane, 2011).*

The quality of the experience in each role is likely to be enhanced, facilitating overall perceptions of role balance. Thus, we propose that individuals more predisposed to mindfulness will be more likely to report work-family balance.

Future research on mindfulness and work/family balance

In future studies, it may be useful to integrate research on mindfulness, work-family balance and detachment. Several studies have shown that being able to detach from work during off-job time has beneficial outcomes (e.g., Fritz et al., 2010; Sonnentag et al., 2010). Killingsworth and Gilbert (2010) report that individuals are frequently thinking about something other than what it is that they are doing. In addition, Killingsworth and Gilbert report that people were less happy when their minds were wandering than when they were not, regardless of the pleasantness of the topic to which their minds wandered. Killingsworth and Gilbert conclude, "a human mind is a wandering mind, and a wandering mind is an unhappy mind" (p. 932). Mindfulness involves noticing that your mind has wandered and bringing it back to the present moment each time it does (Kabat-Zinn, 1990), which may help facilitate the ability to detach from one role while in another.

Another related interesting line of research would be to investigate interruptions, technology use and mindfulness.

> *More mindful individuals may develop boundary-related policies that limit interruptions via email and social media.*

This is important in that Turkle (2011) has described how the use of technology has resulted in individuals who are so busy communicating that the time free of distractions needed for productive work and high quality relationships has declined. Moreover, a considerable body of research has shown that interruptions at work can have serious health and safety consequences (e.g., Monk, Trafton, & Boehm-Davis, 2008). Mindfulness may help individuals more readily collect their thoughts and return to the present moment following interruptions.

Boundary-related policies tend to help individuals compartmentalize their day. Rather than interrupting your work with calls, e-mails or just thinking about home, your family or your children, it is best to stay focused on your work while you are at work and likewise do the same thing while at home by not thinking about work when you are at home. One strategy of being fully engaged at home is to have something fun planned for you and the family.

The Importance of Play

This may sound like an oversimplification, but the family that isn't "working" is the family that isn't playing together. That is the way an article written by Jim Burns (n.d.), titled "Families That Play Together, Stay Together" begins. The author shares a heart-wrenching story about a friend and why playing is so important to the health of families. The article can be retrieved at: http://www.cbn.com/family/parenting/families-that-play-together-burns.aspx

Playing together is an essential trait of happy, healthy families. Certainly our children need to do their chores, and of course they need discipline with consistency, but what they also need desperately from their parents is a rousing game of hide-and-seek or a monthly ping-pong tournament.

> *A great thing happens to families when they play together: They begin to talk and laugh and lighten up.*

Family memories are built, inside jokes are shared and serious moments of intimacy are communicated. Families need special times together to build lifelong memories and to play together.

As most experts will tell you, a family that plays together stays together. But I would add that a family that plays together will also be much happier and healthier. For many families, play is the missing ingredient that glues the family together. Play can even open closed spirits and heal broken marriages.

We know instinctively that play produces family togetherness and support. We know that when we play together, we have a deeper sense of belonging and community in the family. Parents must proactively work at making belonging and community one of their key goals for family togetherness.

> *Playing together as a family may open up the communication lines better than anything else you try,*

so now is the time to be proactive and create those family fun days and events that provide the catalyst for more effective communication. Do whatever it takes to keep the lines open, even if it means picking up a basketball or going to the park on a regular basis. Playing together and having a good time just may be the safety net you need to make a difference in your child's life.

Todd Dean is one of my heroes. I've known him much of my adult life. He is a talented person with an M.B.A. from Stanford University. At the university, Todd was a gymnast. When I first met him, he was teaching students from my youth group to do a standing backflip. All I could do was think about liability, and yet the kids loved watching him do his incredible flips. He invited me to try a backflip. I made a fool of myself, but he still encouraged me.

Todd married Charlotte. They had two beautiful children, and he had a very high-paying job. Todd's career was going through the roof. Then tragedy struck: Charlotte died of a brain tumor. Before Charlotte died, Todd had told me he wanted to coach his children's little league and soccer teams. Because Todd's career would soon include travel, he had to make some difficult decisions about it. Todd was making good money, but it wasn't as important as playing catch with his son or rollerblading with his daughter.

Todd made the decision to quit his high-paying job and become a professor so he could play more with his kids and coach those teams. His annual salary was cut to what was once his annual expense account. His lifestyle had to change. He doesn't live in as large a house as he once did, and his car isn't the same model as some of his Stanford M.B.A. friends, but he is happily coaching his children's teams. He is now married to a lovely woman named Becky who suffered a similar loss. They have four happy, content, and well-adjusted children who play and interact daily with their dad and mom, who have sacrificed financially to help their family thrive. The benefits of playing together are far more valuable than a big paycheck.

These days, we all live with stresses of a fast-paced life. Playing together is one area of our busy lives that we can pretty easily choose to cut out in order to make the other areas of our lives easier to manage. Yet, I challenge you: Don't cut back on playing together. This is one simple area of life that can yield incredible benefits for you and your family.

Family Togetherness with a Spiritual Focus

Bryan Davis wrote an article dated 2/12/13 and titled "Define Family Success in Godly Terms." In the *Charisma Magazine* published article, he crafted a family vision and a strategic plan for the family. The article can be found at: http://www.charismamag.com/life/men/16763-define-family-success-in-goldly-terms

Family Vision. To live my life deliberately to encourage, prompt and foster spiritual, emotional, mental and physical growth in my spouse and children.

The article had a 7-point family strategic plan. Since four of his points have already been stated, I am repeating only three of the eight as follows:

- **To Actively Engage in My Kids' Worlds.** This includes deliberate steps to listen and watch what my kids are listening to and watching and to get to know my children's friends. I know many things in our society encourage kids to rebel and behave wrongly, so I will take steps to limit this influence and instead pour into my children good and pure things.
- **To Take Responsibility for the Proper Education of My Children.** I will not leave learning up to an unknown teacher but will actively partner with my children's educators, and my wife to ensure my children get the best education possible, which will give them a richer and fuller life.

> **To Live With the End in View.** *I recognize my mortality and therefore wish to focus my limited time here on earth on things that are really important—and with God's help—to leave my children an example of an upright man and loving father.*

Healthy Families By the Book

The Grandview Church of Christ (n.d.) offers a number of suggestions for a healthy family and they provide Biblical scriptures as references: A few of those suggestions are listed here:

Respecting Others: Start with respect for self, then learn to respect individual differences within the family. Learn to live with one another. (Respect is not the same as approval.) (Hebrews 12:9)

Trusting: This must begin with parents who trust each other deeply. Give children opportunities to earn trust, and let them learn to accept responsibility for their own behavior. (Psalms 20:7)

Fostering Responsibility: Exhibit a sense of shared responsibility. As children grow, gradually give them more responsibility. This means more than doing chores and does not necessarily mean orderliness and perfection. The consequences of irresponsibility are valuable lessons. (Romans 14:11-12)

Teaching Morals: Parents need to teach clear and specific guidelines about right and wrong. Each family has different values, but the parents should agree on values they consider important. Avoid inconsistency between example and teaching. (Proverbs 22:6)

Enjoying Traditions:

> **Family rituals and traditions give us a sense of stability and a sense of belonging. (Leviticus 23; Exodus 12:26-27)**

Sharing Religion: The potential for satisfying family relationships is far greater among religiously oriented families than among those who do not share a faith. Worship together regularly. Pass on the faith in positive and meaningful ways. (Ephesians 6:4; Deuteronomy 6:4-9)

Respecting Privacy: Respect the right to be alone, to be different, and to change. Have more mutually negotiated rules as children mature. (Matthew 6:6)

Valuing Service: Serve others, whether inside or outside of your family. Be responsive to others' needs. Keep volunteer time under control. (Acts 20:35)

Getting Help: Even the best families have problems. Seek help in the early stages of a problem. Not all problems can be solved within the family. When necessary, seek professional assistance. (James 1:2-4).

Time-Tested Healthy Family Characteristics

Even sources that are over 30 years old still hold true to address the needs of a healthy and productive family. The following are a few of the characteristics that were offered in this source called "Characteristics of Productive Families" (Gilmore, 1976):

- Parents devoted to each other, not competitive
- Have varied and broad interests – community, cultural, educational, etc.
- Do not get over-involved in outside activities (but being involved in social and related activities is very important for developing what might be called social capitol).
- One thing that has worked for my wife and me has been our Friday "date" day. Before we retired, it would be after work; now that we are retired, the entire day is ours – not to be disturbed or interrupted by anyone unless it is a genuine emergency.

Social Capitol and the Family

Some theorists and researchers focus on social capital as a resource that arises out of peoples' family relationships and that enables them to increase their human capital, which then enables them to gain greater economic rewards. For example, James Coleman's work (1988a, 1988b, 1990, 1991) sees social capital as inherent in the structure of family relationships, particularly inter-generationally. He is concerned with explaining how children's educational achievement is driven by parental investment, which then radiates out to the community in the form of the generational passing-on of cohesive social and moral norms of trust and co-operation, sanction and producing economic efficiency.

For Coleman, for example, families are the fundamental bedrock of social capital, where children are socialized into the norms and values of society and their human and social capital are nurtured and developed.

> *Parents invest in their children with time, affective relationships and the transmission of clear guidelines for behavior.*

Rising rates of divorce, mothers' employment and changes in working time, all work against this investment. Where parents are absent rather than physically present with their children, as in single-mother or two-earner families, this means that time and attention for children have to be rationed.

At various points in his body of work, Putnam (1996) also identifies changing working patterns, including longer travel-to-work time and work-intensification stress, women's rising labor market participation and dual earner households and market-based childcare provisions, as possible factors in the decline of social capital, as well as a decline in marriage. Women who were homemakers in the 1950s and 1960s were our best social capitalists, the backbone of neighborhood voluntary associations. In addition, he points to the plight of local communities in which a predominance of work-poor families and an exodus of middle class families has eroded social capital, compounding racial and class inequalities.

<u>REFERENCES</u>
Chapter 6 – "Family Togetherness"

Akerstedt, T., Philip, P., Capelli, A., & Kecklund, G. (2011). Sleep loss and accidents —Work hours, life style, and sleep pathology. *Progressive Brain Research, 190,* 169–188.

Allen, T. D., Shockley, K. M., & Poteat, L. (2010). Anxiety attachment and feedback in mentoring relationships. *Journal of Vocational Behavior, 77,* 73–80.

Allen, T. D., & Kiburz, K. M. (2012). Trait mindfulness and work–family balance among working parents: The mediating effects of vitality and sleep quality. *Journal of Vocational Behavior, 80*(2), 372–37.

Baron, N. S. (1992). *Growing up with language.* Reading MA: Addison-Wesley.

Baumeister, R. F., Bratslavsky, E., Muraven, M., & Tice, D. M. (1998). Ego depletion: Is the active self a limited resource? *Journal of Personality and Social Psychology, 74,* 1252-1265.

Berk, L. E. (2012). *Child Development* (8th ed.). Pearson Education, Inc.

Bostic, T. J., Rubio, D. M., & Hood, M. (2000). A validation of the subjective vitality scale using structural equation modeling. *Social Indicators Research, 52,* 313–324.

Broderick, C. B. (1992). *Marriage and the family.* New Jersey: Prentice Hall.

Brown, K. W., Kasser, T., Ryan, R. M., Linley, P. A., & Orzech, K. (2009). When what one has is enough: Mindfulness, financial desire discrepancy, and subjective well-being. *Journal of Research in Personality, 43,* 727–736.

Brown, K. W., Ryan, R. M., & Creswell, J. D. (2007). Mindfulness: Theoretical foundations and evidence for its salutary effects. *Psychological Inquiry, 18,* 211–237.

Catherine Shaefer.com. (n. d.). *Eight characteristics of strong healthy families.* Retrieved from http://www.catherineshafer.com/families.html

Centers for Disease Control and Prevention, Epidemiology Program Office. (2011). Unhealthy sleep-related behaviors — 12 states, 2009 to March 4, 2011. *Morbidity and Mortality Weekly Report, 60*(8). Retrieved from http://www.cdc.gov/mmwr/PDF/wk/mm6008.pdf

Chambers, R., Lo, B. C. Y., & Allen, N. B. (2008). The impact of intensive mindfulness training on attentional control, cognitive style, and affect. *Cognitive Therapy and Research, 32,* 303–322.

Clark, R. M. (1987). Effective families help children succeed in school. *Network for Public Schools, 13*(1),1-5. Columbia, MD: National Committee for Citizens in Education.

Cohn, M. A. et al. (2009). Happiness unpacked: Positive emotions increase life satisfaction by building resilience. *Emotion, 9,* 361–368.

Coleman, J. S. (1988a). Social capital in the creation of human capital. *American Journal of Sociology, 94*(Supplement), S95-S120.

Coleman, J. S. (1988b). The creation and destruction of social capital: Implications for the law. *Notre Dame Journal of Law, Ethics and Public Policy, 3,* 375–404.

Coleman, J. S. (1990). *Foundations of social theory.* Cambridge: Harvard University Press.

Coleman, J. S. (1991). Prologue: Constructed social organization. In P. Bourdieu & J. S. Coleman (Eds.), *Social theory for a changing society.* Oxford: Westview Press.

Covey, S. (1997). *The 7 habits of highly effective families.* New York: Golden Books.

Creswell, J. D., Way, B. M., Eisenberger, N. I., & Lieberman, M. D. (2007). Neural correlates of dispositional mindfulness during affect labeling. *Psychosomatic Medicine, 69,* 560–565.

Crouter, A. C., Head, M., R., McHale, S. M., Tucker, C. J. (2004). Family time and the psychosocial adjustment of adolescent siblings and their parents. *Journal of Marriage and Family, 66*(1), 147-162.

Curran, D. (1983). *Traits of a healthy family.* Minneapolis, MI: Winston Press.

Daly, K. J. (2001). Deconstructing family time: From ideology to lived experience. *Journal of Marriage and Family, 63*(2), 283-294.

Dane, E. (2011). Paying attention to mindfulness and its effects on task performance in the workplace. *Journal of Management, 37*, 997–1018.

Davis-Laack, P. (2011). *Seven strategies for building your family's resilience.* Retrieved from http://www.psychologytoday.com/blog/pressure-proof/201111/7-strategies-building-your-familys-resilience

Davis, B. (2013). *Define family success in Godly terms.* Retrieved from http://www.charismamag.com/life/men/16763-define-family-success-in-goldly-terms

DeFrain, J., & Asay, S. (Eds.). (2007). *Strong families around the world: Strengths-based research and perspectives.* Binghampton, NY: Haworth Press.

Defrain, J., & Stinnett, N. (2008). *Creating a strong family.* Retrieved from http://www.ianrpubs.unl.edu/live/g1881/build/g1881.pdf

DeGenova, M. K., Stinnett, N., & Stinnett, N. (2010). *Intimate relationships, marriages and families.* New York: McGraw-Hill.

Dekeyser, M., Raes, F., Leijssen, M., Leysen, S., & Dewulf, D. (2008). Mindfulness skills and interpersonal behavior. *Personality and Individual Differences, 44*, 1235–1245.

Dweck, C. (2008). *Mindset: The new psychology of success.* New York: Ballantine Books.

Fleeson, W. (2004). The quality of American life at the end of the century. In Brim et al. (Ed.), *How healthy are we? A national study of well-being at midlife.* London: University of Chicago Press.

Frebel, F. (1907). *The education of man.* W. N. Hailmann, Trans. New York: D. Appleton.

Fritz, C., Yankelvich, M., Zarubin, A., & Barger, P. (2010). Happy, healthy, and productive: The role of detachment from work during nonwork time. *Journal of Applied Psychology, 95*, 977–983.

Gable, S. L., Gonzaga, G. C., & Strachman, A. (2006). Will you be there for me when things go right? Supportive responses to positive event disclosures. *Journal of Personality and Social Psychology, 91*, 904-917.

Gauthier, A. H., Smeeding, T. M., Furstenberg, F. F., Jr. (2004). Are parents investing less time in children? Trends in selected industrialized countries'. *Population and Development Review, 30*(4), 647–671.

Gilmore, J. (1976). *Handout given in family dynamics.* Course at Boston University, 1981.

Glomb, T. M., Duffy, M. K., Bono, J. E., & Yang, T. (2011). Mindfulness at work. In J. Martocchio, H. Liao, & A. Joshi (Eds.), *Research in personnel and human resource management* (pp. 115–157). Bingley, UK: 30Emerald Group Publishing Limited.

Godet-Cayre, V., Pelletier-Fleury, N., Vaillant, M. L., Dinet, J., Massuel, M.-A., & Leger, D. (2006). Insomnia and absenteeism at work. Who pays the cost? *Sleep, 29*, 179–184.

Grandview Bulletin. (2009, December 27). The healthy family. *Grandview Church of Christ, 32*(51). Retrieved from http://grandviewchurchofchrist.org/bulletin/volume-32-number-51/

Greenhaus, J. H., & Allen, T. D. (2010). Work–family balance: A review and extension of the literature. In L. Tetrick & J. C. Quick (Eds.), *Handbook of occupational health psychology* (2nd ed.). Alexandria, VA: American Psychological Association.

Greenhaus, J. H., Collins, K. M., & Shaw, J. D. (2003). The relation between work–family balance and quality of life. *Journal of Vocational Behavior, 63*(2003), 510–531.

Greeson, J. M. (2009). Mindfulness research update: 2008. *Complementary Health Practice Review, 14*(1), 10–18.

Hansen, G. L. (1991). Balancing work and family: A literature and resource review. *Family Relations, 40*(3), 348–353.

Harvard Family Research Project. (2010). *Family engagement as a systemic, sustained, and integrated strategy to promote student achievement.* Cambridge, MA: Author. Retrieved from http://www.hfrp.rog/FE-NewDefinition

Hawkes, S. R. (1991) Recreation in the family. *Family research: A sixty year review, 1930-1990* (pp. 387–433). New York: Lexington Books.

Healthy Life Guides. (2011). *Characteristics of healthy families.* Retrieved from http://healthylifeguides.weebly.com/1/post/2011/7/characteristics-of-healthy-families.html

Chapter 6 – Family Togetherness

Howell, J., Digdon, N. L., & Buro, K. (2010). Mindfulness predicts sleep-related self regulation and well-being. *Personality and Individual Differences, 48*, 419–424.

Howell, J. Digdon, N. L., & Buro, K. & Sheptycki, A. R. (2008). Relations among mindfulness, well-being, and sleep. *Personality and Individual Differences, 45*, 773–777.

Hsin, A. (2009). Parents' time with children: Does time matter for children's cognitive achievement? *Social Indicators Research, 93*(1), 123–126. doi:10.1007/s11205-008-9413-6

Carmody, J. Reed, G. Kristeller, J. & Merriam, P. (2008). Mindfulness, spirituality, and Health related symptoms. *Journal of Psychosomatic Research, 64*, 393–403.

Jamieson, S., & Wallace, L. (2010). *Family strengths.* Retrieved from http://extension.missouri.edu/bsf/strengths/

Kabat-Zinn, J., & Thich, N. H. (1990). *Full catastrophe living: Using the wisdom of your body and mind to face stress, pain, and illness.* New York: Dell Publishing.

Killingsworth, M. A., & Gilbert, D. T. (2010). A wandering mind is an unhappy mind. *Science, 330*, 932.

Kostanski, M., & Hassed, C. (2008). Mindfulness as a concept and a process. *Australian Psychologist, 43*(1), 15–21.

Krystal, M., Moore, K. A., & Zill, N. (1990). *Identifying successful families.* Washington, DC: Child Trends.

Larson, R., & Richards, M. H. (1994). *Divergent realities: The emotional lives of mothers, fathers, and adolescents.* New York: Basic Books.

Lewis, J. M., & Looney, J. G. (1983). *The long struggle: Well-functioning working class black families.* New York: Brunner/Mazel.

Lin, P. L., & Chen, J.-M. (1994). *Characteristics of a healthy family and family strengths: A cross-cultural study.* Retrieved from http://www.eric.ed.gov/PDFS/ED377101.pdf

Lin, Y.-C. (2009). Improving parent-child relationships through block play. *Education, 130*, 461-496. Retrieved from research library.

Mactavish, J., & Schleien, S. (1998). Playing together, growing together: Parents' perspective on the benefits of family recreation in families that include children with developmental disabilities. *Therapeutic Recreational Journal, 32*, 207–230.

Mann, C. (2008). *Research shows lasting benefits of family dinner: Regular family meals linked to healthy habits, academic success.* Retrieved from http://www.suite101.com/content/family-dinner-time-builds-health-success-a69810

Marks, S. R., & MacDermid, S. M. (1996). Multiple roles and the self: A theory of role balance. *Journal of Marriage and the Family, 58*, 417–432.

McCubbin, M. A., & McCubbin, H. I. (1989). Families coping with illness: The resiliency model of family stress, adjustment and adaptation. In C. B. Danielson, B. Hamel-Bissel, & P. Winstead-Fry (Eds.), *Families, health & illness: Perspectives on coping and intervention.* St. Louis. MO: Mosby.

McEwen, B. S. (2006). Sleep deprivation as a neurobiologic and physiologic stressor: Allostasis and allostatic load. *Metabolism, Clinical and Experimental, 55*(10), S20 S23.

Medina, A. M., Lederhos, C. L., Lillis, T. A. (2009). Sleep disruption and decline in marital satisfaction across the transition to parenthood. *Family Systems & Health, 27*(2), 153–160.

Milkie, A., Kendig, S. M., Nomaguchi, K. M., & Denny, K. E. (2010). Time with children, children's well-being and work–family balance among employed parents. *Journal of Marriage and Family, 72*, 1329–1343.

Milkie, M. A., Mattingly, M. J., Nomaguchi, K. M., Bianchi, S. M., and Robinson, J. P. (2004). The time squeeze: Parental statuses and feelings about time with children. *Journal of Marriage and Family, 66*, 739-761.

Monk, C. A., Trafton, J. G., & Boehm-Davis, D. A. (2008). The effect of interruption duration and demand on resuming suspended goals. *Journal of Experimental Psychology Applied, 14*, 299–313.

National Sleep Foundation. (2007). *Sleep in America poll.* Retrieved from http://www.sleepfoundation.org/category/article-type/sleep-america-polls

Nix, G. A., Ryan, R. M., Manly, J. B., & Deci, E. L. (1999). Revitalization through self regulation: The effecvitality. *Journal of Experimental Social Psychology, 35*(1999), 266–284.

Olson, D. H. (1986). Prepared statement before the House Select Committee on Children, Youth, and Families. In *The diversity and strength of American families.* Washington, DC: US Government Printing Office.

Chapter 6 – Family Togetherness

Perrewe, P. L., & Hochwarter, W. A. (2001). Can we really have it all? The attainment of work and family values. *Current Directions in Psychological Science, 10*(1), 29-33.

Putnam, R. D. (1996). The strange disappearance of civic America. *American Prospect, 7*, 24. Retrieved from http://xroads.virginia.edu/~HYPER/DETOC/assoc/strange.html

Putnam, R. D. (1993). The prosperous community: Social capital and public life. *The American Prospect, 4*(13), 11–18.

Reivich, K., & Shatté, A. (2002). *The resilience factor: 7 keys to finding your inner strength and overcoming life's hurdles.* New York: Broadway Books.

Roberts, K. C., & Danoff-Burg, S. (2010). Mindfulness and health behaviors: Is paying attention good for you? *Journal of American College Health, 59*, 165–173.

Ryan, R. M., Deci, E. L. (2008). Self-determination theory and the role of basic psychological needs in personality and the organization of behavior. In O. P. John, R. W. Robbins, & L. A. Pervin (Eds.), *Handbook of personality: Theory and research* (pp. 654–678). New York: The Guilford Press.

Ryan, R. M., & Frederick, C. M. (1997). On energy, personality and health: Subjective vitality as a dynamic reflection of well-being. *Journal of Personality, 65*, 529–565.

Santrock, J. W. (2010). *Life span development.* New York: McGraw-Hill.

Seligman, M. E. P., Steen, T. A., Park, N., & Peterson, C. (2005). Positive psychology progress: Empirical validation of interventions. *American Psychologist, July-August*, 410–421.

Shanea Ellington, A. (2011). *The role of family time on a young child's overall development* (Unpublished masters thesis). University of Alabama, Tuscaloosa, AL.

Shapiro, S. L. Carlson, L. E., Astin, J. A., & Freeman, B. (2006). Mechanisms of mindfulness. *Journal of Clinical Psychology, 62*, 373–386.

Smith, B. W., Shelley, B. M., Dalen, J., Wiggins, K., Tooley, E., & J. Bernard. (2008). A pilot study comparing the effects of mindfulness-based and cognitive-based stress reduction. *Journal of Alternative and Complementary Medicine, 14*, 251–258.

Smith, K. M., Freeman, P. A., & Zabriskie, R. B. (2009). An examination of family communication within the core and balance model of family leisure functioning. *Family Relation, 58*, 79–90.

Sobralske, M. C. (1985). Perceptions of health: Navajo Indians. *Topics in Clinical Nursing, 7*(3), 32-39.

Sonnentag, S., Binnewies, C., & Mojza, E. J. (2010). Staying well and engaged when demands are high: The role of psychological detachment. *Journal of Applied Psychology, 95*, 965–976.

Stinnett, N. (1979). Strengthening families. *Family Perspective, 13*, 3-9.

Stinnett, N., & DeFrain, J. (1985). *Secrets of strong families.* Boston: Little, Brown & Co.

Tanner, K. (n. d.). *Becoming a transitional character: Changing your family culture.* Retrieved from https://foreverfamilies.byu.edu/Pages/challenges/Becoming-a-Transitional-Character-Changing-Your-Family-Culture.aspx

Togliatti, T. (2007). *Stay connected to loved ones.* Retrieved from http://suite101.com/article/most-important-ways-to-connect-a14490

Turkle, S. (2011). *Alone together: Why we expect more from technology and less from each other.* New York: Basic Books.

Valcour, M. (2007). Work-based resources moderators of the relationship between work hours and satisfaction with work–family balance. *Journal of Applied Psychology, 92*, 1512–1523.

Westmoreland, H., & Little, P. M. D. (2006). *Exploring quality standards for middle school after school programs: What we know and what we need to know. A Summit Report.* Cambridge, MA: Harvard Family Research Project. Retrieved from http://www.hfrp.org/ExploringQualityStandardsSummit

Westmoreland, H. (2009). *Family involvement across learning settings: Family involvement and out-of-school time.* Retrieved from http://www.hfrp.org/family-involvement/publications-resources/family-involvement-across-learning-settings

Zabriskie, R., McCormick, B., & Bryan P. (2001). The influences of family leisure patterns on perceptions of family functioning. *Family Relations, 50*, 281–289.

Chapter 7
Passion, Purpose, Vision, Identified & Clearly Focused

You are fired up by your passion, directed by your purpose, empowered, sustained and maintained by your vision. Passion, purpose and vision are all interrelated and all leading to what you end up doing with your life. My immediate thoughts about differentiating between the three would have passion as the driving force. If I am passionate about something there is a built-in motivation present. I don't need a lot of encouragement or help moving on it or getting it done.

> *Your passion is your purpose for your vision. There is a personal drive connected to your actions.*

The caution that must be taken into consideration, however, with passion is that the passion does not turn into obsession.

Purpose for me has a similar built-in motivation present, but it is more foundational or inherently right or appropriate rather than being the driving force behind it. It's more like it is meant to be or it's just the right fit.

> *Your attitude is: "This is the way it is supposed to be."*

Purpose provides that feeling of being right on target, moving in the right direction.

Vision has a similar built-in motivation present, but it is different from the other two in that it is more thoughtful, insightful and more on the intellectual level. Vision is more of a projection based on an accumulation of thoughts, ideas or patterns that you have put together into a single entity. It's more future oriented. And unlike the other two, it tends to require more planning, involving multiple steps or stages.

Passion

In an article titled "Making People's Life Most Worth Living: On the Importance of Passion for Positive Psychology," Robert Vallerand and Jeremie Verner-Filion (2013) give a dualistic model of passion, explaining the difference between harmonious and obsessive passion.

A dualistic model of passion

In line with Self-Determination Theory (SDT; Deci & Ryan, 2000), we propose that people engage in various activities throughout life in the hope of satisfying the basic psychological needs of autonomy (to feel a sense of personal initiative), competence (to interact effectively with the environment) and relatedness (to feel connected to significant others). With time and experience, most people eventually start to display preference for some activities, especially those that are enjoyable and allow the satisfaction of the aforementioned basic psychological needs. Of these activities, a limited few will be perceived as particularly enjoyable and important, and to have some resonance with our identity or how we see ourselves. These activities become passionate activities.

Harmonious passion

Harmonious passion results from an autonomous internalization of the activity into the person's identity and self. An autonomous internalization occurs when individuals have freely accepted the activity as important for them without any contingencies attached to it; they want to act and don't feel that they have to act. This type of internalization emanates from the intrinsic and integrative tendencies of the self (Deci & Ryan, 2000; Ryan & Deci, 2003) and produces a motivational force to willingly engage in the activity that one loves and engenders a sense of volition and personal endorsement about pursuing the activity. When harmonious passion is at play, individuals do not experience an uncontrollable urge to engage in the passionate activity, but rather freely choose to do so.

> *You "want to" rather than feeling like you "have to" be engaged.*

With this type of passion, the activity occupies a significant but not overpowering space in the person's identity and is in harmony with other aspects of the person's life.

Obsessive passion

Conversely, obsessive passion results from a controlled internalization of the activity that one loves into identity. Such an internalization process leads not only the activity representation to be part of the person's identity, but also to values and regulations associated with the activity to be at best partially internalized in the self, and at worse to be internalized into the person's identity but completely outside the integrative self (Deci & Ryan, 2000).

Personally I am passionate about eating a good meal and listening to the news, especially news about politics or news involving financial matters.

If I were obsessive about either, I would have to have a good meal every day and would have to have them perfect just about all the time. If I were obsessive about listening to the news, I would have to listen to it all the time. In other words, I would not feel right until I listened to the news each day and my day would not be complete until I listened to the news. Same thing with a good meal; my day would be incomplete if I did not get that good meal every day. Whereas for the harmonious passion side of things, I thoroughly enjoy both but it's no big deal if I don't get that good meal everyday and/or watch the news all the time.

Another example that is not personal is a person who is passionate about a sport such as playing tennis as often as possible and for a few hours, whereas if he were an obsessive tennis player, his day would not be complete until he played tennis. On the other hand, however, when the obsessive tennis player played, he would have to play for an uncommonly long time, everyday.

> *The obsessively passionate person takes things they are passionate about to the extreme.*

The harmoniously passionate person thoroughly enjoys what they are passionate about but can do or have it in moderation.

A controlled internalization originates from intra- and/or interpersonal pressure typically because certain contingencies are attached to the activity, such as feelings of social acceptance or self-esteem, or because the sense of excitement derived from activity engagement is uncontrollable (Mageau, Carpentier, & Vallerand, 2011). People with an obsessive passion can thus find themselves in the position of experiencing an uncontrollable urge to partake in the activity they view as important and enjoyable. They cannot help but engage in the passionate activity. The passion must run its course, as it controls the person.

Harmonious passion is the passion I am espousing for you to embrace. When you find something you are passionate about, you simply love it; you enjoy it so much that you find yourself (consciously or sometimes unconsciously) trying to find time to do it as often as possible. I am excited about getting to work when I am passionate about my job. My energy level seems to be endless when I am doing something I am passionate about. Acting on my passion just feels right. There is a natural flow to the process rather than a feeling of urgency that it must happen by any means necessary.

Chapter 7 – Passion, Purpose, Vision, Identified & Clearly Focused

Passion and flow

Flow (Csikszentmihalyi, 1975; Csikszentmihalyi, Rathunde, & Whalen, 1993) refers to a desirable state that people experience when they feel completely immersed in the activity (e.g., "I have a feeling of total control"). Based on the Dualistic Model of Passion, it would be expected that harmonious passion facilitates adaptive cognitive processes such as flow, whereas obsessive passion should not, or at least less so. This is so because with harmonious passion, integrative self processes are at play, leading the person to fully partake in the passion activity with an openness that is conducive to mindful attention, concentration, and flow. The situation is different when obsessive passion is at play because ego-invested processes are involved (Hodgins & Knee, 2002), thereby leading individuals to adopt a defensive orientation that only permits a partial investment in the activity. Thus, less flow should be experienced in the process.

Research provides support for this hypothesis.

> *For instance, in Vallerand et al. (2003), results revealed that harmonious passion facilitates the experience of flow, whereas obsessive passion does not.*

These results have been replicated in various fields such as the work domain (Forest et al., 2011; Lavigne, Forest, & Crevier-Braud, 2012) and sports (Philippe, Vallerand, Andrianarisoa, & Brunel, 2009). Of additional interest are the findings of Lavigne et al. (2012) obtained in the work domain. Using a cross-lagged panel design, these authors replicated the above findings. In addition, they showed that passion predicts changes in flow over time, while flow does not affect passion.

The healthy aspect of passion comes into play when you consider the fact that passion engenders excitement, strong interest and energetic involvement. When you have passion in your life, you have excitement, interest and energy as a part of the object of your passion. For example, if I am passionate about helping others every time an opportunity comes up, I am excited about taking advantage of that opportunity. I can't wait to follow through on whatever needs to be done because my energy level is high.

The unhealthy aspect of passion, however, comes into play when my excitement, strong interest and involvement are at such an extreme level that I am compelled to act and that not acting is not even an option. I am obsessed and feel that I must act whether I want to or not. Taking the same example above, instead of taking advantage of an opportunity that comes up, an obsessed person would feel compelled to create such an opportunity and would feel defeated or unsuccessful it they were not able to do so.

Chapter 7 – Passion, Purpose, Vision, Identified & Clearly Focused

> *There is not complete agreement as to whether some obsessive passion is healthy or not.*

For example, Scott Kaufman (2011) disagrees with some commentators who argued that obsessive passion could be useful in the beginning stages of a new endeavor, such as when starting a new company. Kaufman feels that obsessive passion is rarely beneficial. It's not just that those with high levels of obsessive passion are committed, focused and dedicated. Those who are obsessively passionate about their work are inflexibly, excessively and compulsively committed, finding it difficult to disengage. As such, they are setting up bad habits from the start, and risking burnout in the longer run. Kaufman notes that harmonious passion is correlated with flow—the mental state of being completely present and fully immersed in a task. Research shows that it's flow that is conducive to creativity (Vallerand, 2010), not obsessive passion. The positive emotions and intrinsic joy associated with harmonious passion are what propels one to greatness, not the negative emotions, compulsions and unstable ego associated with obsessive passion.

As I mentioned earlier, one of the reasons for writing this book was to bring about balance in my own life. The unhealthy aspect of passion, however, comes into play when my excitement, strong interest and involvement are at such an extreme level that I am compelled to act, and that not acting isn't even an option. I am obsessed and feel I must act whether I want to or not. This is not to say that all obsessions are absolute and completely uncontrollable, but in many cases they are at an unhealthy extreme. **When a person's life is out of balance, it is very possible that their passion has moved from harmonious to obsessive passion with them spending too much time on one, two or even three areas of their life that might be their passion but to the detriment of other areas of their life.**

Kaufman's final note is that all of us have at least a little bit of obsessive and harmonious passion for our work or other things. The key for work productivity and for buffering against work burnout is to increase your harmonious passion while reducing your obsessive passion. Kaufman offers suggestions on how to turn down the dial on obsessive passion and turn up the dial on harmonious passion in an article titled "How to Increase Your Harmonious Passion" (Kaufman 2011). This author agrees with Kaufman that obsessive passion is dangerous and is not likely to be positive. Passion is a good thing and if we can find passion in our lives, we are likely to be better off especially if we spend hours, day in and day out engaged in the activity such as in our work, job or profession.

> *The smart person is the one who finds a way of making a living doing what he/she is (harmoniously) passionate about.*

That is the formula for success. If you are passionate about what you are doing, you will be willing to do it for free or at least for minimum reward since you enjoy it so much. Plus, you will likely do a good job and will likely be willing to learn more about what you are doing.

Chapter 7 – Passion, Purpose, Vision, Identified & Clearly Focused

At some point if you continue to be engaged in your passionate endeavor, you might even become an expert in that area to the extent that you can write about the subject, speak on the subject or even hold seminars or workshops on it or related topics. At any rate, there is potential in pursuing your passion as far as you can take it and still being comfortable with keeping it from become an obsession.

Passion "light"

Passion light, as I am here describing it, is where your focus is on the result rather than the object, activity or entity itself. This passion is more like a determination or a goal or objective that is being seriously sought. The end result is what you are somewhat passionate about getting and the process of getting there is not necessarily enjoyable or even something that you really want to do but you see it as a way to get the desired result. Similar to a regular passion, passion light has a very high level of commitment of time and other resources, but different from a regular passion, it tends to lack the same level of enjoyment, naturalness and effortlessness. The end result is the driving force rather than the personal natural energy.

> *I believe that there are some passions that are born out of necessity.*

These passions might be less enjoyable or satisfying, but they have your complete endorsement. These passions are mostly connected to the results they bring and it is the results you are determined to get. I can explain this passion with a personal example.

I grew up poor even though I cannot recall ever going hungry or not having most of what I needed. I've never been satisfied being poor. I've always wanted to experience the other side. I finally discovered that one way to make it to the other side was through education, so I sought education. After going as far as I could with education, I started to refine my passion to having a variety of experiences. And then finally I started zeroing in on specific things that I enjoy doing such as acquiring knowledge for the sake of just knowing and having the information.

> *I soon discovered that having knowledge is power and that having power would get me to the other side.*

Fortunately, I discovered relatively early in life that education for me was going to be the key to my having a better life. Consequently, acquiring an education became a passion for me. First getting my GED, then my AA degree, my bachelor's degree, masters and finally my doctorate degree.

Now as I look back at my life, I realize I have had several passions throughout my life. I continue to be passionate about my spiritual connection, my health and wellbeing and for the most part, those things that make up a quality life such as an education, family, work, social and civic involvement and financial freedom turn out to be a balanced life. I see my lifestyle as the way to get me to where I need to be.

I believe my passion is beginning to shift away from me and my personal needs to the other person. I'm now wanting to be a good example for others and wanting to be helpful to others; share my knowledge and try to find ways to convince others of the value of education and knowledge, the value and benefits of maintaining good health and ultimately the importance of living a healthy, balanced and consistent lifestyle.

Purpose

> *What is your purpose for being alive?*

Why are you here? What is God's purpose for your life? What purpose does your being who you are serve the people around you: your family, your community, society? Your answer to these questions might help provide an answer to the comment about who you have become and can potentially determine who you are striving to become, your direction in life.

If you have given any thought about what your purpose in life might be, what would you say? Regardless of how you think you would do it, here's at least one way to proceed. Since it's almost a certainty that you will need to be equipped to do what you come up with as your purpose, and probably do it well as a matter of fact.

> *Many people determine their purpose based on what they do well; what they enjoy doing; and what comes naturally to them.*

Many people get their purpose from the work they do. In that case, the woman attorney who works for the state department of vocational rehabilitation might surmise that her purpose in life is to help people with disabilities. The high school teacher might determine that his purpose in life is to help teenage children. Whatever your purpose and however you come about finding it, if you have identified your purpose in life and you are far ahead most others in the world.

> *Most people don't have a clue what their purpose in life is and many have not even given the thought much attention.*

Having an identified purpose in life is a rarity and having identified your purpose and following it is even more rare. This is even true in spite of the abundance of research that shows people who have a purpose in life and are following it are much better off in life and are more likely to outlive those who don't have a clue.

Chapter 7 – Passion, Purpose, Vision, Identified & Clearly Focused

Among the most difficult decisions to make are often about finding purpose in your work and life. In his book *The Power of Purpose: Creating Meaning in Your Life and Work*, author and counselor Richard Leider (2005) believes each individual is born with a reason for being and life is a quest to discover that purpose. He emphasizes that people are overwhelmed at times by the decisions they get to make—and have to make—about their jobs, their families, their businesses, their futures.

If you don't have a way to sort it all out, he states, you can become paralyzed. Among the strategies he suggests are: Ask yourself these questions and answer them honestly: What do you want? (why?) And how will you know when you get it? People really do have their own solutions. The problem is, either they don't know how to discover them, or they avoid discovering them. But if you want to come up with good decisions for your work and your life, simply ask those questions—because it all comes down to very simple things.

Douglas LaBier, a business psychologist and psychotherapist wrote an article titled "5 Steps That Reveal Your Life's Purpose." (Back Off and Tune Inward, Learn From Your Choices and Their Consequences, Get on the Path, Stretch Yourself and Pursue It With Love). In it, he shared an example of a person who found their purpose in a unique and uncommon way: through an event that turned out to be a moment of illumination.

Adam Steltzner is the NASA scientist who headed the team that designed and carried out the successful landing of the Mars rover, Curiosity. In an NPR interview, Steltzner spoke of having played in a rock band after high school rather than going to college. While waiting for stardom, his friends went to college and on with their lives. On his way home from a gig one night he looked up and was suddenly fascinated with the stars, especially the constellation Orion.

Steltzner felt the fact that it was in a different place in the sky at night when he returned home from playing a gig ... That was it ... he was totally turned on by this idea of understanding his world. He had to know all about the laws that govern the universe. Seltzner enrolled in a physics course, and over the next several years earned a Ph.D., which led to where he is today.

LaBier went on to explain that most of us have to work at discovering our purpose. Too often it's clouded over by our conditioning and adapting to life experiences and choices—from family and culture to our educational and career paths and our relationships. We're so enraptured with our outer life—or absorbed by it—that awareness of our true purpose dims to just a flicker.

Consequently, many go through life feeling off-track, out of tune in some way. That creates major stress over time, and research finds that such stress will increase your risk of death from all sources.

Chapter 7 – Passion, Purpose, Vision, Identified & Clearly Focused

Kute Blackman (2013) wrote an article titled "How to REALLY Find Your True Life's Purpose. Once and for All!" In it, he says the real purpose of life is simply to realize and remember who you REALLY are—who you are beyond conditioning and identity—and to be that fully.

> *In his book A Purpose Driven Life, Rick Warren (2002) talks about how people who have identified a purpose for their lives are found to be more "happy" and fulfilled.*

Others have said that a person with vision and purpose has a reason for getting up in the morning and usually it is to benefit someone else or to help someone else to succeed. Some people equate purpose and vision with mission. In his book *First Things First*, Stephen Covey (1995) says that it is a pretty safe assumption that there probably is buy-in when we develop our own mission statement. Covey refers to crafting a mission statement as connecting with your own unique purpose and the profound satisfaction that comes in fulfilling it. He emphasizes the point that the idea is that if you live by a statement of what's really important to you, you can make better time-management decisions. The author asks,

> *why worry about saving minutes when you might be wasting years?*

To me, knowing your purpose in life makes a lot of sense especially if you are truly interested in fulfilling your purpose. If you sincerely believe your purpose in life is to be a nurse helping people to be and stay well, then you are so much more likely to be content with being a nurse or at least having a career in the helping profession.

Purpose connected to your spirituality

> *Part of the problem or the biggest issue is finding your purpose and accepting that as being your purpose.*

If you are a Christian or the follower of some deity, god or spiritual leader, that question might be a little easier than if you are a non-believer. Followers of a certain deity would likely get their direction about their purpose from that source. And even then, it is not an easy task to come up with a specific purpose for your life.

What Scripture says about one's purpose in life

On the website (http://www.openbible.info/topics/purpose_in_life), I found 10 of my favorite scripture-based perspectives on the subject of life's purpose.

Psalm 138:8 The Lord will fulfill his purpose for me; your steadfast love, O Lord, endures forever. Do not forsake the work of your hands.

> **Romans 8:28** *And we know that for those who love God all things work together for good, for those who are called according to His purpose.*

Matthew 5:13-16 You are the salt of the earth, but if salt has lost its taste, how shall its saltiness be restored? It is no longer good for anything except to be thrown out and trampled under people's feet. You are the light of the world. A city set on a hill cannot be hidden. Nor do people light a lamp and put it under a basket, but on a stand, and it gives light to all in the house. In the same way, let your light shine before others, so that they may see your good works and give glory to your Father who is in Heaven.

Job 22:21 Agree with God, and be at peace; thereby good will come to you.

Philippians 4:13 I can do all things through him who strengthens me.

Romans 12:1-5 I appeal to you therefore, brothers, by the mercies of God, to present your bodies as a living sacrifice, holy and acceptable to God, which is your spiritual worship. Do not be conformed to this world, but be transformed by the renewal of your mind, that by testing you may discern what is the will of God, what is good and acceptable and perfect. For by the grace given to me I say to everyone among you not to think of himself more highly than he ought to think, but to think with sober judgment, each according to the measure of faith that God has assigned. For as in one body we have many members, and the members do not all have the same function, so we, though many, are one body in Christ, and individually members one of another.

> **Matthew 6:33** *But seek first the kingdom of God and His righteousness, and all these things will be added to you.*

Mark 12:30-31 "And you shall love the Lord your God with all your heart and with all your soul and with all your mind and with all your strength." The second is this: "You shall love your neighbor as yourself." There is no other commandment greater than these.

Ephesians 1:11 In him we have obtained an inheritance, having been predestined according to the purpose of him who works all things according to the counsel of his will.

Purpose as fundamental to life

According to Carol Ryff and Burton Singer (1998), numerous psychological theorists have emphasized the importance of meaning, purpose, and self-realization/personal growth as fundamental aspects of optimal human functioning. These formulations, extensively reviewed in prior works (Ryff, 1985, 1989a, 1989b), include Allport's (1961) conception of maturity, Roger's (1961) description of the fully functioning person, Maslow's (1955, 1968) characterization of self-actualization, Buhler's (Buhler & Massarik, 1968) basic life tendencies, Jahoda's (1958) criteria of positive mental health, Erikson's (1959) psychosocial stages, Jung's (1933) process of individuation, and Frankl's (1992) will to meaning.

To be sure, these many portrayals of optimal human functioning included other characteristics as well, but themes of leading a life that is purposeful and meaningful and having a sense of one's own growth and development are unmistakably prominent in these psychological accounts. On the sociological side, similar themes of self-realization (Dowd, 1990) and sense of coherence (Antonovsky, 1987) are also evident in efforts to characterize human development or health.

In addition, Ryff and Singer found that purpose in life and personal growth have also been shown in multiple datasets to have strong linkages with education (Marmot, Ryff, Bumpass, Shipley, & Marks, 1997; Ryff & Magee, 1995; Ryff & Singer, 1998). Individuals with college degrees have notably higher levels of these particular aspects of wellbeing than individuals with only high school levels of education, with the differences dramatically evident for women.

> *Casually speaking, it could be argued that varying levels of purpose and personal growth contribute to differences in educational attainment;*

Alternatively, that these aspects of psychological wellbeing may result from differences in education. Although both interpretations likely have merit, the more powerful is most likely the latter, namely, that education is a key mechanism governing opportunities in life: those with limited education are thus blocked in their efforts to pursue meaningful life goals and to experience the sense of personal growth and self-realization. These findings demonstrate that those in lower positions in the social hierarchy also have less likelihood of experiencing the positive in life. As such, they may lack the protective benefits associated with an existence that is purposeful, meaningful, and enabling of an individual's development. The two researchers provide an interesting example to illustrate their point.

Case example: A midlife awakening of true meaning and purpose
The life of John D. Rockefeller (see Hafen, Karren, Frandsen, & Smith, 1996) provides an interesting illustration of the adverse health consequences of negative mental states (e.g., greed, ruthlessness), followed by a fundamental reframing of central life purpose and, in the process, a dramatic shift toward positive physical health. Mr. Rockefeller drove himself relentlessly until his mid-50s, and in the course of accumulating billionaire status, crushed many people. Workers in the Pennsylvania oil fields hung him in effigy; to protect his life, he hired 24-hour bodyguards. Physiologically, he developed alopecia (loss of hair), poor digestion (only crackers and milk were edible), and persistent insomnia. At age 53, physicians gave him about a year to live. In a dramatic life transformation, Mr. Rockefeller redefined his basic life purpose and sense of his own mission in life: He

began to think of and care about others. This led to his 45-year program of generous and well-targeted philanthropy. Accompanying this shift from selfish and ruthless accumulation of wealth to altruism were physiological consequences. For the first time in years, he was able to eat normally and to sleep soundly and, hence, to feel renewed. Defying the physicians' prognosis, he lived until age 98 giving to and caring for others.

Predictability is one of the benefits of purpose

Stacey Schaefer and colleagues (2013) authored an article titled "Purpose in Life Predicts Better Emotional Recovery from Negative Stimuli." In it, they say that purpose in life predicts both health and longevity, suggesting that the ability to find meaning from life's experiences, especially when confronting life's challenges, may be a mechanism underlying resilience.

> *From a study they did, they found that having purpose in life may motivate reframing stressful situations to deal with them more productively, thereby facilitating recovery from stress and trauma.*

In turn, enhanced ability to recover from negative events may allow a person to achieve or maintain a feeling of greater purpose in life over time.

Along those same lines, W. Bradford Swift, author of *Life On Purpose: 6 Passages to an Inspired Life,* identified the following 10 benefits to knowing and living your life purpose:

Focus When you clearly know your life purpose, it becomes a truing mechanism allowing you to focus more clearly on what matters most to you.

Passion The passion becomes the fuel that propels them forward in expressing their life purpose.

Being Unstoppable They've found that often a little patience, coupled with persistence can go a long way, as does surrendering to the timeline of a Higher Power.

Fulfillment Living a life in which you are regularly expressing your life purpose and allowing it to shape your decisions, your thoughts, feelings and actions is simply a whole lot more fulfilling.

Living a Value-based Life an integral component of a person's life purpose are their "core values"—those intangibles of life that mean the most to them. When you are living a life on purpose, you are living a "value-based" life, rather than a lifestyle-based life.

Fun People can bring purposeful play to almost any situation and find or create ways to have each day be a reflection of their true joy and purpose.

Integrity For me, a life on purpose is a life of ultimate integrity. It's a life that is whole and complete. People who know their purpose and are living it know who they are and why they are here.

Trust/Faith As people clarify their life purpose and begin to live true to it, many of them report a surprising increase in synchronicity and serendipity in their lives. It's as though the Universe is rewarding them for the courage to live true to their purpose.

Grace According to the dictionary, grace is "the unmerited divine assistance given man" and people living on purpose often report living a grace-filled life.

> *When you commit to living true to your purpose, something amazing begins to happen.*

The Universe lines up with your intention and commitment.

Flow People living on purpose live in the flow of the Universal stream of consciousness. Rather than fighting against the current, they allow the current of what's wanting to happen to happen.

Purpose provides meaning to life

In his book titled *Purpose in Life*, Kendall Bronk (2014) explains that Victor Frankl (1959) described purpose as "inner strength" (p. 80), "the responsibility which a man has for his existence" (p. 80), "the why of one's existence," (p. 101), and "(that which) life expected from us" (p. 108), "the specific meaning of a person's life at a given moment (p. 110).

I especially liked Chapter 3, "The Role of Purpose in Optimal Human Functioning." He continues to quote Frankl but also shares the perspectives of several other researchers on the topic of purpose.

According to Frankl (1959), purposes are not given to people, instead they are discovered, and discovering a purpose helps individuals withstand the challenges they confront, both in dire conditions and in more typical daily life.

Other researchers have extended and refined Frankl's theory of existential neurosis. For instance, Irvin Yalom (1980) considered meaning to be one of life's ultimate concerns, alongside death, isolation, and the loss of freedom, and he noted that individuals without meaning suffer significantly. As he put it, "the human being seems to require meaning. To live without meaning, goals, values, or ideals seems to provoke... considerable distress" (p. 422).

> *Also confirmed was that chronically bored individuals typically lack a life purpose (Drob & Bernard 1988), and that turning away from or leaving meaningful life projects leads to a sense of being stuck in a chronic state of boredom (Bargdill, 2000).*

While Frankl's ideas were primarily theoretical in nature, other researchers have conducted studies that offer broad, empirical support for many of them. A series of studies, for example, sought to determine if there was an empirical basis for his existential theory—boredom is the result of purposelessness—and results consistently suggest there is. For example, a cluster of studies confirm that boredom is distinct from depression and anxiety (Fahlman et al., 2009) that individuals in a high purpose state report less boredom than individuals in a low purpose state (Fahlman et al., 2009).

Results of a longitudinal study of meaning and boredom conclude that these two factors likely share a bidirectional, causal relationship (Fahlman et al., 2009), whereby a sense of meaninglessness causes boredom and vice versa. Taken together, these studies offer strong support for the inverse relationship between purpose and boredom.

Another series of studies examined the relationship among purpose, hope and depression and concluded that purpose is positively related to hope and inversely related to depression. Other studies have similarly concluded that purpose is inversely related to loneliness (Paloutzian & Ellison, 1982), psychosocial problems (Ho et al., 2010), general anxiety, and depression (Bigler et al., 2001).

> *A greater purpose in life is associated with lower mortality rates.*

Lead researcher Patrick Hill (2009) of Carleton University in Canada said that their findings point to the fact that finding a direction for life and setting overarching goals for what you want to achieve can help you actually live longer, regardless of when you find your purpose.

After adjusting for age, sex, education and race, a higher purpose of life was associated with a substantially reduced risk of mortality. Thus, a person with high purpose in life was about half as likely to die over the follow-up period compared to a person with low purpose. The association of purpose in life with mortality did not differ among men and women or whites and blacks, and the finding persisted even after controlling for depressive symptoms, disability, neuroticism, the number of medical conditions and income. This information was retrieved from: http://www.sciencedaily.com/releases/2009/06/090615144207.htm and
https://www.rush.edu/news/press-releases/having-higher-purpose-life-reduces-risk-death-among-older-adults

Chapter 7 – Passion, Purpose, Vision, Identified & Clearly Focused

Purpose connected to longevity

Rick Nauert (2014), senior news editor for *Psych Central*, wrote an article titled "Purpose, Meaning in Life Can Lower Mortality Risk." In it, he brings out the point that new research suggests that despite one's age, having a sense of purpose in life may help you live longer. The new finding builds on earlier studies that have suggested having a purpose in life lowers risk of mortality.

In the new study, researchers take the concept a step farther as they examined whether the benefits of purpose vary over time, such as across different developmental periods or after important life transitions.

Vision

If you are fired up by your passion and given direction by you purpose, then your vision should empower you, sustain you and provide you with the impetus to maintain your course of action until you reach your ultimate goal. Your vision is your life's work that continues even after you are no longer around. What you feel is the reason you are still alive is your contribution to the world. Your vision is what you are to contribute to society.

> *The thing you feel obligated to carry out, to do, and to accomplish, that's your vision.*

Your vision or purpose in life might be a part of a more global "assignment," or it might be more personal that is peculiar to you. It's a statement of your inspiration, the framework for your strategic planning, a statement of your dreams and hopes for the future.

Dare to dream; stretch your mind; think; ponder; explore the possibilities of the future!
When I was a little boy, I used to dream of being rich. At that time, rich was for me to be able to always have money in my pocket to buy whatever I wanted. I've never needed a lot of money but being broke with no money in my pocket has always bothered me. Even today, I feel uncomfortable unless I have money in my pocket. When I was a boy, I only needed a few dollars; today having $50 to $100 in my pocket feels good and seldom will you find me with less. I will usually not have a lot more, but very seldom will I have less.

Today, my dreams have gone from me being rich to me living comfortably. At my current age, my dreams are basically to maintain in most areas of my life and to continue to grow wherever possible in others.

Mark Batterson (n.d.) authored an article titled "Get a Life: Creating and Sustaining a Personal Life Vision" that had several ideas worth sharing.

> *He emphasized that you will never accomplish the goals you do not set.*

It is that simple. He recommends you schedule a personal retreat. He said part of the reason some people become workaholics is the simple fact they love what they do. Batterson asked the question: You know why most of us do not get what we want out of life? Because we do not know what we want. If all you do is set a bunch of selfish goals, you would be better off if you did not accomplish them. But if you set them in the context of prayer, then life goals become an expression of faith. "Faith is being sure of what we hope for" (Hebrews 11:1).

Batterson ended his article with: You want to sustain a life vision? Stay hungry. Stay foolish. He got those words from Steve Jobs, the late Apple (computer) co-founder being called the Thomas Edison of his time, revealing them in a commencement speech at Stanford University in 2005. *Stay hungry* meaning always be curious to learn more and achieve more. *Stay foolish* meaning dare to make unconventional decisions as Steve Jobs did. Mark Batterson also offered *five principles that will help you discover and define your personal life vision,* which can be found at: http://enrichmentjournal.ag.org/201101/201101_038_Get_Life.cfm

> *In the early 1960s, John Kennedy had a vision of putting a man on the moon by 1970, and in 1969 Neil Armstrong and Buzz Aldrin landed there.*

Importance of having a personal vision

Numerous experts on leadership and personal development emphasize how vital it is for you to craft your own personal vision for your life. Warren Bennis, Stephen Covey, Peter Senge, and others point out that a powerful vision can help you succeed far beyond where you'd be without one. That vision can propel you and inspire those around you to reach their own dreams.

Senge defines vision as what you want to create of yourself and the world around you. What does your vision include? Making a vital change in an area such as health, technology, or the environment? Raising happy, well-adjusted children? Writing a book? Owning your own business? Living on a beach? Being very fit and healthy? Visiting every continent? Helping others with their spiritual development? What are you good at? What do you love to do? What aren't you good at now but would like to be? All of these important questions are part of identifying your personal vision.

Susan Heathfield (n.d.) provided a process of exploration to Prepare to Write the Personal Vision Statement. She suggests you use these questions to guide your thoughts.
- What are the 10 things you most enjoy doing? Be honest. These are the 10 things without which your weeks, months, and years would feel incomplete.
- What three things must you do every single day to feel fulfilled in your work?
- What are your five to six most important values?
- Your life has a number of important facets or dimensions, all of which deserve some attention in your personal vision statement. Write one important goal for each of

166

them: physical, spiritual, work or career, family, social relationships, financial security, mental improvement and attention, and fun.

- If you never had to work another day in your life, how would you spend your time instead of working?

> - ***When your life is ending, what will you regret not doing, seeing, or achieving?***

- What strengths have other people commented on about you and your accomplishments?
- What strengths do you see in yourself?
- What weaknesses have other people commented on about you and what do you believe are your weaknesses?

Do you see common themes in your responses to the questions? Write them down.

Did any of these questions trigger some ideas about what you'd like to be doing with your life? If so, keep thinking about the questions and your answers, and continue your personal research.

Your vision must be unique and appropriate for you. Write out a tentative personal vision based on what you came up with after going through the questions above. Ponder it, reflect on it, share it with others and keep playing with it until you have something that you feel good about.

According to Susanne Madsen (2013), a vision statement is a paragraph that encapsulates everything you would like to be, do and have in your career. She goes on to say:
It defines what success and excellence look like to you.
It expresses your vision for where you want to be in the future.
It reflects your values, goals, and purpose and how you want to operate.
It describes what you want to achieve in the *future*.
It answers the question *"Where do I want to be?"*
It defines the optimal desired future state – the mental picture – of what you want to achieve over time, say in five, ten or more years.
It inspires you to give your best and shapes your understanding of why you are doing what you do.

I offer the following Personal Vision Statement only as an example:

My vision is to follow my passion and purpose for being here on earth: learn and teach; serve and fellowship; and be a blessing for myself and others, especially family and friends. My vision for learning and teaching through serving and fellowship involves each area of my life: spiritual, mental and physical health, family, financial freedom, work and/or school, civic involvement, social connections and personal initiatives, challenges and aspirations. My vision is to have all 10 areas just mentioned in my life be an example for each family member, friend and others with whom I come in contact.

> *My hope is to maintain an acute discernment with the Holy Spirit who lives within me,*

to remain mentally and physically fit and to always be available with love for my family and close friends. My goal is to continue to teach at a university and do research in the areas of counseling, health and wellness. I hope to become an astute entrepreneur and wise investor of my earnings and saved resources. As my financial resources grow, I plan to give more to the many causes that have piqued my interest over the years. I plan to continue my extensive social involvement with the numerous groups and organizations of which I am a member. And finally my vision is to live life to the fullest pursuing my personal initiatives, challenges and aspirations.

Notice in this sample that I have included several areas of life (see Chapters 3 through 13 in this book). This will give you a balanced perspective of your vision. Be sure to solicit the input from others including trusted friends, family members and other people who know you well.

At a website of Beyond-Borders (http://www.beyond-borders.com/articles/are-you-killing-vision/) dated May 31, 2013, they quoted a story and describe what a clear and compelling vision is that I thought was worthy of repeating:

Three stone masons in the Middle Ages were hard at work when a visitor came along and asked them what they were doing. The first stone mason was hard at work, sweat beading his brow. "I am cutting this stone," he grumbled. The second stone mason, though less distraught, responded with a deep sigh, "I'm building a parapet." The third stone mason replied with a radiant face, "I am building a beautiful cathedral that will glorify God for centuries to come." Author unknown.

Personal visions and human motivation

Masuda, Kane, Shoptaugh, and Minor (2010) did a study that examines personal vision and its role in human motivation. In it, they found that a personal vision high on imagery defines in detail a clear and vivid picture of one's desired future (Bass, 1985; Baum et al., 1998; Kirkpatrick et al., 1996; Thoms & Blasko, 1999). By clearly defining one's desired future, a personal vision should better direct one's attention and effort to relevant tasks that facilitate movement toward that vision. Hence, those who clearly know what they want in their future are more likely to set specific task goals that will lead to such a future.

The four researchers also found that a vivid personal vision may reflect stronger, clear, and well-established values.

Chapter 7 – Passion, Purpose, Vision, Identified & Clearly Focused

> **Research has shown that values are related with commitment to projects.**

For example, Lydon (1996) found that the degree to which personal projects affirmed people's core values predicted participants' willingness to commit to their projects, especially when participants perceived these projects as stressful and difficult. In his study, Lydon examined students' commitment to an 8-week volunteer work project. Results revealed that students were more committed to the volunteer project if they reported that the project affirmed their personal values. The findings were more robust when students perceived the project as difficult and stressful.

Likewise, in an article by Berson et al. (2001) titled "The Relationship Between Vision Strength, Leadership Style and Context," the authors talk about the content of vision statements. They say preliminary casework examining the visions of exemplary transformational leaders (e.g., Bennis & Nanus, 1985; Tichy & Devanna, 1990) demonstrate that the content of their visions was highly inspirational, optimistic and future oriented. Visions can distinguish the new direction to be pursued from the old and mobilize (you) to action (Galbraith & Lawler, 1993; Gardner, 1990).

Berson et al. go on to say that vision statements may also include words that will maintain areas that (you) consider important, but may not necessarily represent inspiring content (Conger & Kanungo, 1998). Consequently, we expect that given the same challenge to create a visionary message, a transactional leader's vision will focus more on organizing or agenda setting, maintaining what (you have) already achieved, as well as attaining more specific goals (for the future) (e.g., Kotter, 1990).

> **Not surprisingly, a challenging personal vision should motivate the setting of more difficult and specific proximal goals.**

According to goal-setting theory (Locke & Latham, 1990), motivated effort stems from anticipated satisfaction linked to attaining a difficult goal. In fact, more than 400 field and laboratory studies have shown that people who set difficult and specific task goals are likely to perform better in a task than those who set vague or do-your-best goals (Locke & Latham, 1990).

Whatever your vision, being specific and challenging are key terms to remember. The same can be said for a purpose you might pursue (is it specific and is it challenging?). Or something that you are passionate about (is it specific and is it challenging)? Specificity and difficulty are highly regarded in all three cases.

Chapter 7 – Passion, Purpose, Vision, Identified & Clearly Focused

Passion, Purpose, Vision

As I wrap up the three entities, passion, purpose, vision, I am left with the question, which comes first. This reminds me of another question, which came first, the chicken or the egg? Some people get the vision first and they make it their purpose to become passionate about obtaining their vision. Others see themselves as being visionary when they find their purpose in life and thus become passionate about carrying out that purpose. Still others identify what they are passionate about that will lead them to their purpose and vision. Then there are those who use the three terms interchangeably and don't see a real distinction between them.

Whichever one comes first, second or third for you, I hope that I have shed some light on useful ideas that might be helpful in your pursuit for any one or all three concepts. See your vision, know your purpose and follow your passion.

REFERENCES
Chapter 7 – "Passion, Purpose, Vision Identified & Clearly Focused"

Aron, A., Aron, E. N., & Smollan, D. (1992). Inclusion of other in the self scale and the structure of interpersonal closeness. *Journal of Personality and Social Psychology, 63*, 596-612.

Baltes, P. B., & Smith, J. (1999). Multilevel and systemic analysis of old age: Theoretical and empirical evidence for a fourth age. In V. L. Bengston & K. W. Schaie (Eds.), *Handbook of theories of aging* (pp. 153–173). New York: Springer.

Bass, B. M. (1985). *Leadership and performance beyond expectations.* New York: Free Press.

Batterson, M. (n.d.). *Get a life: Creating and sustaining a personal life vision: Five principles that will help you discover and define your personal life vision.* Retrieved from http://enrichmentjournal.ag.org/201101/201101_038_Get_Life.cfm

Baum, J. R., & Locke, E. A. (2004). The relationship of entrepreneurial traits, skill, and motivation to subsequent venture growth. *Journal of Applied Psychology, 89*, 587–598.

Baum, J. R., Kirkpatrick, S. A., & Locke, E. A. (1998). A longitudinal study of the relation of vision and vision communication to venture growth in entrepreneurial firms. *Journal of Applied Psychology, 83*, 43–54.

Bennis. W. G., & Nanus, B. (19S5). *Leaders: Strategies for taking charge.* New York: Harper and Row.

Berson, Y., Shamir, B., Avolio, B., & Popper, M. (2001). The relationship between vision strength, leadership style and context. *The Leadership Quarterly, 12*, 53–73.

Beyond Borders. (2013). *Are you killing vision?* Retrieved from http://www.beyond-borders.com/articles/are-you-killing-vision/

Blackman, K. (2013). *How to REALLY find your true life's purpose. Once and for all!* Retrieved from http://www.positivelypositive.com/2013/03/26/how-to-really-find-your-true-lifes-purpose-once-and-for-all

Conger, J. A., & Kanungo, R. N. (1998). *Charismatic leadership in organizations.* Thousands Oaks, CA: Sage.

Covey, S. (1997). *Seven habits of highly effective families.* New York: Golden Books.

Covey, S. (n.d.). *The unifying power of a family mission statement.* Retrieved from http://www.success.com/articles/267-the-unifying-power-of-a-family-mission-statement

Covey, S., Merrill, A. R., & Merrill, R. R. (1995). *First things first: To live, to love, to learn, to leave a legacy.* New York: Free Press.

Csikszentmihalyi, M. (1975). *Beyond boredom and anxiety.* San Francisco: Jossey-Bass.

Csikszentmihalyi, M. (1990). *Flow: The psychology of optimal experience.* New York: Harper Perennial.

Csikszentmihalyi, M., Rathunde, K., & Whalen, S. (1993). *Talented teenagers,* Cambridge, UK: Cambridge University Press.

Deci, E. L., & Ryan, R. M. (2000). The "what" and "why" of goal pursuits: Human needs and the self-determination of behavior. *Psychological Inquiry, 11*, 227-268.

Deci, E. L., Egharri, H., Patrick, B. C., & Leone, D. R. (1994). Facilitating internalization: The self-determination perspective. *Journal of Personality, 62*, 119-142.

Dyer, C. B., Pickens, S., & Burnett, J. (2007). Vulnerable elders: When it is no longer safe to live alone. *Journal of the American Medical Association, 298*, 1448–1450.

Erikson, E. (1959). *Identity and the life cycle.* New York: International University Press.

Forest, J., Mageau, G. A., Crevier-Braud, L., Bergeron, E., Dubreuil, P., & Lavigne, G. L. (2012). Harmonious passion as an explanation of the relation between signature strengths' use and well-being at work: Test of an intervention program. *Human Relations, 65*, 1233–1252.

Chapter 7 – Passion, Purpose, Vision, Identified & Clearly Focused

Forest, J., Mageau. A., Sarrazin., & Morin, E. M. (2011). Work is my passion: The different affective, behavioral, and cognitive consequences of harmonious and obsessive passion toward work. *Canadian Journal of Administrative Sciences, 28*, 27–40.

Frijda, N. H., Mesquita, B., Sonnemans, J., & Van Goozen, S. (1991). The duration of affective phenomena or emotions, sentiments and passions. In K. T. Strongman (Ed.), *International review of studies on emotion* (pp. 187-225). New York: Wiley.

Gailbraith, J. R., & Lawler, E. (1993). *Organizing for the future: The new logo for managing complex organizations*. San Francisco: Jossey-Boss.

Gardner, J. W. (1990). *On leadership*. New York: Free Press.

Heathfield, S. (n.d.). *Create your personal vision statement*. Retrieved from http://humanresources.about.com/od/success/a/personal_vision.htm

Ho, V. T., Wong, S. S., & Lee, C. H. (2011). A tale of passion: Linking job passion and cognitive engagement to employee work performance. *Journal of Management Studies, 48*, 26–47. doi:10.1111/j.1467-6486.2009.00878.x

Hodgins, H. S., & Knee, R. (2002). The integrating self and conscious experience. In Deci, E. L., & Ryan, R. M. (Eds.), *Handbook on self-determination researchheoretical and applied issues* (pp. 87-100). Rochester, New York: University of Rochester Press.

Immordino-Yang, M. H. et al (2012). *Reflection is critical for development and well-being*. Retrieved from http://www.medicalnewstoday.com/releases/247409.php

Kaufman, S. B. (2011). *How to increase your harmonious passion*. http://www.psychologytoday.com/blog/beautiful-minds/201109/how-increase-your-harmonious-passion

Kirkpatrick, S. A., Locke, E. A., & Latham, G. P. (1996). Implementing the vision: How is it done? *Polish Psychological Bulletin, 27*(2), 93–106.

Knee, C. R., & Zuckerman, M. (1996). Causality orientations and the disappearance of the self-serving bias. *Journal of Research in Personality, 30*, 76–87. doi:10.1006/jrpe.1996.0005

Knee, C. R., & Zuckerman, M. (1998). A nondefensive personality: Autonomy and control as moderators of defensive coping and self-handicapping. *Journal of Research in Personality, 32*, 115–130. doi:10.1006/jrpe.1997.2207

Knee, C. R., Neighbors, C., & Vietor, N. A. (2001). Self-determination theory as a framework for understanding road rage. *Journal of Applied Social Psychology, 31*, 889–904. doi:10.1111/j.1559-1816.2001.tb02654.x

Kotter, J. P. (1990). *A force for change: how leadership differs from management*. New York: Free Press.

Krause N. (2007a). Evaluating the stress-buffering function of meaning in life among older people. *Journal of Aging and Health, 19*, 792–812.

Krause N. (2007b). A longitudinal study of social support and meaning in life. *Psychology and Aging, 22*, 456–469.

Krause, Neal (2009). Meaning in life and mortality. *Journal of Gerontology B Psychological Sciences and Social Sciences, 64B*(4), 517–527.

Labier, D. (2012). *Five steps that reveal your life's purpose*. Retrieved from: http://www.psychologytoday.com/blog/the-new-resilience/201208/five-steps-reveal-your-lifes-purpose

Lavigne, G. L., Forest, J., & Crevier-Braud, L. (2012). Passion at work and burnout: A two-study test of the mediating role of flow experiences. *European Journal of Work and Organizational Psychology, 21*, 518–546.

Lee, T. W., Ashford, S. J., Walsh, J. P., & Mowday, R. T. (1992). Commitment propensity, organizational commitment, and voluntary turnover: A longitudinal study of organizational entry processes *Journal of Management, 18*(1), 85–32.

Leider, R. (2005). *The power of purpose: Creating meaning in your life and work*. San Francisco: Berrett-Koehler.

Liu, D., Chen, X. P., & Yao, X. (2011). From autonomy to creativity: A multilevel investigation of the mediating role of harmonious passion. *Journal of Applied Psychology, 96*, 294 –309. doi:10.1037/a0021294

Chapter 7 – Passion, Purpose, Vision, Identified & Clearly Focused

Locke, E. A., & Latham, G. P. (1990). *A theory of goal setting and task performance.* Upper Saddle River, NJ: Prentice Hall.

Lydon, J. (1996). Toward a theory of commitment. In C. Seligman, J. M. Olson, & M. P. Zanna (Eds.), *The psychology of values* (pp. 191–214). Mahwah, NJ: Erlbaum.

Madsen, S. (2013). *How to create a personal mission and vision statement for the year.* Retrieved from http://www.liquidplanner.com/blog/create-personal-mission-vision-statement-year/

Mageau, G. A., Carpentier, J., & Vallerand, R. J. (2011). The role of self- esteem contingencies the distinction between obsessive and harmonious passion. *European Journal of Social Psychology, 41,* 720-729.

Masuda, A., Kane, T., Shooptaugh, C., & Minor, K. (2010). The role of a vivid and challenging personal vision in goal hierarchies. *The Journal of Psychology, 144,* 221–242.

Mathieu, J. E., & Zajac, D. M. (1990). A review and meta-analysis of the antecedents, correlates, and consequences of organizational commitment. *Psychological Bulletin, 108,* 171–194. doi:10.1037/0033-2909.108.2.171

Meyer, J. P., Stanley, D. J., Herscovitch, L., & Topolnytsky, L. (2002). Affective, continuance, and normative commitment to the organization: A meta-analysis of antecedents, correlates, and consequences. *Journal of Vocational Behavior, 61,* 20–52.

Musick, M. A., & Wilson, J. (2008). *Volunteering: A social profile.* Bloomington, IN: Indiana University Press.

Newlife.com. (n.d.). *Developing a family mission statement.* Retrieved from http://www.new-life.net/growth/parenting/developing-a-family-mission-statement/

Park, C. L. (2007). Religiousness/spirituality and health: A meaning systems perspective. *Journal of Behavioral Medicine, 30,* 319–328.

Pelletier, L. G., Fortier, M. S., Vallerand, R. J., & Brière, N. M. (2001). Associations among perceived autonomy support, forms of self-regulation, and persistence: A prospective study. *Motivation and Emotion, 25,* 279–306. doi:10.1023/A:1014805132406

Philippe, F. L., Vallerand, R. J. Andrianarisoa, J., & Brunel, P. (2009). Passion referees: Examining their affective and cognitive experiences in sport situations. *Journal of Sport and Exercise Psychology, 31*(1), 77–96.

Phillips-Jones, L. (n.d.). *Creating or revising your personal vision.* http://www.mentoringgroup.com/html/articles/mentee_1.html

Premji, F. (2008). *7 questions to finding your true passion.* Retrieved from http://www.ineedmotivation.com/blog/2008/04/7-questions-to-finding-your-true-passion/

Reker, G. T. (2000). Theoretical perspective, dimensions, and measurement of existential meaning. In G. T. Reker & K. Chamberlain (Eds.), *Exploring existential meaning: Optimizing human development across the life span* (pp. 39–55). Thousand Oaks, CA: Sage.

Richardson, C. (2009, September 9). *Steps to finding your passion.* Retrieved from http://www.oprah.com/spirit/Steps-to-Finding-Your-Passion

Richardson, C. (2009). *Steps to finding your passion.* Retrieved from http://www.oprah.com/spirit/Steps-to-Finding-Your-Passion

Rony, J. A. (1990). *Les passions* (The passions). Paris: Presses universitaires de France.

Rosow, I. (1976). Status and role change through the life span. In R. H. Binstock & E. Shanas (Eds.), *Handbook of aging and the social sciences* (pp. 457–482). New York: Van Nostrand Reinhold.

Rush University Medical Center. (2009, June 18). Having a higher purpose in life reduces risk of death among older adults. *ScienceDaily.* Retrieved from http://www.sciencedaily.com/releases/2009/06/090615144207.htm

Russ, T. C. et al. (2012). *Association between psychological distress and mortality: Individual participant pooled analysis of 10 prospective cohort studies.* Retrieved from http://www.bmj.com/content/345/bmj.e4933

Ryan, R. M., & Deci, E. L. (2000). Self-determination theory and the facilitation of intrinsic motivation, social development, and well-being. *Americasychologist, 55*(1), 58–78. doi:http://dx.doi.org/10.1037/0003-066X.55.1.68

Chapter 7 – Passion, Purpose, Vision, Identified & Clearly Focused

Ryan, R. M., & Deci, E. L. (2003). On assimilating identities of the self: A self determination theory perspective on internalization and integrity within cultures. In M. R. Leary & J. P. Tangney (Eds.), *Handbook of self and identity* (pp. 253-272). New York: Guilford.

Sheldon, K. M. (2002). The self-concordance model of healthy goal-striving: When personal goals correctly represent the person. In E. L. Deci & R. M. Ryan (Eds.), *Handbook of self-determination research* (pp. 65-86). Rochester, New York: The University of Rochester Press.

Tartakovsky, M. (2011). *6 clues for finding your purpose and passion.* Retrieved from http://psychcentral.com/lib/6-clues-for-finding-your-purpose-and-passion/0007053

Thoms, P., & Blasko, D. (1999). Preliminary validation of a visionary ability scale. *Psychological Reports, 85,* 105–113.

Thorgren, S., & Wincent, J. (2013). Passion and role opportunity search: Interfering effects of conflicts and overloads. *International Journal of Stress Management, 20*(1), 20–36.

Vallerand, R. J. (2001). A hierarchical model of intrinsic and extrinsic motivation in sport and exercise. In G. Roberts (Ed.), *Advances in motivation in sport and exercise* (pp. 263–319). Champaign, IL: Human Kinetics.

Vallerand, R. J. (2007). A hierarchical model of intrinsic and extrinsic motivation for sport and physical activity. In M. S. D. Hagger & N. L. D. Chatzisarantis (Eds.), *Self determination theory in exercise and sport* (pp. 255–279). Champaign, IL: Human Kinetics.

Vallerand, R. J. (2010). Chapter 3 – On passion for life activities: The dualistic model of passion. *Advances in Experimental Social Psychology, 42,* 97–193.

Vallerand, R. J., Blanchard, C. M., Mageau, G. A., Koestner, R., Ratelle, C. F., & Léonard, M. (2003). Les passions de l'âme: On obsessive and harmonious passion. *Journal of Personality and Social Psychology, 85,* 756–767.

Vallerand, R. J., Fortier, M. S., & Guay, F. (1997). Self-determination and persistence in a real-life setting: Toward a motivational model of high school dropout. *Journal of Personnality and Social Psychology, 72,* 1161–1176.

Vallerand, R., & Verner-Filion, J. (2013). Making people's life most worth living: On the importance of passion for positive psychology. *Terapia psicologica, 31*(1), 35-48.

Vallerand. J., Paquet, Y., Philippe, F. L., & Charest, J. (2010). On the role of passion burnout process model. *Journal of Personality, 78*(1), 289–312.

Warren, R. (2002). *A purpose driven life.* Grand Rapids, MI: Zondervan.

Warta, T. (2008, June 16). *Fulfilling your purpose in life.* Retrieved from http://www.lifescript.com/Soul/Spirit/Beliefs/Fulfilling_Your_Purpose_In_Life.aspx

174

Chapter 8
Financial Security/Freedom

Money is power, provides conveniences and freedom and is something everybody would like to have more of.

How much money is enough?

What would it take for you to say, "I'm financially secure?" Money can't buy happiness, but the lack of it seems to cause a lot of pain and worry. It takes a certain type of strength and attitude to feel comfortable when you don't have money. The effects that money has on most people is pretty strong whether you are young, middle aged or elderly. I don't know of a single person who does not like having lots of money. We in the American culture (and in many other cultures) treat money as if it were everything.

That said, how does money fit into your financial wellbeing, your current lifestyle and the overall quality of your life?

Financial Security is Based on Personal Perception
Financial wellbeing for many people is based upon the perception people have about the level of financial resources they need or desire to provide themselves (and their families) with a reasonable standard of living. Another element to be considered in determining your perception on this matter is what you are used to having. Some people perceive that for them to be financially "stable," they "need" a certain level of financial security.

Being "secure" financially is in the eyes of each individual.

We will explore principles of financial development, the importance of money in most people's lives, the negative impact of debt and a number of other finance-related topics.

Chapter 8 – Financial Security/Freedom

Principles of Financial Development

There are certain life principles you might want to consider following that can stand the test of time. In this chapter, the 10 principles for financial development espoused by this author are as follows:

1) **Pray**! Pray! Develop a spiritual calmness about money. Meditate on positive thoughts that will put you in a positive frame of mind; be thankful for what you have. Don't make money your most important goal.

2) **Live within your means**; develop a realistic budget that takes into consideration ALL aspects of your fiduciary responsibilities including an emergency fund, taxes, credit and debt;

3) **Educate yourself** as much as you can about what you need to know and don't be afraid to get advice from professionals and other wise counselors whose opinion on the subject you respect; areas you need to know about include investments, credit, taxes, various financial instruments such as insurances and others;

4) **Develop a plan** that you can live with and follow it, even when you don't want to. When you feel the plan needs to be revised, go back to the drawing board and make adjustments as needed. Then follow the new plan; be guided by the best information available that is based on fact, research and best practices whenever possible;

5) **Give back** to the community. Giving is a virtue that has many rewards. The more you give, the more you are likely to receive. Well-known motivational speaker Anthony Robbins (n.d.) has made the comment that,

> *Life is a gift, and it offers us the privilege, opportunity, and responsibility to give something back by becoming more.*

6) **Reach out first to your family**, then your closest friends, your professional organization and others within your sphere of influence; when we reach out to family, friends and others close to us, we are more likely to receive support when we need it.

7) **Be** as **honest**, up front and as transparent as you can in all your dealings, activities and interactions with others; try to avoid even the appearance of wrong doing—try to maintain an impeccable character; even though it might sound trite, "honesty is (in fact) the best policy." Life is so much simpler when you are honest and up front about everything.

8) Even though **home ownership** should be a cornerstone of your investments, all investments should be done wisely and with caution and clear motives—not to "be

176

like the Joneses" or living above your means, or purchase something that you cannot afford;

9) **Protect your** finances and other **resources** with appropriate insurances, wills, living trusts and other financial safeguards, including setting up a mechanism that will provide for your children, grandchildren, great-grandchildren and even great-great-grandchildren;

10) **Plan** as early as you can **for** your **retirement**. If you continue to live, you will eventually retire and if you start planning for retirement early, you will not regret it. Retirement is that part of life when you get a chance to reap the fruits of your (many years of) labor, if and only if, you plan for it sufficiently.

Ten Principles on Financial Development
(1)   *Pray*
(2)   *Live within your means*
(3)   *Educate yourself*
(4)   *Develop a plan*
(5)   *Give back*
(6)   *Help family first, then others*
(7)   *Be of High Character*
(8)   *Work toward home ownership*
(9)   *Protect your resources*
(10)   *Plan for retirement*

Never Ending Financial Concerns
Economic development and the economy have changed dramatically in recent years. Financial concerns for many people have become a primary focus above other areas of concern. Professional counselors and other mental health providers have had to address people's personal and family problems that were caused by the economy-related issues or some other personal tragedy. Retirees concerned about their day-to-day financial viability; home owners continue to worry about keeping their homes from foreclosure; recently hired individuals are worried about their continued employment while employees with more seniority wonder about their own job security; even people who were once considered "safe" from economic downturns have suffered drastic losses from financial schemes of various sorts. Small and large businesses alike are finding it more difficult to secure loans to keep their companies afloat. By and large, financial concerns have increased in recent years.

Money, Money, Money!
Even though financial development is only one of many areas of your life, money is necessarily connected to the average person's life, every day. Money has been the cause of much pain and suffering.

> *Some people rob, steal and even kill to get it, while others invest, borrow and save to have it.*

Money has been nicknamed the "ruler of all evils." And, at the same time, cures have been found for the deadliest diseases because of it and cash contributions have saved lives, successful fundraisers have helped millions find a better life. Money continues to play a significant role in most people's lives, contributing to their happiness and wellbeing.

Your financial status is so affected by other areas of your life that it often determines the health of many other areas of your life. Take, for example, the person who is having financial difficulties. In most cases, the quality of that person's family life is impacted; their social wellbeing is certainly affected; and in many cases, their mental state and even physical state are impacted. **Money plays a major role in most people's lives.** Most of us simply do not have enough money to do the things we would like to do. There is a large segment of our population that doesn't have enough money to meet the bare essentials of living, including having enough money to pay for shelter, food and necessary clothing.

Everyone Impacted at One Time or Another

People facing financial problems can be found among the most wealthy celebrities who overspent during their heydays of fast living, to the upper class corporate executive, the television personality or the once successful sports figure caught up in a financial scheme or legal difficulty, the middle class government official, university professor or small business owner fighting off rising costs for his children's education, the lower socioeconomic class blue collar worker worrying about keeping a job or the rising cost of living while wages are staying the same, on down to the most poverty-stricken single parent struggling to make ends meet, or the homeless grandmother who lost her home six months ago because of a refinancing snafu that was no fault of her own. Financial difficulties do not respect a person based on the position held in life.

> *At one time or another, just about everyone is vulnerable to the clutches of financial woes.*

Even though most of us will never become completely secure in our financial standing, there are some things that can be done to increase the possibility of being protected from many financial entrapments. The literature is replete with very good suggestions, proven strategies and credible models that provide the know-how for anyone willing to follow through on any given plan.

Once you get used to a certain lifestyle it is difficult to not want to keep that lifestyle, as costly as it might be. It is also difficult to keep a certain lifestyle or even improve upon it as time goes on because of the increase in the cost of things. Oftentimes, a person's income does not increase at the same rate. Something that costs $25 today is likely to cost $35 next year and $50 or even $100 five years from now.

Lessons Learned

The person who gets a handle on his finances early on is going to be able to rest somewhat easier than the person who waits until later in life or, even worse, lets things get out of hand. Small, minor concerns and issues oftentimes turn into larger, major problems that could have been avoided. Lessons learned from past experience have taught us that early and wise investments are best for the long-term investor. But just as important are wise short-term investments especially for those who need to have access to their investments soon. The unfortunate thing about investments is that there are few, if any, real guarantees. No one's financial resources are completely secure. Even though there are obvious risks in just about all stocks and mutual funds, there are also risks in bonds and even in certificates of deposit and money market funds.

What is Financial Security?

Few people would argue that "financial security" took on a completely different meaning after the 2008 financial recession. People who once felt optimistic about their job security and/or investment savings are now not as solid as they used to be. Prior to and leading up to the 2008 recession, many people would have said that they were financially secure if they had a high paying job and a significant investment portfolio to look forward to in retirement. Others who own their own business and afforded themselves the fast-living lifestyles of big expensive homes and luxury cars felt secure in their way of life. Today, however, many of those same people might be singing a completely different tune. Financial security is a lot more elusive than it once was seen to be.

> ### *What do the words "financial security" mean to you?*

Think about it. Does the phrase mean having all the money you need? For now? For next year? For the next five years? 10, 15, 20 years? Forever? What about having enough to pass on to future generations? What role does financial security play beyond (purely) money? Like your home or other property and resources? You can look at financial security in a number of ways.

The average person might think about having their home paid for, cars paid off, no credit card or other outstanding debt, having a substantial income, health coverage, long-term care covered. Insurances and other expenses covered, money enough to spend for things they want, a healthy emergency fund, etc. Ultimately, never having to worry about money. So, how much planning and adjusting would that take? It depends on the person and what they believe they need. Some people feel financially secure and happy just to have a job that may or may not include benefits. Others might feel that it would take at least two million in cash.

Chapter 8 – Financial Security/Freedom

The Evils of Debt

Michael Mihalik (2007), author of the book *Debt is Slavery (and 9 Other Things I Wish My Dad Had Taught Me about Money)* shares the 10 lessons he wishes he had learned when he was younger. J.D. Roth (2007) provided a review of the book:

- Debt is slavery. Mihalik discusses secured debt and unsecured debt, credit cards, mortgages, and more. He explains how working to pay off debt is little more than slavery: you're working because you have to.

- Money is time. Whenever you buy something, you're not just spending money on it—you're literally spending time. Money is a representation of hours worked, and when you buy frivolous things, you're squandering hours of your life.

- Possessions are a prison. Mihalik has a few simple rules for controlling the stuff in your life. Don't let advertising brainwash you. Mihalik decries the Great Marketing Machine and its drive to hook us on status and fashion.

> ### • *Money buys freedom (and convenience).*

Money cannot buy happiness, but it can buy freedom. Money can give you more options.

- Don't sell your soul for a salary. Money should not be your primary motive for choosing a career. Consider job fulfillment, educational opportunities, and personal values. Try to find work you love.

- Own something instead of buying all the time. Mihalik admits this advice might seem to contradict his previous notion that possessions are a prison. "Income-consuming assets can imprison us, he writes. Income-producing assets set us free." Don't buy stuff—instead, invest your money in things like mutual funds and real estate, things that make money not consume it.

- Save 50% of your salary. Mihalik writes, "Have you ever asked yourself how people who immigrate to the United States can come here, get a low-paying job, and open their own business five years later? How can they do that, making around minimum wage, when you can't, making more than minimum wage? They save. They save 50 percent or more of their salary. They don't go into debt, they work hard and make other sacrifices, so they can buy their own business and control their financial destinies."

- Control your money. In the book's final chapter, Mihalik lays down an approach to making all of these goals workable. He explains how to eliminate debt, minimize expenses, and create a financial plan.

Chapter 8 – Financial Security/Freedom

Debt's impact on physical and mental health

Four Northwestern University researchers from the diverse specializations of medicine, education, anthropology and health and social policy did a longitudinal study providing evidence that, in addition to known associations with psychological health, financial debt is associated with worse self-reported physical health and blood pressure (Sweet, Nandi, Adam, & McDade 2013). The title of their study is: "The High Price of Debt: Household Financial Debt and Its Impact on Mental and Physical Health."

Our findings show that reporting high financial debt relative to available assets is associated with higher perceived stress and depression, worse self-reported general health, and higher diastolic blood pressure. These associations remain significant when controlling for prior socioeconomic status, psychological and physical health, and other demographic factors.

This nationally representative cohort study has followed participants for over 15 years and is thus an excellent data source for examining the association of debt with health while accounting for prior conditions and events.

The researchers indicate that it is difficult to miss the growing impact of financial debt in the everyday lives of Americans.

> *Since the 1980s, overall debt in American households has tripled (Harvey, 2010).*

Between 1989 and 2006, total consumer credit card debt rose from $211 billion to $876 billion (2006 dollars), and the proportion of indebted households carrying over $10,000 in credit card debt rose from 3% to 27% (Garcia, 2007). Home foreclosures have also gone up; recent foreclosure rates are nearly 5 times higher than at any other time since 1979 (Gruenstein Brocian, Wei, & Ernst, 2010). And, widely publicized in March of 2012, Americans' student loan debt recently surpassed $1 trillion (Mitchell & Jackson-Randall, 2012).

The link between socioeconomic status (SES) and health has long been recognized (Adler et al., 1994; Adler & Stewart, 2010).

Several empirical studies have found that financial strains such as personal debt and home foreclosures are strong predictors of depression, general psychological distress, mental disorders, and suicidal ideation and behavior (Bridges & Disney, 2010; Brown, Taylor, & Price, 2005; Drentea & Reynolds, 2012; Jenkins et al., 2008; McLaughlin et al., 2011; Meltzer et al., 2011; Pollack & Lynch, 2009; Reading & Reynolds, 2001; Selenko & Batinic, 2011). These findings highlight the psychological potency of being indebted and, as others have noted, have implications for other health consequences of debt (Dossey, 2007; Drentea & Lavrakas, 2000).

181

Chapter 8 – Financial Security/Freedom

Psychosocial factors, including stress, and its mental health correlates like depression and anxiety, are thought to be key mechanisms through which SES "gets under the skin" to impact health and health disparities, and a substantial body of work has now investigated this pathway (reviewed in: Matthews & Gallo, 2011). The experience of stress is known to lead to short- and long-term physiological changes that play key roles in several disease processes, particularly those involving metabolic and cardiovascular systems (McEwen, 2004).

Subsequent studies have explored debt only indirectly, finding that debt-related financial stress is associated with worse self-reported health (Kim et al., 2003; O'Neill et al., 2006) and that clients of credit counseling services have higher odds of being overweight or obese than the general population (Munster, Ruger, Ochsmann, Letzel, & Toschke, 2009).

Personal financial debt may result from acute life events, such as job loss, divorce, or medical emergencies, which may themselves be psychosocial stressors or health determinants.

Financial Security is an Illusion

Many of us know of people who thought they were financially secure before the stock market crash of 2008 (http://www.money-zine.com/Investing/Stocks/Stock-Market-Crash-of-2008/), or

> *just before the housing meltdown or when all of a sudden someone in their family started having major health problems that caused them to literally wipe out all their savings and other emergency funds.*

Or, someone who got caught up in legal problems that wiped them out financially; or when they discovered that their 401-K investment funds were being taken care of by some scandalous investment advisor who ran off with their life savings. Literally hundreds of stories could be told that describe why many people no longer feel economically secure. Economic security seems to be an elusive entity that no one can safely claim.

Why Financial Security?

What is the purpose of finances?
Why is this important to you?

The average person might think they would not have to worry about finances. They would be able to focus on other things in their life. It might not make them happier, but it could help. Being financially secure might allow them to do things that they want to do, the way they want to do them, when they want to do them and for whom they want to do them. Being financially secure might allow them to live where they want and have more choices in a number of ways. It could help with self-esteem and confidence. Do they have to be rich to be financially secure? Probably not. How secure do they need to be? As secure as their mind will allow them to be.

> ***When (you feel) you are financially secure, you (feel you) have the ability to give generously to the needs and causes that you feel make the world better.***

Time, physics, and obligations will not allow me to do everything I want to do to promote the causes I support; however, I can financially support those who do this work and share in their fruits. "To fulfill some dreams by proxy and achieve other dreams personally while meeting my obligations is why I would want to be financially secure," said one respondent to the question in a blog whose address I cannot find.

What is Affected by Your Financial Standing and How?
Potentially, just about everything is affected by your financial wellbeing.

I cannot think of a single life area of your personal wellbeing that would not be affected, in some way, both positively and/or negatively, by your financial wellbeing. With financial security, you would be able to spend more time working on hobbies rather than a job; socially, you could spend more time socializing if and when you chose to; your physical health would be enhanced by your being able to afford to choose healthy foods and healthy exercises more freely and have access to health care more freely; the peace of mind that comes from financial security would help your mental health; spiritually, you would have more time to focus on your spiritual development; you would have the time to pursue your vision and have the resources to act on those things involving your vision. Your family would benefit from your financial security due to your ability to assist them financially as well as being able to spend more time with them.

Where Do You Currently Stand? Check One of the Items Below
1) I am in major trouble and need help desperately!
2) I am in trouble and need help.
3) I am having problems in this area.
4) I am having minor problems in this area.
5) I am okay in this area but want to do a lot better.
6) I am okay for now, but probably not for long.
7) I am good in this area but could be better.
8) I need to make minor changes in my life.
9) I am doing well in this area of my life.
10) This area in my life is doing super! I cannot imagine doing any better.

> *If you had to compare, would you consider yourself to be at an average or below average level of financial security?*

How would you begin to assess your current state of financial security? By calculating your current net worth? By looking at your current income or assets versus current liabilities or obligations? You'd have to look at other things like insurances, investments and future obligations.

Is it okay to stay where you are currently?

Any plans to consider changes?

Can you do anything about your current (financial security) standing? When? How?

If you did nothing about your current standing, what is likely to happen?

Do you have things currently in the hopper or planned that will change your standing?

On your satisfaction scale, where does this fall?

Where Do You Want to Be?

What would it look like to move to the next level on the financial scale, say an additional monthly income of $100, $500, $1,000, $5,000 or $10,000? How would life be different? In what ways would it be different? If you were to move from "minor changes are needed" to "this area in my life is fine," what would that look like? How possible is it to get there? How likely is it and how long might it take? How would it be different to move from major to minor problems in this area? What would it take and what would the outcome look like?

Most of us have a desire to do better. Many of us feel that we can do better with the right support or with time or even with a little luck. However, most of us also realize that it will take work and some sacrifice to improve our financial status. How that will play out over the next several months or years will ultimately depend on us and our drive to make it all happen.

Basic Finances 101

Becoming educated about financial matters is important. In most cases, things concerning money and finances could broadly be categorized in one or more of the following areas:

1) income, earnings, cash flow, assets, investments, savings or whatever you choose to call it.

2) outgo, spending, liability, debt, giving, set asides or whatever you choose to call that.

3) there is obviously overlap of the two, for example investing/outgo versus using investments as income or savings-outgo versus using savings as income.

Chapter 8 – Financial Security/Freedom

Once a person has become educated about the finances, the next thing left for them to do might be to make wise decisions concerning their finances:

> ***spend wisely, save wisely, invest wisely and give wisely and generously.***

Immediate Concerns: (taking care of basics, first)
Monthly (income) assets vs. monthly (obligations) liabilities

As simple as this concept might seem, many people fail to understand the delicate balance between the two: One way of looking at this issue is to ask the questions, what monthly (liquid and available) sources of funds do you have? And, what are your annual, monthly, bi-monthly and/or quarterly obligations? In other words, does your income match your spending?

Daily spending is often on small miscellaneous items such as snacks, coffee or during-the-work-week lunch for the working person who does not take a lunch to work.

Weekly spending is usually on items such as minor (perishable) groceries, gas, occasional or regular weekend treats and other such items that become necessary to be purchased on a weekly or bi-weekly basis.

Monthly spending is usually reserved for overall bill paying, more extensive grocery shopping and replacement of necessary personal and/or household items.

When money is not an issue, then most people set their sights on four other financial matters such as saving, giving, set asides and investing. When money is an issue or even a problem, then these last four areas tend to not get the attention they deserve. Budgeting and financial planning can help alleviate that problem.

Budgeting and Financial Planning

> ***Budgeting helps one understand one's current financial situation.***

By first writing down what monies you have to start with, say on a monthly basis, you would need to categorize your spending into areas that make sense to you and your family. Typical categories might include:
* transportation (public or private, including gas, car maintenance, etc.)
* home (mortgage, rent, household supplies, maintenance, etc.)
* food and other groceries
* utilities (phone, cable, Internet, electricity, gas, lights, water, etc.)
* entertainment (events, movies, music, hobbies, travel, memberships, dining out, etc.)
* miscellaneous (cleaners, childcare, credit card payments, gifts, etc.)
The Internet is replete with examples of budget categories that can be used.

Why Budget?

"ConsumerCredit.com" offers 12 good reasons to budget. Retrieved from: http://www.consumercredit.com/financial-education/budgeting/why-use-a-budget/12-reasons-budgeting-can-improve-your-life.aspx

1. A budget is a guide that tells you whether you're going in the direction you want to be headed in financially. You may have goals and dreams but if you don't set up guidelines for reaching them and you don't measure your progress, you may end up going so far in the wrong direction you can never make it back.
2. A budget lets you control your money instead of your money controlling you.

> 3. ***A budget will tell you if you're living within your means.***

   Before the widespread use of credit cards, you could tell if you were living within your means because you had money left over after paying all your bills. The use of credit cards has made this much less obvious. Many people don't realize they're living far beyond their means until they're knee deep in debt.
4. A budget can help you meet your savings goals. It includes a mechanism for setting aside money for savings and investments.
5. Following a realistic budget frees up spare cash so you can use your money on the things that really matter to you instead of frittering it away on things you don't even remember buying.
6. A budget helps your entire family focus on common goals.
7. A budget helps you prepare for emergencies or large or unanticipated expenses that might otherwise knock you for a loop financially.
8. A budget can improve your marriage. A good budget is not just a spending plan; it's a communication tool. Done right, a budget can bring the two of you closer together as you identify and work toward common goals and reduce arguments about money. That's got to be good for your sex life (or not)!
9. A budget reveals areas where you're spending too much money so you can refocus on your most important goals.
10. A budget can (help) keep you out of debt or help you get out of debt.
11. A budget (can) actually create extra money for you to use on things that matter to you.
12. A budget helps you sleep better at night because you don't lie awake worrying about how you're going to make ends meet.

Budgeting and Money Management

What is most important in budgeting and financial planning is money management. Most individuals who have regular jobs or employment with benefits usually have funds taken out of their checks for different insurances, retirement and other benefits.

Chapter 8 – Financial Security/Freedom

Most people get a weekly or monthly (take-home-pay) check that then has to be budgeted until the next check. The more fortunate ones have money left over from check to check. For others, they live from check to check. Even those who have money left from check to check have the residual funds going into some account, usually a checking and/or savings.

One example of how this might work would be a family with a take-home monthly income of $3,000. $1,500 might be set aside for regular monthly obligations while the other $500 could be diverted to:

> $100 saving (for a rainy day)
> $100 set aside for future purchases (such as a new TV, dining room set, etc.)
> $100 for periodic fees such as annual membership renewals and quarterly expenses
> $100 to build an emergency fund
> $100 to be divided among family members for miscellaneous spending money.

On the other hand, however, there are replacements, upgrades, improvements or additions to one's current material things that are often not at the forefront of a person's mind when making out that monthly budget. Most often, when thinking of budgets, many people think about current income and whether their income covers most of their current obligations.

Addressing Today's Needs While Planning for the Future

> *There are a number of things outside your immediate, daily, weekly or even monthly concerns that still need to be addressed and planned for.*

Some of these things might be a part of your immediate concerns and some may not be. There is not necessarily any given priority required even though different people would have things in a different order of priority than is stated here. Regardless of the order, they all need to be addressed.

(1) Wills/Living Trusts—both the will and living trust are designed to provide for the distribution of our assets when we die. The sooner this is done, the better because death is inevitable. According to the Lectric Law Library (www.lectlaw.com or http://www.lectlaw.com/filesh/qfl05.htm), there is a big difference between the two.

What does a Will do?
A Will is the legal document that allows you to distribute your property to those you choose. A Will allows you to designate beneficiaries to receive specific items from your estate and other beneficiaries to receive everything else. For example, if you want your house, your car, or your antique book collection to go to a certain person or organization, you designate that person or organization as the beneficiary.

Who's going to make sure that your antique thimble collection goes to the proper person? It will be the executor of your Will. The executor's the person you designate to carry out your wishes.

A Will also gives parents of minor children the chance to nominate a guardian. The court makes the final decision when appointing a guardian for your children after your death, but the court will usually accept your nomination. A guardian's legal responsibility is to provide for your child's physical welfare.

What does a living trust do?

A Will comes into play only after you die, but a living trust can actually start benefiting you while you are still alive. A living trust is a trust established during your lifetime. It is revocable, which allows for you to make changes. You will transfer substantially all of your property into your living trust during your lifetime, and any omitted assets can be transferred into the trust at the time of death through the use of a simple Pour-over Will. You should always make a Pour-over Will at the time you establish your trust.

> *A living trust will be used as the mechanism to manage your property before and after your death, as well as provide how those assets, and the income earned by the trust, are distributed after your death.*

If you should become incapacitated or disabled, the trust is in place to manage your financial affairs, usually by a successor trustee, if you were serving as trustee. A living trust is not subject to probate; therefore, all provisions of the trust will remain private.

Joint living trusts are also possible. They simply combine the assets of a husband and wife into a single trust, governed by a single trust document. However, if estate tax minimization is important (for combined estates that will exceed $625,000), the joint living trust must be very carefully drafted with the help of an attorney in order to achieve the desired goals.

What happens if I don't have a Will or living trust?

The legal term for dying without a Will is dying intestate. If you do not specify through a valid Will or living trust who will receive your property, state law controls and generally distributes your property to your spouse and/or your closest heirs. This may or may not be what you intended. Furthermore, if you fail to nominate a guardian for your minor children, the state could appoint someone you don't trust as a legal guardian of your minor children. Finally, by failing to appoint someone to carry out your wishes, the state can appoint anyone to be the administrator of your property, and the administrator may have to pay certain fees or post a bond at the expense of your estate before he or she can begin to distribute your assets. It is critical that people at least draw up a will, but a living trust would be even better.

(2) Insurances

The most common types of insurance

According to e-sort.com (n.d.) following are the most common types of insurance.

> ***Basically, the purpose of all insurance is to protect yourself or your family against the financial impact of a tragedy.***

Insurance is not to help you budget moderate-sized expenses, but to protect you against the truly catastrophic.

When shopping for insurance, also look into group policies offered by alumni associations, professional associations, or religious bodies. Usually you can forget about specialized insurance advertised on television with paid endorsers. They usually cover very little.

Health insurance

Don't go without this. Most people have it at work, but if you don't you will really save big by going for a group policy. When comparing policies, consider deductibles and what is or isn't covered. When given a choice, choose one that covers the huge, debilitating conditions over one that is good about routine immunization, but that balks at the larger, more expensive claims.

Health insurance comes in three types, though many policies mix and match traits of the three.

Fee for service, the most expensive, allows you to go to almost any provider and covers almost anything that is medically necessary. You don't have a primary care physician who has to approve visits to specialists.

Preferred provider options (PPOs) allow you to self-refer to any provider in the PPO list and generally cover a wide variety of services recommended by those providers. Some PPOs cover other providers, but with a larger co-payment.

Health maintenance organizations (HMOs) are the least costly, but the most restrictive. They assign you (or let you select) a primary care physician. That physician acts as a gatekeeper in that he or she decides what is medically necessary and when you may see a specialist. Often the HMO itself has to permit certain treatment and can rule against your doctor if it thinks the treatment is too costly.

Chapter 8 – Financial Security/Freedom

Life insurance

> *For most people, the purpose of life insurance should be to replace the financial contribution made by a family member.*

Term life insurance covers you for a certain period, such as 10, 15, 20, or 30 years. Buyers typically choose a policy that covers them until their mortgages and other debts are paid off, or the kids have graduated from college and are living independently. A term life policy pays out if you die during the term while the coverage is in effect. Then your beneficiary collects the proceeds, called the "death benefit." You can't cash in the policy while you're still alive.

Permanent life insurance, such as whole life or universal life, covers you for the rest of your life. The policy pays the death benefit to your beneficiary whether you die tomorrow or in 50 years.
Choose term life insurance if you:
Need only temporary coverage.
- Have no dependents who will need financial help for the rest of their lives.
- Don't own a family business or have a large estate to protect.
Choose permanent life insurance if you:
- Want to provide for lifelong dependents, such as a child with special needs.
- Need to protect a large estate or family business from estate taxes.
- Want to leave a legacy. Want to provide loved ones with money for your final expenses, such as medical bills and funeral costs, no matter when you die.

Most people who need life insurance are better off with pure insurance and saving for retirement through other vehicles. Proceeds from life insurance cover three types of expenses: replacement of the policyholder's income or work, estate taxes, and burial costs.

General sources of insurance information include the American Council of Life Insurers, the Insurance Information Institute, the National Association of Insurance Commissioners, and your state insurance department. You can also visit www.insure.com.

Auto insurance
The requirements for auto insurance vary from state to state. Check with your state insurance regulator to learn more about individual requirements as well as insurers you may be considering for your policy.

> *In most states, you are required to have auto insurance and you don't want to be without it.*

Basically, you buy auto insurance for two purposes: to insure against liability you have to others and to insure against damage that others do to you or your car. You need to have liability insurance. How much you need depends on how much you have in assets. Whether you need insurance to protect your own car depends on your car and how detesting it would be to replace it.

Homeowner's insurance

The purpose of homeowner's insurance is to protect you against damage to your home and property from natural disasters.

When comparing policies, consider differences among deductible, coverage of property other than the house (sheds, garages, etc.), and percent of loss covered. Consider also whether the policy covers resale cost or rebuilding cost. Rebuilding usually provides better coverage, but is more expensive.

Basic homeowner's insurance does not cover the contents, though you can often add it for an additional fee or buy it separately.

> ***When buying contents insurance, consider whether it covers replacement value or fair market value.***

Replacement value is a better buy because it pays to buy a new piece of furniture or appliance, not what your old one is worth.

Consider also buying liability insurance, which covers you if someone sustains an injury or other loss on your property.

Renters and condominium owners need only contents and possibly liability insurance. Many companies have policies tailored to these purposes.

Insure your house, NOT the land under it. After a disaster, the land is still there. If you don't subtract the value of the land when deciding how much homeowners insurance to buy, you will pay more than you should.

Make certain you purchase enough coverage to replace what is insured. "Replacement" coverage gives you the money to rebuild your home and replace its contents. An "Actual Cash Value" policy is cheaper but pays the difference between your property's worth at the time of loss minus depreciation for age and wear.

> ***Remember that flood and earthquake damage are not covered by a standard homeowner's policy.***

The cost of a separate earthquake policy will depend on the likelihood of earthquakes in your area. Homeowners who live in areas prone to flooding should take advantage of the National Flood Insurance Program.

Long-term care insurance

Medical advances have resulted in greater need for nursing home care and assisted living. Most health insurance plans and Medicare severely limit or exclude long-term care. You should consider these costs as you plan for your retirement.

Here are some questions to ask when considering a separate long-term care insurance policy:

What qualifies you for benefits? Some insurers say you must be unable to perform a specific number of the following activities of daily living: eating, walking, getting from bed to a chair, dressing, bathing, using the restroom, and remaining continent.

What type of care is covered? Does the policy cover nursing home care? What about coverage for assisted-living facilities that provide less client care than a nursing home? If you want to stay in your home, will it pay for care provided by visiting nurses and therapists? What about help with food preparation and housecleaning?

What will the benefit amount be? Most plans are written to provide a specific dollar benefit per day. The benefit for home care is usually about half the nursing home benefit, but some policies pay the same for both forms of care. Other plans pay only for your actual expenses.

What is the benefit period? It is possible to get a policy with lifetime benefits, but this can be very expensive. Other options for coverage are from one to six years. The average nursing home stay is about 2.5 years.

Is the benefit adjusted for inflation? If you buy a policy before age 60, you face the risk that a fixed daily benefit will not be enough by the time you need it.

Is there a waiting period before benefits begin? A 20- to 100-day period is not unusual.

Appliance protection

It is usually not recommended that you buy any extended warranties or protection plans when you buy small or major appliances. These plans are pure profit to the appliance stores. That's why the salespeople push them so hard, especially if they are on commission. They usually cover only periods when very little is likely to go wrong and have numerous exclusions.

> **(3) Emergency Funds** – *It has been said that if you keep living, you will eventually experience an emergency.*

Chapter 8 – Financial Security/Freedom

Financial emergencies require funds that are usually outside the regular budget. No one can predict when your next emergency will occur. It certainly feels better to have funds set aside to take care of such situations than not having a reserve designated for that purpose.

Unexpected events come up when we least expect them. Many people have investments, savings and cash on hand that can be used in times of emergencies, but the problem with that is that those funds were probably for some other purpose and it could present a hardship when those funds are used. This is especially true with investments. If the investments are a part of retirement accounts such as a 401(k) or some other investment fund, there are substantial penalties related to those investments if funds are withdrawn prematurely. Many financial advisors suggest that people should have at least three to six months' living expenses saved up and put into an emergency fund that is readily accessible.

Trent Hamm, a guest blogger on csmonitor.com wrote on March 21, 2013 that he liked Dave Ramsey's definition of an emergency fund: An emergency fund is a rainy day fund, an umbrella. It is for those unexpected events in life: a job loss, an unexpected pregnancy, a car transmission going out, and so on. This is not an investment or a Bahamas fund!

Dave went on to suggest that a person have an emergency fund of $1,000 while they're paying off high-interest debt (any debts above 8% interest or so), but grow that to an emergency fund of three to six months of living expenses when they're focused on their lower interest debts.

There are several factors that can help you figure out how big *your* emergency fund needs to be. The absolute first step you need to take is to understand what a month's worth of living expenses is for your family. The easiest calculation is to simply figure out how much money goes out of your checking account in a typical month.

Next, How many people are depending on your paycheck?

> *A good general rule of thumb is to have one month of living expenses for each dependent in your life.*

So, if you're married without children, two months of living expenses is a reasonable target.

I believe that dependent count is the largest factor in determining how big an emergency fund could be. The more dependents you have, the more opportunities there are for a real life-altering emergency that can really affect your life and the greater the impact of something like a job loss can have on the financial stability of your family.

Beyond that, you should have about 2% of your home's value as an additional amount in your emergency fund to take care of inevitable and unexpected home repairs (i.e., roof repairs, air conditioning or your furnace). So, if your home is worth $200,000, you should have an additional $4,000 on top of the months of living expenses indicated above.

Figure out an emergency fund size that's right for your life and start saving for it. When things in your life don't go as planned, you'll be glad you have it.

This information was retrieved from: http://www.csmonitor.com/Business/The-Simple-Dollar/2013/0321/Emergency-funds-How-much-should-you-save-for-a-rainy-day

(4) The Unexpected (not necessarily an emergency)

If you keep living, you can count on it happening. On the positive side, your job has just decided to promote you to the position of division manager. This promotion will add several thousands of dollars to your annual salary, but it will reduce your security at the company. Also on the positive side, you discovered that the antique furnishings your grandmother left you are worth a bundle and it would not be difficult to sell them to an antique buyer. Or, that $500 stock investment you made five years ago in that startup company you thought had potential has finally gone big time. The stock is now worth a lot more than your initial investment.

The other end of the unexpected non-emergencies might include such events as instead of your job giving you a promotion, you find out that the contract you have on your job that is good for the next eighteen months will not be renewed because the plant is closing in two years and will have to let everyone go by then. Or, you discover that the antique furnishings your grandmother left you are actually worth about the same amount of money as regular, modern-day furnishings. And, even though you have not spent any money based on your hopes of a windfall, you had sort of expected that they might be worth more. And finally, that $500 stock investment of five years ago is still worth only about $550 today even though it was worth thousands just a couple weeks earlier.

When unexpected things happen to us that involve finances, we must be prepared to continue to move forward with stated plans and be ready to make adjustments appropriate to the occasion.

(5) What Happens When Very Difficult Financial Decisions Have to be Made?

How are situations resolved when one spouse wants to do one thing with the family finances and the other spouse wants to do something else? How are the nerve-wrenchingly difficult decisions made? Where do you get the advice that's needed? What source do you go to? How do you know that the best decision has been made about a financial decision? When does "tough love" kick in? The wife wants to help one of the children financially and you think your finances are not able to come to the rescue. How is that resolved? Is there a compromise? Is there a hard and fast formula to follow? Where can answers be found? This author's simple answer is "through prayer."

> ***Answer: You struggle with options until you find the right one.***

Usually, there has to be a compromise that will satisfy neither person but that will resolve the issue. One of the two has to come up with an offer that will be close to where the other person wants to be. A compromise is almost inevitable. Decisions that are difficult should not be made in haste. They should grow out of much discussion, thought, deliberation and research, if necessary.

Brainstorm options and eventually come up with the most logical and palatable compromise possible. If it's a couple, one person might trust in the judgment of the other person and hope for the best. No matter what the outcome of this particular situation, everyone involved should learn from this and other such situations for future reference because if you keep living you will need to learn from this experience for the next time you are in such a predicament. If all else fails, consider seeking professional help.

Money talks, from a psychiatrist's perspective

In an article titled "Money Talks: Becoming More Comfortable With Understanding a Family's Finances," two psychiatrists (Jellinek et al., 2008) expound on the reluctance of families to talk about family finances. We routinely gather quite sensitive information about a family history of mental illness, secrets that could be influencing family members, reasons for divorce including affairs, use of substances, and concerns about physical or sexual abuse. However, questioning in one area of family life gives many child and adolescent psychiatrists great pause to ask about money and the family's financial status.

Why is there reluctance to deal with financial issues? Our culture seems to be open about many issues, including some intimate issues that would be taboo in other cultures, such as deeply held emotions, sexual indiscretions, or a family history of mental illness; however, it is clear that how much one earns, one's financial values or financial planning is private.

> ***Money in our culture is equated with self-esteem and success or failure and is often used as the only concrete measure of self-"worth."***

How much you make, like your college SAT score, becomes a broadly acknowledged yardstick for who you are, an easy measure of how you judge yourself, and how society values you (as a teacher, social worker, judge, public defender, nurse, radiologist, child and adolescent psychiatrist, venture capitalist, etc.) Disclosing financial status makes an individual feel exposed and vulnerable.

Money, a powerful tool in the American culture

Money is also used in remarkably powerful ways in our culture. It is a way of showing off, wielding power, and creating an image, a persona for an individual. For people who are poor, their poverty may reflect the shame of failure; for people who are wealthy, their wealth may certify their success or elicit shame if they feel extravagant. Clothing, activities, cars, and vacations are means of communicating financial status and social class. It is noteworthy how many teenagers of the rich and famous choose to wear torn jeans, faded T-shirts, and clothing that looks like a hand-me-down from an older sibling, whether purchased from consignment stores or costly designer boutiques. At the same time, some from poor backgrounds attempt to compensate for their financial limitations or demonstrate their aspirations with selected items such as expensive sneakers or a car, even though such a commitment may put them under serious financial strain. How one feels or attempts to express financial status is a complex personal and social statement that may have little to do with one's actual net worth.

Obviously, the reality of poverty is a critical factor in a person's psychosocial history.

> **On a public health level, living in poverty increases the prevalence of physical and mental illness.**

For an individual family, poverty affects many aspects of daily life, including housing, educational opportunities, safety, and daily stress. Similarly, wealth may provide additional options (e.g., boarding school, home tutoring, summer camps) highly relevant to a comprehensive treatment plan. Nevertheless, regardless of one's actual socioeconomic status, revealing what one makes and the feelings around financial status can expose an individual psychologically more than discussions about sex and drugs or other illegal activities.

Psychiatrist's therapeutic actions sometimes impact family finances

Physicians (and psychiatrists) are not exempt from the impact that money has on self-esteem. I (Michael Jellinek) did not appreciate my own reluctance to ask questions about money until I was essentially required to ask financial questions as part of being a court-appointed guardian ad litem. The judge would supply me with a complete copy of the court filings, including detailed financial disclosure forms that had been subject to dispositions. I soon learned that for some divorces, part of my role was to sort through whether the criticisms and maneuvering by one or the other parent was reflecting the reality of limited resources or was but a legal strategy. Were arguments about private school, travel, childcare expenses, allowance, and visitation based on real financial limitations, a parent's genuine beliefs on what was best for the child, old marital angers, or posturing to influence the court's financial rulings? Understanding the behavior and values regarding money was meaningful and potentially therapeutic. Detailed questions regarding finances became integral to my court-appointed role, and then I began to apply a modified set of questions to the care of most other patients.

Understanding a family's financial planning, values, history, and goals for their children is another window to understanding family myths and dynamics.

> *How the family decides how much to spend on any part of their life communicates their values, beliefs, and priorities, all of which, in addition to the social context, have meaning to the child and practical implications to treatment.*

What are some of these relevant questions?

- Were there any financial issues in either parent's upbringing?
- How much money was available? How was it used in the family (generously, secretively, for control, as a source of tension or pride)?
- Did the parents receive an allowance when they were growing up? How strict were the rules? Did they work or get money from relatives, others?
- Who earns the money and how is it used, shared and determined?
- Do the parents agree on how money is spent? Is this a source of conflict?
- How do the parents feel about spending money on their children? What do they feel are reasonable child-related expenses?
- How much do the children, teenagers, or adult children know of the family's finances?
- How do the parents handle allowances? Chores? Work? Gifts? Major purchases like computers or a car? College costs?
- Are the parents feeling good about their financial situation; is the family headed in the right direction financially?

Of course, not every question needs be asked of every family. However, there are many examples demonstrating the clinical relevance of some of this information. One of the authors was treating a shy, depressed young teenager from an upper middle class family who was having difficulty making friends. I asked whether she was ever invited to the local mall when a group goes to roam or shop. She said yes but never does go because she is embarrassed that she has no money to spend and that her clothes, bought by her mother, were "uncool." When asking the parents about her allowance, the father was clear in that he never got an allowance, but then remembered he always had money from doing chores and had a maternal grandmother who was much beloved and generous. Because there were no grandparents locally and the mother considered whatever her daughter did around the house as "expected, not paid," this shy patient was flat broke.

> *Virtually every interpersonal dynamic—controlling, restrictive, aggressive, secretive, guilt-inducing, ambivalent, generative, altruistic—can be manifested in how money is used in families.*

During the course of treatment, other financial issues came up such as the reluctance of her parents to pay for age-appropriate clothing, revealing their anger about how they were treated as teenagers. To help the teenager have clothes she liked and some money to spend with her friends, the parental beliefs about the use of money, the kinds of clothes she could have and their conflict about paying for chores, an allowance had to be addressed. Moreover, the open discussion allowed the teenager to understand why her parents, who certainly had the means and desire to help, had been so withholding of money and of clothes she wanted. It did not take long for a resolution and development of a new plan that everyone could accept. Clearly finances, like many other aspects of psychiatric interviewing, has both a real factor, usually expressed as a number of dollars, and a dynamic perspective, the meaning of that number in a family's psychological and social context.

Some families use money to motivate by offering too distant, major rewards and setting unreasonable expectations to be worthy of the reward. Other families resist using money as rewards for corrective behavior in a treatment plan, viewing it as a bribe. Some confuse money for luxuries, like designer clothing, with computers that may be central to some children's academic success. Parents may have resentments about financially driven decisions that affect their children. A successful professional parent was harsh and unforgiving of his daughter who was an unconventional teenager. Upon questioning, he noted that he had given up a much-desired unconventional career path to go back to school and "get serious" from a financial perspective. How happy was he with his decision? What does he really want for his daughter? How important should financial success be for the past generation, for the current generation, and for the next?

Money can encourage some autonomy in decision making, including buying gifts for family members or saving for a larger purchase or expense (e.g., gas, car insurance). For the impulsive child, saving money earned to buy or contribute to an expensive item is an excellent means of learning delayed gratification. For teenagers with attention-deficit/hyperactivity disorder, learning disabilities, or low self-esteem, working in the real world after school or during the summer can have a dramatic impact. From feeling worthless or being constantly criticized in school, some of these teenagers find themselves as highly regarded workers in an ice cream shop, restaurant, gas station, summer camp, or hospital. Although expecting to be failures, they experience themselves as competent and productive, getting paid more money than they have ever seen. Many thrive in a working environment, develop relationships with coworkers, and go back to their family or schoolwork with more self-esteem than they expected.

(6) Big Ticket (or expensive) Items

There are certain purchases that most people cannot (afford to) pay for in cash and that many would prefer to not pay for on a credit card. These things are often referred to as big-ticket items. The rich and famous might consider such things as the purchasing of a Lear Jet or a vacation home in Hawaii. A person with few financial means might consider a new dress, pair of shoes or a $75 earring set as a birthday present for a relative as a big-ticket item. For the average middle class person, such things as a dining room, bedroom or kitchen set might be considered big-ticket items. It does not matter what the reason is, if it is not in the regular budget, and it very often is not, then it needs to be planned for.

> *Big-ticket items that are purchased on credit can often end up costing much, much more than the regular retail cost.*

Some consumers make purchases of big-ticket items with no-interest purchases for 12 or 18 months and they pay off the balance over that time period and thereby avoid paying any interest on the purchase. Plus, they have manageable monthly payments that will oftentimes not put a strain on their primary budget.

(7) Overall Debt

MoneyCNN.com posted an article on their website titled Money 101 that had one section on "Controlling Your Personal Debt." This information was retrieved from: http://money.cnn.com/magazines/moneymag/money101/lesson9/index.htm

Among the suggestions included the following:

It's almost impossible to live debt-free; most of us can't pay cash for our homes or our children's college educations. But too many of us let debt get out of hand.

> *Ideally, experts say, your total monthly long-term debt payments, including your mortgage and credit cards, should not exceed 36% of your gross monthly income.*

That's one metric mortgage bankers consider when assessing the creditworthiness of a potential borrower.

Good debt includes anything you need but can't afford to pay for up front without wiping out cash reserves or liquidating all your investments. In cases where debt makes sense, only take loans for which you can afford the monthly payments. Examples of good debt include borrowing to purchase a home a car or to pay for college or some other post-secondary educational training.

Bad debt includes debt you've taken on for things you don't need and can't afford (that trip to Bora Bora, for instance). The worst form of debt is credit-card debt, since it usually carries the highest interest rates.

> *Don't use a credit card to pay for things you consume quickly, such as meals and vacations, if you can't afford to pay off your monthly bill in full in a month or two.*

There's no faster way to fall into debt. Instead, put aside some cash each month for these items so you can pay the bill in full. If there's something you really want, but it's expensive, save for it over a period of weeks or months before charging it so you can pay the balance when it's due and avoid interest charges.

Besides life's big-ticket items—home, car and college—you may be tempted to borrow money to pay for an assortment of other expenses such as furniture, appliances and home remodeling.

Generally speaking, it's best to pay up front for furniture and appliances since they don't add value to your home and are depreciating assets. If you do finance such purchases, however, read the fine print. Also see if you can find a store that will give you a year or more interest free payments so you can avoid paying interest. In that case, you will need to pay off the balance before the end of the interest-free time period. Be sure to read the fine print because some companies will make you pay back interest if you do not pay off the total amount within the given (interest-free) time period.

Most people spend thousands of dollars without much thought to what they're buying. Write down everything you spend for a month, cut back on things you don't need, and start saving the money left over or use it to reduce your debt more quickly.

The wise use of credit could be considered "smart debt." As a matter of fact, in order to build up a good solid credit rating, people need to go into debt.

> *Making purchases with credit cards and paying them off before accruing interest is a smart use of credit.*

The best way to deal with debt is to get out of it as quickly and as cheaply as possible.

The key to getting out of debt efficiently is to first pay down the balances of loans or credit cards that charge the most interest while paying at least the minimum due on all your other debt. Once the high-interest debt is paid down, tackle the next highest, and so on. Even though you must pay at least the minimum, if you just pay the minimum due on credit card bills every time, you'll barely cover the interest you owe, to say nothing of the principal. It will take you years to pay off your balance, and potentially you'll end up spending thousands of dollars more than the original amount you charged.

Watch where you borrow. It may be convenient to borrow against your home or your 401(k) to pay off debt, but it can be dangerous. You could lose your home or fall short of your investing goals at retirement.

> *Don't be so quick to pay down your mortgage.*

Don't pour all your cash into paying off a mortgage if you have other debt. Mortgages tend to have lower interest rates than other debt, and you may deduct the interest you pay on the first $1 million of a mortgage loan. (If your mortgage has a high rate and you want to lower your monthly payments, consider refinancing.)

Get help as soon as you need it. If you have more debt than you can manage, get help before your debt breaks your back. There are reputable debt counseling agencies that may be able to consolidate your debt and assist you in better managing your finances. But there are also a lot of disreputable agencies out there.

(8) Savings

People have savings for different reasons. Banks and other financial establishments offer a number of avenues for you to set up the kind of savings that best meets your needs. Savings generally involve putting money away for future use. Everyone should have at least one savings account if for no other reason but to save for a "rainy day." There are several types of savings accounts depending upon your need to have access to the money. Usually, the sooner you need access to the funds, the less interest you are likely to accrue. Some savings accounts have no interest accruing. People who have developed the habit of saving tend to have money later when they need it as opposed to the person who spends and spends and spends.

> *In four studies, Gulden Ulkumen and Amar Cheema (2011) show that consumers' savings can be increased or decreased merely by changing the way consumers think about their saving goals.*

The two authors emphasize that although the importance of saving is indisputable, most studies conclude that left to themselves, consumers do not save enough (Shefrin & Thaler, 1988). Insufficient savings may be due to errors in spending forecasts (Ülkümen, Thomas, & Morwitz, 2008), errors in calculation (Benartzi & Thaler, 2004), lapses in self-control (Baumeister, 2002), a disproportionate emphasis on the present rather than the future (Lynch & Zauberman, 2006) or the effects of culture (Briley & Aaker, 2006). Therefore, consumers could benefit from mechanisms that help them reach their optimal saving levels (Benartzi & Thaler, 2004; Botti & Iyengar, 2006; Madrian & Shea, 2001).

Such a tool would be beneficial to increase savings among the poor (Bertrand, Mullainathan, & Shafir, 2006), encourage sufficient savings for health care and retirement (Iyengar, Jiang, & Huberman, 2004) and increase wellbeing (Diener, Diener, & Diener, 1995).

A consumer with a goal to save money can either plan to save as much as possible (nonspecific goal) or specify the exact amount to be saved (specific goal).

Wright and Kacmar (1994) show that people are more committed to assigned goals when these goals are specific rather than nonspecific. There are several reasons specific goals may be more beneficial than nonspecific goals. Specific (vs. nonspecific) goals can increase goal commitment by clarifying the required level of performance (Hollenbeck & Klein, 1987).

Saving money requires successful self-regulation of spending impulses (Shefrin & Thaler, 1988). Literature on self-regulation shows that clear rules are more likely to be followed than ambiguous rules (e.g., Ainslie & Haslam, 1992). Specific goals improve resistance to temptation in children (Mischel & Patterson, 1976) and increase persistence (Carter, Patterson, & Quasebarth, 1979). Furthermore, establishing specific subgoals (vs. focusing on long-term goals) improves adult weight loss (Bandura & Simon, 1977). These results suggest that increasing goal specificity should improve performance on saving goals.

Increasing goal specificity will increase goal difficulty. Increased goal difficulty will lead to lower goal attainment for people who focus on how to achieve the goal or those who focus on the feasibility of achieving the goal, but not those who focus on why the goal is important. Consequently, it is better to focus on the why (the goal is important) rather than the how (you plan to achieve it or the feasibility of your being able to achieve it).

When the saving goal is focused on the "how" or "the feasibility," consumers with specific goals will be *less* successful in saving than those with nonspecific goals.

> ***When the saving goal is focused on why the goal is important, consumers with specific goals will be more successful in saving than those with nonspecific goals.***

(9) Investments
In the financial sense, investments are stocks, bonds, Certificates of Deposits, Money Market Funds, Annuities and other instruments and even cash that are primarily designed to increase our current financial standing. In recent years, we have seen that it pays to be careful when making financial investments. Resources needed for immediate (or soon) use should be kept in low-risk investments. Low-risk investments have recently been seen as (U.S.) Treasury Notes and Annuities that have an almost guaranteed return, or at least a very low chance of losing value.

> ***Most financial advisors are supportive of having investments in the stock and bond market. They all, however, warn that every investment has risk.***

Even though the market crash of 2008 (http://www.money-zine.com/Investing/Stocks/Stock-Market-Crash-of-2008/) saw a lot of volatility and people lost money in the short run. Those who have financial resources not needed for the next 8-10 years or later, should continue to consider the stock and bond market as a place to invest.

Chapter 8 – Financial Security/Freedom

A dictionary definition of investing is the laying out of money or capitol with the expectation of earning a higher return. Most people make investments to increase their current financial standing and/or to have money for the future. In another sense, investments could be laying out things of worth such as quality items that will last a long time or purchasing things today that will be worth more tomorrow, or even spending time with a young person who you feel has potential to be an asset to his family and society. In other words, it can be seen as a commitment of time, energy or effort with the expectation of some worthwhile result. However one looks at investments, it is something that everyone should consider participating in. Investments are a key component in planning for the future. No matter how well off or poor, making some kind of investment is important. For most of us, investments are the vehicle by which we acquire moneys that will be used for retirement. The earlier we start investing for our future, the better off we will be.

Investment tips from the U.S. Government
The U.S. government offers investment tips that I thought were noteworthy. This information was retrieved from: http://www.usa.gov/topics/money/investing/tips.shtml
Page Last Reviewed or Updated: June 27, 2013

There is even more extensive financial information concerning a number of areas of interest to consumers found in their (free) consumer action handbook retrieved and ordered from: http://www.usa.gov/consumer-action-handbook/order-form.shtml

Investigate before you invest
What do you want to invest in: stocks, bonds, mutual funds? Do you want to open an IRA or buy an annuity? Does your employer offer a 401(k)? Remember, every investment involves some degree of risk. Most securities are not insured by the federal government if they lose money or fail, even if you purchase them through a bank or credit union that offers federally insured savings accounts. Make sure you have answers to all of these questions before you invest:

- **Define your goals.** Ask yourself "Why am I investing money?" Maybe you want to save money to purchase a house or to save for retirement. Maybe you would like to have money to pay for your child's education, or just to have a financial cushion to handle unexpected expenses or a loss of income.
- **How quickly can you get your money back?** Stocks, bonds, and shares in mutual funds can usually be sold at any time, but there is no guarantee you will get back all the money you paid for them. Other investments, such as limited partnerships, often restrict your ability to cash out your holdings.
- **What can you expect to earn on your money?** While bonds generally promise a fixed return, earnings on most other securities go up and down with market changes. Also, keep in mind that just because an investment has done well in the past, there is no guarantee it will do well in the future.

- **What type of earnings can you expect?** Will you get income in the form of interest, dividends or rent? Some investments, such as stocks and real estate, have the potential for earnings and growth in value. What is the potential for earnings over time?
- **Are your investments diversified?** Some investments perform better than others in certain situations. For example, when interest rates go up, bond prices tend to go down. One industry may struggle while another prospers.

> - *Putting your money in a variety of investment options can help reduce your risk.*

- **How much risk is involved?** With any investment, there is always the risk that you won't get your money back or the earnings promised. There is usually a trade-off between risk and reward: the higher the potential return, the greater the risk. The federal government insures bank savings accounts and backs up U.S. Treasury securities (including savings bonds). Other investment options are not protected.
- **Are there any tax advantages to a particular investment?** U.S. Savings Bonds are exempt from state and local taxes. Municipal bonds are exempt from federal income tax and, sometimes, state income tax as well. For special goals, such as paying for college and retirement, tax-deferred investments are available that let you postpone or even eliminate payment of income taxes.

> ***Many employers encourage their employees to save for their retirement by establishing 401(k), 403(b), or 457(b) plans.***

Employees who participate in these programs elect to have a set amount of their income deducted from their paychecks to save for retirement; these amounts are not subject to income taxes. In many cases, your employer will match a portion of the amount you contribute into your 401(k) account, which is like getting "free" money. If you stop working at a company, remember to take the money from your 401(k) with you. If you "rollover" the total from your old job to an account at your new job, a traditional IRA, you will not have to pay taxes on the money.

Compare investment vehicles
Not all investment vehicles are created equally or work for your personal financial goals. Some provide steady income and are low risk, but yield small returns on investment; others may provide significant returns, but require a long-term investment commitment. There is a wide assortment of investment vehicles available. Some of the most popular include: mutual funds, traditional IRAs, Roth IRAs, savings bonds or bond funds, stocks, and certificates of deposit.

Some investments pay out earnings on a regular (quarterly, monthly, or annual) basis, while others pay out earnings at the end of the investment period or may have age requirements for when you can withdraw your money without a penalty. Make sure your investment income stream matches your investment timeline.

You should also consider the tax ramifications. If you are saving for retirement or for education, consider investments that offer incentives for saving for a particular purpose. Your contributions for some investments are tax deductible, but the earnings are not taxed (e.g., Roth IRA); your contributions to other investments may not be taxed, but the earnings are taxed (e.g., traditional IRA).

You don't have to put all of your money in one investment.

> ***Consider diversifying your investment portfolio by placing your money in several investment vehicles.***

This can (help) protect you from risk; while one of your investments may be performing poorly, another one of your investments can make up for those losses.

Type of Investment	What is it?	Risk level
Traditional IRA	Traditional IRA is a personal savings plan that gives tax advantages for savings for retirement. Investments may include variety of securities. Contributions may be tax-deductible; earnings are not taxed until distributed.	Risk levels vary according to the holdings in the IRA
Roth IRA	A personal savings plan where earnings that remain in the account are not taxed. Investments may include a variety of securities. Contributions are not tax-deductible.	Risk levels vary according to the holding in the IRA
Money Market Funds	Mutual funds that invest in short-term bonds. Usually pays better interest rates than a savings account but not as much as a certificate of deposit (CD).	Low risk.
Bonds and Bond Funds	Also known as fixed-income securities because the income they pay is fixed when the bond is sold. Bonds and bond funds invest in corporate or government debt obligations.	Low risk.
Index Funds	Invest in a particular market index such as the S & P 500 or the Russell 1000. An index fund is passively managed and simply mirrors the performance of the designated stock or bond index.	Risk level depends on which index the fund uses. A bond index fund involves a lower risk level than an index fund of emerging markets overseas.
Stocks	Stocks represent a share of a company. As the company's value rises or falls, so does the value of the stock.	Medium to high risk.
Mutual funds	Invest in a variety of securities, which may include stocks, bonds, and/or money market securities. Costs and objectives vary.	Risk levels vary according to the holdings in the mutual fund.

Most people think a market crash is the biggest danger to investors. Wrong.
Nowhere on your bank or brokerage statement, however, are you likely to get a report on what inflation is doing to the real value of your holdings. If your money is stowed in a "safe" investment, like a low-yielding savings or money market account, you'll never see how inflation is gobbling up virtually all of your return.

(10) Retirement (leaving current employment) or retirement (not working)
Retirement means different things to different people. For my brother who passed away a few years ago, it meant doing the things he enjoyed doing, going to the race track, visiting with his retirement club house buddies and literally doing whatever he felt like doing and could afford to do. Retirement did not include continuing to work at a job, any job. For many people today, I am finding that retirement is simply leaving one job, but fairly soon moving on to another job. For one reason, people today are not saving up enough to live on with their retirement pensions and Social Security. With the rising costs of basic consumer items, it is becoming more and more difficult to manage on the average retirement budget.

Many financial advisors are suggesting that instead of thinking about having a retirement budget of 70 to 80% of your current income, advisors are now recommending 90 to 100% of your current income. Among the main reasons for the higher projections include the fact that people are living longer, the cost of health care is increasing at a much higher rate than previously expected and families are finding they need to financially assist members in their immediate family.

Ways to prepare for retirement
The U. S. Department of Labor suggests that financial security in

> *retirement doesn't just happen. It takes planning and commitment and, yes, money.*

They offer 10 ways to prepare for retirement along with a few facts about retirement in the U.S. This information was retrieved from:
http://www.dol.gov/ebsa/publications/10_ways_to_prepare.html

Facts
- Fewer than half of Americans have calculated how much they need to save for retirement.
- In 2010, 30% of private industry workers with access to a defined contribution plan (such as a 401(k) plan) did not participate.
- The average American spends 20 years in retirement.
  Putting money away for retirement is a habit we can all live with. Remember…Saving Matters!

Chapter 8 – Financial Security/Freedom

1. Start saving, keep saving, and stick to your goals

If you are already saving, whether for retirement or another goal, keep going! You know that saving is a rewarding habit. If you're not saving, it's time to get started. Start small if you have to and try to increase the amount you save each month. The sooner you start saving, the more time your money has to grow. Make saving for retirement a priority. Devise a plan, stick to it, and set goals. Remember, it's never too early or too late to start saving.

2. Know your retirement needs

Retirement is expensive. Experts estimate that you will need about 70% of your preretirement income—lower earners, 90% or more—to maintain your standard of living when you stop working. Take charge of your financial future. The key to a secure retirement is to plan ahead. Start by requesting *Savings Fitness: A Guide to Your Financial Future* and, for those near retirement, *Taking the Mystery Out of Retirement Planning.*

3. Contribute to your employer's retirement savings plan

> *If your employer offers a retirement savings plan, such as a 401(k) plan, sign up and contribute all you can.*

Your taxes will be lower, your company may kick in more, and automatic deductions make it easy. Over time, compound interest and tax deferrals make a big difference in the amount you will accumulate. Find out about your plan. For example, how much would you need to contribute to get the full employer contribution and how long would you need to stay in the plan to get that money.

4. Learn about your employer's pension plan

If your employer has a traditional pension plan, check to see if you are covered by the plan and understand how it works. Ask for an individual benefit statement to see what your benefit is worth. Before you change jobs, find out what will happen to your pension benefit. Learn what benefits you may have from a previous employer. Find out if you will be entitled to benefits from your spouse's plan. For more information, request *What You Should Know about Your Retirement Plan.*

5. Consider basic investment principles

How you save can be as important as how much you save. Inflation and the type of investments you make play important roles in how much you'll have saved at retirement. Know how your savings or pension plan is invested. Learn about your plan's investment options and ask questions. Put your savings in different types of investments. By diversifying this way, you are more likely to reduce risk and improve return. Your investment mix may change over time depending on a number of factors such as your age, goals, and financial circumstances. Financial security and knowledge go hand in hand.

6. Don't touch your retirement savings

> *If you withdraw your retirement savings now, you'll lose principal and interest and you may lose tax benefits or have to pay withdrawal penalties.*

If you change jobs, leave your savings invested in your current retirement plan or roll them over to an IRA or your new employer's plan.

7. Ask your employer to start a plan

If your employer doesn't offer a retirement plan, suggest that it start one. There are a number of retirement saving plan options available. Your employer may be able to set up a simplified plan that can help both you and your employer. For more information, request a copy of *Choosing a Retirement Solution for Your Small Business*. (See below for more information.)

8. Put money into an Individual Retirement Account

You can put up to $5,500 a year (for 2015) into an Individual Retirement Account (IRA); you can contribute even more if you are 50 or older. You can also start with much less. IRAs also provide tax advantages.

When you open an IRA, you have two options: a traditional IRA or a Roth IRA. The tax treatment of your contributions and withdrawals will depend on which option you select. Also, the after-tax value of your withdrawal will depend on inflation and the type of IRA you choose. IRAs can provide an easy way to save. You can set it up so that an amount is automatically deducted from your checking or savings account and deposited in the IRA.

A Roth IRA is designed to help you save for retirement. It allows after-tax contributions in exchange for the potential for tax-free income in retirement. Generally speaking, if you think you might be in a higher tax bracket when you retire, a Roth IRA may be right for you.

A Roth IRA Offers Two Kinds of Flexibility
How and When Money Is Withdrawn

- You can withdraw your contribution dollars at any time tax and penalty free: You can also withdraw earnings tax and penalty free, as long as you have owned a Roth IRA for at least five years and have reached age 59½. The five-year clock starts with the first contribution.
- No Required Minimum Distributions (RMDs): Unlike a traditional IRA, a Roth IRA has no required minimum distributions (RMDs) when you reach age 70½. You control when you want to withdraw money. If you don't need the money in your Roth IRA for living expenses, you can leave it so that it can continue to potentially grow tax free.

Chapter 8 – Financial Security/Freedom

Your Investment Options

With a Roth IRA, you can choose from a wide variety of investments, including stocks, bonds, mutual funds, certificates of deposit (CDs) and money market funds. This variety gives you the opportunity to diversify your savings with an appropriate mix to help meet your retirement objectives.

Roth IRA information retrieved from:
(https://www.edwardjones.com/en_US/products/retire/individual_plans/roth_ira/index.html?gclid=CPTr953P0cYCFQtqfgodFD0GUQ)

9. Find out about your Social Security benefits

Social Security pays benefits that are on average equal to about 40% of what you earned before retirement. You may be able to estimate your benefit by using the retirement estimator on the Social Security Administration's website. For more information, visit their website (https://www.ssa.gov/) or call 1-800-772-1213.

10. Ask Questions

While these tips are meant to point you in the right direction, you'll need more information. Read publications listed below. Talk to your employer, your bank, your union, or a financial adviser. Ask questions and make sure you understand the answers. Get practical advice and act now.

Visit the Employee Benefits Security Administration's (EBSA) website to view the following publications:

- Savings Fitness: A Guide to Your Money and Your Financial Future
  (http://www.dol.gov/ebsa/publications/savingsfitness.html)

- Taking The Mystery Out Of Retirement Planning
  (http://www.dol.gov/ebsa/publications/nearretirement.html)

- What You Should Know About Your Retirement Plan
  (http://www.dol.gov/ebsa/publications/wyskapr.html)

- Filing a Claim for Your Retirement Benefits
  (http://www.dol.gov/ebsa/publications/filingretirementclaim.html)

To order copies, contact EBSA electronically at www.askebsa.dol.gov or by calling toll free 1-866-444-3272.

The following websites can also be helpful:
AARP (**www.aarp.org**)
American Savings Education Council (**www.choosetosave.org**)
Certified Financial Planner Board of Standards (**www.letsmakeaplan.org**)
Consumer Federation of America (**www.consumerfed.org**)
The Actuarial Foundation (**www.actuarialfoundation.org**)
U.S. Securities and Exchange Commission (**www.investor.gov**)

(11) Maintenance, Improvements or Additions and Replacements

Just as maintaining a certain level of lifestyle is important to many people today, that same concept of maintenance applies to our homes, cars, equipment, clothing and many other items that make up key elements of our lives.

> *If things are not maintained on a regular basis, they are likely to not function at an optimum level or even not function at all.*

An automobile that is not regularly maintained will soon break down. The same goes for garage doors, electronic equipment, musical instruments and even the clothing on our backs. Just about everything needs to have some level of tender loving care and maintenance or it will not remain useful or functional for long.

In the same category as maintenance are such things as replacements, repairs and upgrades. No matter how well you maintain your car, things connected to your home or electronic equipment, they will still not last forever. Very few things last forever. Eventually, just about everything needs to be replaced, upgraded, improved upon or added to. Clothing needs to be replaced, repaired and cleaned. Electronic equipment eventually needs to be upgraded. As we go through life, we realize that many things we once relied upon have been improved upon, with a higher quality or a longer functioning life such as certain food products, including milk and hamburger meat. There are certain things in life we need more than we currently have. For example, we might be able to get by with just three or four changes of clothing, but if our circumstances change, such as getting a different job or even a first job, there is always that need for additional changes of clothing or a second pair of eyeglasses.

(12) Credit

Credit cards
There are many types of credit cards with various features, but there is no one best credit card.

> *The card you use depends entirely on how you plan to use it.*

Are you going to use it for everyday purchases or larger purchases? Do you plan to pay your balance off each month?

When you apply for a credit card, consider:
Annual percentage rate (APR). If the interest rate is variable, how is it determined, and when can it change?
Periodic rate. This is the interest rate used to determine the finance charge on your balance each billing period.

Annual fee. While some cards have no annual fee, others expect you to pay an amount each year for being a cardholder.

Rewards programs. Can you earn points for flights, hotel stays, and gift certificates to your favorite retailers? Use the tool on www.creditcardtuneup.com to find the card that offers the best rewards for you.

Grace period. This is the number of days you have to pay your bill before finance charges start. Without this period, you may have to pay interest from the date you use your card or the date the purchase is posted to your account.

Finance charges. Most lenders calculate finance charges using an average daily account balance, which is the average of what you owed each day in the billing cycle. Look for offers that use an adjusted balance, which subtracts your payment from your beginning balance. This method usually has the lowest finance charges. Check whether there is a minimum finance charge.

Credit Card Perks?

Your credit card is good for a lot more than paying bills and racking up miles, according to an article written by Alina Comoreanu, Research Analyst (n.d.) In the article titled "Credit Card Extended Warranty Study: What Type of Credit Card is Best?" The writer lists five little-known perks to most consumers.

- **Lost baggage protection.** If you book a flight using a credit card, you may be covered for up to a few thousand dollars if the airline loses your bags.

- **Refunds and returns**. If you want to return something but the company won't take it back, your credit card company might refund you. The same perk applies if you were wrongfully charged by a merchant and they refuse to refund you. Again, for this to work you have to make the original purchase with your credit card.

- **Extended warranties.** Let's say your brand new big-screen TV or washing machine dies on you just a few months after your warranty is up. If you purchased it with a credit card that has extended warranty coverage, your issuer may offer to replace it, fix it or reimburse you for its value. The limits on reimbursements vary from card to card so check with your company.

- **Trip cancellation.** If you have to a cancel a nonrefundable trip due to illness or weather, your credit card may offer trip cancellation protection. Some cards offer to cover up to $10,000 of flight, hotel and transportation fees. Just read the fine print carefully.

- **Rental insurance.** Just about every major credit card issuer offers some form of car rental insurance, which is a great alternative to purchasing supplemental insurance from a car rental agency. Rental policies may change depending on which state you're in, so definitely call up your credit issuer to ask before you assume you are covered.

These benefits generally do not come from credit card issuers, but rather from the card networks that each card is linked to. In this study, the researchers explored the extended warranty programs offered by the four major card networks: Visa, MasterCard, Discover, and American Express. As a result of the study, extended warranties are generally regarded as being among the biggest money wasters for consumers. However American Express was considered the "best" overall.

The article also mentioned CardHub.com if you need help finding the perfect credit card for your individual needs. This article was retrieved from:
http://www.cardhub.com/edu/credit-card-extended-warranty-study/

FREE CREDIT REPORTS
You can request a free credit report once a year from each of the three major credit reporting agencies—Equifax, Experian, and TransUnion. You may want to request your credit reports one at a time, every four months, so you can monitor your credit throughout the year without having to pay for a report. (If you ask the credit bureaus directly, they will charge you a fee to obtain your report.) To order your free report, you must go through www.annualcreditreport.com or call 1-877-322-8228.

Credit counseling services
Counseling services are available to help people budget money and pay bills. Credit unions, extension offices, military family service centers, and religious organizations are among those that may offer free or low-cost credit counseling.

Local, nonprofit agencies that provide educational programs on money management and help in developing debt payment plans operate under the name Consumer Credit Counseling Service (CCCS).

The counselor should also be certified by the National Foundation for Credit Counseling (NFCC), an organization that supports a national network of credit counselors.

Typically, a counseling service will negotiate lower payments with your creditors, and then make the payments using money you send to it each month. The cost of setting up this debt-management plan is paid by the creditor, not you.

If you are going to use a credit counselor, make certain the agency is accredited by the Council on Accreditation (COA) or the International Organization for Standardization (ISO).

Ask these questions to find the best counselor for you:
- What services do you offer? Look for an organization that offers budget counseling and money management classes as well as debt-management planning.
- Do you offer free information? Avoid organizations that charge for information or make you provide a lot of details about your problem first.
- What are your fees? Are there set-up and/or monthly fees? A typical set-up fee is $10.
- Beware of agencies that charge large up-front fees.

- How will the debt-management plan work? What debts can be included in the plan, and will you get regular reports on your accounts?
- Ask whether the counselor can get creditors to lower or eliminate interest and fees. If the answer is yes, contact your creditors to verify this.
- Ask what happens if you can't afford to pay. If an organization won't help you because you can't afford to pay, go somewhere else for help.
- Will your counselor help you avoid future problems? Getting a plan for avoiding future debt is as important as solving the immediate debt problem.
- Ask for a contract. All verbal promises should be in writing before you pay any money.

Are your counselors accredited or certified? Legitimate credit counseling firms are affiliated with the NFCC or the Association of Independent Consumer Credit Counseling Agencies.

Check with your local consumer protection agency and the Better Business Bureau to see whether any complaints have been filed about the counseling service you're considering.

If you have concerns about approved credit counseling agencies or credit counseling providers, please contact the U.S. Trustee Program at www.justice.gov/ust or call 202-514-4100.

Source: USA.gov/consumer 2013 Consumer Action Handbook
Order your copy of the U.S. Government consumer action handbook at:
http://www.usa.gov/consumer-action-handbook/order-form.shtml
http://www.justice.gov/ust/credit-counseling-debtor-education-information
http://www.justice.gov/ust/contact-program

According to Myfico.com:

> *when you apply for credit – whether for a credit card, a car loan, or a mortgage – lenders want to know what risk they'd take by loaning money to you.*

FICO® scores are the credit scores most lenders use to determine your credit risk. You have three FICO scores, one for each of the three credit bureaus: Experian, TransUnion, and Equifax. Each score is based on information the credit bureau keeps on file about you. As this information changes, your credit scores tend to change as well. Your three FICO scores affect both how much and what loan terms (interest rate, etc.) lenders will offer you at any given time. Taking steps to improve your FICO scores can help you qualify for better rates from lenders.

For your three FICO scores to be calculated, each of your three credit reports must contain at least one account that has been open for at least six months. In addition, each report must contain at least one account that has been updated in the past six months. This ensures that there is enough information, and enough recent information, in your report on which to base a FICO score on each report.

About FICO scores

Credit bureau scores are often called "FICO scores" because most credit bureau scores used in the U.S. are produced from software developed by Fair Isaac and Company. FICO scores are provided to lenders by the major credit reporting agencies.

FICO scores provide the best guide to future risk based solely on credit report data. The higher the credit score, the lower the risk. But no score says whether a specific individual will be a "good" or "bad" customer. And while many lenders use FICO scores to help them make lending decisions, each lender has its own strategy, including the level of risk it finds acceptable for a given credit product. There is no single "cutoff score" used by all lenders and there are many additional factors that lenders use to determine your actual interest rates.

If you've had good credit in the past, just keep doing what you've done, and you can still expect a score that's good enough to keep your rates down. And while those who are trying to make up for poor credit decisions in the past may see the score change as a bump in the road,

> *staying on track by paying down debt and making on-time loan payments is still the best way to improve your score in the long run*

– no matter how they calculate it.

(13) Taxes

State and Federal taxes are necessary obligations of any citizenry.
According to "Infoplease" found at http://www.infoplease.com/ipa/A0005921.html (2007), from 1791 to 1802, the US government was supported by internal taxes on distilled spirits, carriages, refined sugar, tobacco and snuff, property sold at auction, corporate bonds, and slaves. The high cost of the War of 1812 brought about the nation's first sales taxes on gold, silverware, jewelry, and watches. In 1817; however, Congress did away with all internal taxes, relying on tariffs on imported goods to provide sufficient funds for running the government.

In 1862, to support the Civil War effort, Congress enacted the nation's first income tax law. It was a forerunner of our modern income tax in that it was based on the principles of graduated, or progressive, taxation and of withholding income at the source.

The US tax system is progressive. That means that people who make more money have a higher tax rate, and people who make less money have a lower tax rate. Your tax rate will change depending on how much money you made that year. There is a debate over whether our tax rates should be progressive or flat. Politicians who support a flat tax argue that a single tax rate for everybody will greatly simplify people's lives. Politicians who support progressive tax rates argue that it is unfair to ask a person of modest income to pay the same percentage of their income as a wealthier person.

One of the questions you might ask is how to minimize your tax burden.

> ***If you itemize your deductions using a Schedule A, there are a few things you can do that can help lower your tax obligation.***

Stay organized

The key to a relatively painless tax season is organization. Even if you have a tax preparer, she will charge you less if you hand her exactly what she needs neatly organized instead of dumping stacks of paper on her desk. Keeping track of your papers is especially important if you itemize your deductions. Here's what you should save:
Government confirmation of your return and your refund
- Records of charitable donations, including receipts
- Large medical or dental bills
- Records of business or job hunting costs
- Forms from your job showing income you've made
- Purchases, sales, and improvements to real estate property
- All actions in your investment and IRA accounts (Most online brokerages will keep these records for you.)

"Stay Organized," and list of items to save was retrieved from:
http://www.learnvest.com/knowledge-center/taxes-101/
Alden Wicker (2012) "Taxes 101" is at that same site:
http://www.learnvest.com/knowledge-center/taxes-101/

Charitable contributions

According to the IRS (2012), charitable contributions including donations of cash and personal property can be taken as charitable deductions. This includes monetary donations, clothes and other usable items given to organizations and mileage driven for volunteer activities (currently at 14 cents per mile). Just remember to get and keep all receipts from organizations for your good deeds, and keep accurate records of mileage driven for charitable mileage purposes.

Prepay medical expenses

If your medical expenses exceed 7.5% of your adjusted gross income, you can accelerate payments for a deduction. This means an individual with an adjusted gross income of $40,000 can deduct medical expenses above and beyond $3,000. Someone other than your doctor can perform deductible medical services. If you have a condition like a bad back and your doctor says you need a daily massage, this treatment is deductible. However, make sure you get a written note from your doctor saying you need those services.

Retirement accounts

As much as $6,500 (in 2015) can be contributed to a traditional IRA if you are 50 or over and $5,500 if you are under the age of 50. If you have a company-sponsored 401(k) plan, your supplementary contribution may be matched by your employer, adding to the benefits of making additional contributions to your retirement. Accelerating expenses before year-end can add thousands of dollars to your refund check from the IRS. As for all tax issues, contact your tax professional for more information on deductions, or visit the IRS website at www.irs.gov.

(14) The Psychology of Finances

In an article from Patricia Poole (2008) titled: "What makes money such a difficult issue for couples?" in the *Island Connections,* she noted that money is such a powerful and important subject in our culture and has so many hidden meanings in-cluding: feeling loved and cared about, feeling com-petent, feeling safe and secure, accepted, acknowledged and empowered – all of which are core issues.

A certain amount of money is essential for survival. But money is also a tool to enhance life and make it more fun and rewarding. It is not an end in itself and it cannot guarantee health, love, safety, competence, self-esteem or any of the things that are truly important. I try to help couples remember that they are in charge of money; money doesn't control them. Decide together what you want your life to look like and then use money as a tool, not a goal.

This article was retrieved from:
http://pdf.islandconnections.eu/563/pdf/island_connections_050.pdf

(15) Periodic Financial Assessments

Because change is inevitable, it is a good idea to check on your financial health every six months or so. What that means is periodically check up on your monthly spending, saving and investing.

It is almost impossible to avoid credit these days. However, being credit wise by not getting too heavily into credit debt is a good thing. Being able to manage your credit obligations and at the same time not paying heavy finance charges is a skill worth learning.

> *A periodic check to make certain that you are headed in the right direction is being prudent.*

The right direction is where credit balances are going down rather than up. Concerning the issue of credit, if you do not have an automatic credit check made, take a look at your credit report.

Other questions to be asked periodically might include to what extent has your cash flow changed? Has inflation caused you to make financial adjustments in other places? Check to make certain there are no unintended negative consequences.

Periodic checks on your car, home, life and other insurances are also in order. The purchase of new furniture, a computer or other expensive item might need to be added to your insurance policy. A change in your family situation or other life changes might necessitate changes in one or more of your insurances.

Investments need to be checked every six months or so to make sure that your investment balance is where you want it to be. If your investments include say 50% stocks and 50% bonds and the market has favored one over the other, your 50-50 balance might need to be adjusted.

If there have been any changes at your work site, there might need to be changes made in your benefit package or related matters. Similarly, your estate plans might need to be adjusted because of some recent change. It never hurts to check periodically to make certain that whatever is currently in place is where you want things to be. The thing that is most critical is that we are on target with the goals we set earlier and if we are not, then we need to regroup and see where or if we need to make adjustments. If we are on target, then we should reaffirm that these goals are still appropriately set.

Net vs. Gross

> *Some people are not aware that a person's financial health is often determined by not just what they are worth, but their net worth — not simply by their assets, but by their assets minus their liabilities.*

A person who has a $2 million home might be less well off financially than a person with a $200,000 home if the $200,000 home owner only owes $50,000 on their home and the $2 million home owner still owes $1.9 million on their mortgage. If everything else is equal, the $2 million homeowner's net worth is only $100,000 whereas the $200,000 homeowner's net worth is $150,000. That is why it is so important to not only look at the amount of money a person might earn or the amount of money they might have without considering also what they owe, or their financial liabilities.

Another good example is when we look at companies that seem to have lots of business and they seem to be doing quite well until you look at how much they are spending and what their overall overhead (or cost of doing business) might be. I like the way Billionaire Richard Branson, Chairman of Virgin Group, tells the story of how he learned the difference between gross profit and net profit. He says that one of his board members explained to him by telling him to Pretend you're fishing. Net is all the fish in your net at the end of the year. Gross is that plus everything that got away.

Are you still well off after the smoke clears?

Similarly, our own financial resources might be very impressive with reasonably high income, savings and investments. However, if we are spending more than we earn and we still owe thousands on credit cards and tens or hundreds of thousands on home mortgages, then our net worth might not be as impressive as it might first seem. Net worth (generally speaking) is simply assets minus liabilities. For most of us, if we made two columns of figures and under column "A," you list your assets: the value of your home, your vehicles, and securities such as stocks, bonds, even your 401(k) account. Also add in cash contained in bank accounts, savings, and safety deposit accounts, the value of any collectable items, art, and so forth. Generally speaking, that should give you your total assets.

Next, under column "B," list the outstanding balance of your mortgage, credit cards, car notes, personal loans, outstanding medical bills or any other outstanding debt. That should give you a general total of your liabilities.

Your net worth is found by subtracting your liabilities from your assets. A negative figure means you have a negative net worth. A positive figure means you have a positive net worth.

Even though net worth can give you a general idea of your financial health, other things to take into consideration would include current and future financial resources and obligations. Future resources might include additional resources from pay increases, paying off credit cards, car loans or other liabilities and potential windfalls such as income tax returns, job bonuses or unanticipated consulting assignment that pays you extra money. On the other hand, however,

> *future obligations that might be coming up could include education costs for your children, travel plans, big-ticket item purchases and just plain old increase in the cost of living.*

REFERENCES
Chapter 8 – "Financial Security"

Adler, N. E. (2009). Health disparities through a psychological lens. *American Psychologist, 64*, 663–673.

Adler, N. E., & Stewart, J. (2010). Health disparities across the lifespan: meaning, methods, and mechanisms. *Annals of the New York Academy of Sciences, 1186*, 5–23.

Adler, N. E., Boyce, T., Chesney, M. A., Cohen, S., Folkman, S., Kahn, R. L., & Syme, S. L. (1994). Socioeconomic status and health: The challenge of the gradient. *American Psychologist, 49*, 15–24.

Ainslie, G., & Haslam. N. (1992). Self-control. In G. Loewenstein & J. Elster (Eds.), *Choice over time* (pp. 177–209). New York: Sage Publications.

Bandura, A., & Simon, K. M. (1977). The role of proximal intentions in self-regulation of refractory behavior. *Cog- nitive Therapy and Research, 1*(3), 177–193.

Baumeister, R. F. (2002). Yielding to temptation: Self-control failure, impulsive purchasing, and consumer behavior. *Journal of Consumer Research, 28*(March), 670–676.

Benartzi, S., & Thaler, R. H. (2004). Save More Tomorrow™ sing behavioral economics to increase employee saving. *Journal of Political Economy, 112*(February), 164–187.

Bertrand, M., Mullainathan, S., & Shafir, E. (2006). Behavioral economics and marketing in aid of decision making among the poor. *Journal of Public Policy & Marketing, 25*(Spring), 8–23.

Botti, S., & S e t h i - Iyengar, S. (2006). The dark side of choice: When choice impairs social welfare. *Journal of Public Policy & Marketing, 25*(Spring), 24–38.

Bridges, S., & Disney, R. (2010). Debt and depression. *Journal of Health Economics, 29*, 388–403.

Briley D., & Aaker, J. L. (2006). Bridging the culture chasm: Ensuring that consumers are healthy, wealthy, and wise. *Journal of Public Policy & Marketing, 25*(Spring), 53–66.

Brocian, D.G., Wei, L., & Ernst, K. S. (2010). *Foreclosures by race and ethnicity: The demographics of a crisis*. Washington, DC: Center for Responsible Lending.

Brown, S., Taylor, K., & Price S. W. (2005). Debt and distress: Evaluating the psychological cost of credit. *Journal of Economic Psychology, 26*, 642-663.

Carter, D., Bruce, C., Patterson, J., & Quasebarth, S. J. (1979). Development of children's use of plans for self-control. *Cognitive Therapy and Research, 3*(4), 407–413.

Consumercredit.com. (n.d.). *12 reasons budgeting can improve your life*. Retrieved from http://www.consumercredit.com/financial-education/budgeting/why-use-a-budget/12-reasons-budgeting-can-improve-your-life.aspx

Diener, E., Diener, M., & Diener, C. (1995). Factors predicting the subjective well-being of nations. *Journal of Personality and Social Psychology, 69*(November), 851–864.

Dossey, L. (2007). Debt and health. *Explore* (NY), *3*, 83–90.

Drentea, P., & Lavrakas, P. J. (2000). Over the limit: The association among health, race and debt. *Social Science & Medicine, 50*, 517–529.

Drentea, P., & Reynolds, J. R. (2012). Neither a borrower nor a lender be: The relative importance of debt and SES for mental health among older adults. *Journal of Aging and Health, 24*, 673–695.

essortment.com. (n.d.). *Types of insurance*. Retrieved from http://www.essortment.com/types-insurance-19733.html

Garcia, J. (2007). *Borrowing to make ends meet: The rapid growth of credit card debt in America*. Demos.

Garcia, J., & Draut, T. (2009). *The plastic safety net: How households are coping in a fragile economy*. Retrieved from http://www.nyc.gov/html/ofe/downloads/pdf/fenforum_plastic_safety_net.pdf

Chapter 8 – Financial Security/Freedom

Hamm, T. (2013). *Emergency funds: How much should you save for a rainy day?* Retrieved from http://www.csmonitor.com/Business/The-Simple-Dollar/2013/0321/Emergency-funds-How-much-should-you-save-for-a-rainy-day

Hollenbeck, J. R., & Klein, H. J. (1987). Goal commitment and the goal-setting process: Problems, prospects, and proposals for future research. *Journal of Applied Psychology, 72*(May), 212–220.

IRS. (2011). *Charitable contributions.* Retrieved from http://www.irs.gov/publications/p526/ar02.html0

Jellinek, M., & Beresin, E. (2008). Money talks: Becoming more comfortable with understanding a family's finances. *Journal of the American Academy of Child & Adolescent Psychiatry, 46*(3), 249–253.

Jenkins, R., Bhugra, D. Bebbington, P., Brugha, T., Farrell, M., Coid, J.,…Meltzer, H. (2008). Debt, income and mental disorder in the general population. *Psychological Medicine, 38*, 1485–1493.

Lectric Law Library. (n.d.). *Differences between wills and living trusts.* Retrieved from http://www.lectlaw.com/filesh/qfl05.htm

Lynch, J. G., Jr., & Zauberman, G. (2006). When do you want it? Time, decisions, and public policy. *Journal of Public Policy & Marketing, 25*(Spring), 67–78.

Madrian, B. C., & Shea, D. F. (2001). The power of suggestion: Inertia in 401(K) participation and savings behavior. *Quarterly Journal of Economics, 116*(November), 1149–1188.

Matthews, K. A., & Gallo, L. C. (2011). Psychological perspectives on pathways linking socioeconomic status and physical health. *Annual Review of Psychology, 62*, 501–530.

McEwen, B. S. (1998). Stress, adaptation, and disease. Allostasis and allostatic load. *Annals of the New York Academy of Sciences, 840*, 33–44.

McEwen, B. S. (2003).Interacting mediators of allostasis and allostatic load: Towards an understanding of resilience in aging. *Metabolism, 52*, 10–16.

McEwen, B. S. (2004). Protection and damage from acute and chronic stress: Allostasis and allostatic overload and relevance to the pathophysiology of psychiatric disorders. *Annals of the New York Academy of Sciences, 1032*, 1–7.

McEwen, B. S., & Seeman, T. (1999). Protective and damaging effects of mediators of stress. Elaborating and testing the concepts of allostasis and allostatic load. *Annals of the New York Academy of Sciences, 896*, 30–47.

McLaughlin, K. A., Nandi, A., Keyes, K. M., Uddin, M., Aiello, A. E., Galea, S., & Koenen, K. C. (2011). Home foreclosure and risk of psychiatric morbidity during the recent financial crisis. *Psychological Medicine, 42*(7), 1–8.

Meltzer, H., Bebbington, P., Brugha, T., Jenkins, R., McManus, S., & Dennis, M. S. (2011). Personal debt and suicidal ideation. *Psychological Medicine, 41*, 771–778.

Mihalil, M. (2007). *Debt is slavery, and 9 other things I wish my dad taught me about money.* Seattle, WA: October Mist Publishing.

Mischel, W., & Patterson, C. J. (1976). Substantive and structural elements of effective plans for self-control. *Journal of Personality and Social Psychology, 34*, 942–950.

Mitchell, J., & Jackson-Randall, M. (2012). Student loan debt tops $1 trillion. *Wall Street Journal.*

Money Magazine. (2008, August). How billionaire Richard Branson learned the difference between gross profit and net profit. *Money Magazine.* 124.

Money-zine.com. (n.d.). *Stock market crash of 2008.* Retrieved from http://www.money-zine.com/Investing/Stocks/Stock-Market-Crash-of-2008/

MoneyCNN.com. (n.d.). *Controlling your personal debt.* Retrieved from http://money.cnn.com/magazines/moneymag/money101/lesson9/index.htm

MoneyCNN.com. (n.d.). *Understanding how inflation works.* Retrieved from http://money.cnn.com/magazines/moneymag/money101/lesson4/index6.htm

Munster, E., Ruger, H., Ochsmann, E., Letzel, S., & Toschke, A. M. (2009). Over indebtedness as a marker of socioeconomic status and its association with obesity: A cross-sectional study. *BMC Public Health, 9*, 286.

Myfico.com. (n.d.). *About credit scores.* Retrieved from http://www.myfico.com/crediteducation/creditscores.aspx

Onfoplease.com. (n.d.). *History of the income tax in the United States.* Retrieved from http://www.infoplease.com/ipa/A0005921.html

Chapter 8 – Financial Security/Freedom

Pollack, C. E., & Lynch, J. (2009). Health status of people undergoing foreclosure in the Philadelphia region. *American Journal of Public Health, 99*, 1833–1839.

Poole, P. (2008). What makes money such a difficult issue for couples?" *The Island Connection.* Retrieved from http://pdf.islandconnections.eu/563/pdf/island_connections_050.pdf

Reading, R., & Reynolds, S. (2001). Debt, social disadvantage and maternal depression. *Social Science & Medicine, 53*, 441–453.

Roth, J. D. (2007, August 7). *Book review: Debt is slavery.* Retrieved from http://www.getrichslowly.org/blog/2007/08/07/book-review-debt-is-slavery/

Selenko, E., & Batinic, B. (2011). Beyond debt. A moderator analysis of the relationship between perceived financial strain and mental health. *Social Science & Medicine, 73*, 1725–1732.

Sethi-Iyengar, S., Huberman, G., & Jiang, G. (2004). How much choice is too much?: Determinants of individual contributions in 401K retirement plans. In. O. S. Mitchell and S. P. Utkus (Eds.), *Pension design and structure: New lessons from behavioral finance* (pp. 83–97). Oxford: Oxford University Press.

Shefrin, H. M., & Thaler, R. H. (1988). The behavioral life-cycle hypothesis. *Economic Inquiry, 26*(October), 609.

Sweet, E., Nandi, A., Adam, E., & McDade, T. (2013). The high price of debt: Household financial debt and its impact on mental and physical health. *Social Science & Medicine, 91*, 94–100.

Thinkexist.com. (n.d.). *Anthony Robbins quotes.* Retrieved from http://thinkexist.com/quotation/life_is_a_gift-and_it_offers_us_the_privilege/195673.html

U.S. Department of Labor. (n.d.). *Top 10 ways to prepare for retirement.* Retrieved from http://www.dol.gov/ebsa/publications/10_ways_to_prepare.html

U.S. Government. (2013). *Consumer action handbook.* Retrieved from http://www.usa.gov/topics/consumer/consumer-action-handbook.pdf

U.S. Government. (2013). *Investing tips.* Retrieved from http://www.usa.gov/topics/money/investing/tips.shtml

Ulkumen, G., & Cheema, A. (2011). Framing goals to influence personal savings: The role of specificity and construal level. *Journal of Marketing Research, 48*, 958–969.

Ülkümen, G., Thomas, M., & Morwitz, V. G. (2008). Will I spend more in 12 months or a year? The effect of Ease of estimation and confidence on budget estimates. *Journal of Consumer Research, 35*(August), 245–256.

Wicker, A. (2012). *Taxes 101.* Retrieved from http://www.learnvest.com/knowledge-center/taxes-101/

Wright, P. M., & Kacmar, K. M. (1994). Goal specificity as a determinant of goal commitment and goal change. *Organizational Behavior and Human Decision Processes, 59*(August), 242–260.

Chapter 9
Work and/or School

Work hard, get results, for a job or in school the outcome is the same. The amount of education you have is a major determining factor for your success in life.

Unless you are retired, most of us work or go school. A very large part of our day is spent at work, in school or both. The question here is what can be done to make this time as pleasant and as productive as possible?

The Universality of Work/School

At some point in just about every person's life, first going to school, then going to work will be something that will happen after a certain age. For some people, it will be later and others, sooner. This is probably a universal phenomenon that happens pretty much across the board and it transcends culture, ethnicity, religion, gender, age (after and before a certain age) and most other human differences. Most of us are taught at a young age that work is good, healthy and, above all, necessary for survival. We are encouraged to get a good education, find an area of work that we like and pursue the work of our dreams. Research tells us that our parents and others around us provide the models we tend to follow.

> *How far we go in school and the work we gravitate toward tends to be a function of our environment.*

That said, how can the average person take advantage of different ways of maximizing the benefits of a good education and interesting and rewarding work? Once we have mastered the basics in education like reading, writing, speaking, computing and a few other basic skills, the next logical things to master would likely be in areas of work. Hopefully while we are gaining an education, we are also learning about our interests, aptitude, skill sets and special talents.

> *It is through work that we are able to realize our potential.*

Whatever potential we have to become a writer, a doctor, a teacher or a minister, it is through the work we do that will make that happen. Potential is having or showing the capacity (through your work) to become or develop into something in the future. Another definition of potential would be: latent qualities or abilities that may be developed (through the work you do) and lead to future success or usefulness.

More Education, Better Job
It is undisputed that educational attainment has a profound influence on individual labor market prospects. The higher educated earn more, have higher occupational ranks, have better employment contracts, and have a higher probability to be employed than persons with lower levels of qualification. It is also evident that there are several different mechanisms at play that explain this effect (Hannan et al., 1990; Rosenbaum et al., 1990 as cited in Van de Werfhorst, 2011).

Less Education, Different Ways of Being Well
On the basis of older studies that have linked education with wellbeing and education with self-definition (House et al., 1994; Marmot et al., 1997; Ryff & Singer, 1998), the authors hypothesized that wellbeing for the college-educated would involve elements of personal accomplishment and self-fulfillment. The authors also anticipated that the different lives and worlds of the high school-educated respondents would be associated with somewhat different ways of being well, ways that focused more on supportive relationships such as with family members and close friends.

More recent studies, however, will show that high school-educated individuals are likely to find themselves out of work unless they are able to start their own business.

> *Most jobs in the twenty-first century require some level of post-secondary education, training or college.*

The U.S. Bureau of Labor Statistics provides a graphic that depicts data on earnings and unemployment rates by educational attainment.

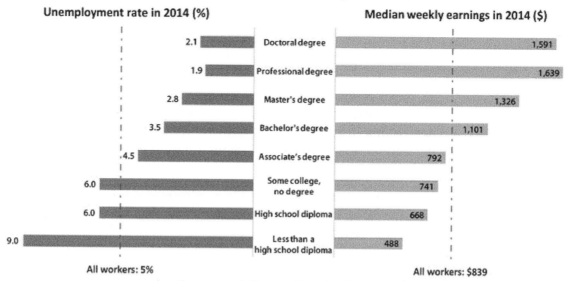

Earnings and unemployment rates by educational attainment

Unemployment rate in 2014 (%) — Median weekly earnings in 2014 ($)

Unemployment rate	Education	Median weekly earnings
2.1	Doctoral degree	1,591
1.9	Professional degree	1,639
2.8	Master's degree	1,326
3.5	Bachelor's degree	1,101
4.5	Associate's degree	792
6.0	Some college, no degree	741
6.0	High school diploma	668
9.0	Less than a high school diploma	488

All workers: 5%   All workers: $839

Note: Data are for persons age 25 and over. Earnings are for full-time wage and salary workers.
Source: Current Population Survey, U.S. Bureau of Labor Statistics, U.S. Department of Labor

Note: Data are for persons age 25 and over. Earnings are for full-time wage and salary workers.
Source: Bureau of Labor Statistics, Current Population Survey.

These education categories reflect only the highest level of education attained. They do not take into account completion of training programs in the form of apprenticeships and other on-the-job training, which may also influence earnings and unemployment rates. For more information on training, see:

http://www.bls.gov/emp/ep_table_education_summary.htm   and
http://www.bls.gov/emp/ep_table_education_by_train.htm

Education Pays

Sandy Baum, Jennifer Ma, and Kathleen Payea wrote a report for the College Board titled "Education Pays 2010" that cited a number of benefits related to higher education. Among those cited included the following:

> - ***Individuals with higher levels of education earn more and are more likely than others to be employed.***

- Median earnings of bachelor's degree recipients working full-time year-round in 2008 were $55,700: $21,900 more than median earnings of high school graduates.

- Individuals with some college but no degree earned 17% more than high school graduates working full-time year-round. Their median after-tax earnings were 16% higher.

- For young adults between the ages of 20 and 24, the unemployment rate in the fourth quarter of 2009 for high school graduates was 2.6 times as high as that for college graduates.

- College-educated adults are more likely than others to receive health insurance and pension benefits from their employers and be satisfied with their jobs.

- In 2008, about 58% of college graduates and individuals with some college education or an associate degree reported being very satisfied with their jobs, while 50% of high school graduates and 40% of individuals without a high school diploma reported being very satisfied.

- *College education leads to healthier lifestyles, reducing health care costs for individuals and for society.*

- Within each age group, college-educated adults are less likely than others to be obese. In addition, children living in households with more educated parents are less likely than other children to be obese.

- College-educated parents engage in more educational activities with their children, who are better prepared for school than other children.

- Among parents whose highest degree was a bachelor's degree, 68% read to their children daily in 2007. This compares to 57% of parents with an associate degree, 47% of parents with some college but no degree, 41% of high school graduates, and 26% of parents who did not complete high school.

Non-Monetary Benefits of Education

These non-monetary occupational outcomes of education are difficult to identify and measure because most of them are subjective; that is, they depend on personal preferences. However, they do increase people's wellbeing and quality of life and must be taken into account when analyzing educational investments (Wolfe & Zuvekas, 1997).

Education and Health

Education is associated with longer life expectancy, improved health and quality of life and health-promoting behaviors like getting regular physical activity, not smoking, and going for routine checkups and recommended screenings (Office of the U.S. Surgeon General, 2011, p. 22).

http://www.politifact.com/georgia/statements/2011/aug/26/regina-benjamin/us-surgeon-general-says-less-education-means-highe/

Beverly Bradley and Amy Greene wrote an article in the May 2013 issue of the *Journal of Adolescent Health* titled "Do Health and Education Agencies in the United States Share

Responsibility for Academic Achievement and Health? A Review of 25 Years of Evidence About the Relationship of Adolescents' Academic Achievement and Health Behaviors." In their article, it was made clear that and health-promoting behaviors like getting regular physical activity, not smoking, and going for routine checkups and recommended screenings (Office of the U.S. Surgeon General, 2011).

> *Education is associated with longer life expectancy, improved health and quality of life.*

To back up their argument, they pointed out that the United States Centers for Disease Control and Prevention monitors health-risk behaviors of adolescents in United States, which include (1) violence, (2) tobacco use, (3) alcohol and other drug use, (4) sexual behaviors contributing to unintended pregnancy and sexually transmitted diseases, (5) inadequate physical activity, and (6) unhealthy dietary behaviors.

They reviewed original research published in peer-reviewed journals between 1985 and 2010 to synthesize evidence about the association of adolescent health-risk behaviors and academic achievement. For all six health-risk behaviors identified to be leading causes of death, disability, and social problems among youth and adults in the U.S., 96.6% of the articles included in this review that were published in peer-reviewed journals from 1985 until the end of 2010 (a 25-year span) reported statistically significant inverse relationships between health-risk behaviors and academic achievement among school-aged populations.

The results of the research reviewed are not evidence of cause and effect; the data do not indicate that poor grades cause health-risk behaviors, nor do they indicate that health-risk behaviors cause poor grades. However, the results support strong positive associations between six health-risk behaviors and poor academic achievement, and inverse associations between six health-risk behaviors and academic achievement.

The results of this review are consistent with data from the 2009 National Youth Risk Behavior Survey that was reported in 2010.

In May of 2012, *Health in Mind*, an initiative of the Healthy Schools Campaign and Trust for America's Health to improve education through wellness, presented actionable policy recommendations to the U.S. Secretary of Health and Human Services and the U.S. Secretary of Education. These recommendations represent a major culture shift in how the nation views health and education—health and education will no longer be separated from one another (Healthy Schools Campaign and Trust for America's Health. Health in mind: improving education through wellness. Available at: http://healthyamericans.org/report/96/)

Education & Work

Two basic facts about education are that individuals and groups change as they receive more schooling and that more educated individuals and groups differ from those with less education. By adopting a wide perspective, it can be argued that both the changes and the differences are basically related to the way people seek, obtain, understand, use, and create new information. Economists think that, as a rule, more educated people have the knowledge, skill, and training required to search for, process, and use information more efficiently in decision-making processes than those who have received less education (Vila, 2000).

The basic idea is that longer schooling promotes a more efficient use of information both on the formation of expectations and on individual choices regarding the labor market (Arrow, 1997).

> *Therefore, highly educated people are thought to form more accurate expectations and to pursue their aspirations more efficiently than poorly educated people do.*

Consequently, they are more likely to reap additional education-enhanced benefits in terms of personal utility arising from a variety of work-related sources. These may include items such as **reduced uncertainty**, **performing more interesting or challenging tasks**, **holding a responsibility level matched to one's qualifications**, **working under healthier or more attractive conditions**, **developing good relationships with co-workers**, **taking on a tenured position**, or **enjoying greater work autonomy** or **higher social prestige** (Vila, 2000).

Occupational Benefits of Education

Empirical analyses on the value of education have traditionally focused on the contribution of formal schooling to increased earning capacity in the labor market, although rate-of-return studies estimate only part of the returns to education. The occupational benefits of education promote not only higher wages but also other non-pecuniary expansions in workers' welfare possibilities (Haveman & Wolfe, 1984; McMahon, 1998).

Human Capital

As noted by many researchers, education—or "human capital"—plays a critical role in driving economic growth. For example, Delong, Golden, and Katz (2002) state that human capital has played the principal role in driving America's edge in twentieth-century economic growth. As such, factors that lead to fewer years of educational attainment for the nation's youth will have substantial consequences for years to come.

Recessions can impact educational achievement in a number of ways. First, a substantial body of literature addresses the importance of early childhood education (e.g., Heckman, 2006, 2007 and the papers cited therein). Because education at this level (either pre-k or even earlier) is primarily driven by parental options and funding, factors that reduce families' resources will impact the level and quality of education available to their children.

For example, Dahl and Lochner (2008) find a direct effect of family income on math and reading test scores.

---

*Furthermore, there is evidence that **early childhood nutrition impacts cognitive development.***

Studies in developing countries have shown that improved nutrition can lead to greater grade attainment, reading comprehension, cognitive abilities, and ultimately wages later in life (e.g., Hoddinott et al., 2008; Ruel & Hoddinott, 2008). The Dahl and Lochner results also suggest that the income impact is larger for families with younger children.

Finally, families struggling to get by are often forced to delay or abandon plans for continuing education. A recent survey of young adults found that 20% aged 18-29 have left or delayed college (Greenberg & Keating, 2009). A survey conducted in Colorado found that a quarter of parents with children in two-year colleges had planned on sending their kids to four-year institutions before the recession (CollegeInvest, 2009).

The Economy and College Attendance

A delay or reduction in college attendance is costly.

Not only does college attendance yield higher earnings, lower unemployment, and other benefits to the individual, but it also conveys myriad social benefits as well, including better health outcomes, lower incarceration rates, greater volunteerism rates, etc. (e.g., Acemoglu & Angrist, 2000; Baum & Payea, 2005).

It is also important to note that the increased educational struggles for many kids and young adults will have lasting effects. Not only does increased educational success lead to higher wages and incomes for individuals and their families down the road (Card, 1999), but it also leads to a greater likelihood of educational achievement for their offspring (Fox et al., 2005; Hertz et al., 2007). Higher-income parents are more likely to have children who complete college, and high degree of correlation between parents and children in educational attainment both in the United States and abroad. As such, the economic downturn will have an impact lasting not just for years, but for generations.

Can Education Bring Happiness?

Juncal Cuñado and Fernando Pérez de Gracia found both direct and indirect effects of education on happiness. First, they found an indirect effect of education on happiness through income and labor status. That is, they found that people with a higher education level have higher income levels and a higher probability of being employed, and thus, report higher levels of happiness. Second, and after controlling by income, labor status and other socio-economic variables, they found that education has a positive (and direct) impact on happiness. They interpret this result as evidence of a "self-confidence" or "self-estimation" effect from acquiring knowledge. Finally, they found that the direct impact of education on happiness does not depend of the level of education (primary, secondary or tertiary).

The two researchers (Cuñado and Pérez de Gracia) go on to say that there are many papers that have analyzed the relationship between educational variables and subjective wellbeing (e.g., Florida et al., 2010; Hartog & Oosterbeek, 1998; Michalos, 2007; Peiro, 2006; Ross & Van Willigen, 1997; Stevenson & Wolfers, 2009; Witter et al., 1984; among many others). For example, some empirical studies obtain a significant positive effect of education on happiness (e.g., Albert & Davia, 2005; Becchetti et al., 2006; Castriota, 2006; Di Tella et al., 2001; Florida et al., 2010; Hayo & Seifert, 2003; Layard, 2005; among many others). In addition, education should increase subjective wellbeing through different channels such as promoting higher job quality with more interesting jobs (e.g., Albert & Davia, 2005; Blanchflower & Oswald, 1994), positive effect on health (e.g., Alesina et al., 2004; Berger & Leigh, 1989; Blanchflower & Oswald 2008; Hartog & Oosterbeek, 1998; among others) and better marriage prospects (e.g., Hartog & Oosterbeek, 1998; Haveman & Wolfe, 1984; among others).

Bottom line, however, although some empirical studies find a positive effect of education on happiness (e.g., Albert & Davia, 2005; Becchetti et al., 2006; Di Tella et al., 2001; Florida et al. 2010; among many others), the empirical evidence on the link between these two variables is not conclusive.

Long Hours of School or Work
The life work you choose, or the development toward that work for you if you are still in training, usually takes up a significant part of your life. People tend to think of working at a job or a business for six, eight, ten, sometimes twelve or even more hours a day. Since this is such a significant part of people's day, it is important to be relatively satisfied with how they spend those hours on the job.

> *Ideally, you would enjoy most of what you do at work.*

For those who feel they are doing something that will make a difference in someone's life, the work tends to be worth the effort. For others, it is a job they do for the pay and benefits and, for them, that is their satisfaction.

Reasons for Working
Regardless of their educational background, generally speaking, most people work to support themselves and their families. Those individuals whose work provides them with job satisfaction, health care and other benefits, such as a retirement pension, are truly fortunate. Unless a person has a very strong substantial financial foundation (i.e., financially independent), achieving at least some college education is a requirement in today's world of

work. This author subscribes to the notion that if you are (college) educated and find work that you truly enjoy doing, especially if it involves helping others, you are headed in the right direction.

For most adults, work is a major part of life.
Retrieved from: http://www.workwithoutlimits.org/individuals/why_work

Work helps us gain a sense of pride and self-satisfaction by reaffirming that we can support ourselves. With work, we earn money to cover bills and pay for activities in our leisure time.

But it's not just about the paycheck. Work makes people happier. If you're a person with a disability and are thinking about work, there is something you should know:

> *People with disabilities who work are healthier and happier than people with disabilities who are unemployed.*

Whether a job is paid or unpaid, people who work tend to:

- **Meet people and expand their social networks.** Work acts as a training opportunity to develop and improve social skills and develop friendly and supportive relationships. The support provided by co-workers can change someone's life experience from one of isolation to one of feeling part of a community.
- **Feel productive and valued** knowing that they are making important contributions.
- **Shape a personal identity.**
- **Build a solid foundation** to advance their goals and their future.
- **Develop new skills**, both work and non-work-related. For example, some individuals with disabilities become comfortable with traveling independently, once learning to travel to and from their job.

The Internet is replete with valuable information on the subject of work. One website I found very useful was http://davetgc.com/Why_People_Work.html. On it, they answered the question why people work and they gave suggestions for choosing a career and a very useful list of occupational survival skills. Following is some of the information gleaned from that site:

WHY PEOPLE WORK
Livelihood – People work to provide themselves and their families with the basic essentials of life: food, clothing and shelter. Once these basic essentials are met, other needs and wants become important.
Human relationships – People basically like companionship. People seek companionship with persons who have interests similar to their own. Working is a means of associating with people who have similar interests.

> ***Being part of a group gives people a feeling of belonging.***

Your work can provide companionship and associations with other persons.

Personal Development – A person's work can provide an opportunity to learn and grow intellectually and socially. It is a means of attaining new goals in life by developing new skills and learning new things. Work allows people to reach their fullest potential.

Job Satisfaction – Since most of your adult waking life will be spent working, it is important to choose an occupation that will bring job satisfaction. You, as well as your family, will be happier if the occupation you choose is satisfying.

Service – Service may be defined as the things a person does that are beneficial or useful to others. People like to make quality products, provide useful services and, in general, make a contribution to society. In addition, people like to feel that the work they do is important and of value to others. Your work can be a service to others.

Security – People look for security in their occupations. We need to know that when tomorrow comes, there will be work for us so money may be earned. People want stability in their lives to make realistic and effective plans for the future. Your work can provide you with this security.

Success – All ambitious young people are interested in securing a beginning job that offers an opportunity for advancement. Employers are interested in employing persons who like a challenge and who want to be successful in life. Your work can give you success.

Happiness – Last, but not least, is happiness with one's work. Thomas Edison, the great inventor, was once encouraged by his wife to take a vacation. He responded by stating that he couldn't think of anything he would rather do than work in his laboratory. Most people who choose their occupations wisely, thoroughly enjoy their work. This contributes to their overall happiness.

SUGGESTIONS FOR CHOOSING A CAREER

> **1. *Choose an occupation because you like the work, not solely because of the rewards in money or prestige.***

2. Choose an occupation that will use the abilities you possess.
3. Choose an occupation in which there is likely to be an active demand for workers when you are ready to go to work.
4. Do not choose an occupation just because a friend or someone else you admire chose it.
5. Avoid occupations that require abilities you do not have.
6. Do not confuse interest and ability.
7. Before making a final choice of occupation, find out what all the things you might have to do in it are. Find out which of these will take most of your time.
8. Do not expect to find a job in which you will never have to do anything you dislike.
9. Beware of biased information from recruiters and other sources.

10.   Take all the advice that is offered, then act on your own judgment.
11.   Do not stay permanently in a job in which you dislike most of the things you have to do.

OCCUPATIONAL SURVIVAL SKILLS

1.   Punctuality/good attendance/promptness/dependability/reliability/maintaining good health-mental/physical.
2.   Being neat, clean in appearance/make a good impression.
3.   Getting along with others/working as a team member.
4.   Knowing what is expected/loyalty to organization/following instructions/working without close supervision.
5.   Adjusting to work situations, changes/working under pressure.
6.   Giving an honest day's work/making independent-interdependent decisions/being ethical/moral/having a sense of integrity.
7.   Managing time and materials effectively: knowing how to use materials/equipment/workplace operating procedures.
8.   Utilizing basic speaking, writing, arithmetic skills.
9.   Locating information/knowing where things are.
10.   Following safety regulations/procedures.
11.   Using initiative/imagination/creativity.
12.   Constantly improving/getting specialized training/furthering your education/knowing your strengths and weaknesses.

The Changing World of Work

According to a study completed in 2009 by the Society for Human Resource Management (SHRM) (2009), "Employee Job Satisfaction, Understanding the Factors That Make Work Gratifying" 86% of employees indicated overall satisfaction with their current position, with 41% of employees reporting they were very satisfied. What's more, the majority of employees (58%) reported that the current economic climate has not made any difference in their level of satisfaction—and this is good news for employers, especially during the economically challenging time.

Job Security and Health Care Benefits, the New Satisfiers

As has already been stated, job security is the number one job satisfier for most employees. The second most popular component for job satisfaction is health care benefits. With the cost of health care continuing to go up and companies and local, state and federal agencies cutting back on health care offerings, health care has become a major concern for most Americans.

The Changing Employee-Employer Relationship

For several years, Randstad tracked a trend of increasingly confident employees—switching jobs, taking risks and demanding benefits. These employees were emboldened by what seemed to be a strong economy in which jobs were plentiful. In 2010, employees are re-evaluating their own on-the-job performance and what is reasonable to expect from employers. Randstad's survey suggests that, as the economy softens and good jobs are harder to find and keep, employees' expectations are lowering and they are more appreciative of their current jobs.

As a result:

> *employers are finding it easier to ensure employees' happiness with less effort and investment than in recent years.*

Despite tightening budgetary constraints in the workplace, businesses should continue to invest in and focus on building professional relationships with their employees, developing employees' skills and recognizing the value that each individual brings to the organization.

Job Satisfaction in the US
Fewer American employees are satisfied with their jobs today than were before the 2008 economic crisis, though the vast majority of American workers remain satisfied with their jobs. The Gallup-Healthways Well-Being Index found 87.5% of workers satisfied with their job in April, continuing the trend of lower levels found since early 2009. Satisfaction is, however, up from the low of 86.9% in July and August 2010, but still below the high of 89.4% in February 2008.

About 9 in 10 American workers reported being satisfied with their jobs throughout 2008. Job satisfaction first dropped below 88% in January 2009, as the effects of the financial crisis started to negatively affect workplaces across the United States. In the summer of 2010, job satisfaction fell to its lowest point of 86.9%.

Job satisfaction is one of four questions the Gallup-Healthways Well-Being Index asks to measure American workers' perceptions of their workplaces. The other three questions ask employees whether they get to use their strengths at work every day, if their supervisor is more like a partner than a boss and if their supervisor creates a trusting and open work environment. Each of these three items has remained steady or even improved since 2008. Overall job satisfaction is the only one of the four that has declined over the past two and half years.

Job Satisfaction Lowest for Low-Income Workers, Blacks, Hispanics
Job satisfaction is down the most among Hispanics and those with less education in the first four months of 2011 compared with 2008. However, workers' satisfaction across all demographic groups is lower or remains statistically unchanged in 2011 when compared with 2008.

> ***Across age groups, young adults' satisfaction has decreased the most and seniors' the least.***

Seniors also have the highest job satisfaction in 2011 among all groups measured, at 94.8%. In general, job satisfaction increases with age, with young adults the least satisfied.

While black American workers' job satisfaction is essentially the same in 2011 as it was in 2008, they have consistently been among the least likely to be content with their work.

Workers with an annual household income of less than $36,000 are also among the least likely to be satisfied with their jobs in 2011, at 82.1%. At the other end of the spectrum are high-income workers—those with an annual income of $90,000 or more—who are among the most satisfied, at 91.9%. Additionally, job satisfaction has declined more among low-income workers than among those with higher incomes.

Job satisfaction has dropped more among men than among women, with both genders now about equally likely to be satisfied.

Bottom Line – Less Fortunate Are Impacted the Most

Job satisfaction provides a broad measure of how content American workers are in their jobs. American workers generally say they are satisfied with their work, though slightly fewer than in 2008. The cause of the decline in job satisfaction is unclear, though in recent years there have been reports of employees taking on more and less-than-ideal work as companies reduced staff and workers had to take jobs they are overqualified for after losing their previous job. Concerns about job security, heightened by high unemployment, are likely playing a role as well.

In 2011, the nationwide African American unemployment rate stood at 15.9%—and in several of the country's large metropolitan areas, the black unemployment rate was significantly higher (Austin, 2012).

- In 2011, the Las Vegas and Los Angeles metropolitan areas had the highest black unemployment rates, at 22.6% and 21.1%, respectively.
- Of the metro areas examined, Las Vegas experienced the largest increase in black unemployment from 2010 to 2011.
- Metro areas in or including parts of Virginia—Virginia Beach, Richmond, and Washington, DC—had the lowest black unemployment rates. However, at around 10%, these areas still had high rates of black unemployment.
- The biggest black-white unemployment rate disparity was in the Minneapolis metropolitan area, where the black unemployment rate was 3.3 times the white rate.

Job Satisfaction Issues

Research on the relationship between job satisfaction and happiness has found that work stress is a significant predictor of job satisfaction.

> *Not surprisingly, the greater the stress, the lower the levels of job satisfaction.*

In addition, work stress and job satisfaction emerged as significant predictors of emotional wellbeing where the greater the job satisfaction, the greater the emotional wellbeing (McPherson & Begawan, 2008).

"Do you get a pleasant satisfied feeling after a hard day at work?" That's a question asked at the website: http://www.spring.org.uk/2011/07/10-psychological-keys-to-job-satisfaction.php. They give 10 Psychological Keys to Job Satisfaction that I thought were worthy of sharing:

1. Little hassles

If you ask doctors what the worst part of their jobs is, what do you think they say? Carrying out difficult, painful procedures? Telling people they've only got months to live? No, it's something that might seem much less stressful: administration. We tend to downplay day-to-day irritations, thinking we've got bigger fish to fry. But actually people's job satisfaction is surprisingly sensitive to daily hassles. Managers should find out about those little daily hassles and address them—your employees will love you for it.

2. Perception of fair pay

Whatever your job, for you to be satisfied, the pay should be fair. The bigger the difference between what you think you should earn and what you do earn, the less satisfied you'll be. The important point here is it's all about perception. If you perceive that other people doing a similar job get paid about the same as you then you're more likely to be satisfied with your job than if you think they're getting more than you.

3. Achievement

People feel more satisfied with their job if they've achieved something. As smaller cogs in larger machines, it may be difficult to tell what we're contributing. That's why the next factor can be so important.

4. Feedback

There's nothing worse than not knowing whether or not you're doing a good job. When it comes to job satisfaction, no news is bad news. Getting negative feedback can be painful but at least it tells you where improvements can be made. On the other hand, positive feedback can make all the difference to how satisfied people feel.

5. Complexity and variety

People generally find jobs more satisfying if they are more complex and offer more variety. People seem to like complex (but not impossible) jobs, perhaps because it pushes them more. Too easy and people get bored.

6. Control

You may have certain tasks you have to do, but *how* you do them should be up to you. The more control people perceive they have in how they carry out their job, the more satisfaction they experience. If people aren't given some control, they will attempt to retake it by cutting corners, stealing small amounts or finding other ways to undermine the system.

7. Organizational support

Workers want to know their organization cares about them, that they are getting something back for what they are putting in. This is primarily communicated through things like how bosses treat us, the kinds of fringe benefits we get and other subtle messages.

> *If people perceive more organizational support, they experience higher job satisfaction.*

Remember: it's not just whether the organization is actually being supportive, it's whether it appears that way.

8. Work-home overflow

Low job satisfaction isn't only the boss's or organization's fault, sometimes it's down to home-life. Trouble at home breeds trouble at the office. Some research, though, suggests that trouble at the office is more likely to spill over into the family domain compared with the other way around (Ford et al., 2007). Either way, finding ways of distancing yourself from work while at home is likely to protect you against job stressors (Sonnentag et al., 2010).

9. Honeymoons and hangovers

Job honeymoons and hangovers are often forgotten by psychologists but are well-known to employees.

> *People experience honeymoon periods after a month or two in a new job when their satisfaction shoots up. But then it normally begins to tail off after six months or so.*

The honeymoon period at the start of a new job tends to be stronger when people are particularly dissatisfied with their previous job (Boswell et al., 2009).

10. Easily pleased?

Some of us are more easily satisfied (or dissatisfied) than others, no matter how good (or bad) the job is. To misquote a famous cliché: You can't satisfy all the people all the time.

"Can Work Make You Sick?" is the title of an article by Nixon et. al in the journal *Work and Stress*. The website at: http://www.spring.org.uk/2011/10/7-ways-work-can-make-you-physically-sick.php did a series on the psychology of work in which this article was reviewed. In it, they mention the authors looked at 72 studies of the effects of occupational stress on physical symptoms including headaches, backaches, sleep disturbances and gastrointestinal problems. Following are the associations with physical symptoms in decreasing order of strength: This information was retrieved from the above mentioned website.

1. Organizational constraints

Overall, the factor most strongly associated with physical symptoms was organizational constraints. These are the aspects of a workplace environment that stop you from getting your job done. It could include things like not having the time, materials or the authority to reach the goals that have been set for you. It seems as though this is likely to be the strongest cause of physical symptoms (although we can't say much about causality, as this was a correlational study). The types of physical symptoms most associated with organizational constraints were tiredness and gastrointestinal problems.

2. Role conflict

This is where one boss tells you to do one thing and another tells you to do something else. Infuriating. This was most associated with gastrointestinal problems.

3. Interpersonal conflict

Interpersonal conflict covers anything from rude or unthinking behavior by co-workers up to all-out bullying. Interpersonal conflict was most associated with sleep disturbances.

4. Workload

This is the first one you might expect to appear higher up the list. We tend to think that it's having too much work that makes us ill. It certainly contributes but not as much as organizational constraints or role conflict. Unsurprisingly, workload was most associated with fatigue.

5. Role ambiguity

Role ambiguity occurs when you don't quite know what the job is. And when you don't know what's expected of you, the stress it causes is associated with illness. In fact, in this analysis it was most associated with fatigue.

6. & 7. Work hours & lack of control

Work hours is most interesting because of how far down the list it comes. You might imagine that working hours would be at the top but it comes down at the bottom with lack of control, which had a similar association with physical symptoms. Both associations were weak, but still there.

> ***Work hours were most associated with eye strain while lack of control was most associated with backache and problems sleeping.***

A Review of Research Literature on Stress at Work

Daniel Ganster from Colorado State University and Christopher Rosen from the University of Arkansas did an extensive review of the latest research on the effects of stress on employees' health (Ganster & Rosen, 2013). They found that research examining the relationship between work stress and wellbeing has flourished over the past 20 years. At the same time, research on physiological stress processes has also advanced significantly.

One of the major advances in this literature has been the emergence of the Allostatic Load model as a central organizing theory for understanding the physiology of stress. In this article, the Allostatic Load model is used as an organizing framework for reviewing the vast literature that has considered health outcomes associated with exposure to psycho-social stressors at work. This review spans multiple disciplines and includes a critical discussion of management and applied psychology research, epidemiological studies, and recent developments in biology, neuroendocrinology, and physiology that provide insight into how workplace experiences affect wellbeing.

The authors critically review the literature within an Allostatic Load framework, with a focus on primary (e.g., stress hormones, anxiety and tension) and secondary (e.g., resting blood pressure, cholesterol, body mass index) mediators, as well as tertiary disease endpoints (e.g., cardiovascular disease, depression, mortality). Recommendations are provided for how future research can offer deeper insight into primary Allostatic Load processes that explain the effects of workplace experiences on mental and physical wellbeing.

More Explicit Findings from the Ganster and Rosen's (2013) Review on Work & Stress

Heaphy and Dutton (2008) suggested that researchers should pay more attention to human physiology across a broad array of management phenomena, as such research has the potential to affirm "the fundamentally important effect of work contexts" (p. 138). Similarly, numerous organizational scholars have argued that organizational research could benefit from the study of human physiology because physiological reactivity may explain the underlying processes that link exposure to workplace stressors to impaired functioning at work, absenteeism, and health care costs incurred by employers (e.g., Ganster, 2005; Greenberg, 2010; Halpern, 2005; Zellars, Meurs, Perrewé, Kacmar, & Rossi, 2009). Consistent with this perspective, authors believe it is important for researchers to be aware of the progress that has occurred in this area and how it can inform the course of work stress research in the management literature.

Thus, in this review, they ignored a broad array of risk factors and exposures such as chemical toxins, noise, temperature, and other physical or safety-related hazards. Some physical complaints, such as lower back pain, might be caused by both physical ergonomic factors and psychosocial stressors, but our interest here is on the psychosocial ones.

> *We thus define work stress as the process by which workplace psychological experiences and demands (stressors) produce both short-term (strains) and long-term changes in mental and physical health.*

Next, the authors provided an overview of the theoretical models of stress that have had the greatest impact on research in the work domain. The discussion of these theories is brief, however, and recent reviews provide more detailed and critical discussions of these models (Cox & Griffiths, 2010; Ganster & Perrewé, 2011; Meurs & Perrewé, 2011).

The most influential model of the psychosocial stress process is Lazarus's transactional model (Lazarus, 1966). It is labeled "transactional" because it asserts that stress resides neither in the person nor the environment, but rather in the interaction between the two. The transactional model describes primary and secondary appraisal processes, whereby individuals cognitively process information about potential stressors in conjunction with their ability to cope with them. It is these cognitions that play the critical role in initiating physiological processes.

Evidence linking work stress to primary outcomes has, by and large, been provided by the vast work stress literature that has considered affective outcomes (e.g., anxiety, psychological distress, emotional exhaustion) or acute stress-related health complaints (e.g., headache, fatigue, gastrointestinal problems). In the great majority of these studies, outcomes are self-reported and represent subclinical measures of wellbeing. These outcomes reflect proximal, relatively immediate reactions to stress exposure and are, therefore, most likely to operate during the acute phase.

Affective Outcomes and Health Complaints

Three patterns emerged across meta-analyses of the work stress literature. First, there is consistent evidence that work stressors demonstrate modest to strong correlations with wellbeing. This pattern of results is best illustrated by Lee and Ashforth (1996) and Nixon, Mazzola, Bauer, Krueger, and Spector's (2011) meta-analyses, both of which summarized how various psychosocial stressors relate to subjective reports of wellbeing. Lee and Ashforth's (1996) study indicated that work stressors (e.g., role clarity, role conflict, role stress, stressful events, workload, and work pressure) demonstrate relatively strong correlations with emotional exhaustion, a dimension of job burnout (Maslach, 1982) that is a commonly used indicator of psychological wellbeing. Similarly, Nixon et al. (2011) focused on relationships between various work stressors and self-reported physical complaints (i.e., backache, headache, eye strain, sleep disturbance, dizziness, fatigue, appetite loss, and gastrointestinal problems).

A second pattern that emerged during our review is that work stressors are most strongly associated with affective outcomes (e.g., emotional exhaustion) relative to physical symptoms. This pattern is corroborated by two meta-analyses that considered the effect of job insecurity (i.e., Cheng & Chan, 2008; Sverke, Hellgren, & Naswell, 2002), both of which indicated that

> *job insecurity demonstrates a stronger association with psychological wellbeing than with physical health.*

Similarly, Herschcovis and Barling's (2010) meta-analysis indicated that supervisor, coworker, and outsider aggression are generally more strongly related to indicators of psychological (e.g., emotional exhaustion) than physical wellbeing.

A third pattern we observed across meta-analyses is that stressors that prevent employees from achieving work goals were more strongly related to wellbeing than stressors that promote personal growth. For example, LePine and colleagues (Crawford, LePine, & Rich, 2010; LePine, LePine, & Jackson, 2004; Podsakoff, LePine, & LePine, 2007) have considered the differential effects of challenge (i.e., job/role demands, pressure, time urgency, and workload) and hindrance (e.g., constraints, hassles, resource inadequacy, role stressors, and organizational politics) stressors on composite measures of strain (e.g., anxiety, depression, emotional exhaustion, frustration, health complaints, illness, physical symptoms) and burnout.

There is also now a small set of randomized field experiments that have tested interventions that manipulated major stressors such as lack of control and role ambiguity.

> *Self-assessments of job satisfaction reflect how people value the whole package of both monetary and non-monetary returns to their effort according to their own personal preferences and expectations.*

Therefore, job satisfaction may be used to clarify the effects of workers' education on utility from work and, ultimately, on general welfare (Vila, 2005).

Current Trend: Employment is Up – Unemployment is Down

The percentage of U.S. adults participating in the workforce in September was 67.5%. This is up from the rate measured in August 2015 (66.9%) and in September of last year (67.2%). Since January 2010, the workforce participation rate has remained in a narrow range, from a low of 65.8% to a high of 68.5%. But since mid-2013, it has typically remained below 67.0%.

Workforce participation is defined as the percentage of adults aged 18 and older who are working or who are not working but are actively looking for work and are available for employment.

The increase in workforce participation in September 2015 coincides with Gallup's decision to include more cellphone-only respondents in the U.S. beginning September 1. This should give slightly more weight to younger respondents, who are more likely to not use landline phones. Most of the seasonal decrease in workforce participation in the fall is from younger Americans ending summer jobs, and weighting these respondents more heavily should actually push the participation rate down. That it has risen in spite of this sample adjustment only strengthens the case that workforce participation had a strong showing this past month.

Unemployment steady at 6.3%

Gallup's unadjusted U.S. unemployment rate was 6.3% in September, steady with August's 6.3% and down three-tenths of a percentage point from the rate measured in September 2014.

Bottom line

The full-time payroll employment rate, otherwise known as Gallup Good Jobs, marked another record this past month with the highest rate measured in any September since Gallup started employment tracking in 2010. So far in 2015, every month except April has seen the highest Gallup Good Jobs rate for that month since Gallup began recording. If this trend holds over the next few months, 2015 will mark the second year in a row with this rate ending higher than it started.

This information was retrieved from:
http://www.gallup.com/poll/185969/gallup-good-jobs-rate-steady-september.aspx?g_source=Economy&g_medium=newsfeed&g_campaign=tiles

REFERENCES
Chapter 9 – "Work/School"

Acemoglu, D., & Angrist, J. (2000). How large are human capital externalities? Evidence from compulsory schooling laws. *NBER Macroeconomics Annual, 15*, 9-59.

Albert, C., & Davia, M. A. (2005). *Education, wages and job satisfaction.* Paper presented at the Epunet Conference 2005, Colchester, UK.

Alesina, A., Di Tella, R., & McCulloch, R. (2004). Inequality and happiness: Are European and Americans different? *Journal of Public Economics, 88*, 2009–2042.

Arrow, K. (1997). The benefits of education and the formation of preferences. In J. R. Behrman & N. Stacy (Eds.), *The social benefits of education.* Ann Arbor: University of Michigan Press.

Austin, A. (2012). *Black metropolitan unemployment in 2011.* Retrieved from http://www.epi.org/publication/ib337-black-metropolitan-unemployment/.

Baum, S., & Payea, K. (2005). *Education pays: The benefits of higher education for individuals and society.* Retrieved from http://www.collegeboard.com/prod_downloads/press/cost04/EducationPays2004.pdf

Baum, S., Ma, J., & Payea, K. (2010). *Education pays 2010: The benefits of higher education for individuals and society.* New York: The College Board.

Becchetti, L., Castriota, S., & Bedoya, D. A. L. (2006). *Climate, happiness and the Kyoto protocol: Someone does not like it hot.* Retrieved from http://www.researchgate.net/publication/24125640_Climate_Happiness_and_the_Kyoto_Protocol_Someone_Does_not_Like_it_Hot

Berger, M. C., & Leigh, J. P. (1989). Schooling, self-selection and health. *Journal of Human Resources, 24*, 433–455.

Blanchflower, D. G. (2008). Happiness economics. *NBER Reporter: Research Summary, 2008*(2). Retrieved from http://www.nber.org/reporter/2008number2/blanchflower.html

Blanchflower, D. G., & Oswald, A. J. (1994). Estimating a wage curve for Britain. *The Economic Journal, 104*, 1025–1043.

Boswell, W. R., Shipp, A. J., Payne, S. C., & Culbertson, S. S. (2009). Changes in newcomer job satisfaction over time: Examining the pattern of honeymoons and hangovers. *Journal of Applied Psychology, 94*, 844–858.

Brim, O. G., Ryff, C. D., & Kessler, R. C. (Eds.). (2004). *How healthy are we? A national study of well-being at midlife.* London: University of Chicago Press.

Card, D. (1999). The causal effect of education on earnings. In O. Ashenfelter & D. Card (Eds.), *Handbook of labor economics (*Vol. 3). North Holland, Netherlands: Elsevier.

Castriota, S. (2006). *Education and happiness: A further explanation to the Easterlin Paradox.* Retrieved from http://www.researchgate.net/publication/24125639_Education_and_Happiness_a_Further_Explanation_to_theEasterlin_Paradox

CollegeInvest. (2009). *Survey: Economy weighing on Colorado parents when planning for college.* Retrieved from http:// www.collegeinvest.org/PDF/CIPollResults_5.29.09.pdf

Cooper, D., Gable, M., & Austin, A. (2012). The public-sector jobs crisis: Women and African Americans hit hardest by job losses in state and local governments. *Economic Policy Institute, Briefing Paper #339.* Retrieved from http://www.epi.org/publication/bp339-public-sector-jobs-crisis/

Cunado, J., & Perez de Gracia, F. (2011). Does education affect happiness? *Social Indicators Research, 108*, 185–196.

Chapter 9 – Work and/or School

Dahl, G., & Lochner, L. (2008). *The impact of family income on child achievement: Evidence from the earned income tax credit.* National Bureau of Economic Research. Retrieved from http://www.nber.org/papers/w14599

Davetgc.com. (n.d.). *Why people work.* Retrieved from http://davetgc.com/Why_People_Work.html

Dean, J. (2011). *10 psychological keys to job satisfaction.* Retrieved from http://www.spring.org.uk/2011/07/10-psychological-keys-to-job-satisfaction.php

Delong, J. B., Golden, C., & Katz, L. (2002). *Sustaining U.S. economic growth.* Retrieved from http://j-bradford-delong.net/ Econ_Articles/GKD_fi nal3.pdf

Di Tella, R., & MacCulloch, R. J. (2006). Some uses of happiness data in economics. *Journal of Economic Perspectives, 20*, 25–46.

Di Tella, R., MacCulloch, R. J., & Oswald, A. J. (2001). Preferences over inflation and unemployment: Evidence from surveys of happiness. *American Economic Review, 91*, 335–341.

Di Tella, R., MacCulloch, R. J., & Oswald, A. J. (2003). The macroeconomics of happiness. *Review of Economics and Statistics, 85*, 793–809.

Florida, R., Mellander, C., & Rentfow, P. J. (2010). The happiness of cities. Working Paper Series—*Martin Prosperity Research 2010–10.*

Ford, M. T., Heinen, B. A., & Langkamer, K. L. (2007). Work and family satisfaction and conflict: A meta-analysis of cross-domain relations. *Journal of Applied Psychology, 92*(1), 57–80.

Fox, M. A., Connolley, B. A., & Snyder, T. D. (2005). *Youth indicators, 2005: Trends in the well-being of American youth.* Washington, DC: U.S. Department of Education.

Ryan, B. (2015, October 1). *U.S. Gallup Good Jobs rate steady in September.* Retrieved from http://www.gallup.com/poll/185969/gallup-good-jobs-rate-steady-september.aspx?g_source=Economy&g_medium=newsfeed&g_campaign=tiles

Ganster, D. C., & Rosen, C. C. (2013). Work stress and employee health: A multidisciplinary review. *Journal of Management, 39*, 1085-1122.

Greenberg, A., & Keating, J. (2009). *Young adults: Trying to weather a recession.* Greenberg Quinlan Rosner Research. Retrieved from http://www.gqrr.com/index.php?ID=2339

Greene, A., & Bradley, B. (2013). Do health and education agencies in the United States share responsibility for academic achievement and health? A review of 25 years of evidence about the relationship of adolescents' academic achievement and health behaviors. *Journal of Adolescent Health, 52*, 523–532.

Hannan, M. T., Schomann, K., & Hans-Peter, B. (1990). Sex and sector differences in the dynamics of wage growth in the Federal Republic of Germany. *American Sociological Review, 55*, 694–713.

Hartog, J., & Oosterbeek, H. (1998). Health, wealth and happiness: Why pursue a higher education? *Economics of Education Review, 17*, 245–256.

Haveman, R. H., & Wolfe, B. (1984). Schooling and economic well-being: The role of non-market effects. *Journal of Human Resources, 19*, 377–407.

Haveman, R. H., & Wolfe, B. L. (1984). Schooling and economic well-being: The role of non-market effects. *Journal of Human Resources, 19*, 377–407.

Hayo, B., & Seifert, W. (2003). Subjective economic well-being in Eastern Europe. *Journal of Economic Psychology, 24*, 329–348.

Heckman, J. J. (2006). Skill formation and the economics of investing in disadvantaged children. *Science, 312*(5782).

Heckman, J. J., & Masterov, D. V. (2007). The productivity argument for investing in young children. *National Bureau of Economic Research.* Working Paper No. W13016. Cambridge, MA: NBER.

Hertz, T., Jayasundera, T., Piraino, P., Selcuk, S., Smith, N., & Verashchagina, A. (2007). The inheritance of educational inequality: international comparisons and fifty year trends. *The B.E. Journal of Economic Analysis & Policy, 7*(2) (Advances).

Hoddinott, J. A Maluccio, J. R. Behrman, R. Flores, and R. Martorell. 2008. Effect of a nutrition intervention during early childhood on economic productivity in Guatemalan adults. *Lancet, 371*, 411–416.

House, J. S., Lepkowski, J. M., Kinney, A. M., Mero, R. P., Kessler, R. C., & Herzog, A. R. (1994). The social stratification of aging and health. *Journal of Health and Social Behavior, 35*, 213–234.

Chapter 9 – Work and/or School

Irons, J. (2009). *Economic scarring: The long-term impacts of the recession.* Retrieved from http://www.epi.org/publication/bp243/

Layard, R. (2005). *Happiness: Lessons from a new science.* New York: Penguin.

Layard, R. (2006). Happiness and public policy: A challenge to the profession. *Economic Journal, 116,* C24–C33.

Marmot, M., Ryff, C. D., Bumpass, L. L., Shipley, M., & Marks, N. F. (1997). Social inequalities in health: Next questions and converging evidence. *Social Science and Medicine, 44,* 901-910.

McMahon, W. W. (1998). Conceptual framework for measuring the total social and private benefits of education. *International Journal of Educational Research, 27,* 453-481.

McPherson, T., & Begawan, B. S. (2008). *Job satisfaction key to overall well-being.* Retrieved from http://www.bt.com.bn/health_fitness/2008/02/12/job_satisfaction_key_to_overall_well_being

Mendes, E. (2011). *U.S. job satisfaction struggles to recover to 2008 levels.* Retrieved from http://www.gallup.com/poll/147833/job-satisfaction-struggles-recover-2008-levels.aspx

Michalos, A. C. (2007). Education, happiness and well-being. *Social Indicators Research, 87,* 347-366.

National Prevention Council. (2011). *National prevention strategy, America's plan for better health and wellness.* U.S. Department of Health & Human Services. Retrieved from http://www.surgeongeneral.gov/initiatives/prevention/strategy/report.pdf

Nixon, A., Mazzola, J., Bauer, J., Krueger, J., & Spector, P. (2011). Can work make you sick? A meta-analysis of the relationships between job stressors and physical symptoms. *Work & Stress: An International Journal of Work, Health and Organization, 25*(1).

Peiro, A. (2006). Happiness, satisfaction and socio-economic conditions: Some international evidence. *Journal of Socio Economics, 35,* 348–365.

Politifact Georgia. (2011, August 26). *U.S. Surgeoon General says less education means higher mortality rates.* Retrieved from http://www.politifact.com/georgia/statements/2011/aug/26/regina-benjamin/us-surgeon-general-says-less-education-means-highe/

Randstad. (2008). *Recession uncertainties impact changes in employee expectations and demands: Employee satisfaction is up dramatically since 2006.* Retrieved from http://us.randstad.com/content/aboutrandstad/news-and-press-releases/press-releases/2008/20080617002b.xml

Rosenbaum, J. E., & Kariya, T., Settersten, R., & Maier, T. (1990). Market and network theories of the transition from high school to work: Their application to industrialized societie. *Annual Review of Sociology, 16,* 263–299.

Ross, C., & Van Willigen, M. (1997). Education and the subjective quality of life. *Journal of Health and Social Behavior, 38,* 275–297.

Ruel, M., & Hoddinott, J. (2008). *Investing in early childhood nutrition.* International Food Policy Research Institute. Retrieved from http://ageconsearch.umn.edu/bitstream/48929/2/bp008.pdf

Ruff, C. D., & Singer, B. (1998). The role of purpose in life and personal growth in positive human health. In P. T. P. Wong & P. S. Fry (Eds.), *The human quest for meaning: A handbook of psychological research and clinical applications* (pp. 213-235). Mahwah, NJ: Lawrence Erlbaum Associates.

Society for Human Resource Management (SHRM). (2009). *2009 employee job satisfaction, understanding the factors that make work gratifying.* Retrieved from https://www.shrm.org/Research/SurveyFindings/Articles/Documents/09-0282_Emp_Job_Sat_Survey_FINAL.pdf

Society for Human Resource Management (SHRM). (2009). *Executive summary, has the U.S. recession affected employee job satisfaction?* Retrieved from http://www.shrm.org/Research/SurveyFindings/Articles/Documents/09-0282_Job_Satis_SR_Exec_Sum.pdf

Sonnentag, S., Binnewies, C., & Mojza, E. J. (2010). Staying well and engaged when demands are high: The role of psychological detachment. *Journal of Applied Psychology, 95,* 965-976.

Stevenson, B., & Wolfers, J. (2009). *Economic growth and subjective well-being: Reassessing the Easterlin Paradox.* Brookings Papers on Economic Activity. New York: Brookings Institution Press.

Chapter 9 – Work and/or School

U.S. Census. (2009). *Income, poverty and health insurance coverage in the United States, 2008.* Retrieved from http://www.census.gov/prod/2009pubs/p60-236.pdf

van de Werfhorst, H. G. (2011). Skill and education effects on earnings in 18 countries: The role of national educational institutions. *Social Science Research, 40,* 1078-1090.

Vila, L. E. (2000). The non-monetary benefits of education. *European Journal of Education, 35*(1), 21–32.

Vila, L. E. (2005). The outcomes of investment in education and people's well-being. *European Journal of Education, 40*(1), 3–11.

Witter, R. A., Okun, M. A., Stock, W. A., & Haring, M. J. (1984). Education and subjective well-being: A meta-analysis. *Educational Evaluation and Policy Analysis, 6,* 165–173.

Wolfe, B. L., & Zuvekas, S. (1997). Nonmarket outcomes of schooling. *International Journal of Education Research, 27,* 491–502.

Wolfe, B., & Zuvekas, S. (1997). Nonmarket outcomes of schooling. *International Journal of Educational Research 27,* 491–502.

Workwithoutlimits.org. (n.d.). *For most adults, work is a major part of life.* Retrieved from http://www.workwithoutlimits.org/individuals/why_work

Chapter 10 Civic Involvement (Responsibility)

One Big Community

> *Serving others is one of the highest honors a person can experience; one of the most noble acts known to man; the more you give, the more you have.*

Since we all are members of one community or another, we all share a certain level of responsibility to provide our "share" of support for the betterment of our community. Giving back is the hallmark of American life. The civic responsibility referred to here includes taking on the responsibility to obey local, state, federal and international laws; support our government by paying taxes; vote in elections and otherwise participate in those affairs that affect us all, in one way or another.

Other areas of civic responsibility lie in the volunteer work we do in our community, the financial contributions we make to charities and the level of outreach we make for the sake of helping others, especially those who are less fortunate than we are. Civic responsibility involves those activities we do that benefit others and is designed for the common good of the communities in which we live. Civic involvement is both a privilege and a responsibility. It is a privilege because it allows us the opportunity to exercise a right that is not universally provided and a responsibility because collectively we are all beneficiaries of the end result.

Civic Engagement Patterns and Transitions

Three college professors each from different east coast, west coast and mid-west universities did a study of civic engagement patterns and transitions. The title of the article detailing the

Chapter 10 – Civic Involvement (Responsibility)

study is "Civic Engagement Patterns and Transitions over 8 Years: The AmeriCorps National Study." Andrea Kinley, Constance Flanagan and Laura Wray-Lake's research results were published in 2011 in the *Journal of Developmental Psychology* where they talked about how young adulthood is a time when individuals make decisions about who they are, what they stand for, and what their plans for the future hold. Studying civic engagement at this developmental stage is important because opportunities to wrangle with civic issues during these years are formative for civic attitudes and behaviors into midlife (Flanagan, 2004; Jennings & Stoker, 2004; Youniss, McLellan, & Yates, 1997).

The life cycle perspective predicts that patterns (i.e., episodic vs. stable) and types of civic engagement (i.e., volunteering, voting, joining organizations, attending meetings, or combinations thereof) change over the life span as individuals become engaged in different social institutions and adopt new social roles (Kinder, 2006).

Civic interest and involvement across the life span is not static, but changes as individuals engage with various institutions (e.g., high schools, universities and community colleges, employment settings, the military). In the years immediately following high school, civic participation is more episodic and less stable compared with the steadier involvement in adolescence and adulthood (Flanagan & Levine, 2010). Several studies have shown that involvement in civic organizations and voting and volunteering are lower for 18- to 24-year-olds compared with such involvement for high-school students or older adults, with some studies showing increases at roughly age 26 (Jennings & Stoker, 2004; Planty, Bozick, & Regnier, 2006; Snell, 2010).

> *Young adults may be less civically engaged due to the episodic nature of their involvement with institutions and the fact that they have not yet settled into adult social roles.*

Whereas the majority of adolescents are in high school and three fourths of adults in their 30s have settled into the roles of marriage and parenthood, young people between the ages of 18 and 25 move in and out of school, change jobs frequently, have high residential mobility and enter and exit several romantic relationships. This instability tends to taper off during the late 20s when young people begin to settle into adult roles such as marriage, parenthood, and full-time employment (Arnett, 2000) and consequently connect with people and institutions that recruit them into civic life.

As the transition to adulthood has become more protracted over the past three decades (Settersten, Fursternberg, & Rumbaut, 2005), young adults also are delaying the acquisition of civic habits. However, at least with respect to voting, they acquire the habit in time: analyses of voting trends show that recent cohorts reached the turnout levels of previous generations but at later times in their life cycle (Flanagan & Levine, 2010). In short, it is not surprising that young people have lower rates of civic engagement during their early adult years as they are sorting out their educational, romantic, and career paths.

Institutions are the venues whereby people get recruited into civic life (Verba, Schlozman, & Brady, 1995) and the nature of these recruitment contexts has changed over the past three decades. College has and continues to be a venue for recruitment and, not surprisingly, levels of civic engagement are higher for young adults who are in college compared with their peers who are not (Zaff, Youniss, & Gibson, 2009).

Workplaces also used to be a venue for the civic recruitment of young adults who did not go on to college. However, over the past three decades, significant changes in the labor market have diminished the recruitment potential of this venue and have contributed to an increasing social class divide regarding civic participation. Compared with their parents and grandparents, today's young adults who terminate their education after high school are less likely to find steady employment in unionized workplaces that heretofore were a venue for civic recruitment (Flanagan & Levine, 2010).

As an alternative or in addition to college, participation in national service offers opportunities for civic engagement. In particular, national service may offer a new route for building social connections and getting recruited into civic life for youth from disadvantaged backgrounds. Their motivations for joining national service programs such as AmeriCorps include making connections, getting job training, and earning stipends to further their education (Finlay & Flanagan, 2008). The social relationships and roles individuals assume in national service programs also are likely to affect subsequent civic actions and habits. Several quasi-experimental studies have examined participation in national service programs, such as AmeriCorps and Teach for America (TFA), to see whether these intense service experiences could have lasting impacts on young adults' civic involvement (Corporation for National and Community Service, Office of Research and Policy Development, 2004, 2008; McAdam & Brandt, 2009).

Civic Engagement Challenges and Opportunities of Tomorrow

Youth involvement in civic affairs is the primary topic of an article by Erik Amna (2012). The author references another writer who points out that political actors and stakeholders in many parts of the world are trying to respond to the purported challenges. Social scientists meet in roundtable discussions (Youniss et al., 2002); national politicians set up special committees (Tong Mycock, 2010). In particular, civic education is put forward as a main vehicle for change (McDevitt & Chaffee, 2000), as too are extracurricular activities (Flanagan, Martínez, & Cumsille, 2011), in order to promote supposedly endangered civic virtues and duties. Yet there is a fear among some that the more the development of civic engagement becomes dependent on initiatives from above, the greater is the risk that adolescents will be tamed and disciplined rather than empowered and skilled.

Chapter 10 – Civic Involvement (Responsibility)

> *When we participate in the political process, we add legitimacy to the political process.*

This leads us to what may trigger even more contemporary studies into adolescents' civic engagement. How will adolescents themselves react to the giant and complex political challenges raised by financial crises, democratization processes, the new world map of politics (where the focus has shifted from West to East), climate change, and access to the Internet? And this is just to mention a few. How will adolescents feel, think and (re)act? In other words, how will they shape their civic identities through various combinations of engagement and disengagement between "fear and hope" (Ojala, 2011)?

Helping Ourselves

When we give our time, money and other resources for the betterment of the community, we are increasing the possibility that someone less fortunate than us might benefit. When we pay our fair share of taxes and participate in community volunteer work, we are helping to provide for a more effective and efficient government and advancing the attitude that we are all in this "community" effort together.

Keyes and Ryff (1998) found that five of seven measures of civic engagement and pro-social behavior predicted positive levels of overall social wellbeing. That is, the level of overall social wellbeing increased as perceived civic responsibilities increased. While it is unclear whether it is a cause or consequence of civic engagement, social wellbeing is clearly linked with civic health and social capital (Putnam, 2000).

Things are Changing

For more than a decade now, there have been pronouncements to the effect that American society is undergoing a fundamental process of social breakdown and alienation. A major example of such a critique is Robert Putnam's research on the decline of civic virtue and participation, which first came to public attention in journal articles (Putnam 1995a, 1995b), especially "Bowling Alone: The Collapse and Renewal of American Community" (Putnam, 2000). The chief culprit, according to Putnam's analysis of these trends, is a turning away from social engagement into excessive amounts of time devoted to television and Internet scanning. The effects of such "thin" social networks and withdrawal into solitary pursuits are illustrated, he claims, by the rising rates of suicide and depression among young people today compared with young adults of 25 years ago (Brim et al., 2004).

"Putnam's work shows how social bonds are the most powerful predictor of life satisfaction. For example, he reports that getting married is the equivalent of quadrupling your income and attending a club meeting regularly is the equivalent of doubling your income. The loss of social capital is felt in critical ways: Communities with less social capital have lower educational performance and more teen pregnancy, child suicide, low birth weight and prenatal mortality. Social capital is also a strong predictor of crime rates and other measures of neighborhood quality of life, as it is of our health. In quantitative terms, if you both smoke and belong to no groups, it's a close call as to which is the riskier behavior."

A Call for Civic Virtue

Putnam argues that Americans' sense of community is waning, the close ties they once had to their community are disappearing.

> *The baby boomers and the Generation Xers display a disconnection from community and a tendency toward individualism.*

Putnam calls for individuals to take the initiative and start educating America's youth about civic virtue, reconnecting with their neighbors, and increasing participation in politics to change this trend and to help them reconnect. Putnam defines three civic virtues: (1) active participation in public life, (2) trustworthiness and (3) reciprocity that is acquired through social connectedness. Putnam feels that only through an understanding of civic virtue will Americans be able to flourish in their communities and play an active role in American democracy.

Civic Responsibility is Devastated by Presumed Moral Breakdown

A wide array of reasons for the presumed social and moral breakdown has been argued:

- excessive individualism with its attendant overemphasis on individual rights and downplaying of social responsibility;
- the residue of counterculture lifestyles from the 1960s;
- the loss of religious faith (or attraction to deviant religious cults);
- overdependence on a bloated federal bureaucracy;
- excessive stridency of the feminist movement;
- the pervasive focus on sex and violence on television;
- the fragility of families as a consequence of premarital cohabitation, births outside marriage, and the high divorce rate;
- the breakdown of social networks and stable communities; and
- as illustrated by Putnam's work discussed above, the withdrawal from social interaction in favor of countless hours of TV viewing and Web surfing.

(From "How Healthy Are We?" by Orville Gilbert Brim, Carol D. Ryff, and Ronald C. Kessler, 2004)

Religious attendance shows a strong effect, but only in the community domain: the more frequent such attendance, the greater the extent of volunteer service, and even so, the greater the financial contributions to organizations and charities. Indeed, religious attendance has the largest net effect on financial contributions of all the predictors in this regard (Brim et al., 2004).

Chapter 10 – Civic Involvement (Responsibility)

> *Frequency of contact with friends may operate in much the way religious attendance does: the greater the frequency of such contact, the greater are both volunteer service and dollar contributions.*

It seems likely that friendships are formed in the course of volunteer work in the community, and friendship networks themselves may provide access to and motivation for volunteer service in sports or social clubs, parish, school or health-related organizations (Brim et al., 2004).

The Minnesota Public Radio news analysts and researchers from The Humphrey Institute (Olesen, 2008) wanted to hear if teenagers want to be involved in their community and in their local governments. Civic involvement was defined as the act of being involved in a community's policies and laws.

Civic Involvement
Findings from a study
The teenagers were from several high schools and community groups in Minneapolis and St. Paul. Everyone broke into small groups for an hour to discuss four approaches to civic involvement.

One approach was mandatory service. A teenager, perhaps upon graduation from high school, would be required to give a period of time (maybe a year?) to community service, a program like AmeriCorps.

> *In one of the groups, several kids said they were averse to anything that had "mandatory" in the title.*

But one young woman pointed out that if she didn't HAVE to do something, she probably wouldn't, even if she thought it was a good idea.

Another approach to civic involvement that was discussed was service learning. Service learning combines community service with classroom instruction. Students could serve as election judges in training, for example, and then reflect on those experiences as part of a broader curriculum. This approach is popular in some high schools. Several students said that service learning was the "fun part" of being in school and that they often got to go to new parts of the city or to an organization they had never heard of.

Higher Education's Role in Civic Learning
How can the knowledge, skills, and dispositions for civic involvement be developed to engender a sense of community and empowerment? (Robert Bringle & Kathryn Steinberg, 2010), answer that question in their article titled "Educating for Informed Community

Chapter 10 – Civic Involvement (Responsibility)

Involvement" by putting that responsibility on institutions of higher education. They begin their article by quoting Wandersman and Florin (1999): One of the presumptions of a well-functioning, viable democracy is that citizens are well-informed about community issues, they participate in various ways in contributing to work around those community issues, and the quality of life is improved as a result of their involvement. Democratic life, then, depends on developing in young adults the inclinations to become involved in civic matters and the capacity to act efficaciously.

Developing good citizens is not a new role for higher education, and Levine (2003) notes that there are numerous pedagogical approaches for civic learning (e.g., classroom instruction on civics, moderated discussions of current events, student governance, community activities, simulations). However, the emergence of service learning as a pedagogical strategy has heightened attention to the civic domain as a set of intentional educational objectives to be addressed seriously in higher education (Battistoni, 2002; Zlotkowski, 1999). Bringle and Hatcher (1995, p. 222) define service learning as:

> a credit-bearing educational experience in which students (a) participate in an organized service activity that meets identified community needs and (b) reflect on the service activity in such a way as to gain further understanding of course content, a broader appreciation of the discipline, and an enhanced sense of personal values and civic responsibility.

> *Although "citizenship cannot be reduced to service" (Dionne & Drogosz, 2003, p. 25), service learning needs to be appreciated and understood as a means for teaching toward civic education objectives.*

Unlike other forms of community-based education (e.g., internship, co-operative education, see Angelique et al., 2002; Furco, 1996), the phrase "civic responsibility" denotes that service learning has the civic education of students as an explicit goal. Thus, service learning is not only about "serving to learn," but also about "learning to serve" and being involved in communities in a variety of ways (e.g., through direct service, political involvement, grassroots organizations, nonprofit sector).

The case for service learning can be strengthened, then, by understanding its capacity to prepare students to assume a civic-minded disposition in their career and acquire the knowledge, skills and dispositions to be active citizens in their communities. For as Cunningham (2006) notes:

> One of [the] goals is the broad-based education of students to be effective and engaged citizens in our democratic society, and to be good citizens in our increasingly international world. Civic learning outcomes from higher education are

difficult to document, but they are one of the most important social and civic contributions our colleges and universities provide to our society. (p. 4)

Conceptual Framework for Student Outcomes

Altman (1996) proposed a new conceptual model for higher education, which included three domains of knowledge: foundational (basic disciplines, liberal education), professional (practitioner skills), and socially responsive knowledge. The goals of education in socially responsive knowledge are to: (a) educate students in society's problems, (b) provide experiences so that students could come to understand community issues first-hand and (c) educate students so they gain the experience and skills to act on social problems.

> *Altman viewed service learning as providing experiences that contribute to the acquisition and development of socially responsive knowledge and civic-minded graduates.*

By linking community service to academic content, service learning courses provide opportunities for students to gain a more detailed understanding of issues in modern society, such as homelessness, environmental issues, illiteracy, juvenile delinquency and health disparities. Altman's construct of socially responsive knowledge resonates with one of the public purposes of higher education, to produce graduates who can contribute to a democratic society.

Institutions of higher education are increasingly focused on infrastructure and programs that produce graduates who are civically minded (Bringle et al., 1999a; Brukardt et al., 2004; Colby et al., 2003; Langseth & Plater, 2004; Zlotkowski, 1999). From the perspective of higher education, we are defining a civic-minded graduate to be a person who has completed a course of study (e.g., bachelor's degree), has a person's inclination or disposition to be knowledgeable of and involved in the community and to have a commitment to act upon a sense of responsibility as a member of that community.

> *In receiving a college education, the civic-minded graduate will have acquired advanced knowledge and skills in at least one discipline that is relevant to issues in the community.*

The authors identified seven elements as the most central components to be manifested in a civic-minded graduate and that can be fostered through undergraduate education that includes service learning. The core elements of the civic-minded graduate domain include:
(a) Academic Knowledge and Technical Skills

(b) Knowledge of Volunteer Opportunities and Nonprofit Organizations: Civic-minded graduates will have a conception of the ways they can contribute to society, particularly through nonprofit organizations and volunteering.

(c) Knowledge of Contemporary Social Issues: Civic-minded graduates have an understanding of the complex issues encountered in modern society at local, state and national levels.

(d) Listening and Communication Skills: In order to help solve problems in society, civic-minded graduates have the ability communicate well with others. This includes written and spoken proficiency as well as the art of listening to divergent points of view.

(e) Diversity Skills: Civic-minded graduates have a rich understanding of, sensitivity to, and respect for human diversity in the pluralistic society in which they live. This can be fostered by students' interactions with persons in the community who are different from themselves in terms of racial, economic, religious, or other background characteristics.

(f) Self-Efficacy: Civic-minded graduates have a desire to take personal action, and also have a realistic view that the action will produce the desired results. Self-efficacy is a key component of personal empowerment.

(g) Behavioral Intentions, Civic Behavior: Behavioral intentions can be viewed as predictors of behaviors. Civic-minded graduates demonstrate that they value civic engagement by stating intentions to be involved in community service in the future and displaying forms of civic involvement. One of the clearest ways students can manifest these attributes is by choosing a service-based career, or by manifesting civic dimensions to a career in any field.

The Relationship Between Civic Behavior and Civic Values

In a study examining the relationships among college students' civic values and behaviors, college culture, and college involvement, accounting for their pre-college inclinations toward civic responsibility, three researchers went on a mission. Alyssa Bryant, Joy Gayles and Heather Davis (2012) wrote an article that was published in the *Research in Higher Education Journal* that opens with a history lesson on the relationship between higher education and civic education.

When colleges were first established in America, civic education was individually focused and closely tied to the religious and moral values that dominated the mission and curricula. In fact, most colleges during this period were affiliated with a religious denomination, and the institutional mission was to educate clergy and produce moral citizens with strong religious beliefs (Colby et al., 2003; Kezar, 2004;). However, as colleges and universities have evolved, the goal of preparing educated citizens for participation in a democratic society has lost its place as a core value of undergraduate education (Bok, 2001; Boyte &

Hollander, 1999; Jacoby, 2009). By the early 1900s, colleges began to educate a more diverse segment of the population.

> *As the purpose of higher education broadened, the nature of civic education and responsibility shifted from an individual focus to community involvement and solving social problems (Jacoby, 2009; Malone, 1968).*

For example, during the World War period, the federal government formed partnerships with higher education institutions to address new problems and respond to societal needs. Two such partnerships included the creation of the G.I. Bill and The National Science Foundation. By the 1960s, civic education took on more of a political focus with government and current events courses taught at the secondary educational level. There was also a surge in community service and volunteerism with the establishment of the Peace Corp in 1961 and the Volunteers in Service to America in 1965 (Jacoby, 2009). In the decades that followed, organizations committed to improving undergraduate education and maintaining civic responsibility and engagement as core values were founded, such as Campus Compact, a group of over 500 college and university presidents dedicated to promoting civic responsibility through service learning, and the Wingspread Group, the outgrowth of a meeting of key constituents about the role of higher education in promoting civic responsibility (Jacoby, 2009).

Contrary to the surge in public service efforts, the 1980s were met with great concern over the growing lack of interest in community involvement and the common good expressed by Americans in general and college students in particular (Jacoby, 2009). Cooperative Institutional Research Program (CIRP) freshman data show a sharp decline in students' interest in politics over the decades since 1984 (Pryor et al., 2010). Further evidence of a shift away from civic values is reflected in students' declining commitment to social responsibility and the increase in self-interest, materialism, and being well-off financially reported over the past 40 years (Astin et al., 1997; Astin & Sax, 1998; Pryor et al., 2007, 2010).

Defining Citizenship

> *The meaning and nature of responsible citizenship has varied over time and has been operationalized in various ways in the literature.*

Further, not all disciplines agree on how the term should be defined. Some definitions of citizenship are narrow, limiting the term to voting, running for public office, and expressing interest in politics (Hunter & Brisbin, 2000). Other definitions are broad and encompass a range of social, political, and psychological attitudes, values, and behaviors (Perry & Katula, 2001; Sherrod et al., 2002). Perry and Katula (2001) offer a three-part definition of citizenship that captures various dimensions of what citizenship represents in today's society. The first dimension, individual motivations and skill, is defined by the authors as personal attitudes that can be expressed through interest in and connections to the community. Defining citizenship along this dimension also involves cognitive skills such as problem solving and a deeper awareness and understanding of social issues. The second dimension of citizenship as defined by Perry and Katula (2001) includes philanthropic and civic behaviors. The authors describe this aspect of citizenship in terms of nonpolitical behaviors, such as charitable donations and volunteerism. The last dimension of citizenship, political behaviors, represents the behaviors one typically associates with citizenship (e.g., voting, campaigning, and running for an elected office).

There is a growing body of empirical evidence to support the positive benefits of service learning for civic responsibility, such as enhancing critical thinking skills, teaching problem solving, and increasing awareness of social problems (Astin & Sax, 1998; Astin et al., 1999; Einfeld & Collins, 2008; Hunter & Brisbin, 2000; Taylor & Trepanier-Street, 2007).

On the whole, the outcomes of service participation are numerous and extend beyond the citizenship development/civic engagement outcomes. Various studies, in fact, have linked service participation to academic achievement (Astin & Sax, 1998), multicultural competence (Einfeld & Collins, 2008; Taylor & Trepanier-Street, 2007), social consciousness (Einfeld & Collins, 2008; Jones & Abes, 2003, 2004; Taylor & Trepanier-Street, 2007), identity development (Jones & Abes, 2004), and even physical and mental health (Wilson, 2000).

> *Attitudes and values also play a role in inclinations to behave in civically responsible ways (Marks & Jones, 2004; Ozorak, 2003; Vogelgesang & Astin, 2005).*

Students who are socially responsible, optimistic, religious, and non-materialistic maintain their commitment to community service from high school to college (Marks & Jones, 2004), and students who feel connected to their communities and who perceive serious community needs tend to volunteer (Hellman et al., 2006).

One's sense of responsibility for action is shaped primarily by one's perception of his or her influence over an event or situation (Guskey, 1981; Silverman & Davis, 2009; Weiner, 1995). Based on these conjectures, students who enter college expecting to serve in charitable roles and valuing civic engagement are much more likely to seek civic and charitable activities and sustain their engagement throughout the transition to college.

Civic Capacity

In an article by Peter Sun and Marc Anderson concerning how community leaders might get the most out of civic involvement, they discuss a study they did and introduce the term "civic capacity."

Chapter 10 – Civic Involvement (Responsibility)

> **Jonathan Dent (2008) claimed that a community's civic capacity is composed of three components: civic enterprise, civic capital, and civic competency.**

Civic enterprise is the shared history of the community in joint actions and the expectation that the community will be entrepreneurial in identifying and engaging in future joint actions. Civic capital is the network of social and cultural institutions that can be mobilized for joint public actions. Civic competency refers to the collective knowledge, skill, and capability of the community, and the pragmatic use of these sets of competencies in fostering joint actions.

In the Sun and Anderson study, however, they propose a new form of "civic capacity" that occurs at the individual leader level. We suggest that since transformational leaders engender trustworthiness and honesty (Lowe et al., 1996) and are trusted by others to overcome obstacles and to engage in self-sacrificial behaviors (van Knippenberg & van Knippenberg, 2005), they are likely to exceed the "threshold level" of trustworthiness required to be engaged as an integrative public leader (Shmueli et al., 2009).

However, their transformational leadership style needs to be augmented with a moral perspective regarding public interest. They must have an altruistic motive (care for others) that will propel them to be involved in community service. Bono, Shen, and Snyder (2010) found that those who have such altruistic motives are more likely to be involved in community leadership activities. They must also have the capacity to work collaboratively with partners and be pragmatic in the institutionalization and in the use of collaborative structures and mechanisms to foster collaboration.

Collectively, we refer to these as "civic capacity." We define civic capacity at this individual level of analysis as the combination of interest and motivation to be engaged in public service and the ability to foster collaborations through the use of one's social connections and through the pragmatic use of processes and structures. We suggest that there are three components to this individual-level construct of civic capacity (only one of which is a direct analog to the community-level construct).

These components are civic drive, civic connections, and civic pragmatism, and they help explain the integrative leadership resources and the integrative structures and processes needed for effective integrative public leadership.

Civic drive refers to the desire and motivation to be involved with social issues and to see new social opportunities. Integrative leaders need to have civic drive and be social entrepreneurs who have the ability to see new opportunities for creating public value. Social entrepreneurship combines the passion of a social mission with the business-like characteristics of innovation and creativity that are often seen in Silicon Valley businesses (Van Slyke & Newman, 2006).

Chapter 10 – Civic Involvement (Responsibility)

Similar to civic capital at the community level, which is the network of cultural and social institutions that can be mobilized for joint actions, civic connections at the individual leader level refer to the social capital found in the leader's internal and external social networks that specifically enable and promote the success of the collaboration.

And finally,

> *civic pragmatism refers to the ability to translate social opportunities into practical reality by pragmatically leveraging structures and mechanisms for collaboration.*

Fostering multi-sector collaboration requires a pragmatic approach to leadership (Huxham & Vangen, 2000; Redekop, 2010). It involves setting up effective structures such as forums, workshops, or committees where collaboration can take place and mechanisms for governance and accountability. It also involves the co-creation of fair and transparent processes, ground rules and dialogues for considering issues and making decisions jointly.

Voluntarism

President Kennedy established the Peace Corps to aid both the United States and other countries. Generally, those who join the Peace Corps spend two years serving as volunteers, often abroad in underdeveloped countries. Following the start of the Peace Corps, VISTA (Volunteers in Service to America) was also established to encourage voluntarism within the United States. The Peace Corps is a good way for individuals to immerse themselves in voluntarism for a significant period of time.

Voluntarism has played a major role in both American and world history. In addition, it is important in terms of economics. Since volunteer labor is free, in organizations that use volunteers effectively, funding becomes available for other expenses. Also many corporations and for-profit entities are encouraging voluntarism on the part of their employees. In some cases, companies claim that these voluntarism efforts raise employee morale and can increase corporate profits in the long run. In addition, associations are important for maintaining democracy in America.

Civic Engagement

In a publication titled *Civic Engagement in California*, Harper+Company Community Research (2004) describe civic engagement as the inclusion and meaningful participation of community members in the process of deliberation, prioritization and decision-making regarding public programs, services, projects or policy-making.

In the public policy arena, civic engagement has become a key concept. It is increasingly common for communities to be included and have meaningful participation on issues of land-use planning, public education, transportation and services for young children and their families. A civic engagement approach to policy-making mandates that the community be considered when policy decisions are made. Community activists and policymakers use the term civic engagement widely, even while there is sometimes only a limited understanding of why it is important, or what its benefits are. As used by the Civic Engagement Project for Children and Families (Harper+Company Community Research, 2004), civic engagement refers to the process of involving community residents in creating the public policies that govern their communities, using the approach that fits best with those communities' characteristics.

Religion, Civic Engagement and Social Networks

Religion, civic engagement and social networks is the topic of an article by Valerie Lewis, Carol MacGregor and Robert Putnam that is worthy of sharing. The three researchers indicated that they build on this notion by suggesting that religious involvement is positively related to civic engagement largely due to the impact of social networks.

> *An individual's social networks have been shown to impact his or her civic engagement, both formal and informal.*

For example, extensive social networks have been shown to increase the likelihood of volunteering, and research suggests that face-to-face invitations to volunteer are much more effective than impersonal appeals (Wilson, 2000).

Numerous studies have examined the association between religion and civic engagement, and there is widespread agreement in the literature that religious Americans are more civically and socially engaged than their less religious peers across a range of outcomes (Lam, 2002; Park & Smith, 2000; Putnam & Campbell, 2010; Wilson & Musick, 1997, 1998).

Religious Americans Give More

Higher levels of religiosity have been linked to higher levels of both formal and informal civic and social engagement. Religious Americans also engage in neighborly activities that we term informal helping behaviors, such as helping a neighbor with housework or giving money to a homeless person (Brooks, 2006; Putnam & Campbell, 2010). With a few notable exceptions, most research to date has examined how religiosity has impacted one, or at most two, of these citizenship or neighborly activities, most often focusing on volunteering and charitable giving.

Religious Americans give more money and time to charitable causes than their secular counterparts. These findings are robust across a wide set of data sources and over several decades of research; in addition, the impact of religion on volunteering and giving extends not only to religious causes but secular causes as well. In fact, Americans who give to or volunteer with religious congregations also give more of their money to non-religious charitable causes than non-religious Americans (Brooks, 2006; Hall, 2005; Nemeth & Luidens, 2003; Putnam & Campbell, 2010; Regnerus et al., 1998; Wilhelm et al., 2007; Wuthnow, 1990).

Chapter 10 – Civic Involvement (Responsibility)

In short, religious Americans are not giving more simply because they are giving to religious charities. In numerical terms, Brooks (2006) used the Social Capital Community Benchmark Survey to show that religious people gave to non-religious causes on average about three and a half times more dollars per year than their secular counterparts. In addition to increased financial contributions, religious people are more active volunteers and community participants than their secular counterparts (Campbell & Yonish, 2003; Lam, 2002, 2006; Lazerwitz, 1962; Loveland et al., 2005; Park & Smith, 2000; Putnam & Campbell, 2010; Ruiter & De Graaf, 2006; Uslaner, 2002). For example, according to Giving and Volunteering survey, 45% of those who regularly attend religious services volunteer, while only 26% of non-attendees, volunteer (Putnam & Campbell, 2010).

> *Religious Americans have also been shown to be more civically active and engaged in their communities (Loveland et al., 2005; Putnam & Campbell, 2010; Smidt, 2008; Wald & Calhoun-Brown, 2007).*

In terms of community engagement, religiosity is positively associated with belonging to community organizations, serving as an officer or committee member of an organization, working on a community project and working with others to solve a problem in the community. Looking toward civic and political life, religiosity is associated with increased chances of voting in local elections, attending public meetings (such as school board meetings), and participating in protests, marches, or demonstrations. Finally, religiosity has been shown to impact informal helping outcomes as well. Religious Americans are also more likely to give blood, give money or food to a homeless person, to return change mistakenly given to them by a cashier, to help someone outside their own household with housework, offer a seat to a stranger and help someone find a job (Brooks, 2006; Putnam & Campbell, 2010).

It's Not All Positive

An important qualification to this literature is that there are related arenas in which religion has important negative effects and this has not been explored as extensively in the literature (Smilde & May, 2010). Religious organizations are highly segregated along racial lines and conservative Protestantism in particular may solidify or intensify existing racial divisions (Emerson, 2006; Emerson & Smith, 2000).

It is possible that religious Americans' civic engagement is focused on activities promoting conservative political and religious causes, such as signing petitions supporting pro-life causes or going to school board meetings to support teaching creationism. In these cases, religion may not generate social capital but collective goods that are only accessible to those who are part of the religious community (Iannaccone, 1988, 1994).

However, although religious Americans tend to be more politically conservative, the current evidence suggests that religious Americans' civic engagement is not primarily focused on conservative causes, either political or religious. Quantitative surveys often ask respondents directly about religious and non-religious volunteering and giving, finding the relationship between religiosity and civic engagement exists in non-religious activities

Social Interaction and Social Networks

Finally, another type of work has focused on the importance of social interactions and social networks in explaining links between religion and civic outcomes (Djupe & Gilbert, 2009; Putnam & Campbell, 2010; Wuthnow, 2004). In essence, researchers have argued that the participatory nature of religion in the United States may impact members' civic engagement (Lam, 2002; Verba et al., 1995). We take this one step further, arguing that participation is important because people form important social ties through religious participation. Religious congregations provide places where Americans make friends, join small discussion groups to study scripture, share worries and concerns in prayer groups and socialize at church potlucks and suppers (Djupe & Gilbert, 2009; Stroope, 2012; Wuthnow, 2004).

> *It is possible that the social connections formed in congregations are the foundation of the link between religiosity and civic engagement.*

Specifically, we argue that the connection of religiosity and civic engagement may be due to the strong friendships and social networks formed in religious congregations. We contend that religious congregations in the United States are likely places where Americans form close relationships, and it is these networks (rather than other aspects of religiosity) that underlie the religiosity-civic engagement relationship.

We theorize that religious social networks may matter for several reasons beyond the impact of general social networks, as the literature suggests several plausible possibilities. First, it may be that the enhanced social resources and social support offered by religious networks contribute to increased civic engagement. Second, it is possible that religious networks promote norms of helping behavior more than other social networks, either through encouragement or coercion.

Our findings echo previous research that has found a positive relationship between religious engagement and civic engagement or informal helping.

Civic Participation Cuts Work Absenteeism

> *Can civic involvement help you not miss days at work?*

Two researchers, Bram Lancee and Claartje L.ter Hoeven (2010) think so. In a study published in the *Social Science and Medicine Journal,* the two researchers reported that those who perceive themselves as unhealthy, and who participate more, report fewer days absent from work. We conclude that with regard to absence, civic participation matters for people who do not feel physically well. Perhaps civic participation gives people something to look forward to, which can help them overcome health-related obstacles. This supports the notion that people preserve resources and if they experience resource loss in one life domain, they benefit from compensating for this lack with resources from another category (Hobfoll, 1989).

At this point, other mechanisms can be thought of to explain the relationship reported in this study. Role commitment as a psychological trait is an example of such an explanation: being more committed to fulfill different life roles in general means that one will more likely go to work when feeling unwell and participate more in civic life anyhow.

Although the exact underlying processes may not be entirely clear, this study offers several practical implications. Certain scholars (e.g., Poelmans & Caligiuri, 2008) assert that organizations can no longer afford to assume that the ideal employee has no responsibilities outside work. This study adds that those responsibilities might even be beneficial to the organization. Although organizations can hardly facilitate civic participation for their employees, they can facilitate maintenance of a social network through work-life policies (Poelmans & Caligiuri, 2008), facilitate social capital at work (Oksanen et al., 2008) and adjust company policies to facilitate contact with other members of the community.

Skills Building

How does skills building promote civic engagement?

> *Skills building through training and technical assistance promotes civic engagement by providing people with the tools they need to be leaders in their own community.*

Training and technical assistance can be provided on a variety of topic areas to build technical and leadership skills. Skills building is beneficial not only to community members, but also for Commission staff and Commissioners. For instance, training can be provided on: facilitation, conflict resolution, community organizing, advocacy, grant proposal writing, writing a memorandum of understanding, decision-making processes, working in partnerships, needs assessments, asset mapping, budget development, evaluation, community capacity-building, community engagement strategies, child development and cultural competency (Harper+Company Community Research, 2004).

To get started, one would need to identify training and technical assistance needs and community assets. This can be accomplished through community outreach, needs assessments and by word of mouth.

Determine what kind of trainings and one-on-one support to give, to whom, where and how often. These questions can be answered after determining the needs and available resources.

Chapter 10 – Civic Involvement (Responsibility)

Advertise the available trainings and other resources in the community using multiple strategies. Methods include (multi media), bilingual flyers, announcements at meetings, presentations, word-of-mouth and information on mini-grant applications.

Provide skills building assistance. This can be done in group settings (bilingually, as needed), as well as one-on-one to make it more accessible for people with various needs.

Provide follow-up support by telephone or in person for those who need additional assistance. Follow-up is important to ensure that people are getting the assistance they need.

Neighborhood Civic Values

The Institute for the Study of Civic Values has developed 10 Neighborhood Civic Values (n.d.) that deserve repeating:

1. **Build Strong Communities** – Strengthen human relations, promote harmony, and improve the condition of all racial, ethnic, religious and economic groups in the community, within the framework of civic values set forth in the Preamble to the Constitution: to establish justice, insure domestic tranquility, promote the general welfare, and secure the blessings of liberty to ourselves and our posterity.

2. **Broaden Citizen Participation** – Increase the number of people who participate in organizations that strengthen blocks, neighborhoods, schools, and the community as a whole.

3. **Encourage Community Service** – Expand the number of people at all ages who perform community service, especially for our schools, after-school programs, and people in need.

4. **Improve Neighborhood Appearance** – Work together to insure that neighbors and businesses are doing their best to improve their blocks and corridors and fight for the resources needed to preserve neighborhood housing and rehabilitate vacant buildings. Support ongoing efforts to reduce blight.

5. **Uphold the Law** – Reduce crime in neighborhoods and throughout the community.

6. **Promote Youth Civic Responsibility** – Work to insure that young people attend school, obey the law, and respect the principles set forth in the Declaration of Independence, the Preamble to the Constitution, and the Bill of Rights.

7. *Reduce Recidivism and Support* – *comprehensive programs that help repeat juvenile and adult criminal offenders become responsible citizens.*

8. **Support Civic Education** – Build support for expanded civic education in schools, colleges, and adult education that creates a deeper understanding of the country and of all groups in our communities, helps citizens debate public policy within the

framework of America's civic values, and conveys the knowledge, skills, and attitudes needed for effective participation in the democratic process.

9. **Expand Economic Opportunity** – Work to expand economic opportunity for all residents of the neighborhood and work to insure that all levels of government are providing the resources needed to "establish justice, insure domestic tranquility, promote the general welfare, and secure the blessings of liberty to ourselves and our posterity."

10. **Increase Voter Participation** – Increase the number of people who vote in every election and strengthen the accountability of government and the schools to the citizens whom they serve.

Social Capital

"'Social capital' – an analytic term used to explain the stratification process at individual and aggregate levels" (Dominguez & Watkins, 2003, p. 112). Civic engagement would certainly be impacted by this social capital.

> *"On the individual level, social capital refers to one's access to resources through reciprocal social networks" (Ciabattari, 2007, p. 35).*

A cross-disciplinary concept generally referring to the benefits of social networks, including problem solving related to mutual interests (Putnam, 2000). This is an example of a win-win situation in which both the individual and the community benefit.

Another strand of social capital work stresses the trust and reciprocity between people that facilitates collective action in terms of economic and political development at regional and national levels. For example, Robert Putnam (1993, 1995, 2000; Leigh & Putnam, 2002) sees social capital as a distinct form of public good, embodied in civic engagement and having knock-on effects for economic prosperity, rather than an individual good related to human capital. He highlights voluntary associations as creating and sustaining the bridging social capital that enables people to get ahead. The bridging form of social capital refers to co-operative connections with people from different walks of life, and is more valuable than bonding social capital.

Broadly, social capital concerns the norms and values people hold that result in, and are the result of, collective and socially negotiated ties and relationships. It is integrally related to other forms of capital, such as human (skills and qualifications), economic (wealth), cultural (modes of thinking) and symbolic (prestige and personal qualities). For example, economic capital augments social capital, and cultural capital can be readily translated into human and social capitals. (Edwards, 2002).

REFERENCES
Chapter 10 – "Civic Involvement (Responsibility)"

Altman, I. (1996). Higher education and psychology in the millennium. *American Psychologist, 51*, 371–378.

Amnå, E. (2006). Still a trustworthy ally? Civil society and the transformation of Scandinavian democracy. *Journal of Civil Society, 2*(1), 1–20.

Amnå, E. (2010). Active, passive or stand-by citizens? In E. Amnå (Ed.), *New forms of citizen participation: Normative implications* (pp. 191–203) Baden-Baden: Nomos.

Amnå, E., & Zetterberg, P. (2010). A political science perspective on socialization research: Young Nordic citizens in a comparative light. In C. Flanagan, L. Sherrod, & J. Torney-Purta (Eds.), *Handbook of research on civic engagement in youth* (pp. 43–65). Hoboken, NJ: Wileys.

Amnå, E., Ekström, M., Kerr, M., & Stattin, H. (2009). Political socialization and human agency: The development of civic engagement from adolescence to adulthood. *Statsvetenskaplig Tidskrift, 111*(1), 27–40. Retrieved from http://oru.diva-portal.org/smash/get/diva2:231686/FULLTEXT01

Angelique, H. L., Reischl, T. L., & Davidson, W. S. (2002). Promoting political empowerment: Evaluation of an intervention with university students. *American Journal of Community Psychology, 30*, 815–835.

Astin, A. W. (1984). Student involvement: A developmental theory for higher education. *Journal of College Student Personnel, 25*, 297–308.

Astin, A. W. (1993a). *What matters in college: Four critical years revisited*. San Francisco: Jossey-Bass.

Astin, A. W. (1993b). An empirical typology of college students. *Journal of College Student Development, 34*, 36–46.

Astin, A. W., & Sax, L. J. (1998). How undergraduates are affected by service participation. *Journal of College Student Development, 39*, 251–263.

Astin, A. W., Parrott, S., Korn, W. S., & Sax, L. J. (1997). *The American freshman: National norms for fall 1996*. Los Angeles: Higher Education Research Institute, UCLA.

Astin, A. W., Sax, L. J., & Avalos, J. (1999). Long term effects of volunteerism during the undergraduate years. *Review of Higher Education, 22*, 187–202.

Battistoni, R. M. (1995). Service learning, diversity, and the liberal arts curriculum. *Liberal Education, 81*(1), 30–36.

Battistoni, R. M. (1997). Service learning and democratic citizenship. *Theory into Practice, 36*, 150–160.

Battistoni, R. M. (2002). *Civic engagement across the curriculum: A resource book for service-learning faculty in all disciplines*. Providence, RI: Campus Compact.

Bok, D. (2001). Universities and the decline of civic responsibility. *Journal of College and Character*. Retrieved from http://www.collegevalues.org/articles.cfm?id=570&a=1

Bono, J. E., & Anderson, M. H. (2005). The advice and influence network of transformational leaders. *The Journal of Applied Psychology, 90*, 1306–1314.

Bono, J. E., Shen, W., & Snyder, M. (2010). Fostering integrative community leadership. *The Leadership Quarterly, 21*, 324–335.

Boyte, H. C., & Hollander, E. L. (1999). *Wingspread declaration on renewing the civic mission of the American research university*. Retrieved from http://www.compact.org/civic/Wingspread/Wingspread_Declaration.pdf

Boyte, H. C., & Kari, N. N. (2000). Renewing the democratic spirit in American colleges and universities: Higher education as public work. In T. Ehrlich (Ed.), *Civic responsibility and higher education* (pp. 37–59). Phoenix: American Council on Education and Oryx.

Chapter 10 – Civic Involvement (Responsibility)

Brim, O. G., Ryff, C. D., Kessler, R. C. (Eds.). (2004). *How healthy are we? A national study of well-being at midlife.* London: University of Chicago Press.

Bringle, R. G. & Steinberg, K. (2010). Educating for informed community involvement. *American Journal of Community Psychology, 46,* 428-441. (Several other references included in this article)

Bringle, R. G., & Hatcher, J. A. (1995). A service-learning curriculum for faculty. *Michigan Journal of Community Service Learning, 2,* 112–122.

Bringle, R. G., & Hatcher, J. A. (2000, Fall). Meaningful measurement of theory-based service learning outcomes. *Michigan Journal of Community Service Learning,* 68–75.

Bringle, R. G., & Hatcher, J. A. (2006, October). *Where's the community impact in service learning research.* Paper presented at the 6th annual international conference on service learning research, Portland, OR.

Bringle, R. G., & Hatcher, J. A. (in press). Student engagement trends over time. In H. E. Fitzgerald, C. Burack, & S. Seifer (Eds.), *Handbook of engaged scholarship: The contemporary landscape* (Vol. 2). Community-campus partnerships. East Lansing, MI: Michigan State University Press.

Bringle, R. G., Hatcher, J. A., & McIntosh, R. (2006). Analyzing Morton's typology of service paradigms and integrity. *Michigan Journal of Community Service Learning, 13*(1), 5–15.

Bringle, R. G., Phillips, M., & Hudson, M. (2004). *The measure of service learning: Research scales to assess student experiences.* Washington, DC: American Psychological Association.

Brukardt, M. J., Holland, B., Percy, S. L., & Zimpher, N. (2004). *Calling the question: Is higher education ready to commit to community engagement? A wingspread statement.* Milwaukee, WI: Milwaukee Idea Office, University of Wisconsin- Milwaukee.

Bryant, Alyssa N., Gayles, J. G., & Davis, H. A. (2012). The relationship between civic behavior and civic values: A conceptual model. *Research in Higher Education, 53,* 76-93. (Several other references included in this article)

Ciabattari, T. (2007). Single mothers, social capital, and work-family conflict. *Journal of Family Issues, 28*(1), 34–60.

Colby, A., Beaumont, E., Ehrlich, T., & Corngold, J. (2007). *Educating for democracy: Preparing undergraduates for responsible political engagement.* San Francisco: Jossey-Bass.

Colby, A., Ehrlich, T., Beaumont, E., & Stephens, J. (2003). *Educating citizens: Preparing America's undergraduates for lives of moral and civic responsibility.* San Francisco: Jossey-Bass.

Corporation for National and Community Service, Office of Research and Policy Development. (2004). *Serving country and community: A longitudinal study of service in AmeriCorps.* Washington, DC: Author.

Corporation for National and Community Service, Office of Research and Policy Development. (2008). *Still serving: Measuring the eight-year impact of AmeriCorps on alumni.* Washington, DC: Author.

Corporation for National and Community Service. (2001). *Serving country and community: A study of service in AmeriCorps. A profile of Ameri-Corps members at baseline.* Cambridge, MA: Abt Associates.

Cunningham, A. (2006). *The broader societal benefits of higher education.* Retrieved from http://jcu.edu/academic/planassess/planning/files/Planning%20articles/Broader%20Social%20Benefits.pdf

Dent, J. (2008). Civic capacity and community response to government action: The endangered species act and state water law in the Methow and Walla Walla Basins in the Pacific Northwest. *International Journal of Public Administration, 31,* 262–276.

Dionne, E. J., Jr., & Drogosz, K. M. (2003, Winter). United we serve: The debate over national service. *Campus Compact Reader,* 23–26.

Dominguez, S., & Watkins, C. (2003). Creating networks for survival and mobility: Social capital among African-American and Latin-American low-income mothers. *Social Problems, 50*(1) 111-135.

Edwards, R. (2002). *Social capital.* A Sloan work and family encyclopedia entry. Chestnut Hill, MA: The Sloan Work and Family Research Network.

Einfeld, A., & Collins, D. (2008). The relationships between service-learning, social justice, multicultural competence, and civic engagement. *Journal of College Student Development, 49,* 95–109.

Erik A. (2012). How is civic engagement developed over time? Emerging answers from a multidisciplinary field. *Journal of adolescence, 35,* 611–627. (Several other references included in this article)

Chapter 10 – Civic Involvement (Responsibility)

Finlay, A. K., Flanagan, C., & Wray-Lake, L. (2011). Civic engagement patterns and transitions over 8 years: The AmeriCorps National Study. *Developmental Psychology, 47,* 1728–1743. (Several other references included in this article)

Flanagan, C. (2004). Volunteerism, leadership, political socialization, and civic engagement. In R. M. Lerner & L. Steinberg (Eds.), *Handbook of adolescent psychology* (2nd ed., pp. 721–745). Hoboken, NJ: Wiley.

Flanagan, C., & Levine, P. (2010). Youth civic engagement during the transition to adulthood. *Transition to Adulthood, 20,* 159–180.

Flanagan, C., & Sherrod, L. (1998). Youth political development: an introduction. *Journal of Social Issues, 54,* 447–457.

Flanagan, C., Martínez, M. L., & Cumsille, P. (2011). Civil societies as cultural and developmental contexts for civic identity formation. In L. A. Jensen (Ed.), *Bridging cultural and developmental approaches to psychology: New syntheses in theory, research and policy* (pp. 113–137). Oxford: Oxford University Press.

Furco, A. (1996). Service-learning: A balanced approach to experiential education. In Corporation for National Service (Ed.), *Expanding boundaries: Serving and learning* (pp. 26). Columbia, MD: The Cooperative Education Association.

Guskey, T. (1981). Measurement of the responsibility teachers assume for academic successes and failures in the classroom. *Journal of Teacher Education, 23,* 44–51.

Harper+Company Community Research. (2004). *Civic engagement in California: An evaluation of the civic engagement project for children and families.* Final Report: author.

Hellman, C. M., Hoppes, S., & Ellison, G. C. (2006). Factors associated with college student intent to engage in community service. *Journal of Psychology, 140,* 29–39.

Hunter, S., & Brisbin, R. A. (2000). The impact of service learning on democratic and civic values. *Political Science and Politics, 33,* 623–626.

Huxham, C., & Vangen, S. (2000). Leadership in the shaping and implementation of collaboration agendas: How things happen in a (not quite) joined-up world. *Academy of Management Journal, 43,* 1159–1175.

Jacoby, B. (2009). *Civic engagement in higher education: Concepts and practices.* San Francisco: Jossey-Bass.

Jennings, K. M. (1989). The crystallization of orientations. In M. K. Jennings & J. van Deth (Eds.), *Continuities in political action* (pp. 313–348). Berlin, Germany: DeGruyter.

Jennings, K. M., & Stoker, L. (2004). Social trust and civic engagement across time and generations. *Acta Politica, 39,* 342–379. doi:310.1057/ palgrave.ap.5500077

Jones, S. R., & Abes, E. S. (2003). Developing student understanding of HIV/AIDS through community service-learning: A case study analysis. *Journal of College Student Development, 44,* 470–488.

Jones, S. R., & Abes, E. S. (2004). Enduring influences of service-learning on college students' identity development. *Journal of College Student Development, 45,* 149–166.

Keys, C. L. M., & Ryff, C. D. (1998). Generativity in adult lives: Social structural contours and quality of life consequences. In D. McAdams & E. de St. Aubin (Eds.), *Generativity and adult development Perspectives on caring for and contributing to the next generation* (pp. 227-263). Washington, DC: American Psychological Association.

Kezar, A. (2004). Obtaining integrity? Reviewing and examining the charter between higher education and society. *Review of Higher Education, 27,* 429–459.

Kinder, D. (2006, June 30). Politics and the life cycle. *Science, 312,* 1905–1908.

Lancee, B., & Hoeven, C. L. (2010). Self-rated health and sickness-related absence: The modifying role of civic participation. *Social Science & Medicine, 70,* 570–574.

Langseth, M., & Plater, W. M. (Eds.). (2004). *Public work and the academy: An academic administrator's guide to civic engagement and service-learning.* Bolton, MA: Anker.

Leigh, A. K., & Putnam, R. D. (2002). Reviving community: What policy-makers can do to build social capital in Britain and America. *Renew,10,* 2, 15-20.

Levine, P. (2003, November). *Service-learning research and the movement for youth civic engagement.* Keynote address at the 3rd annual international service-learning research conference, Salt Lake City, UT.

Lowe, K. B., Kroeck, K. G., & Sivasubramaniam, N. (1996). Effectiveness correlates of transformational and transactional leadership: A meta-analytic review of the MLQ literature. *The Leadership Quarterly, 7,* 385–425.

Chapter 10 – Civic Involvement (Responsibility)

Malone, W. C. (1968). Civic education. *Peabody Journal of Education, 46*(2), 110–114.

Marks, H. M., & Jones, S. R. (2004). Community service in the transition: Shifts and continuities in participation from high school to college. *Journal of Higher Education, 75,* 307–339.

McAdam, D., & Brandt, C. (2009). Assessing the effects of voluntary youth service: The case of Teach for America. *Social Forces, 88,* 945–970. doi:910.1353/sof.1350.0279

Ojala, M. (2011). Hope and climate change: The importance of hope for environmental engagement among young people. *Environmental Education Research,* 1–18.

Olesen, N. (2008). *Youth speak up about civic involvement.* Retrieved from http://minnesota.publicradio.org/collections/special/columns/hows_the_family/archive/2008/05/youth_speak_up_about_civic_inv.shtml

Ozorak, E. W. (2003). Love of God and neighbor: Religion and volunteer service among college students. *Review of Religious Research, 44,* 285–299.

Perry, J. L., & Katula, M. C. (2001). Does service affect citizenship? *Administration & Society, 33,* 330–365.

Planty, M., Bozick, R., & Regnier, M. (2006). Helping because you have to or helping because you want to? Sustaining participation in service work from adolescence through young adulthood. *Youth & Society, 38,* 177–202. doi:10.1177/0044118X06287961

Pryor, J. H., Hurtado, S., DeAngelo, L., Palucki Blake, L., & Tran, S. (2010). *The American freshman: National norms fall 2009.* Los Angeles: Higher Education Research Institute, UCLA.

Pryor, J. H., Hurtado, S., Saenz, V. B., Santos, J. L., & Korn, W. S. (2007). *The American freshman: Forty year trends.* Los Angeles: Higher Education Research Institute, UCLA.

Putnam, R. (2000). Bowling alone: America's declining social capital. *Journal of Democracy, 6*(1), 65-78.

Putnam, R. (2000). *Bowling alone: The collapse and renewal of American community.* New York: Simon & Schuster.

Putnam, R. D. (1993). The prosperous community: Social capital and public life. *American Prospect, 13,* 35-42.

Redekop, B. (2010). "Physicians to a dying planet": Helen Caldicott, Randall Forsberg, and the anti-nuclear weapons movement of the early 1980s. *The Leadership Quarterly, 21,* 278–291.

Settersten, R. A., Jr., Fursternberg, F. F., Jr., & Rumbaut, R. G. (Eds.). (2005). *On the frontier of adulthood: Theory, research and public policy.* Chicago, IL: University of Chicago Press.

Sherrod, L. R., Flanagan, C., & Youniss, J. (2002). Dimensions of citizenship and opportunities for youth development: The what, why, where, and who of citizenship development. *Applied Development Science, 6,* 264–272.

Shmueli, D., Warfield, W., & Kaufman, S. (2009). Enhancing community leadership negotiation skills to build civic capacity. *Negotiation Journal, 25,* 249–266.

Silverman, S. K., & Davis, H. A. (2009, April). *Exploring pre-service teachers' sense of responsibility for working with diverse students.* Paper presented at the Annual Conference of the American Educational Research Association, San Diego, CA.

Simola, S. K., Barling, J., & Turner, N. (2010). Transformational leadership and leader moral orientation: Contrasting an ethic of justice and an ethic of care. *The Leadership Quarterly, 21,* 179–188.

Snell, P. (2010). Emerging adult civic and political disengagement: A longitudinal analysis of lack of involvement with politics. *Journal of Adolescent Research, 25,* 258–287. doi:10.1177/0743558409357238

Sun, P. Y. T., & Anderson, M. H. (2012). Civic capacity: Building on transformational leadership to explain successful integrative public leadership. *The Leadership Quarterly, 23,* 309–323. (Several other references included in this article)

Taylor, J. A., & Trepanier-Street, M. (2007). Civic education in multicultural contexts: New findings from a national study. *The Social Studies, 98*(1), 14–18.

The Institute for the Study of Civic Values. (n.d.). *Neighborhood civic values.* Retrieved from http://www.phillyneighborhoods.org/civicvalues/

Tonge, J., & Mycock, A. (2010). Citizenship and political engagement among young people: The workings and findings of the youth citizenship commission. *Parliamentary Affairs, 63*(1), 182–200.

van Knippenberg, B., & van Knippenberg, D. (2005). Leader self-sacrifice and leadership effectiveness. *The Journal of Applied Psychology, 90,* 25–37.

Chapter 10 – Civic Involvement (Responsibility)

Van Slyke, D. M., & Newman, H. K. (2006). Venture philanthropy and social entrepreneurship in community redevelopment. *Nonprofit Management & Leadership, 16*, 345–368.

Verba, S., Schlozman, K. L., & Brady, H. E. (1995). *Voice and equality: Civic voluntarism and American politics*. Cambridge, MA: Harvard University Press.

Vogelgesang, L. J., & Astin, A. W. (2005). *Post-college civic engagement among graduates*. Los Angeles: Higher Education Research Institute, University of California, Los Angeles.

Wandersman, A., & Florin, P. (1999). Citizen participation and community organizations. In J. Rappaport & E. Seidman (Eds.), *Handbook of community psychology* (pp. 247–272). New York: Kluwer/Plenum.

Weiner, B. (1995). *Judgments of responsibility: A foundation for theory of social conduct*. New York: The Guilford Press.

Wilson, J. (2000). Volunteering. *Annual Review of Sociology, 26*, 215–240.

Youniss, J. (2011). Civic education: What schools can do to encourage civic identity and action. *Applied Development Science, 15*(2), 98-103.

Youniss, J., Bales, S., Christmas-Best, V., Diversi, M., McLaughlin, M., & Silbereisen, R. (2002). Youth civic engagement in the twenty-first century. *Journal of Research on Adolescence, 12*(1), 121–148.

Youniss, J., McLellan, J. A., & Yates, M. (1997). What we know about engendering civic identity. *American Behavioral Scientist, 40*, 620–631. doi:610.1177/0002764297040005008

Zaff, J. F., Youniss, J., & Gibson, C. M. (2009). *An inequitable invitation to citizenship: Noncollege bound youth and civic engagement*. Washington, DC: Philanthropy for Active Civic Engagement.

Zlotkowski, H. (1999). Pedagogy and engagement. In R. G. Bringle, R. Games, & E. A. Malloy (Eds.), *Colleges and universities as citizens* (pp. 96–120). Boston: Allyn & Bacon.

Chapter 11
Social Connection

To be social is to be human. Or, better still, to be human is to be social.

Social "medicine" fights anxiety and depression!

People who are social are happier than those who are not. They have more friends; they fit in and get along with others better; and to the extent their social behavior has personal connotations, their associations last longer.

In our social interactions with other people, we tend to get back what we put out. If we stay on the surface with our conversation and talk about the weather or current events, we tend to get back weather talk and current events. On the other hand, if we risk saying something of significance, sharing a personal interest or hobby we might get back something more significant such as how they spend their spare time or something about what seems to be important to them. The level of one's social interaction tends to be reciprocal.

As I reflect on my own social involvement, I find myself being more social with people who are most like me. On some (fairly rare) occasions I am the big talker. Most of the time, I am more of a listener. The people whose company I resonate with most are those who are quiet and don't have a lot to say, at least at first. I especially appreciate those who seem to be sensitive of others' potential desire to be heard, intermittently initiating conversation and not taking every opportunity there is for something to be said and otherwise being socially engaged in a non-domineering and friendly kind of way. People can sometimes surprise you, however, and seem quiet at first but you get them in a one-on-one conversation and they turn out to be non-stop talkers about just about everything. That is what makes socializing both interesting and fun. Different people at different times have different ways of interacting with one another.

Chapter 11 – Social Connection

> **"The human is a social animal, dependent on trust. And trust comes from a sense of common values and beliefs.**

We seek commonality, which is why we love social networks, the immediate friendships on Facebook and the instantaneous connections on Twitter. It's why when we're riding the Paris Metro, and we hear an American accent, we say 'Hello.' Those are the words of Simon Sinek, author of *Start With Why* who was the first speaker at the 3rd annual 99% Conference in New York City. Retrieved from:
http://thenextweb.com/media/2011/05/05/why-the-human-is-a-social-animal-report-from-the-99-conference/
Article by Cortney Boyd Myers (2011).

Anthropologist Paula Gray (2010) says that human beings are social animals. Our lives depend on other humans. Human infants are born unable to transport or care for themselves. Their survival depends on another human's efforts. We develop and learn about the world around us through the filter of other people. Our connections to others are key to not only our survival, but also to our happiness and the success of our careers.

Richard Taflinger (1996) would agree, only he says it differently by saying that we are the only creatures on earth (as far as we know) that can remember the past as discrete events, then connect those events with present conditions. Then, on the basis of those connections, we can consciously decide what to do, and project possible present actions into the future consequences of those actions. Thus, unlike other animals that react to stimuli as they occur, humans live not only in the present, but in the past and the future. A dog may bristle at a threat, but not at a threat that's long gone or hasn't occurred yet. Humans will do all three. It is this ability to remember the past, relate it to the present, and project into the future that is a special province of humans. This ability allows us to manipulate our environment, communicate across distance and time, and evolve incredibly complex societies and cultures.

Social Connectedness

> *Social connectedness refers to the relationships people have with others and the benefits these relationships can bring to the individual as well as to society.*

It includes relationships with family, friends, colleagues and neighbors, as well as connections people make through paid work, sport and other leisure activities, or through voluntary work or community service.

People who feel socially connected also contribute toward building communities and society. They help create what is sometimes called "social capital," the networks that help society function effectively.

272

Chapter 11 – Social Connection

Social connectedness is fostered when family relationships are positive and when people have the skills and opportunities to make friends and to interact constructively with others. Good health, employment, and feeling safe and secure all increase people's chances of developing positive social networks that help improve their lives. The above few paragraphs on social connectedness was retrieved from:
http://www.socialreport.msd.govt.nz/documents/social-connectedness-social-report-2010.pdf

Social Wellbeing

> *Some experts have defined social wellbeing as an individual's self-report of the quality of their relationship with other people, their neighborhood, and their community (Keyes, 1998; Larson, 1993).*

Social wellbeing is operationalized as an individual's perceptions of their integration into society, acceptance of other people, coherence of society and social events, sense of contribution to society, and the potential and growth of society (Orville Brim, Carol Ryff, & Ronald C. Kessler (Eds.), *Midlife in the United States)*.

In 1948, the World Health Organization identified social wellbeing as one of the several facets of an individual's overall health (U.S. Department of Health and Human Services, 1999; WHO, 1948). However, the construct of social wellbeing is often equated with social indicators that are operationalized by economic measures (e.g., the Growth Domestic Product and the Poverty Rate) that reflect the "health" of narrow sectors of society (Andrews & Withey, 1976; Bell & Olson, 1969). According to Larson (1996), "The key to deciding whether a measure of social well-being is part of an individual's health is whether the measure reflects internal responses to stimuli – feelings, thoughts and behaviors reflecting satisfaction or lack of satisfaction with the social environment" (p. 186) (Keyes & Shapiro, 2004). For example, how does an individual feel about interacting, socializing and otherwise making contact with others in their environment? Does their behavior reflect their satisfaction or dissatisfaction with others in that environment?

All else being equal, social interaction is associated with positive affect (Emmons & Diener, 1986; Watson, Clark, McIntyre, & Hamaker, 1992). For example, people report more positive affect on days in which positive social events occur (e.g., lunch with friends) than on days in which they do not (Clark & Watson, 1988; Gable, Reis, & Elliot, 2000; Reis, Sheldon, Gable, Roscoe, & Ryan, 2000), and these increases operate independently of increases associated with positive, personal achievements on those days (e.g., Nezlek, 2002; Nezlek, Feist, Wilson, & Plesko, 2001; Reis et al., 2000).

Gregory Walton and colleagues (2012) provided a quote by David Hume that was noteworthy along with comments from their research article titled "Mere Belonging: The Power of Social Connections."

Chapter 11 – Social Connection

No quality of human nature is more remarkable, both in itself and in its consequences, than that propensity we have to sympathize with others, and to receive by communication their inclinations and sentiments, however different from, or even contrary to our own. That's according to Hume, A Treatise on Human Nature.

> *Among the most powerful human motives is the desire to form and maintain social bonds (Baumeister & Leary, 1995).*

Research underscores the role of social connections in diverse domains of functioning.

When people's sense of social connectedness is threatened, their ability to self-regulate suffers; for instance, their IQ performance drops (Baumeister, Twenge, & Nuss, 2002). Feeling lonely predicts early death as much as major health risk behaviors like smoking (Cacioppo & Patrick, 2008).

Given the importance of social relationships for human functioning and wellbeing, an important question involves how social relationships affect people's personal interests and motivated behavior—qualities that form an important basis of people's sense of self-identity.

Anthropologist Paula Gray (2010), who was mentioned earlier, said she was reading an excellent book titled *Connected: The Surprising Power of Our Social Networks and How They Shape Our Lives* (2009) by Nicholas Christakis and James Fowler. They delve into the social theory underlying the impact that our social networks have on our lives.

> *The bottom line is that we are influenced by, and we are able to influence, people up to three degrees removed from us.*

With that thought in mind, now look at your social network within three degrees from yourself. Are these the people you want shaping nearly every aspect of your life? Does this group have enough depth and breadth? Should you expand this group?

One way to grow your social network, especially benefiting your career, is to join a professional association. Once you do, you must decide how to utilize that membership to gain the greatest value. Some people believe an association membership is something that is passively done *to them*, rather than an active starting point for *their own action*. Being an active member in a professional association can:

- Open doors to new opportunities
- Connect you with like-minded individuals
- Connect you with respected colleagues holding differing opinions or perspectives
- Provide a venue to share solutions

- Land you your next job
- Even set you apart as a thought leader

It is all in how you use it to your advantage.

You can also gain additional credibility and recognition as a product manager by writing and submitting articles, which you can do from anywhere in the world, or participate in online boards or forums.

Simon Sinek, author of *Start with Why*, who was also mentioned in the first paragraph of this chapter, brings home the point of why it is to your advantage to expand your sphere of influence and the importance of giving, trusting and otherwise connecting with others in a significant way.

> *Simon Sinek emphasized that when we trust, we're more willing to experiment. We have the confidence that if we fail or trip over, that those who trust us will look after us.*

Our very survival depends on this. We're not good at everything and we're not good by ourselves... The goal is to amplify your strength and surround yourself with people who can do what you can't do. He also talked about the win-win aspect of giving by saying: Generosity is doing something for someone else and expecting nothing in return, ever. Giving isn't an equation. It's designed to help you feel good. Sex feels good because it was designed to feel good so that we will continue to procreate. When we inspire those around us, it feels good because it's supposed to feel good. That sense of fulfillment that we get was designed so that we'll do it more. It's how the human species progresses.

Not only do we want the human species to progress but we want people to be able to bounce back from hardship and other negative encounters. That's where resilience comes into play.

What Is Social Resilience?

According to John Cacioppo, Harry Reis and Alex Zautra (2011), social resilience is the capacity to foster, engage in, and sustain positive relationships and to endure and recover from life stressors and social isolation. Its unique signature is the transformation of adversity into personal, relational, and collective growth through strengthening existing social engagements, and developing new relationships, with creative collective actions. Social resilience emphasizes an individual's capacity to work with others to achieve these endpoints and, consequently, the group's capacity to do so as well.

Social resilience, unlike other forms of personal resilience, therefore is intrinsically multilevel and includes an individual's (a) characteristic ways of relating (e.g., agreeableness, trustworthiness, fairness; compassion, humility, generosity, openness); (b) interpersonal resources and capacities (e.g., sharing, attentive listening, perceiving others accurately and empathically, communicating care and respect for others, responsiveness to the needs of others, compassion for and forgiveness of others); and (c) collective resources and capacities (e.g., group identity, centrality, cohesiveness, tolerance, openness, rules for governance).

Even though the three authors provide an excellent definition of social resilience, in their article about the value of social fitness, they include a great example through a story provided by a person they thanked by the name of William Patrick. Following is the story:
On January 3, 1864, the *Grafton*, an English schooner piloted by Captain Thomas Musgrave, was struck by a hurricane that broke its anchor chains and sunk it on the rocky beach on the southern end of Auckland Island. The captain and his crew of four men made it to shore but not to safety. Auckland Island is one of the most inhospitable places on earth, with freezing rain, howling winds, and little to eat year round.

On May 10th of the same year, the *Invercauld*, an Aberdeen clipper piloted by Captain George Dalgarno was struck by a heavy gale and driven between two steep cliffs on the northern side of Auckland Island and sunk. Nineteen of the twenty-five men aboard the *Invercauld* made it ashore, unaware of the existence of the other crew despite their spending more than a year together on the desolate and inhospitable island.

The survivors of the *Grafton* abandoned formalities from the past and adopted group problem solving and decision making, whereas the survivors of the *Invercauld* retained the formal hierarchy that served them so well on the high seas. Although the challenges to survive were quite similar, the outcomes for these two crews could not have been more different.

The crew of the *Grafton* worked together to find food and water, consulted with and looked after one another, constructed shelter, and contributed to their rescue by building a vessel and setting out to sea where they were found by Captain Cross of the *Flying Scud*. The crew of the *Invercauld*, on the other hand, fought and splintered, lost 16 of the 19 to cold or hunger, descended into cannibalism, and was found only by chance. The *Julian*, a Peruvian ship, had sprung a leak off the island and set a boat ashore to seek assistance. There they found and rescued the three remaining crewmembers of the *Invercauld* (Druett, 2007). (We thank William Patrick for suggesting this example of social resilience)."

> *We may aspire to be self-sufficient and celebrate our individual achievements, but our remarkable accomplishments as a species are attributable to our collective action, not our individual might.*

Human evolutionary heritage has endowed us with the capacity to feel the pain of social isolation and the rewards of social connection. Importantly, it has also endowed us with the capacity to feel others' social pain and the compassion to care for the sick and the elderly far beyond their reproductive or instrumental utility.

Chapter 11 – Social Connection

Social species generally do not fare well when forced to live solitary lives, and we are certainly no exception. Humans, born to the longest period of utter dependency of any species and dependent on conspecifics across the life span to survive and prosper (Cacioppo & Patrick, 2008; Hartup & Stevens, 1997), do not fare well when living solitary lives or when it simply feels that way. Social isolation is associated not only with lower subjective wellbeing (Berscheid, 1985; Burt, 1986; Myers & Diener, 1995) but with broad-based morbidity and mortality (Cacioppo & Hawkley, 2009; House, Landis, & Umberson, 1988).

Humans are a social species, and by definition, social species create emergent structures that extend beyond the individual. Whales swim in pods, wolves hunt in packs, penguins share warmth in huddles, fish swim in schools and birds migrate in flocks. The emergent social structures created by humans are more abstract, flexible, and variable than those of other species. These structures range from dyads and families to nations, international alliances, and virtual global communities. The captains and crews of the *Grafton* and the *Invercauld* developed different governance structures and group norms when confronted with conditions that to solitary individuals meant likely death.

The captain and crew of the *Grafton* eliminated the formal hierarchy and norms that functioned well at sea in favor of group consultation and cohesion in the face of these new and dire challenges. They instead created a culture in which everyone's survival was tied to the survival of one another. These norms encouraged individuals to work for the good of the group rather than for themselves at the expense of the group because they believed their contributions would be repaid in kind, a social rule promoting cooperation and effective collective action: what Bowles (2006) termed network reciprocity.

The captain and crew of the *Invercauld*, in contrast, maintained the hierarchical structure and privileges that existed at sea even though the challenges faced on the island demanded a more flexible authority structure. The behaviors of the crew were guided by individual self-interests rather than group interests, which resulted in a high rate of mortality. In short, the social structures of these two groups differed in their resilience, leading to survival and rescue for one crew and disastrous outcomes for the other.

Social resilience also modulates the development and expression of individual resilience.

> *For instance, social resilience leads to growth through enhancing relationships, meaning-making, social engagement, and coordinated social responses to challenging situations.*

Of course, other forms of resilience—for example, emotional or spiritual resilience—may also strengthen and preserve, but social resilience emphasizes the role of connections with other individuals, groups, and large collectives as a means of fostering adaptation through new learning and growth. Importantly, social resilience does not imply monolithic pressures toward uniformity nor an uncritically rosy view of the joys of relating. Both fair competition and cooperation, for instance, can contribute to resilience.

What is unique about social resilience is an appreciation for the key contributions to human welfare of coordinated social activity and feelings of connectedness and "we-ness." In other words, when people work together toward their common benefit, taking into account their differences and seeking to profit from them while recognizing and valuing the bonds that link them to each other, their collective outcomes typically transcend those that would be obtained from more solitary activities and promote the development and expression of individual resilience.

How Does Social Resilience Operate?

Consider the capacity and motivation to perceive others accurately and empathically. One's ability to see others from the same lens through which one views oneself, and to respond supportively to them, is a cornerstone of social relations. To be socially resilient, one needs to understand how other persons perceive the diverse experiences and situations of life because successful coordination of activity requires shared perspectives and coordinated goals. Also, heightened awareness of and concern for the needs of another person promotes positive interpersonal bonds.

Although many resilience-enhancing qualities reside within individuals, it is valuable to recognize that they are effective primarily when mutual and reciprocal and when social tasks and situations encourage their expression. Resilience resources contribute to social resilience in a manner that is both interactive and iterative—in other words, they are constructive because one interacting partner's display of resilient behaviors fosters complementary behaviors by interacting others, and this process then unfolds repeatedly through ongoing interaction. Thus, ongoing virtuous cycles of resilient behaviors enhance problem solving and the maintenance and growth of relationships and groups, whereas downward spirals of nonresilient behavior lead to poor problem resolution and the deterioration of relationships and groups.

The rigid hierarchy of the *Invercauld* discouraged prosocial behavior, inhibited empathy, caring, and shared problem-solving, and made it unlikely that a sense of "we-ness" would emerge. Social resilience, therefore, is a *multilevel construct* because it represents a feature of groups as well as a feature of the individuals in the group.

Building Social Resilience

> *One of the outstanding features of resilience is that it can be thought of as a systemic process (or processes) inherent in virtually any type of organized entity,*

from a simple biological system to a person, an organization, a neighborhood, a community, a city, a state, or even a nation (Zautra & Reich, 2011). In essence, social resilience represents a paradigmatic shift in our ways of thinking about people and their problems and thus requires a fresh look at the design of interventions to promote the kinds of qualities that increase the likelihood of resilient outcomes.

Final Comments about Social Resilience

Social resilience depends on the development of greater awareness of our connections with others and multiple capacities for social action that can lead to the attainment of both personal hopes and social purposes. Choices informed by social connection as well as personal values lead to resilient outcomes that are sustainable with respect to the social worlds in which we live as well as personal motivations for success and long life.

Don't Hide Your Happiness!

Positive Emotion Dissociation, Social Connectedness, and Psychological Functioning are the topics of an article written by seven university professors. I. B. Mauss et al. (2011) quote a number of references that agree with the position that positive emotions are often associated with good outcomes (Fredrickson, 1998, 2001; Harker & Keltner, 2001; Isen, 2000; King, Hicks, Krull, & Del Gaiso, 2006). In terms of cause and effect, evidence is accumulating that positive emotions are not just the to-be-expected consequence of good things. Rather, they appear to causally contribute to good outcomes, including enhanced psychological functioning (Fredrickson, 1998; Lyubomirsky, King, & Diener, 2005).

Positive Emotions and Psychological Functioning

Positive emotions are associated with enhanced psychological functioning, including higher levels of wellbeing and lower levels of mental health problems (Bonanno & Keltner, 1997; Folkman & Moskowitz, 2000; Fredrickson, 1998, 2001; Lyubomirsky et al., 2005). Such correlations may seem unsurprising because of course it feels good to be healthy and to do well. Moreover, positive feelings are part of the very definition of some facets of psychological functioning. For example, wellbeing is often defined as including high levels of positive emotion (Diener, 2000; Kahneman, 1999).

> *What is somewhat more surprising is that positive emotions also seem to causally contribute to psychological functioning.*

This is suggested by both experimental and longitudinal evidence (for reviews, see Fredrickson, 1998; Lyubomirsky et al., 2005). For example, Fredrickson, Cohn, Coffey, Pek, and Finkel (2008) randomly assigned participants either to a meditation practice aimed at enhancing positive emotion or to a control group. Over time, the group assigned to the positive-emotion condition exhibited increased positive emotion, which in turn predicted greater wellbeing and decreased depressive symptoms. These effects were mediated by gains in resources, including social resources.

Chapter 11 – Social Connection

How Do Positive Emotions Enhance Psychological Functioning?

The finding that positive emotions produce good outcomes leads to the crucial question of how positive emotions might do so. According to the social-functional perspective (Frijda & Mesquita, 1994; Keltner & Haidt, 1999), a key function of emotions is to coordinate a person's social interactions and relationships.

In particular, *positive* emotions serve these functions by communicating to others affiliative intent and approachability and by inducing positive emotional states in others (cf. Anderson, Keltner, & John, 2003; Borkenau & Liebler, 1992; Frank, Ekman, & Friesen, 1993; Frijda & Mesquita, 1994; Keltner & Haidt, 1999; King, 2000; Shiota, Campos, Keltner, & Hertenstein, 2004). In this way, positive emotions foster social connectedness (engagement in close, mutually satisfying relationships) and the formation of long-term cooperative bonds (Anderson et al., 2003; Reis & Patrick, 1996).

> *The key proposition here is that positive emotions will have these adaptive social outcomes to the extent that they are communicated accurately to others (Buck, 1994; Keltner & Kring, 1998).*

When positive emotions are not communicated accurately, they should lose some of their positive functions. Thus, to understand when and how positive emotions are adaptive we must focus on the question of whether they are accurately communicated.

We argue that accuracy is achieved—and communication is thus most effective—when positive behavior matches a person's feelings. When emotional behavior is dissociated from experience and thus inaccurate, it may disrupt communication (cf. Berry & Pennebaker, 1993; Bonanno et al., 2007; Boone & Buck, 2003; Keltner & Kring, 1998). For instance, a person who smiles when she does not feel happy or who keeps a stoic face when she is delighted would disrupt rather than enhance communication. We suggest that such experience—behavior dissociation—impedes social connectedness because it confuses others about the actual internal states of the individual or makes the individual appear inauthentic and thus not trustworthy (e.g., Berry & Pennebaker, 1993; Bonanno et al., 2007; Boone & Buck, 2003; English & John, 2011).

How and why do positive emotions lead to good outcomes? We argued from a social-functional perspective that one key to answering these questions lies in the social-communicative function of emotions: Positive emotions should be adaptive inasmuch as they are accurately communicated. In turn, accurate communication is ensured when positive emotional behaviors are tightly coupled with positive experiences.

Social Activity and Aging

Maintaining supportive relationships is an important element of effective aging. The more contact we have with others as we age, the better we may be at retaining mental sharpness.

Chapter 11 – Social Connection

A large study reported in the *New England Journal of Medicine* found that people who engaged in leisure activities such as learning to play a musical instrument or dancing were less likely to develop dementia (http://www.neurological.org.nz/brain-health/mental-workout).

> ***Dancing may be especially beneficial to the brain because it combines physical activity with social interaction and often involves a cognitive challenge in learning dance steps.***

Research studies suggest that people with the most limited social connections are twice as likely to die over a given period than those with the widest social networks. Many experts believe that social isolation may create a chronically stressful condition that accelerates aging.

This information is especially important to older people, who may be more likely to lead solitary lives—especially if family and friends have moved away or died. Of course, combating loneliness requires time and energy, both in establishing new relationships and in deepening existing ones. But the benefits are well worth the effort.

As soon as you become captive in your room or your chair, you've got a problem, says Michael Merzenich, PhD, a neurobiologist at University of California, San Francisco. You become removed from the possibilities for excitement, for learning, and for engaging your brain with fun and surprise. Your brain needs you to get out and have those 1,000 daily surprises (AARP, 2006, "Stay Socially Connected").

AARP offers options available to any age group for staying connected
- Pursue social activities, lecture programs, hobby clubs or traveling with friends.
- Get involved in projects that require regular contact with others, like planning a gathering for a club, organizing a card game with friends or helping with a church event.
- Seek out people who may share your interests by getting involved at your place of worship or other organizations.
- Volunteer at a local nonprofit organization, such as a charity, school or museum.
- Join a walking or cycling club or fitness center, go golfing, or take yoga or cooking classes.
- Take an adult education or college course in something that interests you.
- Stay in touch with your neighbors and participate in neighborhood activities.
- Take advantage of programs and services offered at community and senior centers, or at your local offices for aging.
- Furry, finned, and feathered friends can bring great joy and love into our lives. Animal shelters are full of potential companions looking for good homes.

Specific subcategories pertaining to qualities of social relationships that emerged within relations with others help illuminate what it is about the company of other people that seems crucial to living a good life. The high-frequency subcategories included (1) a positive evaluation of others (490% of respondents mentioned relations with others); (2) loving and caring (37%), an indication that relationships with other people are important because people love, care, and support each other emotionally; (3) advising and respecting (30%), an indication that relationships with other people are important because people advise each other, teach each other new things, and enable each other to feel respected and worthy; and (4) spend time/physical presence together (27%). (From "How Healthy Are We?" by Orville Gilbert Brim, Carol D. Ryff, and Ronald C. Kessler, 2004.)

> *Whether defining the good life, identifying the causes of life going well, or expressing hopes for the future, respondents mentioned relationships with other people (especially with one's parents, spouse, and offspring) most often in their narratives.*

The importance of good health was also frequently mentioned, especially when describing what is necessary for a good midlife and future life.

Benefits of Social Capital

In terms of social capital in which people share a sense of identity, hold similar values, trust each other and reciprocally **do things for each other**, this is felt to have an impact on the social, political and economic nature of the society in which we live. Thus, the concept of social capital has gained a considerable influence in policymaking circles.

Social capitol is covered in much more detail in *Handbook of Social Capitol, the Troika of Sociology, Political Science and Economics*, edited by Gert Tinggaard Svendsen and Gunnar Lind Haase Svendsen, both of Denmark (2009).

Social Interaction

According to succeedsocially.com a fairly common social issue people have is that they're not sure how to make friends and put together a social life for themselves. There are quite a few ways someone can find themselves in this situation:

- They've moved to a new city and don't know very many people yet.
- They've been in a long-term relationship and have let their social life wither.
- Their old friends have slowly been dropping out of the picture (moving away, busy with work or a new family, etc.) and haven't been replaced by new ones.
- They feel like they've grown apart from their current friends and want to make entirely new ones.
- Their lifestyle has changed and the people they used to be around no longer support the new lifestyle.

Chapter 11 – Social Connection

In the past they were happy being alone a lot of the time, but now they want to be around people more often. They never really knew how to make friends and have always wished their social lives were better.

Social Network Changes Across the Life Span

Cornelia Wrzus et al. (2013) did a meta-analysis that provides comprehensive evidence of how the size of social networks changes from adolescence to old age. Referencing a number of other studies, the four researchers show how social networks comprise a person's social relationships, that is, "the set of people with whom an individual is *directly involved* [emphasis added]" (C. S. Fischer, 1982, p. 2), such as family members, friends, and acquaintances. Direct involvement implies that there is a social relationship between the individual and the network partner that is characterized by repeated interactions between the dyad members and a mental representation of the relationship as such (Baumeister & Leary, 1995).

This definition distinguishes social networks in the current meta-analysis from approaches that focus on the maximum number of persons an individual knows at least by name (Hill & Dunbar, 2003; Killworth, Johnsen, Bernard, Shelley, & McCarty, 1990). Furthermore, the definition distinguishes social networks from social groups: Members of social groups can, but do not have to, entertain social relationships (e.g., Asendorpf & Banse, 2000; Baumeister & Leary, 1995). Group belonging can occur without (repeated) interaction (e.g., research using the minimal group paradigm: Brewer, 1979; Tajfel, Billig, Bundy, & Flament, 1971). Finally, groups are often performance oriented and share goals (Sherif, 1966), whereas this does not necessarily characterize social networks such as friendship or family networks (Baumeister & Leary, 1995; Duck, 1988; Hinde, 1979).

> *The size of social networks is an important characteristic because it indicates social resources.*

Social resources often bear beneficial effects for people's health, wellbeing and accomplishment of life tasks (Bastani, 2007; Carstensen, 1991; Granovetter, 1973; Kahn & Antonucci, 1980; Pinquart & Sörensen, 2000). The assessed social network size can vary with the assessment method and several other methodological factors such as sample representativeness or gender distribution (Bien, Marbach, & Neyer, 1991; Cross & Madson, 1997; Kogovšek, & Ferligoj, 2005). The strength of meta-analyses is that they incorporate studies with varying methods because these effects can be analyzed in moderator analyses (Rosenthal, 1991).

Chapter 11 – Social Connection

During adolescence and young adulthood, when the remaining lifetime seems unlimited, information acquisition goals are relatively more prevalent compared with other life periods.

People focus on gathering knowledge and information from diverse relationships and sources, which is achieved best in large networks with diverse relationship partners. After young adulthood and throughout the rest of adult life, when remaining lifetime is perceived as increasingly limited, emotion regulation goals become increasingly important.

People emphasize emotional aspects of relationships and focus on close relationships, such as those with family members, with expected pleasant interactions that most likely satisfy emotion regulation goals. Accompanying decreases in network size in older adulthood are assumed to be actively sought and not merely passively experienced because of deaths of network members (Carstensen, Isaacowitz, & Charles, 1999; Lang & Carstensen, 1994). Decreases especially in peripheral, but less in close and familial relationships, support these assumptions (Lang, 2000; Lang, Staudinger, & Carstensen, 1998).

In an article titled "A Social Life Improves Health" by Mike Davison (n.d.), he indicates that friends are excellent stress busters because they provide consistent psychological support, assistance in times of need, and contribute to overall feelings of contentment and acceptance. Davison provides a list of ways you can improve your social life and ultimately improve your overall health:

5 Ways to boost your social life:
1 – Renew old friendships
Why not call up some buddies you haven't seen in awhile and arrange to do a fun activity like fishing or bowling?

2 – Get a romantic partner
Studies show that married men live several years longer than their unmarried counterparts. Also, men tend to feel more comfortable opening up about certain issues to their partners, and bouncing ideas off the other half sometimes sheds new light on problems.

3 – Spend time with family
Your family can be your nearest, dearest and most consistent means of support.

4 – Meet new people
Join a co-ed slow pitch team, get involved in a local reading group, or do some volunteer work. There are endless ways for you to make new connections, learn new skills and increase leisure time in your life.

5 – Listen and learn

Take time to *have a 20-minute conversation with at least two friends a week.* Talking with others can help reduce the burden of coping with stressors alone and can increase feelings of support between individuals. Retrieved from: http://www.askmen.com/money/body_and_mind_60/69b_better_living.html

Social Contacts

A holistic approach to health always involves nurturing all aspects of your life, especially social contacts.

Large, extended families that were often available for support are now fewer. The number of one-person households has increased. People often move far from their families to work or retire. But staying connected to family, friends and activities has never been more important.

> ***Several studies report fewer colds, lower blood pressure and lower heart rates in participants with strong social ties.***

Statistics show that marriage, perhaps the strongest tie, adds years to life expectancy. And suicide, mental illness and alcoholism rates are much lower when people feel a sense of belonging. Evidence of the benefits of social interactions was found in these studies:

In one study, medical students who were assigned to work in pairs had lower stress levels than those who were assigned to work alone.

Another study reported that elderly people who like to eat out, go to movies and take part in other social activities live an average of two and a half years longer than people who spend most of their time alone. The physical health benefits of socializing were equal to physical exercise, (not to replace either) even though the social activities involved almost no physical exertion. It wasn't physical activity or physical health but feeling worthwhile that led to longer life. Good health and eating counted, but it was social interaction that was responsible for the results.

In one experiment, paid volunteers had a cold virus sprayed in their noses. The people with very few or no social contacts were four times more likely to come down with cold symptoms than those with lots of social contacts (Gold, 2006).

According to thirdage.com, many studies show that people who are well-connected to others are less likely to get sick than those who are socially isolated. And, if they do become ill, they are also more likely to recover. Even death seems to be staved off by love and support;

Chapter 11 – Social Connection

> *A Harvard University study noted that death rates among socially isolated men were almost 20% higher than men with stronger social connections.*

Also, according to Dr. Valerie Ulene, in another study, healthy volunteers received identical exposure to a cold virus, and then researchers monitored them for cold symptoms. The volunteers with diverse and positive social networks developed colds 35% of the time versus those volunteers with fewer types of social relationships who developed colds 60% of the time. Therefore, improving your social life could cut your chances of getting a cold in half! Retrieved from: http://www.askmen.com/money/body_and_mind_60/69_better_living.html

Social Butterfly

Wisegeek.com asks, What is a social butterfly? If you've ever watched a butterfly in action, you'll note that they busily work a garden, flitting from flower to flower to glean a little nectar before moving on.

Gradually, social butterfly has migrated into a descriptive term, mostly applied to females, who are extroverted, comfortable in social situations, can talk to just about anyone, and who seem to have a certain grace and ease at parties. Social butterflies in a party setting could move from group to group, briefly sipping in the nectar of each engagement and sharing a few pleasant words with partygoers. Their social adeptness makes it simple for the social butterflies to be quite at home in large group settings.

> *Just as the actual butterfly enhances the lives of flowers, the social butterfly tends to be an asset at parties.*

She or sometimes he can start conversations, praise the looks of the other guests, and keep the party atmosphere more interesting. It would be more difficult to throw a party with no extroverted guests, since most introverted guests need a little encouragement to move about a room, engage in conversation and keep a party lively. A combination of extroverts and introverts tend to balance social engagements more appropriately.

Some people seem to be innately extroverted, and there are now various personality tests that can tell you whether you tend to be more outgoing or less. Generally, you may already know whether you fit social butterfly standards if you've had opportunities to take part in social engagements. Do you like to walk about the room talking with various guests, or do you prefer one deep conversation with a kindred spirit? If the answer is yes to the former, you probably are the extroverted social butterfly type.

The term can sometimes be misapplied to people who are obnoxiously social, overbearing, loud, and who make rude comments. They may stomp from guest to guest vociferously voicing their opinions; they don't flit and they don't have a light touch and innate social grace. These are not true social butterflies because they detract from a social scene rather than enhance it.

Retrieved from: http://www.wisegeek.com/what-is-a-social-butterfly.htm

Social Development

Social development can be summarily described as the process of organizing human energies and activities at higher levels to achieve greater results. Development increases the utilization of human potential (Gary Jacobs & Harlan Cleveland, 1999). http://www.icpd.org/development_theory/SocialDevTheory.htm

Hartup (1992) notes that peer relationships in particular contribute a great deal to both social and cognitive development and to the effectiveness with which we function as adults.

> *Hartup states that the single best childhood predictor of adult adaptation is not school grades, and not classroom behavior, but rather, the adequacy with which the child gets along with other children. (Hartup, 1992).*

Retrieved from: http://www.ericdigests.org/2001-4/assessing.html

Social Networking

Although there is some debate as to an actual definition, social networking basically refers to a community where one connects and communicates with others on the Internet. Although the actual format may vary from website-to-website, communication is accomplished using a variety of methods, such as web logs or blogs, instant messaging, email, video, chat rooms or forums.

Social networking allows people to connect with others worldwide in the privacy of one's home; it is usually free and instantaneous. Social networking allows people to stay in touch with old friends, or establish new friendships. People are instantly able to share music, videos, photographs or one's deepest, darkest thoughts and secrets with one person, or with many. Social networking sites provide an outlet for creativity and expression and can be just plain fun!

> *For those who are shy or awkward in "real life," social networking sites allow people to hone their social skills without the dreaded face-to-face contact.*

Some social networking sites are devoted to a particular category or specific interest group such as dating, religion, music, pets or business. People can browse or search for others who share those interests or hobbies. Social networking sites are not just for teenagers either. There are sites targeted toward the much younger audience, grandparents and yes, even the four-legged friends can have their very own site and communicate with other animals!

Chapter 11 – Social Connection

Once registered on a social networking site, a user profile is then completed. Profiles generally include the person's name or user-name (commonly known as nickname or handle), as well as various other identifying information (age, date of birth, sex, location, address, email, etc.). A variety of interests may also be included (favorite movies, foods, schools, likes and dislikes, etc.).

The amount of information one provides in their user profile, is generally up to that particular person. Many profiles include a photograph or photos as well as videos, and may also provide information about last log in time. Some profiles are public, while others are considered "private" (only those who are specifically listed in a friend's listing, or other specific criteria set by that website, can view that particular profile), keeping online strangers from viewing that profile, in theory.

There are hundreds of social networking websites online today. MySpace, Facebook, Bebo, and Xanga are just a few of the sites you may be familiar with. The popularity of social networking sites has skyrocketed in recent years and isn't expected to diminish (Jace Shoemaker-Galloway, 2007, "Social Networking Defined").

- Facebook is a popular free social networking website that allows registered users to create profiles, upload photos and video, send messages and keep in touch with friends, family and colleagues. According to statistics from the Nielsen Group, Internet users within the United States spend more time on Facebook than on any other website.
- Twitter is a free microblogging service that allows registered members to broadcast short posts called tweets. Twitter members can broadcast tweets and follow other users' tweets by using multiple platforms and devices.
- Google+ (pronounced *Google plus*) is Google's social networking project, designed to replicate the way people interact offline more closely than is the case in other social networking services. The project's slogan is "Real-life sharing rethought for the web."
- Wikipedia is a free, open content online encyclopedia created through the collaborative effort of a community of users known as Wikipedians. Anyone registered on the site can create an article for publication; registration is not required to edit articles. Wikipedia was founded in January 2001.
- LinkedIn is a social networking site designed specifically for the business community. The goal of the site is to allow registered members to establish and document networks of people they know and trust professionally.
- Reddit is a social news website and forum where stories are socially curated and promoted by site members. The site is composed of hundreds of sub-communities, known as "subreddits." Each subreddit has a specific topic such as technology, politics or music. Reddit site members, also known as, "redditors," submit content which is then voted upon by other members. The goal is to send well-regarded stories to the top of the site's main thread page.

Chapter 11 – Social Connection

<u>Pinterest</u> is a social curation website for sharing and categorizing images found online. Pinterest requires brief descriptions but the main focus of the site is visual. Clicking on an image will take you to the original source, so, for example, if you click on a picture of a pair of shoes, you might be taken to a site where you can purchase them. An image of blueberry pancakes might take you to the recipe; a picture of a whimsical birdhouse might take you to the instructions.

These examples were retrieved from: http://whatis.techtarget.com/definition/social-media

Another Perspective on Social Networking

Another perspective is offered by the website whatissocialnetworking.com. They say it's the way the 21st century communicates today. Social networking is the grouping of individuals into specific groups, like small rural communities or a neighborhood subdivision, if you will. Although social networking is possible in person, especially in the workplace, universities, and high schools, it is most popular online.

This is because unlike most high schools, colleges, or workplaces, the Internet is filled with millions of individuals looking to meet other people and to gather and share firsthand information and experiences about a myriad of different topics.

Online Networking

Whatissocialnetworking.com also explains that when it comes to online social networking, websites are commonly used. These websites are known as social sites. Social networking websites function like an online community of Internet users. Depending on the website in question, many of these online community members share common interests in hobbies, religion, or politics. Once you are granted access to a social networking website, you can begin to socialize.

The friends you can make are just one of the many benefits to social networking online. Another one of those benefits includes diversity because the Internet gives individuals from all around the world access to social networking sites.

As mentioned, social networking often involves individuals or organizations together. While there are a number of social networking websites that focus on particular interests, there are others that do not. The websites without a main focus are often referred to as "traditional" social networking websites and usually have open memberships. This means that anyone can become a member, no matter what their hobbies, beliefs, or views are. However, once you are inside this online community, you can begin to create your own network of friends and eliminate members who do not share common interests or goals.

> *As I'm sure you're aware, there are dangers associated with social networking including data theft and viruses, which are on the rise. The most prevalent danger, though, often involves online predators or individuals who claim to be someone that they are not.*

Potential Dangers of Social Networking

By being aware of your cyber-surroundings and who you are talking to, you should be able to safely enjoy social networking online. It will take many phone conversations to get to know someone, but you really won't be able to make a clear judgment until you can meet each other in person.

Once you are well informed and comfortable with your findings, you can begin your search from hundreds of networking communities to join. This can easily be done by performing a standard Internet search. Your search will likely return a number of results, including MySpace, FriendWise, FriendFinder, Yahoo! 360, Facebook, Orkut, and Classmates, to name a few.

Retrieved from: http://www.whatissocialnetworking.com/

REFERENCES
Chapter 11 – "Social Connection"

This first reference (Wrzus, et al.) is out of alphabetical order to highlight the other (*) references that were included in this meta-analysis.

Wrzus, C., Hänel, M., Wagner, J., & Neyer, F. J. (2013). Social network changes and life events across the life span: A meta-analysis. *Psychological Bulletin, 139*(1), 53–80. References marked with an asterisk indicate studies included in the meta-analysis.

*Antonucci, T. C., Lansford, J. E., Akiyama, H., Smith, J., Baltes, M. M., Takahashi, K., & Dartigues, J.-F. (2002). Differences between men and women in social relations, resource deficits, and depressive symptomatology during later life in four nations. *Journal of Social Issues, 58*, 767–783. doi:10.1111/1540-4560.00289

*Antonucci, T. C., Lansford, J. E., Schaberg, L., Smith, J., Baltes, M., Akiyama, H., . . . Dartigues, J.-F. (2001). Widowhood and illness: A comparison of social network characteristics in France, Germany, Japan, and the United States. *Psychology and Aging, 16*, 655–665. doi:10.1037/0882-7974.16.4.655

*Asendorpf, J. B. (2000). A person-centered approach to personality and social relationships: Findings from the Berlin Relationship Study. In L. R. Bergman, R. B. Cairns, L.-G. Nilsson, & L. Nystedt (Eds.), *Developmental science and the holistic approach* (pp. 281–298), Mahwah, NJ: Erlbaum.

*Asendorpf, J., & Wilpers, S. (1998). Personality effects on social relationships. *Journal of Personality and Social Psychology, 74*, 1531–1544. doi:10.1037/0022-3514.74.6.1531

*Bost, K. K., Cox, M. J., Burchinal, M. R., & Payne, C. (2002). Structural and supportive changes in couples' family and friendship networks across the transition to parenthood. *Journal of Marriage and Family, 64*, 517–531. doi:10.1111/j.1741-3737.2002.00517.x

*Cronenwett, L. R. (1985a). Network structure, social support, and psychological outcomes of pregnancy. *Nursing Research, 34*, 93–99. doi:10.1097/00006199-198503000-00009

*Cronenwett, L. R. (1985b). Parental network structure and perceived support after birth of first child. *Nursing Research, 34*, 347–352. doi:10.1097/00006199-198511000-00007

*Feiring, C., & Lewis, M. (1991). The transition from middle childhood to early adolescence: Sex differences in the social network and perceived self-competence. *Sex Roles, 24*, 489–509. doi:10.1007/BF00289335

*Fischer, J. L., Sollie, D. L., & Morrow, K. B. (1986). Social networks in male and female adolescents. *Journal of Adolescent Research, 1*, 1–14. doi:10.1177/074355488611002

*Fischer, J. L., Sollie, D. L., Sorell, G. T., & Green, S. K. (1989). Marital status and career stage influences on social networks of young adults. *Journal of Marriage and the Family, 51*, 521–534. doi:10.2307/352513

*Guiaux, M., van Tilburg, T., & Broese van Groenou, M. (2007). Changes in contact and support exchange in personal networks after widowhood. *Personal Relationships, 14*, 457–473. doi:10.1111/j.1475-6811.2007.00165.x

*Hammer, M., Gutwirth, L., & Phillips, S. L. (1982). Parenthood and social networks: A preliminary view. *Social Science & Medicine, 16*, 2091–2100. doi:10.1016/0277-9536(82)90258-1

*Heller, K., & Mansbach, W. E. (1984). The multifaceted nature of social support in a community sample of elderly women. *Journal of Social Issues, 40*, 99–112. doi:10.1111/j.1540-4560.1984.tb01109.x

*Hughes, R., Jr., Good, E. S., & Candell, K. (1993). A longitudinal study of the effects of social support on the psychological adjustment of divorced mothers. *Journal of Divorce & Remarriage, 19*, 37–56. doi:10.1300/J087v19n01_03

Chapter 11 – Social Connection

*Imamoglu, E. O., Küller, R., Imamoglu, V., & Küller, M. (1993). The social psychological worlds of Swedes and Turks in and around retirement. *Journal of Cross-Cultural Psychology, 24*, 26–41. doi:10.1177/0022022193241002

*Jerusalem, M., Hahn, A., & Schwarzer, R. (1996). Social bonding and loneliness after network disruption: A longitudinal study of East German refugees. *Social Indicators Research, 38*, 229–243. doi:10.1007/BF00292047

*Johnson, M. P., & Leslie, L. (1982). Couple involvement and network structure: A test of the dyadic withdrawal hypothesis. *Social Psychology Quarterly, 45*, 34–43. doi:10.2307/3033672

*Lang, F. R. (1998). Einsamkeit, Zärtlichkeit und subjektive Zukunftsori- entierung im Alter. Eine Untersuchung zur Sozioemotionalen Selektivitätstheorie [Loneliness, tenderness, and subjective future orientation in old age: A study on socioemotional selectivity theory]. *Zeitschrift fu·r Klinische Psychologie, 27*, 98–104.

*Lang, F. R. (2000). Endings and continuity of social relationships: Maximizing intrinsic benefits within personal networks when feeling near to death. *Journal of Social and Personal Relationships, 17*, 155–182. doi:10.1177/0265407500172001

*Lang, F. R., & Carstensen, L. L. (1994). Close emotional relationships in late life: Further support for proactive aging in the social domain. *Psychology and Aging, 9*, 315–324. doi:10.1037/0882-7974.9.2.315

*Lang, F. R., Staudinger, U. M., & Carstensen, L. L. (1998). Perspectives on socioemotional selectivity in late life: How personality and social context do (and do not) make a difference. *Journals of Gerontology: Series B. Psychological Sciences and Social Sciences, 53*, P21–P30. doi:10.1093/geronb/53B.1.P21

*Milardo, R. M. (1989). Theoretical and methodological issues in the identification of the social networks of spouses. *Journal of Marriage and the Family, 51*, 165–174. doi:10.2307/352377

*Milardo, R. M., Johnson, M. P., & Huston, T. L. (1983). Developing close relationships: Changing patterns of interaction between pair members and social networks. *Journal of Personality and Social Psychology, 44*, 964–976. doi:10.1037/0022-3514.44.5.964

*Morrison, E. W. (2002). Newcomers' relationships: The role of social network ties during socialization. *Academy of Management Journal, 45*, 1149–1160. doi:10.2307/3069430

*Murphy, S. A., Lohan, J., Dimond, M., & Fan, J. (1998). Network and mutual support for parents bereaved following the violent deaths of their 12- to 28-year-old-children: A longitudinal prospective analysis. *Journal of Personal and Interpersonal Loss, 3*, 303–333. doi:10.1080/10811449808409708

*Neyer, F. J. (1999). Die Persönlichkeit junger Erwachsener in verschiedenen Lebensformen [Personality of young adults with different life styles]. *Kölner Zeitschrift für Soziologie und Sozialpsychologie, 51*, 491–508.

*Neyer, F. J., & Lang, F. R. (2004). Die Bevorzugung von genetischen Verwandten im Lebenslauf [Preference for genetic kin across the life course]. *Zeitschrift für Sozialpsychologie, 35*, 115–129. doi:10.1024/0044-3514.35.3.115

*Neyer, F. J., & Lehnart, J. (2007). Relationships matter in personality development: Evidence from an 8-year longitudinal study across young adulthood. *Journal of Personality, 75*, 535–568. doi:10.1111/j.1467-6494.2007.00448.x

*Shaver, P., Furman, W., & Buhrmester, D. (1985). Transition to college: Network changes, social skills, and loneliness. In S. Duck & D. Perlman (Eds.), *Understanding personal relationships: An interdisciplinary approach* (pp. 193–219). Thousand Oaks, CA: Sage.

*Sollie, D. L., & Fischer, J. L. (1988). Career entry influences on social networks of young adults: A longitudinal study. *Journal of Social Behavior & Personality, 3*, 205–225.

*South, S. J., & Haynie, D. L. (2004). Friendship networks of mobile adolescents. *Social Forces, 83*, 315–350. doi:10.1353/sof.2004.0128

*Tracy, E. M. (1990). Identifying social support resources of at-risk families. *Social Work, 35*, 252–258.

AARP. (2006). *Stay socially connected.* Retrieved from http://www.aarp.org/health/brain-health/info-2006/brain_socially_connected.html

Allan, G. (2006). Social networks and personal communities. In A. L. Vangelisti & D. Perlman (Eds.), *The Cambridge handbook of personal relationships* (pp. 657– 671). Cambridge, England: Cambridge University Press.

Chapter 11 – Social Connection

Allan, G. (2008). Flexibility, friendship, and family. *Personal Relationships, 15*, 1–16. doi:10.1111/j.1475-6811.2007.00181.x

Anderson, C., Keltner, D., & John, O. P. (2003). Emotional convergence between people over time. *Journal of Personality and Social Psychology, 84*, 1054–1068. doi:10.1037/0022-3514.84.5.1054

Andrews, F. M., & Withey, S. B. (1976). *Social indicators of well-being: Americans' perceptions of life qu*ality. New York: Plenum.

Antonucci, T. C. (1986). Hierarchical mapping technique. *Generations, 10*, 10–12.

Antonucci, T. C., & Akiyama, H. (1987). Social networks in adult life and a preliminary examination of the convoy model. *Journal of Gerontology, 42*, 519 –527. doi:10.1093/geronj/42.5.519

Asendorpf, J., & Banse, R. (2000). *Psychologie der Beziehung* [Relationship psychology]. Bern, Germany: Huber.

Back, M. D., Schmukle, S. C., & Egloff, B. (2008). Becoming friends by chance. *Psychological Science, 19*, 439–440. doi:10.1111/j.1467-9280.2008.02106.x

Bastani, S. (2007). Family comes first: Men's and women's personal networks in Tehran. *Social Networks, 29*, 357–374. doi:10.1016/ j.socnet.2007.01.004

Baumeister, R. F., & Leary, M. A. (1995). The need to belong: Desire for interpersonal attachments as a fundamental human motivation. *Psychological Bulletin, 117*, 497–529. doi:10.1037/0033-2909.117.3.497

Bell, D., & Olson, M. (1969). Toward a social report-I. The idea of a social report, II. The purpose and plan of a social report. *Public Interest, 15*, 72-97.

Berge, Z. L. (1996, Summer). Where interaction intersects time. *MC Journal: The Journal of Academic Media Librarianship, 4*(1). Retrieved from http://wings.buffalo.edu/publications/mcjrnl/v4n1/berge.html

Berkman, L. (1995). The role of social relations in health. *Psychosomatic Medicine, 57*, 245–254.

Berkman, L. F., & Breslow, L. (1983). *Health and ways of living: The Alameda County Study*. London: Oxford University Press.

Berkman, L. F., & Syme, S. L. (1979). Social networks, host resistance, and mortality: A nine-year follow-up study of Alameda county residents. *American Journal of Epidemiology, 109*(1979), 186-204.

Berry, D. S., & Pennebaker, J. W. (1993). Nonverbal and verbal emotional expression and health. *Psychotherapy and Psychosomatics, 59*, 11–19. doi:10.1159/000288640

Berscheid, E. (1985). Interpersonal attraction. In G. Lindzey & E. Aronson (Eds.), *Handbook of social psychology* (3rd ed., pp. 413–484). New York: Random House.

Bien, W., Marbach, J., & Neyer, F. (1991). Using egocentered networks in survey research: A methodological preview on an application of social network analysis in the area of family research. *Social Networks, 13*, 75–90. doi:10.1016/0378-8733(91)90014-K

Bloem, B. A., van Tilburg, T. G., & Thome´se, F. (2008). Changes in older Dutch adults' role networks after moving. *Personal Relationships, 15*, 465–478. doi:10.1111/j.1475-6811.2008.00210.x

Bonanno, G. A., & Keltner, D. (1997). Facial expressions of emotion and the course of conjugal bereavement. *Journal of Abnormal Psychology, 106*, 126–137. doi:10.1037/0021-843X.106.1.126

Bonanno, G. A., Colak, D. M., Keltner, D., Shiota, M. N., Papa, A., Noll, J. G., . . . Trickett, P. K. (2007). Context matters: The benefits and costs of expressing positive emotion among survivors of childhood sexual abuse. *Emotion, 7*, 824–837. doi:10.1037/1528-3542.7.4.824

Boone, T. R., & Buck, R. (2003). Emotional expressivity and trustworthiness: The role of nonverbal behavior in the evolution of cooperation. *Journal of Nonverbal Behavior, 27*, 163–182. doi:10.1023/A: 1025341931128

Borkenau, P., & Liebler, A. (1992). Trait inferences: Sources of validity at zero acquaintance. *Journal of Personality and Social Psychology, 62*, 645– 657. doi:10.1037/0022-3514.62.4.645

Brewer, M. B. (1979). In-group bias in the minimal intergroup situation: A cognitive-motivational analysis. *Psychological Bulletin, 86*, 307–324. doi:10.1037/0033-2909.86.2.307

Brim, O. G., Ryff, C. D., & Kessler, R. C. (Eds.) (2004). *How healthy are we? A national study of well-being at midlife*. London: University of Chicago Press.

Brooks, J. G., & Brooks, M. G. (1999). *In search of understanding: The case for constructivist classrooms*. Alexandria, VA: Association for Supervision and Curriculum Development.

Brown, D. R., & Gary, L. E. (1985). Social support network differentials among married and nonmarried Black females. *Psychology of Women Quarterly, 9*, 229–241. doi:10.1111/j.1471-6402.1985.tb00874.x

Chapter 11 – Social Connection

Brown, J. S., & Duguid, P. (1989). Situated cognition and the culture of learning. *Educational Researcher, 18*(1), 32-42.

Buck, R. (1980). Nonverbal behavior and the theory of emotion: The facial feedback hypothesis. *Journal of Personality and Social Psychology, 38*, 811–824. doi:10.1037/0022-3514.38.5.811

Buck, R. (1994). Social and emotional functions in facial expression and communication: The readout hypothesis. *Biological Psychology, 38*, 95–115. doi:10.1016/0301-0511(94)90032-9

Burt, R. S. (1986). *Strangers, friends, and happiness* (GSS Tech. Rep. No. 72). Chicago, IL: National Opinion Research Center, University of Chicago.

Byrne, D. (1971). *The attraction paradigm*. New York: Academic Press.

Byrne, D., Griffitt, W., & Stefaniak, D. (1967). Attraction and similarity of personality characteristics. *Journal of Personality and Social Psychology, 5*, 82–90. doi:10.1037/h0021198

Cacioppo, J. T., & Hawkley, L. C. (2009). Perceived social isolation. *Trends in Cognitive Sciences, 13*, 447–454. doi:10.1016/j.tics.2009.06.005

Cacioppo, J. T., & Patrick, B. (2008). *Loneliness: Human nature and the need for social connection*. New York: W. W. Norton.

Cacioppo, J. T., Fowler, J. H., & Christakis, N. A. (2009). Alone in the crowd: The structure and spread of loneliness in a large social network. *Journal of Personality and Social Psychology, 97*, 977–991. doi:10.1037/a0016076

Cacioppo, J. T., Reis, H. T., & Zautra, A. J. (2011). Social resilience: The value of social fitness with an application to the military. *American Psychologist, 66*(1), 43–51. (Several other references included in this article)

Caldwell, M. A., & Peplau, L. A. (1982). Sex differences in same-sex friendship. *Sex Roles, 8*, 721–732. doi:10.1007/BF00287568

Caldwell, R. A., Bloom, B. L., & Hodges, W. F. (1983). Sex differences in separation and divorce: A longitudinal perspective. *Issues in Mental Health Nursing, 5*, 103–120. doi:10.3109/01612848309009435

Carstensen, L. L. (1991). Socioemotional selectivity theory: Social activity in life-span context. *Annual Review of Gerontology and Geriatrics, 11*, 195–217.

Carstensen, L. L. (1992). Social and emotional patterns in adulthood: Support for socioemotional selectivity theory. *Psychology and Aging, 7*, 331–338. doi:10.1037/0882-7974.7.3.331

Carstensen, L. L. (1995). Evidence for a life-span theory of socioemotional selectivity. *Current Directions in Psychological Science, 4*, 151–156. doi:10.1111/1467-8721.ep11512261

Carstensen, L. L., Isaacowitz, D. M., & Charles, S. T. (1999). Taking time seriously: A theory of socioemotional selectivity. *American Psychologist, 54*, 165–181. doi:10.1037/0003-066X.54.3.165

Christakis, N., & Fowler, J. (2009). Connected: *The surprising power of our social networks and how they shape our lives*. New York: Little, Brown & Company.

Cross, S. E., & Madson, L. (1997). Models of the self: Self-construals and gender. *Psychological Bulletin, 122*, 5–37. doi:10.1037/0033-2909.122.1.5

Daniels-Mohring, D., & Berger, M. (1984). Social network changes and the adjustment to divorce. *Journal of Divorce, 8*, 17–32. doi:10.1300/ J279v08n01_02

Dankwa-Mullan, I., Rhee, K. B., Williams, K. et al. (2010). The science of eliminating health disparities: Summary and analysis of the NIH summit recommendations. *American Journal of Public Health, 100*(S1), S12---S18.

Darwin, C. (1965). *The expression of the emotions in man and animals*. Chicago, IL: University of Chicago Press. (Original work published 1872).

Davison, M. (n.d.). *A social life improves health*. Retrieved from http://www.askmen.com/money/body_and_mind_60/69b_better_living.html

Diener, E. (2000). Subjective well-being: The science of happiness and a proposal for a national index. *American Psychologist, 55*, 34–43. doi:10.1037/0003-066X.55.1.34

Diener, E., Emmons, R. A., Larsen, R. J., & Griffen, S. (1985). The satisfaction with life scale. *Journal of Personality Assessment, 49*, 71–75. doi:10.1207/s15327752jpa4901_13

Druett, J. (2007). *Island of the lost: Shipwrecked at the edge of the world*. New York: Algonquin Books.

Duck, S. (Ed.). (1988). *Handbook of personal relationships: Theory, research, and interventions*. New York: Wiley.

English, T., & John, O. P. (2011). *Social effects of emotion regulation are mediated by authenticity, not emotion expression, in East Asians and Westerners and in young and old*. Manuscript submitted for publication.

Festinger, L. (1954). A theory of social comparison processes. *Human Relations, 7*, 117–140. doi:10.1177/001872675400700202

Festinger, L., Schachter, S., & Back, K. (1950). *Social pressures in informal groups: A study of human factors in housing*. New York: Harper.

Filipp, S.-H. (1990). Ein allgemeines Modell für die Analyse kritischer Lebensereignisse [A general model for the analysis of critical life events]. In S.-H. Filipp (Ed.), *Kritische Lebensereignisse* (pp. 3–52). München, Germany: Psychologie Verlags Union.

Fischer, C. S. (1982). *To dwell among friends: Personal networks in town and city*. Chicago, IL: University of Chicago Press.

Fischer, C. S. (2009). The 2004 GSS finding of shrunken social networks: An artifact? *American Sociological Review, 74*, 657–669. doi:10.1177/000312240907400408

Folkman, S., & Moskowitz, J. T. (2000). Positive affect and the other side of coping. *American Psychologist, 55*, 647–654. doi:10.1037/0003066X.55.6.647

Forabettermemory.com. (2012). *Practical tips for increasing social interaction*. Retrieved from http://4abettermemory.com/memory/?p=224

Frank, M. G., Ekman, P., & Friesen, W. V. (1993). Behavioral markers and recognizability of the smile of enjoyment. *Journal of Personality and Social Psychology, 64*, 83–93. doi:10.1037/0022-3514.64.1.83

Fredrickson, B. L. (1998). What good are positive emotions? *Review of General Psychology, 2*, 300–319. doi:10.1037/1089-2680.2.3.300

Fredrickson, B. L. (2001). The role of positive emotions in positive psychology: The broaden and build theory of positive emotions. *American Psychologist, 56*, 218–226.

Fredrickson, B. L., Cohn, M. A., Coffey, K. A., Pek, J., & Finkel, S. M. (2008). Open hearts build lives: Positive emotions, induced through loving-kindness meditation, build consequential personal resources. *Journal of Personality and Social Psychology, 95*, 1045–1062. doi: 10.1037/a0013262

Frijda, N. H., & Mesquita, B. (1994). The social roles and functions of emotions. In K. Shinobu & H. R. Markus (Eds.), *Emotion and culture: Empirical studies of mutual influence* (pp. 51–87). Washington, DC: American Psychological Association.

Gold, E. (2006). *Benefits of social interaction*. Retrieved from http://www.valueoptions.com/april06_newsletter/benefits_of_social_interactions.htm

Gollust, S. E., Lantz, P. M., & Ubel, P. A. (2009). The polarizing effect of news media messages about the social determinants of health. *American Journal of Public Health, 99*, 2160–2167.

Granovetter, M. S. (1973). The strength of weak ties. *American Journal of Sociology, 78*, 1360–1380. doi:10.1086/225469

Gray, P. (2010). *Humans are social animals*. Retrieved from http://www.aipmm.com/anthropology/2010/05/humans-are-social-animals-1.php#trackbacks

Hammer, M. (1983). "Core" and "extended" social networks in relation to health and illness. *Social Science & Medicine, 17*, 405–411. doi:10.1016/0277-9536(83)90344-1

Harker, L., & Keltner, D. (2001). Expressions of positive emotion in women's college yearbook pictures and their relationship to personality and life outcomes across adulthood. *Journal of Personality and Social Psychology, 80*, 112–124. doi:10.1037/0022-3514.80.1.112

Hartup, W. W. (1992). *Having friends, making friends, and keeping friends: Relationships as educational contexts*. Retrieved from ERIC. (ED345854)

Hartup, W. W., & Stevens, N. (1997). Friendships and adaptation in the life course. *Psychological Bulletin, 121*, 355–370. doi:10.1037/0033-2909.121.3.355

Heider, F. (1958). *The psychology of interpersonal relations*. New York: Wiley. doi:10.1037/10628-000

Hill, R. A., & Dunbar, R. I. M. (2003). Social network size in humans. *Human Nature, 14*, 53–72. doi:10.1007/s12110-003-1016-y

Hinde, R. A. (1979). *Towards understanding relationships*. London, England: Academic Press.

Chapter 11 – Social Connection

Hofer, M., & Pikowski, B. (2002). Familien mit Jugendlichen [Families with adolescents]. In M. Hofer, E. Wild, & P. Noack (Eds.), *Lehrbuch Familienbeziehungen: Eltern und Kinder in der Entwicklung* (pp. 241–264). Göttingen, Germany: Hogrefe.

Holmes, T. H., & Rahe, R. H. (1967). The social readjustment rating scale. *Journal of Psychosomatic Research, 11*, 213–218. doi:10.1016/0022-3999(67)90010-4

House, J. S., Landis, K. R., & Umberson, D. (1988). Social relationships and health. *Science, 241*, 540–545. doi:10.1126/science.3399889

Hughes, R., Jr. (1988). Divorce and social support: A review. *Journal of Divorce, 11*, 123–145.

Hurlbert, J. S., & Acock, A. C. (1990). The effects of marital status on the form and composition of social networks. *Social Science Quarterly, 71*, 163–174.

Isen, A. M. (2000). Positive affect and decision making. In M. Lewis & J. Haviland-Jones (Eds.), *Handbook of emotions* (2nd ed., pp. 417–435). New York: Guilford Press.

Jacobs, G., & Cleveland, H. (1999). *Social development theory*. Retrieved from http://www.icpd.org/development_theory/SocialDevTheory.htm

John, O. P., & Gross, J. J. (2004). Healthy and unhealthy emotion regulation: Personality processes, individual differences, and life span development. *Journal of Personality, 72*, 1301–1333. doi:10.1111/j.1467-6494.2004.00298.x

Johnson, M. A. (1989). Variables associated with friendship in an adult population. *Journal of Social Psychology, 129*, 379–390. doi:10.1080/ 00224545.1989.9712054

Kahn, R. L., & Antonucci, T. C. (1980). Convoys over the life course: Attachment, roles and social support. In P. B. Baltes & O. G. Brim Jr. (Eds.), *Life-span development and behavior* (Vol. 3, pp. 253–286). New York: Academic Press.

Kahneman, D. (1999). Objective happiness. In D. Kahneman, E. Diener, & N. Schwarz (Eds.), *Well-being: The foundations of hedonic psychology* (pp. 3–25). New York: Russell Sage Foundation.

Keltner, D., & Haidt, J. (1999). Social functions of emotions at four levels of analysis. *Cognition & Emotion, 13*, 505–521. doi:10.1080/ 026999399379168

Keltner, D., & Kring, A. M. (1998). Emotion, social function, and psychopathology. *Review of General Psychology, 2*, 320–342. doi:10.1037/1089-2680.2.3.320

Keyes, C. L. M., & Ryff, C. D. (1998). Generativity in adult lives: Social structural contours and quality of life consequences. In D. McAdams & E. de St. Aubin (Eds.), *Generativity and adult development: Perspectives on caring for and contributing to the next generation* (pp. 227-263). Washington, DC: American Psychological Association.

Keyes, C. L. M., & Ryff, C. D. (1998). Generativity in adult lives: Social structural contours and quality of life consequences. In D. McAdams & E. de St. Aubin (Eds.), *Generativity and adult development: Perspectives on caring for and contributing to the next generation* (pp. 227-263). Washington, DC: American Psychological Association.

Keys, C. L. M., & Shapiro, A. D. (2004). Social well-being in the United States. In O. G. Brim, C. D. Ryff, & R. C. Kessler (Eds.), *How Healthy are we? A national study of well-being at midlife* (Chapter 12). London: University of Chicago Press.

Killworth, P. D., Johnsen, E. C., Bernard, H. R., Shelley, G. A., & McCarty, C. (1990). Estimating the size of personal networks. *Social Networks, 12*, 289–312. doi:10.1016/0378-8733(90)90012-X

King, L. (2000). Why happiness is good for you: A commentary on Fredrickson. *Prevention & Treatment, 3*, Article 4. doi:10.1037/1522-3736.3.1.34c

King, L. A., Hicks, J. A., Krull, J. L., & Del Gaiso, A. K. (2006). Positive affect and the experience of meaning in life. *Journal of Personality and Social Psychology, 90*, 179–196. doi:10.1037/0022-3514.90.1.179

Kogovšek, T., & Ferligoj, A. (2005). Effects on reliability and validity of egocentered network measurements. *Social Networks, 27*, 205–229. doi:10.1016/j.socnet.2005.01.001

Koh, H. K., Oppenheimer, S. C., Massin-Short, S. B., Emmons, K. M., Geller, A. C., Viswanath, K. (2010). Translating research evidence into practice to reduce health disparities: A social determinants approach. *American Journal of Public Health, 100*(S1), S72–S80.

Chapter 11 – Social Connection

Kreppner, K. (1993). Eltern-Kind Beziehungen: Kindes und Jugendalter [Parent– child relationships: Childhood and adolescence]. In A. E. Au- hagen & M. von Salisch (Ed.), *Zwischenmenschliche Beziehungen* (pp. 81–104). Göttingen, Germany: Hogrefe.

Lang, F. R. (2004). Social motivation across the life span. In F. R. Lang & K. L. Fingerman (Eds.), *Growing together: Personal relationships across the lifespan* (pp. 341–367). Cambridge, England: Cambridge University Press.

Larson, J. S. (1993). The measurement of social well-being. *Social Indicators Research, 28*, 285-296.

Larson, J. S. (1996). The World Health Organization's definition of health: Social versus spiritual health. *Social Indicators Research, 38*, 181-192.

Lee, R. M., & Robbins, S. B. (1995). Measuring belongingness: The social connectedness and the social assurance scales. *Journal of Counseling Psychology, 42*, 232–241. doi:10.1037/0022-0167.42.2.232

Lee, R. M., & Robbins, S. B. (1998). The relationship between social connectedness and anxiety, self-esteem, and social identity. *Journal of Counseling Psychology, 45*, 338–345. doi:10.1037/0022-0167.45.3.338

Lehman, D. R., Wortman, C. B., & Williams, A. F. (1987). Long-term effects of losing a spouse or child in a motor vehicle crash. *Journal of Personality and Social Psychology, 52*, 218–231. doi:10.1037/0022-3514.52.1.218

Lyubomirsky, S., King, L. A., & Diener, E. (2005). The benefits of frequent positive affect: Does happiness lead to success? *Psychological Bulletin, 131*, 803–855. doi:10.1037/0033-2909.131.6.803

Masten, A., & Wright, M. O. (2009). Resilience over the lifespan: Developmental perspectives on resistance, recovery and transformation. In J. W. Reich, A. J. Zautra, & J. S. Hall (Eds.), *Handbook of adult resilience* (pp. 213–237). New York: Guilford Press.

Mauss, I. B., Levenson, R. W., McCarter, L., Wilhelm, F. H., & Gross, J. J. (2005). The tie that binds? Coherence among emotion experience, behavior, and physiology. *Emotion, 5*, 175–190. doi:10.1037/1528-3542.5.2.175

Mauss, I. B., Shallcross, A. J., Troy, A. S., John, O. P., Ferrer, E., Wilhelm, F. H., & Gross, J. J. (2011). Don't Hide Your happiness! Positive emotion dissociation, social connectedness, and psychological functioning. *Journal of Personality and Social Psychology, 100*, 738–748. (Several other references included in this article)

McPherson, M., Smith-Lovin, L., & Brashears, M. E. (2006). Social isolation in America: Changes in core discussion networks over two decades. *American Sociological Review, 71*, 353–375. doi:10.1177/000312240607100301

McPherson, M., Smith-Lovin, L., & Brashears, M. E. (2009). Models and marginals: Using survey evidence to study social networks. *American Sociological Review, 74*, 670–681. doi:10.1177/000312240907400409

McPherson, M., Smith-Lovin, L., & Cook, J. M. (2001). Birds of a feather: Homophily in social networks. *Annual Review of Sociology, 27*, 415–444. doi:10.1146/annurev.soc.27.1.415

Ministry of Social Development. (2010). *Social connectedness: The social report*. Retrieved from http://www.socialreport.msd.govt.nz/documents/social-connectedness-social-report-2010.pdf

Myers, C. B. (2011). *Why the human is a social animal* [Report from the 99% Conference]. Retrieved from http://thenextweb.com/media/2011/05/05/why-the-human-is-a-social-animal-report-from-the-99-conference/

Myers, D. G., & Diener, E. (1995). Who is happy? *Psychological Science, 6*, 10–19. doi:10.1111/j.1467-9280.1995.tb00298.x

Neurological Foundation of New Zealand. (n.d.). *Brain health: Mental workout*. Retrieved from http://www.neurological.org.nz/brain-health/mental-workout The material in "Brain Health – Mental Workout" originally came from the Dana Alliance for Brain Initiatives. www.dana.org/stayingsharp.

Neyer, F. J., & Asendorpf, J. B. (2001). Personality–relationship transaction in young adulthood. *Journal of Personality and Social Psychology, 81*, 1190–1204. doi:10.1037/0022-3514.81.6.1190

Neyer, F. J., & Lang, F. R. (2003). Blood is thicker than water: Kinship orientation across adulthood. *Journal of Personality and Social Psychology, 84*, 310–321. doi:10.1037/0022-3514.84.2.310

Neyer, F. J., Wrzus, C., Wagner, J., & Lang, F. R. (2011). Principles of relationship differentiation. *European Psychologist, 16*, 267–277. doi:10.1027/1016-9040/a000055

Chapter 11 – Social Connection

Niederdeppe, J., Bu, Q. L., Borah, P., Kindig, D. A., Robert, S. A. (2008). Message design strategies to raise public awareness of social determinants of health and population health disparities. *Milbank Quarterly, 86*, 481–513.

Niederdeppe, J., Robert, S. A., & Kindig, D. A. (In press.). Societal responsibility for obesity: Qualitative research about attributions, narratives, and support for policy. *Preventing Chronic Disease.*

Pinquart, M., & Sörensen, S. (2000). Influences of socioeconomic status, social network, and competence on subjective well-being in later life: A meta-analysis. *Psychology and Aging, 15*, 187–224. doi:10.1037/0882-7974.15.2.187

Putnam, R. D., Felstein, L. M., & Cohen, D. J. (2003). *Better together: Restoring the American community.* New York: Simon & Schuster.

Rands, M., & Milardo, R. M. (1988). Changes in social networks following marital separation and divorce. In R. M. Milardo (Ed.), *Families and social networks* (pp. 127–146). Thousand Oaks, CA: Sage.

Reis, H. T., & Patrick, B. P. (1996). Attachment and intimacy: Component processes. In E. T. Higgins & A. W. Kruglanski (Eds.), *Social psychology: Handbook of basic principles* (pp. 523–563). New York: Guilford Press.

Roberts, S. A., & Booske, B. C. (2011). U.S. opinions on health determinants and social policy as health policy. *American Journal on Public Health, 101*, 1655–1663.

Rosenthal, R. (1991). *Meta-analytic procedures for social research.* Thousand Oaks, CA:Sage.

Ryff, C. D., & Singer, B. (2008). Know thyself and become what you are: A eudaimonic approach to psychological well-being. *Journal of Happiness Studies, 9*, 13–39.

Ryff, C. D., Love, G. D., Muller, D., Urry, H., Friedman, E. M., Davidson, R., & Singer, B. (2006). Psychological well-being and ill-being: Do they have distinct or mirrored biological correlates? *Psychotherapy and Psychosomatics, 75*, 85–95. doi:10.1159/000090892

Sattikar, A. A., & Kulkarni, R. V. (2001), A review of security and privacy issues in social networking, International *Journal of Computer Science and Information Technology, 2*, 2784–2787. Retrieved from http://ijcsit.com/docs/Volume%202/vol2issue6/ijcsit2011020657.pdf

Seeman, T. E. (1996). Social ties and health, *Annals of Eidemiology, 6*, 442–451.

Seeman, T. E. et al (1993). Intercommunity variations in the association between social ties and mortality in the elderly: A comparative analysis of three communities. *Annals of Epidemiology, 3*, 325–335.

Seligman, M. E. P., Steen, T. A., Park, N., & Peterson, C. (2005). Positive psychology progress: Empirical validation of interventions. *American Psychologist, 60*, 410–421. doi:10.1037/0003-066X.60.5.410

Shallcross, A. J., Troy, A. S., Boland, M., & Mauss, I. B. (2010). Let it be: Accepting negative emotional experiences predicts decreased negative affect and depressive symptoms. *Behaviour Research and Therapy, 48*, 921–929. doi:10.1016/j.brat.2010.05.025

Sherif, M. (1966). *In common predicament: Social psychology of inter-group conflict and cooperation.* Boston, MA: Houghton Mifflin.

Shiota, M. N., Campos, B., Keltner, D., & Hertenstein, M. J. (2004). Positive emotion and the regulation of interpersonal relationships. In P. Philippot & R. S. Feldman (Eds.), *The regulation of emotion* (pp. 127–155). Mahwah, NJ: Erlbaum.

Socially.com. (n.d.). *How to make friends and get a social life.* Retrieved from http://www.succeedsocially.com/sociallife

Sprecher, S., & Felmlee, D. (2000). Romantic partners' perceptions of social network attributes with the passage of time and relationship transitions. *Personal Relationships, 7*, 325–340. doi:10.1111/j.1475-6811.2000.tb00020.x

Sprecher, S., Felmlee, D., Schmeeckle, M., & Shu, X. (2006). No breakup occurs on an island: Social networks and relationship dissolution. In M. A. Fine & J. H. Harvey (Eds.), *Handbook of divorce and relationship dissolution* (pp. 457–478). Mahwah, NJ: Erlbaum.

Svenden, G. T., & Svendsen, G. L. H. (Eds.). (2009). *Handbook of social capitol, the Troika of sociology, political science and economics.* UK: Edward Elgar Publishing Limited.

Taflinger, R. (1996). *Taking ADvantage social basis of human behavior.* Retrieved from http://public.wsu.edu/~taflinge/socself.html

Chapter 11 – Social Connection

Tajfel, H., Billig, M. G., Bundy, R. P., & Flament, C. (1971). Social categorization and intergroup behaviour. *European Journal of Social Psychology, 1*, 149–178. doi:10.1002/ejsp.2420010202

U.S. Department of Health and Human Services. (1999). *Mental health: A report of the Surgeon General.* Rockville, MD: Author.

van der Poel, M. G. M. (1993). Delineating personal support networks. *Social Networks, 15*, 49–70. doi:10.1016/0378-8733(93)90021-C

Walton, G. M., Cohen, G. L., Cwir, D., & Spencer, S. J. (2012). Mere belonging: The power of social connections. *Journal of Personality and Social Psychology, 102*, 513–532.

Whatissocialnetworking.com. (2009). *What is social networking?* Retrieved from http://www.whatissocialnetworking.com/

Wisegeek.com. (n.d.). *What is a social butterfly?* Retrieved from http://www.wisegeek.com/what-is-a-social-butterfly.htm

World Health Organization (WHO). (1948). *WHO defines health.* Retrieved from http://www.who.int/about/definition/en/print.html

World Health Organization. (1948). World Health Organization constitution. In *Basic documents.* Geneva: Author.

World Health Organization. (1997). *Twenty steps for developing a healthy cities project* (3rd ed.). Copenhagen, Denmark: World Health Organization Regional Office for Europe.

Zautra, A. J., & Reich, J. W. (2011). Resilience: The meanings, methods, and measures of a fundamental characteristic of human adaptation. In S. Folkman (Ed.), *The Oxford handbook on stress, health, and coping* (pp. 173–185). New York: Oxford University Press.

Zautra, A. J., Hall, A. J., & Murray, K. E. (2008). Resilience: A new integrative approach to health and mental health research. *Health Psychology Review, 2*, 41–64. doi:10.1080/17437190802298568

Zettel, L. A., & Rook, K. S. (2004). Substitution and compensation in the social networks of older widowed women. *Psychology and Aging, 19*, 433–443. doi:10.1037/0882-7974.19.3.433

Chapter 12
Personal Initiatives, Challenges & Aspirations

Something Just for You!

Initiatives you start, challenges you get and overcome, aspirations you choose and pursue, it's all up to you!

Can we now focus just on you—purely, simply and totally focus on what makes you happy, satisfied and excited about life? Where can we fit you into the total scheme of things?

When you're not on task and you're free to just do something for yourself, something personal, that's the time to take the initiative to take on a personal challenge, do something that you've been inspired by or initiate that project that you've thought about for years. It might even be something you've put off and never got around to doing even thought you meant to. Sometimes you have to give yourself permission to do something personal, outlandish, maybe even crazy for yourself—something just for YOU.

> *Life can get so busy with work, school, family and other obligations and "must-do"*
> *things that we often neglect our own personal needs and desires.*

For the lack of a better word, let's just call this area "personal." If there is an area of your life that does not "fit" the other areas previously mentioned, then this is the one that is purely personal. For example, what home improvements would you personally consider making? How do you feel about a person at work, at church, or in the neighborhood that you think you should investigate to see if you need to act on those feelings or maybe even consider trying to change those feelings?

Other examples of personal initiatives, challenges and aspirations might include such questions as: What can I do to improve upon the esthetics of my surroundings that fit my personal taste? This aspect of your life can challenge your creative tastes. As you consider your taste in jewelry, articles of clothing, home or office furnishings, art objects or other such items, this feature comes into play. From time to time, people decide to change their hairstyle, eyeglass frames and even preferences in automobiles. As we grow older, our personal tastes change. Sometimes we are fortunate enough to move into a different tax bracket and can afford to make changes in our surroundings. If money were no object, what personal changes would you make in your surroundings, your personal appearance or choice in automobiles? You're not sure? But then again, given your current state of affairs, what changes would you want to make without anything else changing?

Hobbies

> *What hobby can you consider taking up in order to add variety to your lifestyle?*
> *Hobbies are designed to allow for an "escape" from life's daily chores.*

Hobbies are oftentimes avocations that people take up. Some people become so good at their hobby that the hobby becomes a source of income. Usually, however, hobbies are designed to provide personal satisfaction and is often a way for people to engage in activities that are interesting, fun, captivating or sometimes social in nature.

Generally speaking, hobbies give us something to do that is a distraction from our main source of activities. For example, collecting stamps, coins and teddy bears allows us an opportunity to see how many different stamps, coins or teddy bears we can collect before we become bored with it and until we can pick up another hobby.

Hobbies can oftentimes present us with a challenge or provide a way to get involved with something that can satisfy another need. For example, some people take up tennis or golf to get exercise and at the same time have fun or socialize with other people. Some hobbies can even turn into a means of investments such as collecting antique furniture or rare coins.

> *Hobbies can sooth the mind, calm the soul or become the distraction you need to take your mind off life's challenges.*

For example, some people choose gardening, sewing or reading. Hobbies can also serve to entertain, such as collecting and watching old movies or attending sports events. Playing games can become a hobby as can fixing things around the house, which can end up being very useful and productive.

Chapter 12 – Personal Initiatives, Challenges & Aspirations

Doing something to pass the time away can become a hobby such as playing different games, going to the movies or reading a good book. I think lately my wife has picked up a new hobby: surfing the Internet and checking out different things on Living on the Edge, a religious program that offer spiritual messages and Bible lessons. Whatever the reason, hobbies serve a purpose and can certainly embellish a person's life for the better.

One strategy for following through on learning the different functions on your various electronic gadgets is to pick a day each week to dedicate time to that specific task: learning how to more effectively and or efficiently use one of your electronic gadgets. The interesting and fortunate thing about that is there is usually nothing to keep you from doing just that. Now that you just read that, why don't you pick every Saturday for the next two months to spend a minimum of one hour on one of your electronic devices (computer, cell phone, camera or GPS, etc.)?

Why having a hobby is important

Here are eight reasons why having a hobby is important. Retrieved from: http://thinklink.in/why-is-it-important-to-have-a-hobby/

1. As a remedy for fatigue: A hobby is the easiest way to restore your balance whenever you are overworked or stressed. Since it is an activity of your choosing, it will always give you pleasure and help you unwind. Even if you indulge in your hobby for a short period of time, you still can feel the difference in your energy level and spirit.

2. As a chance to connect with yourself: Perhaps one of the best active ways to get in touch with yourself is to explore yourself through your hobby. It does not matter as much what your hobby is as it does to have a hobby of your own. It is the private time you have with yourself.

> *Interestingly, when you have a hobby, you will strive to create time for yourself and manage your schedule well to keep that appointment with yourself.*

3. As an alternative career option: Many people have made a flourishing career out of their hobby. What can be more rewarding and enjoyable than the fact that your career and work is also the source of your unwinding and relaxation! When you take up a hobby or pursue the one you have with a sense of purpose, you can think of adding value to yourself.

4. As a life-long pleasure: Most people think that the time to pursue their hobby is when they retire. They miss a very important aspect that by the time you retire, you would have lesser ability and agility required of a person to learn a hobby. However, those who have pursued a certain hobby at a younger age would continue to do so well into their old age. By then it has become their second nature.

5. As an independent and intrinsic source of pleasure: Instead of depending upon external sources of pleasure and entertainment like movies and friends, a hobby is something you do with an urge from within. You cannot always look to others for relaxing or spending your free time. Having something to do of your own keeps you in control of yourself and gives you a sense of freedom regarding the way you wish to spend your precious time.

6. As a means to discover and re-discover your talents: Your job can recognize and utilize your competence to some extent, but it takes more than that to bring out what talents lie hidden with an individual. While you pursue a hobby, you may discover that you have a talent for something unusual as well which you did not know about so far!

7. As a chance to meet people of similar taste: When you procure material, equipment, etc. required for your hobby, you are likely to find people who pursue your hobby. You may be further surprised to know how serious some people are about their hobbies and, therefore, would have immense knowledge of their chosen pastime.

> *Instead of being forced to meet people from your work or those from whom you have gradually grown apart, it is a great way to meet people with whom you have something in common.*

8. As a chance to share: What you create or learn through your hobby gives you something to share with others. People who learn card-making and pottery can use them as gifts. Hobbies like music and theatre enable you to share the fine experience of the arts. People who like photography like to click pictures and share their photos. It gives you a reason to reach out and share with another person. Invest some time in cultivating a hobby. It is a gift you can give to yourself that shall be an enriching and rewarding experience for the rest of your life.

Personal Projects

A personal project is YOUR project to do what you want to do, potentially to show the skills you have developed over the years and through approaches to learning, and to apply them to an area or topic on which you decide. Ultimately, you will be proving to yourself that you can get something done that you want to do.

Coming up with a project is one of the single best ways to develop a plan to get something done that you have wanted to get done for a long time. When you decide to do a project, you make a commitment; set goals; set quotas; set timelines; create a useful structure for your idea, collect accompanying materials, data or relevant information, and polish the strategy for your efforts so the idea will be well thought out.

Make a commitment. Making a commitment is perhaps the single best thing you can do to advance your idea. You've already made a commitment to consider doing this. Now make a commitment to present your idea in the very best light. You deserve it.

Chapter 12 – Personal Initiatives, Challenges & Aspirations

Once you make a commitment, the chances for success will grow exponentially. The type of project you pick will determine your level of commitment.

Above all, seek feedback. Seek feedback from people with diverse perspectives whose opinions you value and trust. One thing you can always use, that you can never provide for yourself, is an outside perspective. Remember, feedback is food for thought, not gospel. Set a timeline. A timeline can be used to combat procrastination and/or distraction and encourage you to make progress on your idea. Set realistic timelines. Unrealistic timelines simply produce frustration. Focusing your efforts into a project will help you produce a useful product or a meaningful result. A project gives your work a definite, presentable structure. A finished project makes work more useful and accessible. Once your project is done, your work will have a significantly greater likelihood of seeing the light of day. Who knows? Public acclaim may follow. Come what may, your satisfaction is guaranteed. You can work on multiple projects at a time. Be careful that you don't get scattered. Starting projects is easy. Finishing them is hard.

Note: Some ideas for this introduction were retrieved from the following website: http://www.johnpaulcaponigro.com/blog/7410/define-a-personal-project/

Following is an example of an idea I decided to come up with and follow through on:
Question: What do I want to do?
Answer: Let's say I want to learn how to use my new iphone to the max

Question: Why do I want to do it?
Answer: To be able to take full advantage of this expensive piece of hardware

Question: How do I get started?
Answer: Gather all the information I can about the iphone:
start with the instructions that came with the phone
look for tutorials I can find
take classes offered at the Apple store
set a schedule for one month to learn what I can

Question: What resources do I have at my disposal to get the job done?
Answer: I am fairly good at following directions.
I know several people who have the iphone who can help

Question: Do I know someone who has done such a thing before? Is there someone who can help?
Answer: I know several people who can at least answer questions that I might have if I run into problems understanding parts of the instructions

Chapter 12 – Personal Initiatives, Challenges & Aspirations

Question: What obstacles are there that could keep me from doing it or slow me down?

Answer:

1. *Finding the time to do this*
2. *Being distracted or losing interest after a short time*
3. *I'm not real good with mechanical things*
4. *Finding the time to not only learn but to practice so I don't forget*
5. *Losing interest after a short period*

Question: Can I overcome the obstacles?

Answer:

1. *If I commit myself to doing it and ask my wife to help me stay on schedule, I think I can overcome this obstacle.*
2. *If I tell my wife or someone else that I will give them money if I quit, then I probably won't quit.*
3. *I can usually "hang in there" with things that are frustrating if I am really committed.*
4. *Schedule the time on my calendar and promise myself to strictly follow my calendar*
5. *If I am committed, I don't think I will lose interest and even if I do, my commitment will override my lack of interest.*

Question: Do I want to move forward on this or not?

Answer: Yes, I do

Question: When do I get started?

Answer: The first of next month, I will get started.

Following is a list of project ideas that I retrieved after Googling "personal projects." (https://www.google.com/?gws_rd=ssl#q=personal+project+ideas). The ideas came from a pdf file from the Gaston County Schools in South Carolina, which sent the pdf but had no website identification. I also mixed in a few of my own ideas:

- Writing a book
- Writing a poem
- Writing a song
- Developing a marketing campaign to address a teen issue, like teen pregnancy
- Training a pet
- Building something - like a guitar, furniture, etc.
- Developing a plan for a solar-powered car
- Learning how to play an instrument
- Learning to play a sport
- Developing a new strategy for chess, poker or another game
- Starting a business
- Developing a recipe

- Designing and making jewelry
- Producing and directing a music video
- Producing and directing an exercise video
- Demonstrating how to do something
- Doing a research/lab report for an original idea
- Drawing a mural
- Throwing pottery
- Going on an archeological dig
- Researching your genealogy
- Debating
- Building a proposal/plan
- Forming a club
- Raising money for charity
- Inventing something
- Developing a speech
- Conducting an experiment
- Performing (dance, music, comedy)
- Providing a photo essay
- Building a model
- Developing your own video game
- Creating an e-commerce website
- Creating a blog
- Creating software programs
- Developing a business plan
- Designing clothes
- Remodeling using eco-friendly material
- Launching a Recycling Program
- Learning a foreign language

Initiatives

Personal initiatives tend to come out of need. Having the need to do something you know needs to be done and finally, you have decided to do something about it.

For whatever reason, you are ready now to act and follow through on this oftentimes bold and new project. Several years ago, a friend told me about his taking part in a statewide private foundation's initiative to address violence in California schools. The foundation allocated millions of dollars to the initiative and put a plan together to tackle the problem. Similarly, a personal initiative can be started. Instead of millions of dollars being allocated, a commitment to follow through and the designation of focused time can get you started.

Soliciting the support of family, friends and interested colleagues is usually recommended. Identifying others who have taken on similar projects or even engaging others who can be helpful along the way is also recommended. The old adage that two heads are better than one can certainly come into play on personal initiatives.

A few personal initiatives that I decided to take on at different times have included my unceasing desire to organize and categorize the books in my library, something I had thought about doing for years.

The thing about personal initiatives that you are serious about carrying out is they grate on your mind a lot. And, sometimes they seem to be overbearing and very complicated. However, as you continue to persist, seek help if necessary and do your part, you are very likely to get a very positive and appropriate outcome, in due time.

As long as you are working through the issues, pinpointing what needs to be done all along the way, you will realize you are making progress. For each initiative you might designate very specific time each week to deal with each issue. You might also find yourself, from time to time, doing something that will be helpful toward addressing this initiative while you are doing something else completely unrelated. It is during those times that have proven to be very helpful and encouraging.

Personal Challenges
Life has a way of bringing on personal challenges that cannot be ignored. The person who handles personal challenges well and appropriately is likely to weather future challenges without a lot of fanfare.

> *Major setbacks can sometimes be the best thing that could have happened to you*

—a major health problem, separation from a spouse or job, foreclosure on your home or some other major financial problem like bankruptcy—whatever the situation, going back to business as usual is probably not an option. Challenges oftentimes test our ability to make necessary adjustments to life's situations.

> *We find ourselves stretching the boundaries of our normal way of thinking and being forced to think differently.*

Personal challenges can be positive or they can be seen as negative. Sometimes the response to a personal challenge can be demanding and sometimes it can be stimulating; either way, it usually requires more than an ordinary response. The key thing to keep in mind is that personal challenges usually require some kind of action or deliberate non-action. Doing nothing is sometimes the right course of action as long as it is done deliberately. Oftentimes, after the challenge is over, we are grateful for having gone through a challenge than if we never experienced the challenge in the first place. The other potential positive side of a challenge is that it helps us appreciate life a little bit more during those non-challenging times. You learn a lot about yourself as well.

> *In most cases, challenges can make us just a little bit more humble and appreciative of what we have, especially during the good times after the challenging times.*

Above all else, however, is to keep in mind that sometimes, things can get out of hand and beyond your own capabilities of resolution. After you have done all you can, by all means, seek professional assistance if necessary. Depending upon the severity of the situation, seeking professional assistance in the very beginning might even be the best response.

If you are a Christian, seek the Holy Spirit.

Opportunities

Sometimes opportunities come about because you are at the right place at the right time.

> *Opportunities are also born from previous planning whereby the thing planned for has finally come to pass. Still other opportunities come about as a result of your perseverance.*

I cannot recall who said it, but someone mentioned that out of a crisis or failed situation comes opportunity. Sometimes the crisis or failed situation causes you to re-think the situation or "forces" you to consider things you might not have otherwise thought. You are more likely to at least try to get more creative in your thinking than if the crisis or failure had not happened. Without the crisis, things would likely have gone on as usual. Crises are sometimes (oftentimes) opportunities to grow and become stronger. Research has shown that one way to build self-esteem and self-confidence is to see yourself solving your own problems, especially those problems and challenges that at first seem insurmountable.

I remember a few years ago the opportunity came for me to spend much more time on writing this book that I had been trying to write for years. That opportunity came as a result of the State of California giving state workers a three-day furlough each month. After doing the math, I realized that I would be bringing home more money if I retired than if I continued to work and receive my regular furlough check. I loved my job and enjoyed the people at work, but I was not willing to continue losing money so I left one great job and went back to another by returning to teaching at the university.

Aspirations

Ralph Waldo Emerson once wrote that without ambition (or aspiration) one starts nothing. Without work one finishes nothing. The prize will not be sent to you. You have to win it (First Quotes.com). If you aspire for nothing, nothing is likely what you will get. Most people will agree that you get out of it what you put into it—nothing in, nothing out. Our aspirations are the things we look forward to achieving in the future. To have an earnest desire or ambition as for something high and good is how the dictionary defines aspiration—to rise or reach upward.

Most people want to improve their lot. Some people even have the will to succeed at something they want in life. One way to look at aspirations is to treat them as life goals. Albert Einstein once said that if you want to live a happy life, tie it to a goal, not to people or things (Marshall, 2008). There are short-term goals and there are long-term goals. Those goals that are within reach in the next one to three years or sooner would be considered short-term. Long-term goals are more likely to take five, maybe even 10 years or more down the road to achieve. Oftentimes, the short-term goals are mini steps toward the long-term goals, but not necessarily. Whether long-term or short-term, however, the key is to get started, as soon as possible.

Robert Marzano wrote an article about self-efficacy that focused on long- and short-term aspirations. In it, he indicated that many frameworks that outline the skills necessary for success in the 21st century emphasize the importance of self-efficacy (Marzano & Heflebower, 2012).

And, even though the article talks about how teachers can help their students, the article is relevant for adults as well. Self-efficacy is the belief that one has control over one's own life; it's accompanied by a set of skills that include the ability to:

> - *Identify long- and short-term aspirations that are personally meaningful and that contribute to one's sense of wellbeing.*

- Set concrete long- and short-term goals relative to one's aspirations.
- Monitor progress toward long- and short-term goals and revise actions or goals as needed.
- Identify, monitor, and change personal beliefs and habits that are impediments to successfully completing one's goals.

Intuitively, these seem like powerful skills to teach, and many classroom teachers try to foster them at every turn. However, they're difficult to teach in the artificial, academic context that's so often embedded in traditional subject areas.

Rather, students can more easily learn these skills in the context of strong personal aspirations. I've found that teachers can use a certain type of classroom project—what I refer to as a personal project—to enhance self-efficacy skills (Marzano, Pickering, & Heflebower, 2011).

Chapter 12 – Personal Initiatives, Challenges & Aspirations

Self-Efficacy—In Seven Phases. Personal projects entail seven phases, each of which begins with a question that fosters self-efficacy.

Phase 1: What do I want to accomplish?

In phase one, students identify personal aspirations of interest. Typically, they don't share these with other students; rather, they record them in a journal that's accessible to the teacher only to help students articulate their aspirations. A teacher might ask, "What would you do if you knew you wouldn't fail?" One female high school student might respond, "I want to go to the U.S. Air Force Academy and eventually fly military jets." A powerful addition to student projects is for the teacher to identify an aspiration and follow the same phases as the students.

Phase 2: Who else has accomplished the same goal, and who will support me?

During the second phase, students look for role models and mentors. The student who wants to fly jets might find her role model in Nicole Malachowski, who not only graduated from the U.S. Air Force Academy and flew F-15s in combat over Kosovo, but also was the first female to be selected to the Air Force's elite flying team, the Thunderbird. The student might approach her own parents to be her mentors, just as Nicole Malachowski's parents were mentors for their daughter.

Phase 3: What skills and resources will I need to accomplish my goal?

> *Whereas Phase 1 encourages students to "dream big" without any limitations, Phase 3 asks them to confront the realities of their aspirations.*

During this phase, the young female student might find she has to maintain a high grade point average, procure a letter of recommendation from a U.S. senator or representative, and be in superb physical condition to be accepted into the Air Force Academy.

Phase 4: What will I have to change about myself to achieve my goal?

This phase directly addresses the fourth self-efficacy skill: the ability to identify personal beliefs and habits that get in the way of accomplishing one's goals. It's probably the most confrontational of all the phases. Here, the student might realize she gets discouraged easily when positive feedback begins to wane. As a result, she might resolve to work against this tendency.

Phase 5: What is my plan for achieving my goal, and how hard will it be?

This phase directly addresses the second self-efficacy skill: the ability to set concrete long- and short-term goals. Students develop written plans that detail the steps they will take to accomplish their goals. With guidance from the teacher, the student who wants to fly jets might develop a detailed two-year plan that, when executed, would most likely result in a higher grade point average and enhanced physical conditioning.

Phase 6: What small steps can I take right now?

This phase partially addresses the third self-efficacy skill: the ability to monitor one's progress. Teachers might ask students to identify something they can accomplish within the next month or two that would be a small step toward their ultimate goal. Because Air Force cadets must regularly run long distances, the student might set the goal of being able to run the mile in less than eight minutes by the end of two months. An effective addition to this phase is for the teacher to ask students to write their small step on a piece of paper and put it in a self-addressed envelope. The teacher then mails these envelopes to students after two months.

Phase 7: How have I been doing, and what have I learned about myself?

In the last phase, students evaluate their overall progress and draw conclusions regarding what they have learned about themselves. The student who wants to fly jets might conclude that she's right on schedule, proud of herself because she's willing to dream big, and ready to celebrate her current progress. This phase is also a time when students can make adjustments in their efforts or time lines. Our student might find that she really isn't as committed to flying as she thought she was but that she's very committed to a career in the military. Such changes in direction are a natural consequence of exercising self-efficacy and are also to be celebrated.

Personal Projects

One nice feature about personal projects is that the teacher doesn't have to attend to each phase every day. Rather, he or she might devote one class period to the first phase and then wait a few days to address the second. After that, the teacher could space each of the remaining phases one or two weeks apart.

Personal projects are most easily embedded in skill-based courses, such as those that teach study skills. Teachers might also embed them in classes that focus on understanding human psychology or in traditional subject-matter classes, in which short periods are set aside to address the seven phases.

Short-term goals

Short-term goals are goals that are on your to-do list for the day or something you want to do in the next few years.

> *Goals ranging from a day to a week should go on your to-do list. Month-long goals might be mapped out as weekly goals. Goals you want to obtain in a year might be broken down into monthly goals. One to five year goals might be taken one year at a time.*

Chapter 12 – Personal Initiatives, Challenges & Aspirations

A university colleague once told me that looking down the road two to three years from now, he can see one of his immediate aspirations or short-term goals is to get a book written that he has been working on for two years and at the same time find part-time consulting work that is compatible with his completing the book. His current financial situation is such that either he or his wife will need to find additional work six to eight months from now or they will need to make some financial adjustments. He explained that his family can maintain their current level of lifestyle with as little as $1,500 to $2,000 a month more income. However, since they are wanting to purchase another home within the next two to three years, they will need to increase their annual income by a lot more for the next three to five years. After that, they can probably go back to their current working situation and not have to do additional work to maintain their current level of lifestyle.

Long-term goals

> *Long-term goals are goals that would take five to ten years, or even longer to obtain.*

A colleague told me that in the next eight to ten years, he and his wife both should be able to be retired and not have to work if they can maintain the goal of taking only $1,000 a month from their retirement investments. If, however, either of them chooses to work, then, of course that is always an option. In that timeframe, their goal is to have their home either completely paid off or very close to being paid off. They should have very little or no other outstanding debt and there should be enough income available for them to live comfortably, taking vacations and traveling almost as frequently as they wish as long as the trips are relatively inexpensive.

A long-term goal that another friend has for both him and his wife is to find ways they can effectively and efficiently help their family members improve their lifestyle and, ultimately, quality of life. The wife would work on her family (primarily) in California and he would work on his family (primarily) in and around Gary, Indiana.

Another colleague with whom I am currently working, said that one of his long-term goals is that he wants to one day be independently wealthy. He wants to become an authority on the concept of "resiliency," and/or "turning problems into opportunities." He would like to write and do research on each of these topics and become an authority on each of these and possibly others that are related. He would like to set up a private (or non-profit) foundation that focuses on helping others enjoy a better life and be able to sustain it.

Chapter 12 – Personal Initiatives, Challenges & Aspirations

Getting Started

> *How does one get started on this personal journey of identifying initiatives, taking on challenges and pursuing lifetime aspirations?*

Well, one of the first things needing to be done is to see where you are now and where you want to be in the future.

A good place to start might be to ask yourself, "How content am I with certain aspects of my life or with life in general? What things that are going on in my life that I think I need to change? Am I relatively happy with the way things are going in my personal life? If I looked at my daily schedule, would I be happy with how I spend my time? Is life fun, boring, a little of both? How much stress do I have in my life? What about fun?" Are you in a rut routine and need to consider making changes? Your routine is your life. Gradually change the routine and start a new one so the new one becomes routine.

Looking at where you are and where you want to be might be a good place to start. Since this chapter is titled personal initiatives and challenges and aspirations, you might want to ask yourself, "What are my personal initiatives, challenges and aspirations? What do I do for fun? Do I have any hobbies or fun things in my life that make my life interesting and worthwhile? What about the challenges and/or opportunities? Do I have any of those?" Whether you want to admit it or not, you do. We all do. A better question to ask might be, "How well am I handling them?" Most people have aspirations, but many of us don't have a viable plan to actually act on them. And, there are very few people who have identified real initiatives tied to their personal life goals. These and other questions are certainly a good place to start in assessing your current personal state of affairs.

Serendipity

Cuna, Clegg, and Mendonca (2010) wrote an article on serendipity and organizing that I thought connected very well with personal initiatives, challenges and aspirations.

> *Sometimes we get ideas from "out of the blue."*

Have you ever considered following up on some of those seemingly crazy ideas that make little sense but still pique your interest? Maybe you were working on a project and by accident you discovered an unexpected connection to a new idea, completely separate and different from your original project. Personal initiatives, challenges and aspirations can sometimes come from where we least expect them. And, they might be worthy of our serious pursuit. This might be an example of serendipity.

Denrell et al. (2003) defined serendipity as effort and luck joined by alertness and flexibility. Dew (2009, p. 735) defined it as a search leading to unintended discovery.

> ***Serendipity, defined as the accidental discovery of something that, post hoc, turns out to be valuable, is "the art of making an unsought finding" (Van Andel, 1994, p. 631).***

Merton and Barber (2004, p. 293) see serendipity working when one stumbles on an "unanticipated, anomalous and strategic datum that becomes an occasion for developing a new theory or for extending an existing theory." Unanticipated, because serendipitous discovery is a fortuitous by-product, an unexpected observation; anomalous, because serendipitous discovery is surprising as it appears inconsistent with previous theories or expected facts, and strategic when serendipitous discovery permits implications that bear upon generalized theory.

It is sometimes presented as an element of organizational learning. At its core, serendipity is a process of metaphorical association—seeing something in another thing. New ways of seeing may provide the necessary ingredients for creativity and exploratory learning.

In research and development, serendipity is often mentioned as a vital ingredient. In researching mergers and acquisitions, Graebner (2004, p. 752) described that there were often serendipitous value consequences from acquisitions, "such as windfalls that were not anticipated by the buyer prior to the deal. Examples include new strategic ideas, improved product development techniques, and unexpectedly useful technologies."

Columbus discovered America because he was looking for the Orient.

Chance plays an enormous role in many major scientific discoveries. Examples of serendipitous or chance findings in medical and technological research include the Scottish bacteriologist Alexander Fleming, who stumbled upon penicillin when his poor housekeeping allowed mold to start growing on a petri dish of bacteria and amateur inventor George de Mestral, who took a walk, noticed burrs adhering to his clothing, examined their structure under his microscope, and went on to create Velcro.

Chance, luck and happenstance may be as relevant in organizational life as in other domains, however far they may appear to be from the predictable matter of science. The idea that there may be logic in disorder (Warglien & Masuch, 1995) and mess (Abrahamson & Freedman, 2006) is not quite theoretical heresy but is largely excluded from the core of formal theory. That there is logic to disorder does not mean that organizations are irrational or incoherent but rather that there is an element of unpredictability and emergence in the fabric of organizations that needs to be considered and studied.

Serendipity travels in good social networks too. People are willing to open up to friends, and friends with knowledge may provide adequate if unexpected solutions: "meetings and social events provide the unplanned and unstructured opportunities for the accidental coming together of ideas that may lead to the serendipitous development of new intellectual capital" (Nahapiet & Ghoshal, 1998, p. 258).

Whether people and resources are mobilized to push a connection further inside the organization in a spirit of resolve or it is simply forgotten often bears no necessary relation to the quality of insight, innovation and creativity embedded in such a connection but more to political phenomena such as the "rule of anticipated reaction" (Friedrich, 1963). The rule applies where the instigator of an idea refrains from promoting it because they anticipate the reaction to it will be sufficiently negative that it is unlikely to garner much support.

> *"Dr. Spencer Silver, a 3M researcher discovered the Post-It Note adhesive accidentally, while trying to discover the opposite – super strong adhesives.*

The two processes of resolve and anticipated reaction are well-known in the context of invention but may equally apply to the process of discovery. As is the case of the Post-It. Although the adhesive wasn't his original target, Silver was convinced of its merits. He took it to others within 3M and asked how they thought it might be used. There was a definite lack of enthusiasm for his discovery" (Fry, 1987, p. 5).

The rest of the story is well-known. Given the championing of the idea by a bunch of researchers, and the ultimate support of a number of people in high places, including a divisional Vice-President, Post-It Notes finally emerged from the laboratory. It was the collective effort that made the discovery valuable through connecting it to several uses (some of which were not even recognized as a need). The collective revelation/creation of needs fitted the discovery, and thus made it serendipitous.

Motivation and Commitment

> *Commitment and motivation go hand and hand. If you are committed to acting on your own personal initiatives, challenges and aspirations, your motivation will likely come from your desire to keep your word.*

Making a commitment to this effort is saying that you will make the time to follow through on doing whatever is necessary to carry out your personal initiatives, challenges and aspirations. You are sufficiently inspired or "ready" to act. Having the mental state of mind to do something is also motivation. Because of your commitment, you are almost automatically ready for the next steps, which might be to start putting together a plan to make it happen.

REFERENCES
Chapter 12 – "Personal Initiatives, Challenges & Aspirations"

Abrahamson, E., & Freedman, D. H. (2006). *A perfect mess. The hidden benefits of disorder.* London: Weidenfeld & Nicolson.

Adler, P. S., Forbes, L. C., & Willmott, H. (2007). Critical management studies. *Academy of Management Annals, 1*, 119–179.

Cunha, M., Clegg, S. R. & Mendon, S. (2010). On serendipity and organizing. *European Management Journal, 28*, 319–330.

Denrell, J., Fang, C., & Winter, S. G. (2003). The economics of strategic opportunity. *Strategic Management Journal, 24*, 977–990.

Dew, N. (2009). Serendipity in entrepreneurship. *Organization Studies, 30*, 735–753.

First Quotes. (n.d.). *Ambition quotes.* Retrieved from http://www.finestquotes.com/select_quote-category-Ambition-page-0.htm

Friedrich, C. J. (1963). *Man and his government: An empirical theory of politics.* New York: McGraw-Hill.

Fry, A. (1987). The post-it note: An entrapreneurial success. *SAM-Advanced Management Journal, 52*, 4–9.

Garud, R., & Karnoe, P. (2003). Bricolage versus breakthrough: Distributed and embedded agency in technology entrepreneurship. *Research Policy, 32*, 277–300.

Graebner, M. (2004). Momentum and serendipity: How acquired leaders create value in the integration of technology firms. *Strategic Management Journal, 25*, 751–777.

Marshall, N. (2008). *Rescue our world: 52 brilliant little ideas for becoming an eco-hero.* United Kingdom: The Infinite Ideas Company Limited.

Marzano, R. J. (2012). Teaching self-efficacy with personal projects. *Educational Leadership, 69*(8), 86–87.

Marzano, R. J., & Heflebower, T. (2012). *Teaching and assessing 21st century skills.* Bloomington, IN: Marzano Research Laboratory.

Marzano, R. J., Pickering, D. J., & Heflebower, T. (2011). *The highly engaged classroom.* Bloomington, IN: Marzano Research Laboratory.

Merton, R. K., & Barber, E. (2004). *The travels and adventures of serendipity.* Princeton, NJ: Princeton University Press.

Nahapiet, J., & Ghoshal, S. (1998). Social capital, intellectual capital, and the organizational advantage. *Academy of Management Review, 23*, 242–266.

Think link Inc. (n.d.). *Why is it important to have a hobby?* Retrieved from http://thinklink.in/why-is-it-important-to-have-a-hobby/

Van Andel, P. (1994) Anatomy of the unsought finding: Serendipity: origin, history, domains, traditions, appearances, patterns and programmability. *British Journal for the Philosophy of Science, 45*, 631–648.

Warglien, M., & Masuch, M. (1995). *The logic of organizational disorder.* Berlin: De Gruyter.

Part III
Implementation:
Noteworthy components of
Getting things Done &
Getting Desired Results

This is the part that makes the first two parts count!

Part III is designed to provide a mechanism to implement Parts I and II. Once you have identified **balance** needs, desired **lifestyle** changes and which of the **10 other areas** in your life needing improvement, the next thing to be done is to develop and implement a plan to bring about the desired changes. That is why the next section is titled "Noteworthy components of getting things done and getting desired results." This is where the rubber meets the road. In other words, part III completes the process. Mission accomplished once you master part III.

It is my belief that most people, young, old and in between at some point in our lives have learned to get results (in something) at one time or another. In many cases we just needed to be motivated (by something) to really want to get the results we desire.

After many years of study, research and trial and error, I have identified thirteen key components that are connected to success in getting things done. If you work consistently hard at the desired goal you will get the desired result using one or more of these

components. Different components are needed by different people at different times, depending upon what they need at a particular time. At some point in time most people will need one or more of the following components to get the desired result:
(1) motivation, (2) organization, (3) self-assessment, (4) commitment, (5) support, (6) time, (7) deal with change, (8) be empowered, (9) confront excellence, (10) make clear and concise decisions, (11) problem solve, (12) act, by 'just doing it' and (13) recognize and own up to their own resilience.

For example, after reading chapter 1 about *balance*, I realize that for me to obtain more balance in my life, I lack the motivation to make that happen, so the chapter on **motivation** is going to be one of the first chapters that will be helpful for me to get started. Or, let's say that I'm motivated but fall short on organization; in that case, **organization** is going to be the chapter for me to read up on.

Another person who has tried a number of diets to lose weight has come to the realization that what they really need is a *lifestyle* change and not another diet. This person might identify **self-assessment** as the chapter in the implementation phase that will be most helpful or maybe they need to become more committed to a long-term regimen that is going to be needed for a lifestyle change.

Another example would be the person who realize that they have been spending so many hours at work that they have neglected their family to the point of causing major problems in the family. They also realize that all their previous efforts have failed and they now realize that they need **support** from other sources to make that happen or in some cases they know what to do because they have weighed the pros and cons of the matter and just need to act. Here the chapter on action or (just do it) might be helpful.

Other examples can be given by different people who need different implementation mechanisms for different purposes. The chapter on **change** can be helpful for any and everyone to better understand the complexities of change when it comes to getting a desired outcome within a certain timeframe. The chapter on **time** is another one that can be an eye opener for many people who have not done a time analysis recently to recognize how easily and quickly time can slip away and before you know it you have run out of time for certain things. Most of us waste time in so many areas of our lives without even knowing it.

My personal favorite chapter and one that I think has had a great impact on my life is the chapter on **resilience**. Not only does the resilience chapter help us to focus on the positive and look at what is right in our lives but it also provides a mechanism for us to get an overall picture of our lives by identifying the risk and protective factors in our lives. We all have both. Some of us have more protective factors working for us than risk factors working against us, while others are just the opposite. The beauty of the resiliency concept is that once you learn how to differentiate between the two, you can build more protective factors in your life and eliminate risk factors that are more harmful to your wellbeing.

Part III – Implementation

"Can do" versus "Do"

I have always been fascinated by successful people. Not just financial success but success in the broader since of the word including those people who successfully complete a degree program or those who successfully follow through on a stated goal.

How is it that some people seem to get things done and get results while others seem to somehow miss the mark? The answer is relatively simple. Those who get things done and get results tend to be focused, determined, motivated risk takers who think positive much of the time and who have the "just do it" attitude. They don't fear failure. These are usually very productive people who can get things done even when conditions for getting things done are not ideal. They have learned to improvise, make due with what they have to work with and in many cases get started on a task even when they don't know or can't see at the time how the end will look. They tend to not ponder too long before getting started on a task. They don't need everything to be planned out or in place before they get started because in many cases they realize that they can go back to make corrections and changes later. They know they need to just get started.

Bottom line, are you getting, or, can you get results? It does not matter how much information you have, how much you want to do it or how much you are doing, the big question seems to always come back to "are you getting results?" If the answer is "yes" then you are (at least) on the right track. Whether you are getting the level of results you want is another matter, If you are not getting results, then either some things simply take more time for (positive) results to show up, or, you need to reassess the situation and see what changes need to be made.

The author and motivational speaker David Allen has trademarked "Getting Things Done." He has developed seminars and workshops around the topic of getting things done. His strategy in an over-simplified explanation is to collect the things needing to be done, process and organize them in a way that makes sense to you and in such a way that they can either be acted upon, filed away, thrown away or delegated to someone else to do, review to make sure the correct action is being contemplated and then do what needs to be done (Allen, 2001). *Getting Things Done: The Art of Stress-Free Productivity*

A book reviewer at amazon.com says that this book is for all those who are overwhelmed with too many things to do, too little time to do them, and a general sense of unease that something important is being missed.

Getting Results

The reviewer (Mitchell, 2001) explains the essence of the process is that you write down a note about everything when you take on a new responsibility, make a new commitment, or have a useful thought. All of this ends up in some kind of "in" box. You then go through your "in" box and decide what needs to be done next for each item. For simple issues, this includes identifying the action you should take first and when to take it. For tougher issues, you schedule an appropriate time to work the problem in more detail. You organize the results of this thinking, and review your options for what you should be doing weekly. Then you take what you choose to do, and act. Think of this process as the following five steps:

(1) collect

(2) process

(3) organize

(4) decide

(5) act

For the tougher problems, you start with identifying your purpose and principles so you know why you care how it all turns out. Then you imagine the potential good outcomes that you would like. Following that, you brainstorm with others the best way to get those outcomes. Then you organize the best pathway. Finally, you identify the first actions you need to take. Then you act, as in step 5 above.

Sources on the Topic

There are a lot of references in the literature on getting results that refer to how employees in the corporate world might go about getting results. Longenecker and Simonetti's book "Getting Results: Five Absolutes for High Performance" (2001) is an example. Then there are other books like JD Meier's book "Getting Results the Agile Way" (Meier 2010) that gives a recipe for getting results. Longenecker and Simonetti's approach include focus on purpose, be prepared, create a climate for results, nurture relationships with people and practice continuously. Getting Results the Agile Way' and the Agile Results system is the author's way to offer everyone the insight and information needed to develop the skills vital for personal and business success and for getting results. Meier comments that the Agile Results details a principles-based approach to making the most out of work and life. Among other benefits he believes readers will learn is how to find a work/life balance, how to find a flow state for more engaging work, how to focus on what really counts, how to create more value for yourself and others, and how to find your passion and purpose.

Important Elements of Getting Things Done

Borrowing from these and other authors, I believe that there are a number of elements that are involved in getting things done and getting results. According to the research that I have done, among those elements would include such things as change, commitment, time, motivation, decision making, excellence, resiliency, focus on building strengths, problem solving, support, self assessment, empowerment and an element entitled "action".

The following next several chapters cover the key elements of getting things done and getting results are presented in the order that I have chosen to put them. However, they need not be followed in the exact order that they are here presented.

<u>REFERENCES</u>
Part III – "Implementation: Noteworthy Components of Getting Things Done & Getting Desired Results"

Allen, D. (2001). *Getting things done: The art of stress-free productivity*. New York: Penguin Group.

Longenecker, C. O., & Simonetti, J. L. (2001). *Getting results: Five absolutes for high performance*. San Francisco: Jossey-Bass & Sons.

Meier, J. D. (2010). *Getting results the agile way*. Bellevue, WA: Innovation Playhouse. Interactive table of contents of book retrieved from from http://www.gettingresults.com/wiki/Getting_Results_the_Agile_Way_Table_of_Contents

Mitchell, D. (2001). Review of *Getting things done*. Retrieved from http://www.amazon.com/Getting-Things-Done-Stress-FreeProductivity/dp/0142000280

Chapter 13
Action

Just do it!!

Move, now!

I've heard writers say if you want to overcome writers block, just start writing. I've also heard the saying, "An object in motion, tends to stay in motion." That is the same principle behind "just do it."

> *"Put one foot in front of the other and just keep moving."*

Remove tempting obstacles, such as doing nothing by having a plan in place. And, whenever possible, act with intention. Act with decisiveness. Act as if you mean it. If you are going to go after something, go after it with the forcefulness that shows the seriousness with which you take this action.

Just do it can happen at several levels. One level is you have been wanting or meaning to do something and just have not gotten to the point of getting started. Here the issue is to move from the thought or idea to following up on the thought or idea by developing a plan or setting goals and objectives to make this thought or idea a reality. Here it is just do it! Stop thinking or pondering on it, do it. Begin developing the plan.

Once you have a plan, the next level of just do it comes into play to follow the plan. Just do it. If you find that the plan needs to be adjusted, adjust it.

An action plan is a blueprint for action. It's a personal performance structure with specific tasks, timelines and resources to get the job done.

Among the best reasons to have an action plan include such things as the following:

Chapter 13 – Action

It lend credibility to the person planning
It increases the possibility that you are not overlooking something important
It helps for understanding what is and is not possible
It provides a level of efficiency that would not otherwise be present
It adds a level of accountability for the person doing the planning
It also adds a level of confidence that you are prepared and now ready to move forward with the plan.

The internet and the library have lots of resources on different action plans and strategies on how to get things done. Surely you can find a plan that works for you.

Usually the biggest issue is not finding the right plan or strategies to get something done, the problem is usually with follow through or immobility or plain and simple procrastination. Consequently, this chapter is primarily dealing with issues concerning moving into action. Develop a plan, follow the plan, or do whatever is necessary to move forward. Just do it.

What is it about action, just doing it that might be captured and duplicated? What happens in the mind and body that causes or allows a person to move to action? There are certain actions that occur as a result of habit. Other actions result from deliberate thought and decision-making processes. In some cases, action is the result of impulse or even a reaction to something like a threat, a reward or other incentive. Acting also can come from having the confidence in a plan that has been thought out and now ready for implementation.

A good question to ask might be what moves a person to action? A better question might be what moves a person to action if they don't really want to act. They question whether they should act or not, or, they are afraid to act. What is happening in the mind and body of a person who simply tells himself to "just do it" and they do it? On some things I go into what I call my "no think" mode. Things that I know I "should" do or have really committed myself to doing, I tend to not think about not doing it.

For example, I am committed to going to the gym to work out at least three to four times a week. Because I don't particularly like doing this, I have scheduled it for the very first thing in the morning so I can simply "roll" out of bed, put on my gym clothes, jump into my car and go. For me, this "just do it" concept works best for those things for which there is little or no question that I "should" do it. I don't have time to think about whether I "feel like" doing it or not. If I "thought" about it, I would possibly rationalize my way out of doing it.

Some people think that you've got to have everything in perfect order before you act on it. Or, everything has to all be in place before you act, but sometimes you have to trust that it will all come together once you get started. Sometimes, the question becomes how much of a thing needs to be together before you act. Surely you should have a clue of the end result, or where you're going, before you act. If you're 80 or 90% sure of something, then maybe that's enough to act on.

Chapter 13 – Action

There are numerous reasons many people never reach this stage: fear of failure, uncertainty, afraid to risk, lack of self-confidence, lack of reliable information, lack of faith.

> ***Once you have acted, then there is the concern of continuing to act; acting the second time; and the third, etc.***

Maintenance

Oftentimes, the second time is easier than the first and action becomes even easier as you continue to act. This step is probably the most critical in the series of decision-making. After you have begun to act, the next step is to maintain. Depending upon the situation, an appropriate level of maintenance needs to be decided upon. Once the action step has been taken, it can move you to a different level of decision-making. Unless you are really sorry you took that action step, you might consider moving forward and really try to make the best of the situation.

Following through—doing, carrying out, moving forward—all are positive actions. To act on a certain thing is to start doing it. Acting is beginning a task. Acting does not guarantee that something will be completed or that it will be done well or correctly or that it will be done with an appropriate attitude. However, without action, it is very likely to not get done. If it is not started, then it is likely to not get done.

Just get started, first

Acting on something is often the best way to get started without necessarily knowing whether you are going in the right direction, whether you are doing right or not, or whether you will complete it or not; just start acting on it and continuing to act and see what you get or start the "juices" to move. Oftentimes, just getting started is necessary because it is often easier to make corrections later. Sometimes it just takes getting started and letting your thoughts flow as they come to you and eventually you end up on the right track and can move forward in a more appropriate direction as you move along. It is often easier to continue moving than it is to get started moving.

> ***Ideas have a short shelf life—that's why we must act before the expiration date."Procrastination is the ability to keep up with yesterday Even if you are on the right track, you'll get run over if you just sit there. Anyone who brags about what he is going to do tomorrow probably did the same thing yesterday.*** (Taken from "You're Born an Original, Don't Die a Copy" by John L. Mason, 1993)

Acting on impulse, through coercion, after a short or long deliberation or just because it is the right thing to do, taking action is the bottom line. Once the action is initiated, the next "concern" might be whether to follow through and continue acting or whether to switch directions or simply stop.

Chapter 13 – Action

Missed Opportunity from Not Acting

People differ in how they cope with missed opportunities and bad decisions. Some people dwell on missed opportunities, feel bad about them for a long time and do not seem to be able to leave the past behind them. Others get over those failures relatively quickly and focus on how to improve the here and now instead. Van Putten, Zeelenberg, and Dijk (2009) did a study that highlights the different types.

Extensive research has demonstrated that these differences in coping reflect a fundamental dimension in how people approach current challenging situations and referred to it as state vs. action orientation (see for a review, Kuhl & Beckmann, 1994). The present research investigates how this orientation influences an important behavioral consequence of missed opportunities called inaction inertia (Tykocinski, Pittman, & Tuttle, 1995). Inaction inertia refers to the effect that people, after missing out on an initial attractive opportunity, are less likely to act on further opportunities despite their objective attractiveness.

It is proposed that if people differ in the way they cope with missed opportunities, the influence of missed opportunities on current decisions should differ accordingly. The Van Putten et al. (2009) article reports three experiments that demonstrate a weaker inaction inertia effect for action-oriented people than for state-oriented people.

> *Inaction inertia implies that decisions to act on an attractive opportunity in the present are negatively influenced by inactions from the past.*

For example, although people may find the opportunity to book a vacation on discount for $900 instead of $1,000 very attractive, they will decline it when they missed an earlier opportunity to book it for $400. Inaction inertia is demonstrated when likelihood to act on an attractive current opportunity is lower because the difference in attractiveness between the missed and the current opportunity is large rather than small. Thus, the more attractive the missed opportunity (initial inaction) was, the lower the likelihood that people will act on an attractive action opportunity now (inertia).

This effect is very robust and has been found for numerous different decisions, such as for buying shoes or beer, joining fitness centers, booking vacations, investing in the stock market and registering for college courses (Arkes, Kung, & Hutzel, 2002; Butler & Highhouse, 2000; Kumar, 2004; Sevdalis, Harvey, & Yip, 2006; Tykocinski, Israel, & Pittman, 2004; Tykocinski & Pittman, 1998, 2001, 2004; Van Putten, Zeelenberg, & Van Dijk, 2007, 2008; Zeelenberg, Nijstad, Van Putten, & Van Dijk, 2006; Zeelenberg & Van Putten, 2005).

Because of its robustness, one might expect that whenever people miss a more attractive opportunity to act, all else being equal, the likelihood that they will act on a subsequent opportunity will inevitably decrease. However, because some people seem to get over negative outcomes quicker than others, an important determinant of the influence of missing a more attractive opportunity on behavior might be the way people cope with missing a more attractive opportunity.

> ***Action oriented people typically get over negative events quickly and focus on taking action to solve them,***

while state-oriented people find it typically difficult to overcome a negative event and keep ruminating about it and how it affects their current state (see Dieffendorff, Hall, Lord, & Strean, 2000; Kuhl & Beckmann, 1994). We expect that, compared to state-oriented people, action-oriented people are less influenced by missing a more attractive opportunity when initiating action on the current opportunity and, hence, less likely to show the inaction inertia effect.

Note that the main characteristic that distinguishes action-oriented people from state-oriented people is the ability to disengage from unpleasant events. This does not mean that action-oriented people feel less negatively about unpleasant events. Put differently, action- and state-oriented people will feel equally bad about missing an attractive opportunity, but only state-oriented people will let the previous opportunity influence current decisions.

Missed opportunities may influence current opportunities because they are used as an anchor to evaluate the current opportunity (Arkes et al., 2002; Zeelenberg et al., 2006). As a result, people do not act on the current opportunity because it is devalued under the influence of the missed opportunity. Thus, we think action-oriented people will show weaker inaction inertia effects than state-oriented people. This decrease in inaction inertia is not the result of action-oriented people experiencing less regret after missing a more attractive prior opportunity, but is due to them being better able to overcome this negative experience when evaluating subsequent events; thus, they are less likely to devalue the current opportunity.

Some Thought is Necessary, but Not Too Much

As the old saying goes, "actions speak louder than words." People who act on things are known to get things done. Hopefully, action is preceded with deliberate and sufficient thought. Most action requires some kind of subsequent activity. Because that is the case, it helps when that initial action took into consideration the subsequent activity and is prepared to follow through. Some actions are irreversible and others are retractable. Generally speaking, the irreversible ones are those that require the most deliberate thought and planning.

> ***You do it or you don't. If you do it, do the best you can, otherwise don't.***

Doing your best is usually the best policy so that not only will you likely feel better about the final product, but so will others. Acting requires taking that first step. The rest is usually much easier. Once you have begun to do something, it is much simpler to continue, even if you are not acting in the exact way you want, you are at least moving. If you feel you need to change courses, then make the change, but keep moving.

A point of caution is always in order. This author is not saying act without thinking or act prematurely or inappropriately. The main point here is to not get caught up in procrastination or not getting things done that need to be done. Don't become that person who fails to get things done because of failing to act.

J. D. Roth (Aug. 30, 2010), shares a few lessons learned while moving from talker to doer in an article titled: "Action Not Words: The Difference Between Talkers and Doers:"

Make **time for the things you want to do.** One of the keys to getting things done is setting aside time for the things you want to accomplish. You have to *make* time to get stuff done. As the Kevin J. Anderson article I mentioned above demonstrates, you don't just become a best-selling author or an Olympic athlete. Talking doesn't make it so. You have to carve out time to do this stuff. You have to put your Big Rocks first and fit the small stuff in around them.

Have a goal in mind. I truly believe that the biggest reason I used to struggle with getting stuff done is that I didn't have any sort of plan. I had no goals. Goals give you purpose. It wasn't until I became committed to digging myself out of debt that I was able to actually start moving in the right direction. Part of my current problem is that I've recently achieved a bunch of big goals, but now have nothing planned for the future.

Don't take on too much. While it's important to set goals, don't take on too many tasks at once. I try to set just one or two major goals at a time. Any more and I find I can't pursue any of them effectively.

Don't let failures deter you. This is huge. One of the reasons the article's author used to talk so much without acting is that he was afraid of failure. He says he is not sure where he learned to be afraid of defeat, but that's the way he was. And when he *did* try something but failed, he would give up. This is no way to get stuff done. Talkers let fear of failure keep them on the sideline; doers overcome fear and move on, and when they fail, they simply try again.

Don't find reasons that something *can't* be done; instead, find ways that something *can* be done. The author of the article said he hated when people come to him for advice, but when he gave it, they told him all the reasons it wouldn't work for their circumstances. (This often happens when he suggested people take a second job to boost their income, for example.)

Chapter 13 – Action

> *One of the biggest differences between successful people and those who aren't is that the successful don't make excuses.*

If something looks difficult or impossible, they find ways to make it happen anyhow. Retrieved from: http://www.getrichslowly.org/blog/2010/08/30/action-not-words-the-difference-between-talkers-and-doers/

Talkers Versus Doers

Karen Hinds (Jan. 30, 2013) wrote a blog titled: "6 Signs You Are Working with a Talker, Not a Doer" that I thought was worthy to share:

> *Some people have mastered the art of talking, yet fail miserably at the art of doing. Bottom line: They talk a good game.*

It's frustrating to work with these individuals as they project a very positive public image but do nothing to back it up. Colleagues dread being paired with them on projects because they know the outcome. These are a few telltale signs that you might be stuck working with a talker and not a doer.

Always criticizing. They spend their time criticizing the people and issues at hand, yet fail to offer a solution or even suggestions to solve the problem. Companies seek out problem-solvers not criticizers, and although they may have valid points, their constant negative energy actually does more harm than good.

Spending more time discussing problem. Sometimes people gain more personal satisfaction rehashing a problem simply to hear themselves talk. They are only interested in repeating the facts and emotions of the issue and never really move past that point to a possible resolution.

Having no plan to execute. Talkers consistently talk about what should and could be done, but they themselves have no plan in place and have no interest in executing the ideas they may present. They come from the standpoint of "somebody should do this" but that somebody is never them.

Always seeking an audience. Talkers always have an audience, voluntary or involuntary. They actively seek out anyone who will listen to them.

Broken promises. They offer many excuses as to why they are not able to accomplish the tasks requested of them, and each excuse actually sounds legitimate, but the result is always the same—nothing or little is accomplished. Unfortunately, many also promise too much and leave many disappointed people.

Riding on others' coattails. Talkers know how to position themselves on winning teams, so when the team is successful, they end up getting the credit for work they did not contribute to. They know how to do just enough to appear as a contributor when, in fact, their efforts are unproductive.

Retrieved from: http://powerofdistinction.com/6-signs-you-are-working-with-a-talker-not-a-doer/

A Different Perspective on Doers Versus Thinkers
Jeffrey Phillips (April 21, 2006) wrote a blog on "Innovate on Purpose" titled "Thinkers Versus Doers" where he talks about the balancing act many business firms have to do concerning innovation. He states that there are at least two "camps" of people in any business, and keeping these folks working together and in the appropriate proportion is a challenge and an opportunity.

I'm identifying the two camps as "Thinkers" and "Doers."

> *Thinkers are the people who are open to new ideas, new concepts and are constantly trying to improve or change the way things are done.*

They are the creative types, always experimenting. Their strengths are their willingness to experiment and change and try new things, new processes, invent new products or services. The weakness of many Thinkers is that they don't understand the processes and issues required to bring these new concepts to market.

Contrast the Thinkers with the Doers. Frankly, the Doers are the people who get things done. They recognize an efficient, optimized process and don't appreciate tinkering with the process or with people who introduce a lot of change. Doers don't really like change all that much, since change is disruptive to the existing norms and processes.

Clearly, a firm needs both Thinkers and Doers and people who can be the bridge between the two camps. What's interesting is that a firm composed completely of Thinkers is basically a research lab or a think tank, while a firm composed completely of Doers would eventually run itself, very efficiently, right out of business because it never changed or created new products or services. We need both of these skill sets to be effective in any business.

The trick to understand:
1. the appropriate proportion of each skillset in every product group or team
2. the different approaches to compensating and motivating these very different people within the same teams
3. how to bridge between them and make both kinds of people successful in an organization

Chapter 13 – Action

This article was retrieved from:
http://innovateonpurpose.blogspot.com/2006/04/thinkers-versus-doers.html

The Origin of "Just Do It"

> **Psychologist Jennifer Kunst discussed the "Just do it" slogan in A Headshrinker's Guide to the Galaxy that was published July 18, 2012.**

Retrieved from:
http://www.psychologytoday.com/blog/headshrinkers-guide-the-galaxy/201207/just-do-it

She comments that Nike's golden slogan resonates with the wisdom of psychoanalysis: just do it! Indeed, we all need that kind of urging at critical points in our lives when we are faced with fear and indecision, at the crossroads of the same-old same-old and the new venture. Call it cutting the cord or taking the plunge. Sometimes we just have to screw up our courage and take the leap of faith.
She also said,

> **To be sure, as a psychoanalyst, I am not known for recommending that people just jump into things.**

My profession's reputation is one of thorough reflection and careful consideration. Even navel-gazing, if you believe the caricature. So, I'll bet a lot of people wonder if we ever get around to helping our patients *do* anything!

Take Freud's famous paper, "Formulations on Two Principles of Mental Functioning." In this short paper, Freud puts forth the idea that the psychological shift from infancy to maturity—from the pleasure principle to the reality principle—is essentially about *delaying* action. The baby goes right from impulse to action, with nothing in between. "I want it, I take it," is the language of the young mind. But with maturity, we learn to interrupt the chain. We add a step in-between. Now, after impulse and before action, we think. This idea became fundamental in understanding how people develop psychologically. It has trickled down into modern psychology (and parenting, too!) in concepts such as "impulse control," "delayed gratification," and "frustration tolerance."

> **Civilized people think before they act.**

But, psychoanalysis practiced well encompasses more than just thinking. The whole point is about *living*. And when it comes to living, thinking is a big help but it only takes you so far. There comes a point where one must act. When all the feelings are reflected upon, all the pros and cons considered, and all the unconscious dynamics understood, one must have the courage to live. And that means *doing* something.

An Act of Freedom

In his work on therapeutic change in psychoanalysis, Neville Symington puts forward the idea that a shift from the old routine to a new way of being requires what he calls *an act of freedom*. This kind of freedom means having a mind of one's own, acting in faith in oneself and one's good objects, and taking a chance. We must cut the ties to the old way in order to try something new. Whether we succeed or fail in that one moment, we have succeeded in the big picture because we have invested in real change.

> *Psychological progress occurs in the face of anxiety and conflict. If we wait for the anxiety and conflict to subside first, we will never do anything…at some point, you have to just do it.*

REFERENCES
Chapter 13 – "Action"

Arkes, H. R., & Blumer, C. (1985). The psychology of sunk costs. *Organizational Behavior and Human Decision Processes, 35*, 124–140.

Arkes, H. R., Kung, Y., & Hutzel, L. (2002). Regret, valuation, and inaction inertia. *Organizational Behavior and Human Decision Processes, 87*, 371–385.

Breathnach, S. B. (n.d.). *The world needs dreamers and the world needs doers. But above all, the world needs dreamers who do.* Retrieved from http://www.brainyquote.com/quotes/quotes/s/sarahbanbr108282.html

Butler, A., & Highhouse, S. (2000). Deciding to sell: The effect of prior inaction and offer source. *Journal of Economic Psychology, 21*, 223–232.

Dieffendorff, J. M., Hall, R. J., Lord, R. G., & Strean, M. L. (2000). Action-state orientation: Construct validity of a revised measure and its relationship to work-related variables. *Journal of Applied Psychology, 85*, 250–263.

Freud, S. (1911), Formulation on two principles of mental functioning, *Standard Edition, 12*, 213-226. London: Horgarth Press.

Hinds, K. (2013). *6 signs you are working with a talker not a doer.* Retrieved from http://powerofdistinction.com/6-signs-you-are-working-with-a-talker-not-a-doer/

Kuhl, J. (1981). Motivational and functional helplessness: The moderating effect of state versus action orientation. *Journal of Personality and Social Psychology, 40*, 155–170.

Kuhl, J., & Beckmann, J. (1994). *Volition and personality: Action versus state orientation.* Seattle: Hogrefe & Huber.

Kumar, P. (2004). The effects of social comparison on inaction inertia. *Organizational Behavior and Human Decision Processes, 95*, 175–185.

Kunst, J. (2012, July 18). *Just do it!* Retrieved from http://www.psychologytoday.com/blog/headshrinkers-guide-the-galaxy/201207/just-do-it

Mason, J. L. (1993). *You're born an original, don't die a copy.* Tulsa, OK: Insight International.

Phillips, J. (2006). *Thinkers versus doers.* Retrieved from http://innovateonpurpose.blogspot.com/2006/04/thinkers-versus-doers.html

Roth, J. D. (2010). *Action not words: The difference between talkers and doers.* Retrieved from http://www.getrichslowly.org/blog/2010/08/30/action-not-words-the-difference-between-talkers-and-doers/

Sevdalis, N., Harvey, N., & Yip, M. (2006). Regret triggers inaction inertia – But which regret and how? *British Journal of Social Psychology, 45*, 839–853.

Symington, N. (2007). The analyst's act of freedom as agent of therapeutic change. In *Becoming a person through psychoanalysis* (Chapter 3). London: Karnac Books, LDT.

Tykocinski, O. E., Israel, R., & Pittman, T. S. (2004). Inaction inertia in the stock market. *Journal of Applied Social Psychology, 34*, 1166–1175.

Tykocinski, O. E. Pittman, T. S. (1998). The consequences of doing nothing: Inaction inertia as avoidance of anticipated counterfactual regret. *Journal of Personality and Social Psychology, 75*, 607–616.

Tykocinski, O. E., & Pittman, T. S. (2001). Product aversion following a missed opportunity: Price contrast or avoidance of anticipated regret. *Basic and Applied Social Psychology, 23*, 149–156.

Tykocinski, O. E., & Pittman, T. S. (2004). The dark side of opportunity: Regret, disappointment, and the cost of prospects. In I. Brocas & J. D. Carillo (Eds.), *The psychology of economic decisions: Reasons and choices* (Vol. 2, pp. 179–196). New York: Oxford University Press.

Tykocinski, O. E., Pittman, T. S., & Tuttle, E. E. (1995). Inaction inertia: Foregoing future benefits as a result of an initial failure to act. *Journal of Personality and Social Psychology, 68*, 93–803.

Chapter 13 – Action

Van Putten, M. (2008). *Dealing with missed opportunities: The causes and boundary conditions of inaction inertia*. Ridderkerk, Netherlands: Ridderprint.

Van Putten, M., Zeelenberg, M., & Van Dijk, E. (2007). Decoupling the past from the present attenuates inaction inertia. *Journal of Behavioral Decision Making, 20*, 65–79.

Van Putten, M., Zeelenberg, M., & Van Dijk, E. (2008). Multiple options in the past and the present: The impact on inaction inertia. *Journal of Behavioral Decision Making, 21*, 519–531.

Van Putten, M., Zeelenberg, M., & Van Dijk, E. (2009). Dealing with missed opportunities: Action vs. state orientation moderates inaction inertia. *Journal of Experimental Social Psychology, 45*, 808–815.

Zeelenberg, M., & Van Putten, M. (2005). The dark side of discounts: An inaction inertia perspective on the post-promotion dip. *Psychology and Marketing, 22*, 611–622.

Zeelenberg, M., Nijstad, B. A., Van Putten, M., & Van Dijk, E. (2006). Inaction inertia, regret and valuation: A closer look. *Organizational Behavior and Human Decision Processes, 101*, 89–104.

Chapter 14
Organization

> *People who are organized stress less, lose less time looking for lost or misplaced items and are extremely valuable employees to have around.*

Things are in their rightful place!

So Much Better

People are also more likely than not to think systematically which is an asset, especially in most businesses, agencies and other organizations.

Being organized saves time and money, holds down frustration and provides needed structure for effective and efficient action. Organization is critical for many tasks. On the other hand, chaos or non-organization breeds confusion. When you are organized, you can compartmentalize your thoughts and ideas; you can put things in their proper place; and you can think more clearly about your goals, your progress toward the goals and how much more needs to be done before the goal is accomplished. To be organized helps you focus. Organization helps the mind to better see how to proceed. This is especially true if others are involved in the same project. The division of labor can be made much simpler.

To be organized is to be prepared. Organization entails putting things in a logical order to simplify or to make it conveniently arranged. Organization improves efficiency. Organization helps minimize mistakes, it provides for a clearer picture or presentation. Oftentimes, there are several potential ways to organize something. People tend to organize things in a way that makes sense to them. Some systems of organization are from broad, general "big picture" to narrow, specific, or "little picture" or vice versa—micro to macro. Organizations are best seen displayed in some manner, in writing, in a picture or some other graphic display.

Chapter 14 – Organization

To organize is to put into order, to arrange such that a compilation of things makes sense or is conveniently ordered. Putting something in place so it can be easily found later. Sorting or separating things such that things with similar characteristics or things that have something in common are put together or separated from other things.

It Makes Sense

> *I put things where I am likely to look when I want to see them again.*

When I organize my files, I design or come up with categories or characteristics that make sense to be together. When I organize my kitchen, I put things in places I am likely to remember when I want to use them. I also put things in places that make sense. The things that I am likely to use most often are put in easy to get to places. When I organize my desktop, I arrange things such that I have clear spaces to work, I throw away stuff that is no longer needed or wanted. I put things away in their proper places.

Organization helps you see the "big picture" of a situation or circumstance or thing. Organization is putting things in order, into sequences or providing a structure that makes sense to the organizer. Organization saves time and other resources. Organization provides a sense of confidence that you might not otherwise have. Organization sometimes requires consolidation and elimination of unnecessary items and the weeding out of unnecessary duplication. Organization can also help you see where there are gaps or other areas of need. In many cases, organization simplifies and provides clarity. A person who is organized tends to be more focused on the next steps needed to proceed with whatever needs to be done.

> *Organization provides a picture that might not have otherwise been possible.*

Benefits of Being Organized

Danielle Gaylord and Rita Smeyak, owners of S.O.S., Signature Organizing Services (n.d.), in Lafayette, IN talk about benefits of being organized on their website at: (http://www.organizinglafayette.com/organizing-services/benefits-of-being-organized/)
They introduce their comments by reminding the reader how time and money are precious commodities….Consider the cost of being unorganized and then think about the money you can save or generate by getting organized. Their Reduce, Reuse and Recycle approach to de-cluttering any space will help you critically analyze the use of your space, and then feel better knowing that the items that will be sold, donated or repurposed will benefit you, someone else and the environment. More of Danielle Gaylord and Rita Smeyak's tips follow.

Rewards of Organization:

- Immediate relief and peace of mind
- Satisfaction from knowing you helped create an organizing system you can maintain.

338

- Peace knowing you have eliminated excess in your home in an environmentally friendly fashion.
- You have implemented a storage system that will keep your important documents and heirlooms safe.
- You can find anything and everything in a moment's notice.
- You and your family will enjoy your space together.
- You will feel more productive and clear minded.
- You will be more confident and inclined to entertain family and friends in your home.

The Cost of Being Unorganized

The financial cost
- Duplicate purchases, credit card late fees, late payment penalties and unclaimed rebates.
- The average American has between $2,500 and $5,000 worth of perfectly usable stuff they aren't using while carrying $10,000 in credit card debt.
- Credit card companies collect $7 billion in late fees annually
- Banks collect more than $37 billion in overdraft fees
- Millions of dollars in tax refunds and rebates go unclaimed.
- Self-storage is a $22 billion dollar a year industry

The emotional and psychological cost
- Many underestimate the significance of or don't consider home inventory as critical until there is a crisis and such items are not easily located.
- Clutter increases the amount of cleaning. Eliminating clutter reduces housework by up to 40%.
- It has been estimated that the average person spends over an hour daily looking for things. This translates into two weeks every year! By age 50, you could have spent over a year of your life looking for things.

> *– Depression can cause clutter and clutter can cause depression*

- Over 85% of couples say they argue about clutter and disorganization.

Ways you can save and make money getting organized:
- Implementing a filing system will help you avoid missed payments, late fees and missed rebates.
- Take your nearly new items to a local consignment shop. There are many advantages to placing your gently used items in consignment and each store has rules for resale. We can help you decide which store is best for your well-cared-for items.

- If you prefer the Internet for resale, Ebay, Amazon and Craig's Lists have proven to be highly lucrative options. Again, there are rules, but once you understand how it works, resale could be your method of removing clutter and making money.
- Yard sales are the conventional tried and true method to eliminate large-scale excess in one fell swoop. What you don't sell, you can donate.
- Donate your unwanted items to a charity and be sure to obtain a tax deduction form. If you want to record your donations as well as get an idea of what those items are worth, create an account with its deductable.com.

More Benefits of Being Organized

Other benefits of being organized were offered by Julie Bonner (2007) in an article titled "10 Benefits of Being Organized." Following are a few that are not repeated in the previous article:

- **You will have more time for yourself, your friends and your family**.

> *When you live an organize life, you get things done faster.*

You spend less time looking for lost things and more time with the people you love. Freeing up your time will also allow you to read that book you've been meaning to get to for the past year or take that tennis class. We never get yesterday back. Make sure you get the most out of each day.

- **You will achieve balance in your life.**
  You can spend less time on the little things of life and more time on the big things, like your health and your family. Achieving balance sets the stage for an amazing life.

- **Your professional life will improve.**
  Not only will you make a better impression on your co-workers and boss, but you will also feel great about yourself. When you feel like you have it all together at work, your professional life can take off and you can achieve things you have always dreamed of.

- **You will be able to set and achieve your goals.**
  People who write down their goals are much more likely to achieve them. Being organized can help you recognize what your goals are and map out a plan to achieve them.

- **You will be an example to those around you.**

> *Your children are watching and learning from you everyday. Showing them how to be organized and get the most out of each day will be a lesson they can take with them for the rest of their lives.*

If you don't want your children to be raised in chaos, make it your goal to get life under control. They will someday thank you and appreciate everything you did for them.

Chapter 14 – Organization

You Can't Organize Everything

Sarah Aguirre had an interesting way of introducing her article titled "3 Reasons You Can't Organize Everything." She starts off with letting you know that it's happened before. You had a revelation to organize everything in your home. Maybe you saw a magazine article, heard a motivational speech, saw a friend's new closet system. More likely you spent an eight-hour block of time searching for someone's baseball uniform, ballet slippers, or worse yet, car keys. You've seen the blissful light of homemaking simplicity and eagerly run towards it, but midway you trip over your own excuses. Can you really organize everything? Knock down these 3 roadblocks and speed away to uncluttered success. She also came up with three myths and solutions to the myths.

Myth #1
I don't have the time to get organized. I have way too much to do to set aside time to organize my life.

Many people believe they are unable to set aside time to organize because of their hectic schedules. Those same schedules that have us running everywhere all day are the reasons to get and stay organized. Without an organized home base, we run the risk of clutter and chaos spreading to other parts of our lives. Think about the time saved when we eliminate lost items and keep last-minute time emergencies from being an every day occurrence.

Solutions
A. So you don't have a lot of time. Begin in a slow way by identifying areas of your home that cause chaos and disorder in your life. Don't be afraid to work slowly toward your goals. Try Baby Steps For Organization.

B. Start with a project that only takes a small portion of the day like Organizing Your Medicine Cabinet. Accomplishing just one tiny goal can give you the motivation to keep going and eventually organize everything.

C. Find help. Get together with your family or friends in an effort to organize your home. Partner up with a friend to help you get started. One weekend work together to weed out her pantry and the next weekend do the same for yours.

> ## Myth #2
> *I can't afford to get organized. All the tools, shelving systems, racks, etc. cost way too much for me to be able to organize everything in my home.*

For many people, spending a chunk of money on a professional organizer and designer shelving is not an option. There are ways to organize without emptying the wallet.

Solutions

A. It doesn't take bucks to clear out clutter. It only takes four containers and an iron will against the spread of stuff.

B. Scour garage, yard, and estate sales for organizational equipment you need. This can be a great way to get storage options to organize everything without stretching your budget.

C. Ask for organizational items for holiday presents. Sure a shelving system may not seem like a romantic anniversary gift, but the time saved in finding and putting away the contents of your closet can be used to rekindle the flame.

Myth #3
I'm naturally disorganized and I have no desire to change. My disorganization doesn't cause any problems in my life.

It's great when you find a system that works for you, and for some people disorganization seems to be it. They work best in an atmosphere of chaos. If this is you, then you may not need to be organized. But, if your disorganization spills over to affect other people then you may need to adjust your thinking. Do you pay bills late? Do you frequently forget appointments or show up late to functions? Is your home an inviting place, or one that your friends and family can't really feel comfortable in because of disorder?

Solutions

A. Try reaching a compromise in your life by organizing areas that affect other people or that have given you problems in the past. If you're usually late for meetings, try creating a calendar system for yourself. Don't just assume that your lack of organization doesn't cause any problems for those around you. Don't be afraid to ask for feedback from those you care about.

B. Consider a trial run of some new organizational ideas. You may find that changing your way of thinking and grouping allows you more freedom than you had before.

C. Allow yourself to be you. If you have systems that seem like chaos to the casual observer, but that work for you, don't just discard them because of public opinion. There's no reason for your sock drawer to be organized by color, type, and texture if it's not important to you. Even if you don't organize everything in your home, organizing the important things can give you more time and freedom.

Chapter 14 – Organization

> *So there it is. Even with no money, no time, and no motivation, you can give yourself the skills to organize everything in your home. Throw out these 3 excuses with the clutter, and you'll find the efficient and user-friendly home of your dreams.*

The article "3 Reasons You Can't Organize Everything" was retrieved from: http://housekeeping.about.com/cs/organizing101/a/3excuses.htm

Adrianne Cohen, author of *Help, It's broken!: A Fix-it Bible for the Repair-Impaired* (2011), wrote an article titled "8 Organizing Strategies from Professional Purgers" that I thought was worthy of sharing.

Organize Your Stuff!

You know those closets and drawers and cupboards that are so full, they won't quite close? It turns out they could be bad for your health: Every time you look around and feel anxious that the mess is getting out of hand, your body releases cortisol, one of the classic stress hormones, says Steven Maier, PhD, a neuroscience professor at the University of Colorado at Boulder.

1. Keep Your Kitchen Clean

Purging: Even Emeril doesn't need six spatulas and four whisks; two of each will do, so start by tossing extras. While you're at it, check expiration dates on foodstuffs and pitch anything that's past its prime. Next, tackle seldom-used appliances like cappuccino and bread makers. Those things don't need to live in the kitchen, put up a rack in the garage, or store them on a hallway closet shelf. **Prevention:** The number one rule: Keep the counters clear. Counter space is only for items you use daily, according to Barry Izsak, president of the National Association of Professional Organizers. Everything else can be stored in a cabinet or pantry.

2. Dust Off That Desk!

Purging: Begin by throwing away the no-brainers, including junk mail, expired coupons, brochures, and catalogs. Next, create desk zones. Have a bill-paying zone, a stationery zone, a mail zone, and a reading zone. Keep everything you need for each activity in neat containers. **Prevention:** Tackle your zones weekly, particularly bills and mail. For incoming papers such as children's art or tax information, keep one folder or container for each category, and at the end of the year (or month, if things really pile up fast), choose the keepers and purge the rest.

3. Liberate Your Library

Purging: Some people would consider it a sacrilege to ever get rid of a book, but if you've decided it's time to winnow, donate all books that don't meet any of these three criteria:

books you love, books you read regularly, books whose content can't be found on the Internet. **Prevention:** Librarian's rules: No stacking or double shelving allowed. Group your books into categories like fiction, nonfiction, and travel, so you can see what you have. And, good news: Regifting is perfectly acceptable with books.

4. Tossing Tchotchkes
Purging

> ***You should own nothing that is not useful, beautiful, or loved.***

If a tchotchke (trinket, wooden object, etc.) can't pass this test, out it goes. **Prevention:** When a new tchotchke comes in, Kosloff suggests immediately rejecting it if you already own something similar. Keep only the little objects you'll use (a vase, a pretty bowl) or that are uniquely meaningful (a handmade gift or travel memento).

5. A Picture Perfect System
Purging: Keep the gems, toss the rest. According to Julie Morgenstern, author of *Never Check E-mail in the Morning,* throw away or delete all the blurry, unflattering, redundant, or bad shots. This strategy is especially effective if you or your partner is a lousy photographer. **Prevention:** Don't feel compelled to label every photo. Instead, organize them into broad categories such as "Venice vacation" or "work events," and store them in a labeled photo box or digital folder. Weed out new shots as you take them or as soon as you receive prints.

6. Reclaim Your Garage
The Garage Purging: The garage is not a warehouse! Begin by attacking one shelf or corner at a time, and tossing or donating all items you no longer use. Sports equipment your kids have outgrown, the gardening tools for the yard you no longer use—out! Then arrange items by category. Your garage should be zoned. You might have a zone for car equipment and a sports zone. **Prevention:** Never pile items on the floor; buy new shelves or wall hooks as needed. Kosloff suggests keeping a large donation bin so family members always have a place to put unused belongings.

7. Sort Through Makeup
Purging: Sort through all your half-empty bottles of shampoo, lotion, and makeup, and toss anything you haven't used in six months. Group what's left in containers of like products (i.e., rather than having 18 kinds of makeup sitting out on the counter, put it all in one easily accessible container). Morgenstern also uses extra toiletries (unopened, of course) to make hostess baskets for overnight guests. **Prevention:** Avoid impulse purchases by buying products only to replace those you're done with.

8. Cleanse Your Closet

Purging: Remember that 80% of the time, we wear only 20% of our clothes. So go through your wardrobe and jettison anything that's one of the four S's: stretched, small, smelly (ew!), or stained (sure, you could clean the stained and smelly pieces, but the idea is to let things go). Another great tip: Turn all your hangers in one direction, and for the next six months, flip the hanger (and leave it flipped) when you wear something. Donate the untouched clothes. **Prevention:** The rule of thumb is that when something new comes in, at least one thing—preferably two—must go. And be realistic. If you're a size 10, hold on to the 8s but not the 6s.

This article, "8 Organizing Strategies from Professional Purgers," was retrieved from: http://www.oprah.com/home/The-Urge-to-Purge/1#ixzz2qZeToxd3

Being Organized Helps

In their Jan.-Feb. 2010 Newsletter "Organizing," Lisa Montanaro (of LM Organization Solution, LLC) wrote an article covering 10 points on organizing.

> *According to Lisa, one of the best benefits of being organized is when life throws you a curve ball, you can hit it and get on base. You can't avoid the curve ball, but being organized helps you deal with it better by having systems in place to fall back on.*

1. Multi-tasking actually reduces productivity 20 to 40%. Studies have shown that we reduce our cognitive abilities and IQ points every time we try to do two things at once. Think "uni-tasking"—the act of doing tasks one at a time. You will feel less stressed and accomplish more, actually improving your overall productivity. (In fact, most of the time when we believe we're multitasking, we're actually switching between two tasks. Switching from one task to another is hard because different tasks follow different rules and call for different types of responses) (Monsell, 2003).

2. Learn to say no. As someone said once, "No is a complete sentence." We have to learn how NOT to deliberately overload ourselves and more importantly, our brains. This means your activities and tasks need to be prioritized and sometimes even taken off our plates all together.

3. You don't have to be the keeper of an object forever. At some point, things emotionally depreciate, and we need to move on. Remember—you can always say the hurricane took it!

4. When organizing in a room, use sorting boxes labeled as "keep," "toss," "charity," and "other rooms." Stay in the room you're working on, and take all the items that belong to other rooms back after you finish what you're doing. Otherwise, you're going to wander from room to room, doing bits and pieces here and there and not finish what you were doing.

5. Create a Command Center for your home. This is where the mail, bills, and other items go so you can find what you need, and stock it with scissors, a letter opener, staple remover, sticky notes, pens, the checkbook, and stamps. Every house also needs a charging station for cell phones, MP3 players, and other electronic equipment, and the charging station can be next to the Command Center.

6. Make your organizing tools cute. Never underestimate the power of cute. If an inbox or file folder is cute, you are more likely to use it.

7. Before bedtime, put on some music and everyone in the family (adults included) do the Seven Minute Sprint to put everything back where it belongs and get things ready for the next morning. This helps put the house in order before bedtime and makes for a faster morning. Organizers in New Zealand also refer to this as the 10 Minute Tidy.

> **8. To avoid procrastination, do the worst first.**

Think of your projects as a gigantic chocolate cake. To eat the cake and to complete your tasks, break your tasks into smaller, bite-sized pieces and visualize where you want to go. This will help keep your work flowing.

9. Use Outlook Rules and Alerts and other electronic and digital items to help you save time and work smarter, not harder. To set a rule, right click on an Outlook email, scroll to "Create a Rule" and on the dialogue box select the "from" or "subject line" and then select "Folders." You can choose to send your emails to deleted items, a reading folder, or a project folder.

10. Take a vacation. Seriously. Take one. The vacation is not just for you, it's for the people who work around you as well.

Brynn Mannino (n.d.) offers expert tips on how to get rid of clutter for good on the Womansday.com website. In the article titled "8 Secrets of Personal Organizers," he says that there's no right way to organize your home. Whatever strategy you choose just has to work with your lifestyle, habits and tastes. But there are a few tried-and-true strategies that can enhance the effectiveness of any system. From being aware of clutter hot spots to identifying red flags that your organizing method isn't working, we learned some smart approaches to getting organized from the pros so you can save the time, money and stress that come with living in a den of disorder.

1. Make it easier to put things away than to take them out.
Kate Brown, certified professional organizer and owner of Impact Organizing LLC comments that she is always surprised how difficult people make organizing for themselves. (http://www.impactorganizing.com/). Her suggestion is to make everything a one-handed operation.

> *For example, don't hide your laundry basket in the back of the closet. Instead, use an open bin that you can throw your clothes into from across the room. And avoid lids at almost all costs.*

Using open containers for things you use often like toiletries and cooking supplies makes it easier to put them away. This advice even applies to garbage cans. Brown recommends investing in one with a lever you can step on to pop the lid open. The fewer steps, the better the organizing system.

2. Don't buy storage containers until you've purged.

When people want to get organized, the first thing they usually do is run out and buy storage supplies. (http://www.unclutteredhome.com/). But that's actually backwards. The point, she explains, is to evaluate why you have so much stuff to begin with—not find new ways to house your junk.

> *You won't have any idea of what you really need in terms of containers or shelving until you've purged.*

While deciding what to keep and what to toss, always remember the "80/20 rule." It's the theory that most of us only use 20 percent of what we have. That's a good starting point to realizing you are surrounded by a lot of things you probably don't need. Plus, not only will slimming down your stuff save you money on storage supplies, but it'll also save you the headache of going through excess items in an emergency or last-minute situation.

3. There are red flags that let you know your system isn't working.

If a room still somehow looks messy after you've cleaned, it's time to improve your organizational system, which, according to Brown, should allow you to tidy up in 15 minutes or less. Once you've pulled out what you don't need—to either throw away or donate—the next step is to group things together based on use or occasion and store them in open, square containers (round ones take up too much space). Now that everything has a place, Brown recommends labeling. If you don't like labeling, find some other way to communicate your organizational system to yourself and your family, either by using translucent bins or by simply involving everyone in the purging process so they have a better idea of your goals.

4. Use containers as visual signals that it's time to purge.

Not only do containers keep items grouped and easier to find, but they also make it obvious when you're at capacity. For instance, most organizing experts would recommend keeping a basket or open container for magazines beside the couch. Brown recommends an 11" x 14" container that's 4" to 6" deep. When the magazine container is full, you've [got] more reading material than you can handle. A pile of magazines, which has no literal limit, doesn't relay the same message.

5. Don't treat drawers like catchalls.

According to interior decorator Christopher Lowell, author of Seven Layers of Organization, there isn't a drawer in your house that should not have container organizers in them. (http://www.christopherlowell.com/books.php). They can be any material you want—wood, wire mesh or clear plastic—and are available at most home goods stores. This allows you to separate the drawers into defined areas for specific things versus throwing everything into one big space. For the bedroom, store everyday items—like underwear and socks—in top drawers, workout clothes in the second or third drawers and pants in the bottom drawers. In the bathroom, keep cotton swabs and other daily use items on the counter within arm's reach, and tools you use occasionally under the cabinet.

> *Lowell says with the things you only use now and then separated out and away from the things you need every day, those daily essentials will be better organized and easier to get to.*

6. Eliminate clutter hot spots.

Flat surfaces like your dining room table, entryway table and kitchen counters tend to accumulate piles faster than any other spot in the house. Make clearing all flat surfaces part of your nightly routine—right along with washing your face and brushing your teeth. But if that doesn't work, her last-ditch trick is to physically block any surface that has become a clutter haven. For instance, if you put a flower arrangement in the middle of the dining room table and set it with placemats, you're sending the message that the space is no longer a dumping zone.

7. Store a discard bag in the closet.

 I keep a shopping bag with a handle in the front of my closet. Every time I try on a piece of clothing and then take if off again because it's unflattering, doesn't fit, is pulled, stained or out of style, I put it in the bag, Brown says. If you've taken the piece of clothing off for any reason other than that it's dirty or doesn't match, that means it's not right and will probably. When the bag is full, donate the clothes or trade them with a friend at a swap party.

8. The items you use most frequently should be easiest to get to.

Keep the items you use every day in plain sight—or at least at eye level. According to Lowell, the things you use daily should be the easiest to get to. While the things you use once in a while should require a step stool. This is where high shelving comes in handy. Things you use only once a year should require a ladder. (Think attics or out-of-reach shelving in a garage.) Not only will this storage system make it easier for you to find the things you use often, but also the items you don't use regularly will stay organized until you need them.

<u>How to Get Organized</u>

Another source found at (http://getsetorganize.com/) offered a few other worthy suggestions:
•   Move away from old "bad" habits and form new "good" habits.

- ensure you have scheduled routine maintenance into your day – 30 minutes each for five days should do, along with a serious purging session every 6 months or so.
- ensure there is room for growth in your storage solutions. It is no good fitting your current items into closets and cabinets perfectly, there needs to be some spare capacity for future items.

How to De-Clutter Your Home—for Good

In her years as a professional organizer, Julie Morgenstern (2011) says she has learned that most people desperately want to get organized, but are held back by hidden obstacles they don't understand. Clutter is actually caused on three different levels" (technical problems, external realities and psychological obstacles).

Level 1: Technical Problems

All messes can be attributed to at least *one* technical problem. Technical problems are simple mistakes in your organizing system that can be as easy to fix as changing a light bulb. Identify your problem area, and try one of these solutions to get started.

- **Items Have No Home**

Simply put, you can't put things away if there's no place to put them. If items are piles all over the place, it is likely that you never designated a particular spot for them. In other words, the item has no "home."
Solution: Take the time to assign each item a single, consistent home, e.g., hats always go in this basket; scissors always go in this drawer. Label everything so you'll always remember where it belongs and can easily find it when you need it.

- **More Stuff Than Space**

If your closets, drawers, cabinets and shelves are all packed full—and you *still* have lots of surface piles—you've got more stuff than storage space.
Solution: You've got two options: (1) Lighten your load, or (2) Add more storage space. Make sure you're using the space you do have as efficiently as possible. Find hidden pockets of storage between cabinet shelves spaced too far apart, under the hanging clothes in your closet, and on the insides of closet doors. Maximize vertical wall space and look for dual function furniture (end tables, coffee tables and ottomans) items that feature storage.

- **Storage Is Inconvenient**

Is it too much of an ordeal to put things away? If you have to go climb a ladder, move a piece of furniture out of the way, or cross the length of your house just to put something away—you'll never do it.
Solution: Store things where you use them to make them easily accessible. For example, if you do your bills in the kitchen, store your financial files and calculator there, *not* in the spare bedroom upstairs. Look for where your piles are and create storage there.

Chapter 14 – Organization

- **Organizing Is Boring**

Let's face it—organizing and putting things away everyday is a dull, repetitive chore.

Solution: Make it more appealing and fun by adding a sense of personal style. Get containers you love instead of withering baskets, broken-filing cabinets and leftover moving boxes. Don't underestimate the power of pizzazz—it can make a big difference in whether you feel inspired to use and maintain your organizing system.

Level 2: External Realities

These are environmental forces that limit how organized you can be. Recognizing them empowers you to address the true source of the problem, and stop feeling like there's something wrong with you. Identify the source(s) of your disorganization and use the solutions below to put them into perspective.

- **The "Other" Person**

There's nothing more frustrating than having your organizing efforts undermined or disregarded by someone you live or work with.

> **Solution:** *Whether it's your spouse, child, roommate, co-worker, or employer, appeal to their own priorities by finding out what the clutter is costing them —your spouse may hate being late for work everyday, your child may be frustrated by losing game pieces, your boss may be embarrassed in front of visiting clients.*

Design systems together so you both have ownership—and they'll be more motivated to put things away.

- **An Unrealistic Workload**

Running a home, taking care of kids, helping your aging parents, and holding down a job are huge responsibilities. If you're trying to jam 20 hours worth of tasks into a 10-hour day, it's going to be nearly impossible to stay organized. Who has time to clean up?

Solution: Track yourself for a week, noting everything you get done, as well as what you don't. Then take a hard look to see what tasks on your list are superfluous. If everything must get done, get help. Consider delegating tasks to other family members or hiring an outside service.

- **Speed of Life/Technology**

Technology has sped up the pace of life, allowing us to work faster, learn more, do more, and be reachable 24 hours a day. It's easy to get caught up in the frenzy of pursuing every opportunity, but perpetual motion will burn you out.

Solution: Apply the brakes from time to time, and be willing to say "no" occasionally. Just because emails and calls arrive instantaneously, doesn't mean you need to answer them immediately. Don't be afraid to turn off the ringer on your phone or the message alert on your email, and slow down to keep your life in order and calm.

Chapter 14 – Organization

- ## During Transitions and Life Changes

Each time we go through a major life change (getting married or divorced, moving, having a family, switching careers, starting a new business, going back to school), we experience a breakdown of our organizational systems. It's inevitable—we are dealing with a new set of realities—and it takes time to process the information and to actually see what there is to organize.

Solution: Wait for things to settle a bit, so you have a clearer idea of your new priorities and needs, before setting up any new organizing systems.

- ## Limited Space

Living or working in a tiny home or office with little storage space will challenge even the most organized person. If you are already down to just the essentials—and have utilized every square inch of space—you may have simply run out of room. Trying to store more things than is physically possible will only increase your frustration.

Solution: If the needs of your (growing) family or (changing) job have increased, it may be time to look for a bigger space. Until that's possible, use an off-site storage facility to hold off-season items, memorabilia, and other items you don't need to access daily.

Level 3: Psychological Obstacles

Hidden internal forces may be pulling you toward disorganization—no matter how much you crave control! You may be subconsciously sabotaging your organizing systems and holding yourself back. If you see yourself in the categories below, try one of the solutions to get started.

- ## Need for Abundance

Did you grow up with scarce resources and feel like you never had "enough" (money, clothes, food, attention, or love)? If so, possessing large quantities of stuff now, as an adult, is probably comforting. It gives you a sense of fullness, comfort, and security while the idea of a spare, clutter-free environment makes you feel anxious and empty.

> *Solution: Instead of fighting your personality and forcing yourself to throw things out—try celebrating the abundance by organizing everything you own.*

Once everything is accessible and orderly, it may be easier for you to see what's truly excess and part with items bit by bit. No matter what, you'll have the chance to enjoy your belongings, instead of feeling lost under them.

- ## Sentimental Attachment

Do you get so emotionally attached to objects, it's hard to get rid of anything—even if you don't use it anymore? When items symbolize a part of ourselves, a time in our lives, or people we knew, it can be tough to let go. Saving some items is fine, but if you save everything—you won't be able to enjoy any of it.

Solution: Limit how much you keep for sentimental reasons and hold on to only the most important 20% in each category: kid's artwork, old clothes, etc. Make letting go of the rest easier by giving it away to a friend or charity. Remember, you can still own all of the memories of your past without holding onto every physical reminder of it.

- **Conquistador of Chaos**

Some people keep their lives or spaces disorganized because they love the thrill of coming to their own rescue and seeing their way through almost impossible situations. Often, people like this grew up under challenging circumstances and more so than anyone know how to handle a crisis. Actually capable of setting up wonderful organizing systems, they are always dismantling them and starting over in search of an even better solution.

Solution: Instead of constantly rebuilding your organizing systems, direct your talents to a new challenge. Learn a language. Become a better parent. Get involved in your community. Put those expert-problem solving talents to better use than living in constant chaos!

- **Thriving On Distraction**

Clutter can serve as a wonderful and convenient distraction from life's more complex challenges. In other words, as long as you have a closet to clean or a stack of papers to sort, you can avoid thinking about more perplexing problems.

Solution: If you are using clutter to distract yourself from bigger problems, search for a more direct way of coping with major stress. Reach out to a friend or professional who can help you sort out the real issues you're avoiding, and then you'll begin to enjoy your orderly home again.

- **Need for Retreat**

If your disorganization gets so extreme that you won't let anyone into your home or office, or if you frequently turn down social invitations to spend all your time "organizing" and "re-organizing" your stuff, consider whether you are using clutter as a protective shield—a way of insulating yourself from the outside world. It can be okay to want some private space, but living in that chaos may increase your anxiety level.

Solution:

> *Don't organize your whole space all at once. Go slowly. Start by creating one clutter-free room in which you keep nothing but items you use and love.*

If the experience feels good, create another room like that, then another. Remember, an organized work or living space is a much nicer "retreat" than a cluttered one.

This article "How to De-Clutter Your Home—for Good," was retrieved from: http://www.oprah.com/home/Discover-Your-Clutter-Problem/1#ixzz2qZS1GK5v

Chapter 14 – Organization

Organizing Your Paperwork

A few excellent ideas on organizing paperwork came from a web site at:
http://www.dummies.com/how-to/content/eight-tips-for-organizing-your-paperwork.html

They very appropriately suggest that coming up with a system of organization for all the paper in your life takes thought and planning. And making use of it requires time and effort. In the short run, letting papers pile up is a lot easier. But in the long run, doing so can turn into a major headache.

> *Taking the time and effort to develop a systematic way of organizing your papers can result in a lot less stress and hassle in your life.*

Try the following as you create your filing system:

- **Start simple:** Come up with a filing system that's relatively easy to use. You don't want your filing system to be more stressful than the stress it's supposed to alleviate.

- **Be colorful:** Files of different colors or tabs and labels of different colors can not only turn your filing system into a work of art but also make it easier to find different subjects and interests.

- **Don't scrimp when you buy a filing cabinet:** Invest in a cabinet of good quality. Poorly made filing cabinets tend to break down in the crunch. When your files get larger and heavier, their weight can strain a cheap filing cabinet and make it difficult for the drawers to open smoothly—or to open at all, for that matter. And try to find a cabinet that won't make your room look like a claim-adjusters office. Many of the traditional office cabinets are big and, frankly, pretty unattractive.

- **Keep important papers where you know they're safe:** Keep your documents in a safe place, but make sure you can easily get ahold of them when you need them. Keep track of the following

  Automobile information

  Bank account numbers

  Birth certificates

  Credit card numbers

  Deeds

  Important receipts

  Instructions

  Insurance policies

  Loan agreements

  Marriage certificate

  Medical records

Mortgage agreements

Passports

PIN numbers

School transcripts

Service contracts

Tax returns (last 7 years)

Warranties

Wills

- Some of these categories warrant their own separate file. Some, like your important numbers, can be combined. For the more important documents, you may want to keep the originals in a safe or in a safe-deposit box, and keep available copies in your files.

- **Avoid Lower Moravia:** The most common error people make when creating a filing system is to come up with categories that are too specific. For example, a file titled "Travel articles about Lower Moravia" won't fit well in your system unless you're definitely planning on going there or you're writing your master's thesis on this topic. If you continue in this vein, you'll be overrun with file folders in no time, and you'll have a heck of a time ever finding anything — if you ever want to. Start with fewer, broader categories.

- **Never put all your papers in one basket:** An approach described by organizational expert Stephanie Culp suggests that you have four baskets for your paper (in addition to the extremely important wastepaper basket):

    A To Do basket: The wire see-through kind works best.

    A To Pay basket: Again, wire works best here.

    A To File basket: Use a larger wicker basket.

    A To Read basket: Try an even larger wicker basket with handles.

- Culp recommends that you stack your To Do basket on top of your To Pay basket on your desk. Keep the To File basket under your desk, out of the way of your more immediate paper needs. You can keep the To Read basket in a different part of your home—such as your bedroom or study—so you can catch up on your reading whenever the opportunity arises.

> - *Make filing a habit: Find a time during the week to empty your To File basket and file those needed papers away. This task really shouldn't take long — 15 or 20 minutes should do it.*

- **Fine-tune later:** At a later date, take a look at what's in your files. Usually, you find that a file is either underused or bulging. If you find that you have only one or two things in a file folder, find or create a file that's broader in scope. Alternatively, if you find that a folder is overflowing with contributions, create subcategories, either by topic or by dates.

REFERENCES
Chapter 14 – "Organization"

Aguirre, S. (n.d.). *3 reasons you can't organize everything: The top three excuses we use to keep our clutter.* Retrieved from http://housekeeping.about.com/cs/organizing101/a/3excuses.htm

Bonner, J. (2007). *10 benefits of being organized.* Retrieved from http://www.blisstree.com/2007/11/08/sex-relationships/10-benefits-of-being-organized-207/

Cohen, A. (2005, September 27). *8 organizing strategies from professional purgers.* Retrieved from http://www.oprah.com/home/The-Urge-to-Purge/1#ixzz2qZeToxd3

Cohen, A. (2011). *Help, It's broken!: A fix-it Bible for the repair-impared.* New York: Hachette Filipacchi Media U. S., Inc.

Dummies.com. (n.d.). *Eight tips for organizing your paperwork.* Retrieved from http://www.dummies.com/how-to/content/eight-tips-for-organizing-your-paperwork.html

Getsetorganize.com. (n.d.). *How to get organized and stay organized.* Retrieved from http://getsetorganize.com/

Mannino, B. (n.d.). *8 secrets of personal organizers.* Retrieved from http://www.womansday.com/home/organizing/8-secrets-of-personal-organizers-124034

Monsell, S. (2003). Task switching. *Trends in Cognitive Sciences, 7*(3).

Montanaro, L. (2010). *Organizing. Jan.-Feb. 2010 Newsletter Organizing, University of Texas M.D.* Anderson Cancer Center. Retrieved from http://www.mdanderson.org/education-and-research/education-and-training/faculty---academic-career-enhancement/files/go-jan-feb-2010.pdf

Morgenstern, J. (2011). *How to de-clutter your home—for good.* Retrieved from http://www.oprah.com/home/Discover-Your-Clutter-Problem/1#ixzz2qZS1GK5v

Pashler, H. E. (1998). *The psychology of attention.* Cambridge, MA: MIT Press.

S.O.S. (Signature Organizing Services). (n.d.). *Benefits of being organized.* Retrieved from http://www.organizinglafayette.com/organizing-services/benefits-of-being-organized/

Spring Rhythm.com. (2012). *The importance of being organised.* Retrieved from http://springrhythm.com/2012/the-importance-of-being-organised

Willingham, D. T. (2010). Have technology and multitasking rewired how dtudents learn? *American Educator, Summer 2010.*

Chapter 15
Time

All you have for certain is now. Use it or lose it. Later might not get here and the past has past!

Too Precious to Waste

Time is one of the most precious items in a person's life. Once it's gone, it's gone forever. It cannot be recaptured. It is something that's divided equally among everyone. Everyone has the same amount of it, and it also depends on how we each use it. When I think of time, I think of a commodity I wish I had more of. More time to sleep; more time to read and relax; more time to be with family and friends. Most people I know wish they had more time. That being the case, the more wisely and efficiently we use our time is of utmost importance. How much is your time worth? If you could find a way to spend your time more productively and enjoyably would you take advantage of it?

> *The next time you make a decision that involves the use of your time, think about this value. Will you be wasting your time? Is it worth what you will get from it?*

For the typical, average person (as you look at your day,) about one third of your time is spent sleeping, another one third is spent "working" (or somehow earning a living), so the final one third has to be shared with everything else. A person might ask, "How do I find the time to do all the things I do?" It's called "making time"—multi-tasking, getting up early, going to bed late, "stealing" an hour here and an hour there. Or simply not "wasting" time on insignificant, less-priority, unimportant things. If a person followed us around, they could see just how much time we "waste" either doing "nothing" (even though there is no such thing) or doing trivial things that could be left undone, done at a more appropriate time or done more efficiently by someone else.

Chapter 15 – Time

It Goes Fast

Time is a commodity that is in limited supply. It is one thing that everyone shares in common. We all have an equal share of it—no more, no less. It's how we use our time that makes the difference. A certain amount is necessary for sleeping, eating, taking care of bodily functions, grooming and hygiene and other "necessary" functions. It's been estimated that most people have from 8 to 16 hours a day to "live life."

5 to 9 hours sleeping

1 to 3 hours eating (breakfast lunch, dinner)

1/2 to 1 hour grooming, bathing, etc.

1/4 to 1/2 hour bodily functions

1 to 3 hours traveling from place to place

7-3/4 to 15-1/2 hours (rounded to 8 to 16 hours) working

That leaves 8 to 16 hours to divide among such things as the following:

Physical/mental development

Spiritual development

Social development

Financial development (beyond regular job)

Family development

School/work

Vision/purpose/passion

Civic involvement

Personal development (entertainment, etc.)

Each of us devotes a different amount of time to these activities. We might call them something else, but they could all fit into these categories.

A Priority Measure

> *Time is a measure of importance. The amount of time you spend on something indicates its level of priority or importance.*

Time seems to "fly by" when you are having fun, or engrossed in something. When you are fully engrossed into your work or some activity, the time goes by quickly. Conversely, when you are bored with your work or some activity, time seems to drag on and on. In similar fashion, at "special" times with loved ones or even when you are alone, the time allotted for the day seems to never last long enough. No matter what you are doing, eventually, it will end. It seems that just about everything lasts "just for a little while." Good times and bad times alike come and go.

The measure of a person with a "good" life might be one whose time is "mostly" spent on positive, enjoyable things and less time is spent on not-so-positive or non-pleasurable things.

Chapter 15 – Time

My philosophy of life is that it is not all roses. If my time is spent mostly on positive or enjoyable things, then I am pretty satisfied. Currently, I think about 80% of my time is positive. Time spent on things like cleaning house and paying bills is not my favorites.

> *Be jealous of your time; it is your greatest treasure. Killing time is not murder, it's suicide.* (Taken from "You're Born an Original, Don't Die a Copy" by John L. Mason, 1993).

The Temporariness of Time

Time is an interesting phenomenon. It is here one minute and gone the next. I recall the great time I had when I was in Key West Florida and again the time I was in Kirkwood, near Lake Tahoe. That time is gone and now here I am at home typing. Tomorrow will find me doing something else. Everything comes and goes, good times and bad. I remember some time ago, my neck was hurting, a week later, it was fine. If you are bored with what is happening at one time, all you have to do is wait it out and things will be different later (for better or for worse). Everything lasts for but a moment in time and then it's gone. All you are left with are the memories of the past and thoughts of things to come. Time is but a moment in your life that can never be recaptured as an exact duplicate. Oftentimes, we have an enjoyable time and have a desire to repeat it (or at least come close) and sometimes we can, but more often we can't. Time waits for no one, ready or not.

Use It or Lose It

> *Time comes and goes like a thief in the night. One minute it's here, now, the next minute, it's gone, then.*

Time is so temporary, yet so permanent at the same time. We have as much of it as we need, but not nearly enough for what we want. Time is so elusive; as soon as you think you have it right, it's time to start all over again. Enjoy the time you have now, because things will change. You can count on it.

An important part of focusing on results is working out what to focus on with your time—how to best use your time such that the quality of your life and how you use your time is maximized—clarifying what you enjoy, understanding what your strengths (talents) and weaknesses are. A good way to get an idea of identifying these things is to carry out a SWOT analysis (Strengths and Weaknesses and Opportunities and Threats that you face). Sometimes developing an Action Plan can also save time and other resources. An action plan is a list of tasks that you have to carry out to achieve an objective. It differs from a To Do List in that it focuses on the achievement of a single goal. An action plan allows you to concentrate on the stages of that achievement, and monitor your progress towards it.

Different strokes for different folks

Some people rely on an Activity Log, which helps you find out how you actually spend your time, hour by hour. The first time you use, it you may be shocked to see the amount of time that is wasted. You may also be unaware that your energy levels may vary throughout the day. Most people function at different levels of effectiveness at different times depending on the amount of sugar in your blood, the length of time since you last took a break, routine distractions, stress, discomfort, or a range of other factors. There is evidence that most people have daily rhythms of alertness and energy.

> *Keeping an activity log helps you understand how time is spent and when you perform at your best. Once you have logged your time for a few days, analyze the log, (while logging, note how you feel, whether alert, flat, tired, energetic, etc.)*

"Make" time (turn off TV, get up earlier, use lunch period, set aside one day a week, ID a particular hour that works best for you).

How to save time

The Internet is replete with suggestions on how to save time. I have included a few examples:

Susan Ward provides Time management tips worth noting.
Retrieved from: http://sbinfocanada.about.com/cs/timemanagement/a/timemgttips.htm

- Create time management goals. "I will (goal + performance measure) BY (specific actions)." For example, "I will lose 10 pounds in two months BY running on a treadmill for half an hour six days a week." Remember, the focus of time management is actually changing your behaviors, not changing time.

- Prioritize ruthlessly. You should start each day with a time management session prioritizing the tasks for that day and setting your performance benchmark.

> - *Establish routines and stick to them as much as possible. While crises will arise, you'll be much more productive if you can follow routines most of the time.*

- Get in the habit of setting time limits for tasks. For instance, reading and answering email can consume your whole day if you let it. Instead, set a limit of one hour a day for this task and stick to it.

- Be sure your systems are organized. Are you wasting a lot of time looking for files on your computer? Take the time to organize a file management system.

- Don't waste time waiting. Always take something to do with you when you go on appointments or other meetings that cause you to wait before getting started.

Susan provides additional time management techniques for super-busy people:

- Recognize you can't do it all. Too many of us are stretched too thin because we've bought into the myth that everyone can (and should) do it all.

- Learn to say "Yes" and "No." The inability to say "No" is the cause of an incredible amount of misunderstanding and frustration. Instead of saying "No," people say "Maybe" or "I might be able to do that" or "I'll see," causing a huge waste of time. Make it a general rule not to say "Maybe" at all when you're asked to commit to something. Learn to make quick decisions and say "Yes" or "No" instead.

> - ***Unplug. There are times when it's important or useful to be unreachable to everyone or everything except the person or the task immediately in front of us.***

Make yourself the manager of your technology rather than being managed by it. Do not read every piece of email as soon as it comes in, for example, or feel that you have to personally answer every phone call.

- Take time off. Incorporate time off into your schedule. When you take time off, whether it's an afternoon or a weekend or a week, you return to your work refreshed and more productive, able to accomplish so much more in the amount of time available.

The Mayo Clinic staff offers time management tips to reduce stress and improve **productivity (Mayo clinic staff) (n.d.)**
Among those tips included are:

> - ***Break large, time-consuming tasks into smaller tasks. Work on them a few minutes at a time until you get them all done.***

- Evaluate how you're spending your time. Keep a diary of everything you do for three days to determine how you're spending your time. Look for time that can be used more wisely. For example, could you take a bus or train to work and use the commute to catch up on reading? If so, you could free up some time to exercise or spend with family or friends.

- Get plenty of sleep, have a healthy diet and exercise regularly. A healthy lifestyle can improve your focus and concentration, which will help improve your efficiency so you can complete your work in less time.

More on Time Management

More time management tips are summarized in the University of Nebraska at Lincoln's NebGuide, written by Kathleen Prochaska-Cue, Carla Mahar and Sandra Preston (2007). These tips can also be found online at:

(http://www.ianrpubs.unl.edu/pages/publicationD.jsp?publicationId=860).

Be Flexible. Allow time for interruptions and distractions. Time management experts often suggest planning for 50% or less of one's time. With just 50% of your time planned, you will have the flexibility to handle interruptions and any unplanned "emergency." When you expect to be interrupted, schedule routine tasks. Save larger blocks of time for priorities. When interrupted, ask Alan Lakein's question, What is the most important thing I can be doing with my time right now? to help you get back on track fast.

Consider Your Biological Prime Time. That's the time of day when you are at your best. Are you a "morning person," a "night owl," or a late afternoon "super person?" Know when your best time is and plan to use that time of day for your priorities, if possible.

Do the Right Thing Right. According to noted management expert, Peter Drucker, doing the right thing is more important than doing things right. Doing the right thing is effectiveness; doing things right is efficiency. Focus first on effectiveness (identifying what is the right thing to do), then concentrate on efficiency (doing it right).

Eliminate the Urgent. Urgent tasks have short-term consequences while important tasks are those with long-term, goal-related implications. Work toward reducing the necessary urgent things so you'll have more time for your important priorities. Flagging or highlighting items on your "to do" list or attaching a deadline to each item may help keep important items from becoming urgent emergencies.

Practice the Art of Intelligent Neglect. Eliminate from your life trivial tasks or those tasks that do not have long-term consequences for you. Can you delegate or eliminate any of your "to do" list? Work on those tasks which only you can do.

Avoid Being a Perfectionist. Many cultures have a belief that only gods are considered capable of producing anything perfect. When people in these cultures make something, a flaw is left on purpose so the gods will not be offended. Some things need to be closer to perfect than others, but perfectionism, paying unnecessary attention to detail, can waste time and be a form of procrastination.

Learn to Say "No." Such a small word—and so hard to say. Focusing on your goals may help. Blocking time for important, but often unscheduled, priorities can also help. But first you must be convinced that you and your priorities are important—that seems to be the hardest part in learning to say "no." Once convinced of their importance, saying "no" to the unimportant in life gets easier.

Reward Yourself. Even for small successes, celebrate achievement of goals. Promise yourself a reward for completing a task or finishing the total job. Then keep your promise to yourself and indulge in your reward.

Procrastination

Procrastination seems to be a problem that most of us have at one time or another. James Manktelow and Amy Carlson provided a few strategies to "Stop procrastinating."

> *"Stop procrastinating." They say the key to controlling this destructive habit is to recognize when you start procrastinating, understand why it happens and take active steps to manage your time and outcomes better.*

Are you procrastinating?

Here are some useful indicators that will help you know when you're procrastinating:

- Filling your day with low priority tasks from your To Do List.
- Reading e-mails several times without starting work on them or deciding what you're going to do with them.
- Sitting down to start a high-priority task and almost immediately going off to make a cup of coffee.
- Leaving an item on your To Do list for a long time, even though you know it's important.
- Regularly saying "Yes" to unimportant tasks that others ask you to do, and filling your time with these instead of getting on with the important tasks already on your list.
- Waiting for the "right mood" or the "right time" to tackle the important task at hand.

> *Why you procrastinate can depend on both you and the task. But it's important to understand which of the two is relevant in a given situation, so you can select the best approach for overcoming your reluctance to get going.*

Following are a few reasons for procrastination:

- Unpleasant task or job – try to get it done and over with as soon as possible.

- Disorganized—get organized with an action plan; prioritize and schedule to identify precisely when it is due.

- Feel overwhelmed by the task—break the project into a set of smaller, more manageable tasks; start with some quick, small tasks that you can get done and feel some achievement in the matter.

What the "experts" suggest for time management

An article in the *Wall Street Journal* by Sue Shellenbarger titled "No Time to Read This? Read This" had an interesting twist on how this columnist investigated time management systems. (http://deltawaverlyrotary.com/ryla/No_Time_to_Read_This.pdf) She says many readers seem to think they need a time-management system, based on the email response to my recent column on the importance of taking time off. Dozens asked me to recommend a time-management method that would help them get on top of their work and home duties. In response, I asked a half-dozen executive coaches to help me pick the most widely used time-management systems—not just software tools or high-tech to-do lists, but behavioral-change techniques that help people get organized, clarify thinking and increase output. Then, for a week each, I tried out of the three methods they mentioned most often—including one that involved a ticking plastic tomato.

Of course, a week isn't long enough to reap the full benefits of these methods. Still, I learned a lot from this experiment. Like many people, I am often my own worst enemy in managing my time, distracting myself from the task at hand, or setting myself up for failure by starting each day with an unrealistically long to-do list. Second, the key to getting more important stuff done is often doing less of everything else. And finally, getting control of your time requires a significant up-front investment of mental effort—and, well, time.

> *Mr. Allen has since sold more than one million books about Getting things Done and attracted 1.2 million followers on Twitter. GTD's aim is to corral all the projects and tasks floating around in your head into an organizing system you update weekly.*

Here, in no particular order, are the methods I (Sue Shellenbarger) tried:

• **Getting Things Done:** The reigning gorilla of time management, "GTD," as its followers call it, was created in the 1980s by David Allen, an Ojai, CA, consultant whose coaching, training materials and seminars can be found at **davidco.com**. No matter what chaos erupts, the system in theory enables you to quickly identify the next step to take on every front to keep all your projects moving forward, while keeping your mind clear to relax, think and be creative.

I start GTD with a weekly "mind sweep," writing down all the stuff I should be doing, want to do or dream of doing. The resulting list ranges from essentials, like meeting my next deadline, to nagging worries, like updating college-financing plans for my kids, to future hopes, like volunteering as a writing coach for needy kids. Next, I sort it all and create new files, action lists, calendar items or reminders based on what is needed next—for example, whether a project requires action (the deadline); input from someone (a talk with my accountant about college financing); or deferral (the tutoring plan). My daily calendar is reserved for only the most urgent items, such as the deadline.

When all the collecting, reviewing and categorizing required by GTD is portrayed visually on a "workflow map," the result resembles a cross between a corporate organization chart and a map of Middle-earth in *The Lord of the Rings*. GTD fans liken it to learning a new sport, such as tennis, and say mastering it can take two years.

Nevertheless, I see some benefits right away. GTD has me clump tasks together by context; phone calls, for example, are grouped so I can run through them quickly during a spare moment. And GTD ends sloppy habits, such as stashing piles under my desk, forcing me instead to decide what to do with all the stuff and either file or discard it. As I comply, I revel in the vast expanse of clear desktop that appears before me. I doubt, however, that I have the perseverance to stick to this system.

• **The Pomodoro Technique:** This quirky method had me working in intense spurts guided by a kitchen timer shaped like a tomato—or pomodoro, in the inventor's native Italian. Developed by Francesco Cirillo, director of XPLabs, a software design firm based near Rome, this technique is spreading via Twitter and other social networks. It can be learned in a few hours from a free guide at **pomodorotechnique.com**, making it a habit takes up to 20 days.

While any timer will do, I purchased my own tomato for $14.95. I start each day by making a log of things to do, then tackle each in 25-minute intervals called Pomodoros. When a Pomodoro is over, I mark an X on the log next to the item I am working on, then take a refreshing 3- to 5-minute break. Nothing must be allowed to interrupt a Pomodoro. If co-workers barge in, Mr. Cirillo advises trying to defer the conversation.

> *The Pomodoro Technique —The method is based on the idea that time-management tools and techniques should be simple; that frequent breaks can improve mental agility; and that changing the way people think about time can ease anxiety, freeing them to concentrate better.*

Although I found this method laughable at first, its simplicity is deceptive. Working with my ticking tomato made me aware that I constantly interrupt myself. Users are asked to put an apostrophe over the "X" on the log each time they are tempted to break a Pomodoro. I had no less than eight apostrophes over one "X"—marking impulses ranging from reading email to ordering a toner cartridge to running outside to see if my car had a flat tire (seriously).

This method offers less help than the others with organizational problems; it is narrower in scope. However, it eased my anxiety over the passing of time and also made me more efficient; refreshed by breaks, for example, I halved the total time required to fact-check a column.

> *"Sharpening the saw" metaphor for setting aside time to take care of your health so you can work (and play) with more vigor.*

• **Franklin Covey's Focus:** This method, subtitled, "Achieving Your Highest Priorities," hits workaholics where it hurts—in their upside-down priorities. Created by Franklin Covey, Salt Lake City (franklincovey.com)(http://deltawaverlyrotary.com/ryla/No_Time_to_Read_This.pdf). Focus aims to help users jettison busywork and wasted time and devote themselves to their most valued pursuits. Franklin Covey has trained more than two million people in the method. Some of its concepts are widely known, such as another well-known symbol, its four-quadrant "time matrix" helps users distinguish among tasks based upon whether they are truly urgent and important; important but not urgent; urgent but not important; or neither. A pretest shows I squander one-third of my time on unimportant stuff. To remedy this, I settle down for a half-hour planning session, a weekly Focus requirement, to think through my values, identify the roles and goals most important to me, and block out time in advance to pursue them. I enter other tasks day-by-day on my calendar, prioritizing them based on their importance. Like GTD, Focus requires a fairly high up-front investment of mental effort to be useful.

Focus aims to break users' "urgency addiction," the habit of rushing around needlessly. By week's end, I am surprised at how much calmer I feel, as I let insignificant stuff slide; in a spillover benefit, I am able to help my teenage son see that his race to finish a college research project early isn't truly urgent. Also, in pursuit of the value I place on generosity, I start working early on a holiday gift for my extended family, a photo calendar; not only do I take more pleasure in making it, but I know it won't be the usual slapdash, last-minute affair. In an era when values are often neglected, this system is a worthy antidote.

In the end, I expect I will embrace elements of each of these systems—the approach experts recommend for most people. The essence of good time management is sticking to rituals that make you more productive, and rituals are largely a matter of personal preference. According to Luke Iorio, president of iPEC Coach Training, Shrewsbury, NJ, the only system that matters is the one that works for each individual.

Time Management Secrets Anyone Can Use

Helen Coster wrote an article that was updated by Forbes staff writer Susan Adams titled "Time Management Secrets Anyone Can Use." In it, she talked about how much time people lose or waste. According to a survey by Salary.com, the average worker admits to wasting 2.09 hours of each eight-hour workday, not including lunch or scheduled breaks. The Web is like the next-door neighbor who keeps asking us to play when we know we have homework to do. Thankfully, there's an entire community of people who specialize in productivity and time management. Their guru is David Allen, author of the 2001 book *Getting Things Done: The Art of Stress-Free Productivity*. Others include Merlin Mann, founder of the blog 43 Folders, and the highly addictive Lifehacker.com. Here are some of their best ideas to help you declutter your life and make way for big, creative boosts of productivity.

Some of their advice, like "don't multitask," is counter-intuitive. Apparently you'll be much more productive if you check your e-mail only a few times a day, rather than incessantly, as most of us do. But much of it is common sense, in an "I know I should do that, but I never actually do" kind of way. Allen's mission is to help people rein in all the to-do-list items that float around in their heads, and then organize them systematically. A system allows you to identify the next step to take on every project and keep those projects moving forward, while freeing up your mind to relax and dwell on loftier things. Keeping things out of your head and managing a clear and complete inventory of your commitments brings a great increase in clarity, focus, and control. And, it provides the critical background for then making the important distinctions about where you're going and what's really important, so you can make decisions about what to do, and not do, *on* those lists.

> *Allen says that if replying to or disposing of an e-mail takes less than two minutes, you should always do so right away.*

A lot of productivity-speak involves managing technology. Gretchen Rubin, author of the bestselling book *The Happiness Project*, describes technology as a great servant but a terrible master. Turn off those annoying e-mail alerts–do not have a sign flash up on your screen every time a new e-mail comes in. Send less to receive less: Keep your e-mails short, and write fewer of them.

Allen is also a huge proponent of to-do lists. He says that everyone should have an organized, clear and simple way of writing down everything they need to remember. That way you never need to lie in bed at night trying to recall some crucial thing you're sure you've forgotten. Productivity experts say to keep multiple lists, including a short list of one to three things that you absolutely need to do each day. Hand off anything that can be delegated, and be realistic about what you can reasonably accomplish every day. Don't set yourself up for failure by starting each day with an unrealistically long agenda.

Time Management Equals Self-Management

According to Patrick Forsyth author of *Successful Time Management*, time management must be seen as synonymous with self-management. It demands discipline, but discipline reinforced by habit. He goes on to say the good news is that it gets easier as you work at it. Good habits help ensure a well-organized approach to the way you plan and execute your work. On the other hand, bad habits—as many of us are aware—are difficult to shift. And the changing of habits is something that may well be a necessary result of any review of how you work.

> *Making time management work for you is based on two key factors: how you plan your time and how you implement the detail of what you do.*

Chapter 15 – Time

The first of these, which is reviewed in the early part of this book, creates an important foundation upon which you can then build and work. The second consists of a multitude of operational factors, practices, methods and tricks, all of which can individually and positively affect the way in which you work. Such factors may be absurdly simple, for example, visibly checking your watch from time to time will tend to make visitors less likely to overstay their welcome, especially if such checks are accompanied by the appropriate look of concern. Or they may demand more complexity, for example, a well-set-up filing system can save time, ensuring that you can locate papers quickly and accurately.

Other factors may be downright sneaky, like having a private signal to prompt your secretary to interrupt a meeting with news of something demanding its rapid curtailment or your prompt departure. Furthermore, there is a cumulative effect at work here. This means that the more you adopt or adapt the tricks of the trade that work for you, the more time-efficient you become. This is a process most of us can continue to add to and work on throughout our career. So, unless you are a paragon of time-efficient virtue, a review of whether you are working in the best possible way is nearly always worthwhile. Indeed, it can pay dividends to keep a regular eye on this throughout your working life. This too can become a habit.

Forsyth also shares what he calls the greatest time wasters.

The Greatest Time Waster?

1. *Do not put off the things you find difficult.* The time wasted here can occur in two ways. First, decision making is delayed, then implementation is delayed and both let time leak away.
   Of course, the thought, consideration, checking, or whatever needs to be done, must be done and in many contexts should not be skimped, but once you are able to make the decision or take the action, or both, then there is merit in doing so. Watch out for any tendency you have in this respect; controlling it can save considerable time and aggravation.
2. *Do not put off the things you do not like.* There is a difference between what you find difficult and what you simply do not like. The likely effect of delay and avoidance of tasks is very similar to that referred to above…but the motivation is different, though not less powerful.

   The only real help here is self-discipline and a conscious effort in planning what you do to make sure that such things do not get left out and that this, in turn, does not lead to worse problems. Some flagging system to highlight things on your list may act as a psychological prompt. Experiment here to see if it makes a difference.

   If all this seems minor and you disbelieve the impact of this area, it is likely that any time log exercise you undertake will confirm the danger. Again, it seems simple, but the correct approach can save a worthwhile amount of time.

3. *Beware of your favorite tasks*. This is potentially even more time wasting than putting off things that you do not like or find difficult, and often the most difficult to accept. But many people spend a disproportionate amount of time on the things they like doing best—and perhaps also do best. This is perfectly natural and there are various reasons for it. An important one is that any concentration on what you like is what seems to produce the most job satisfaction.

Is There Really Such a Thing as Time Management?

Self management is the focus of another article written by Ken Fairweather titled "Fairweather: does time management really exist?"

Is there really such a thing as time management? With the plethora of books and articles on the subject, one might conclude that it must be next to impossible. Even if we could hang on to the minute hand of a clock as it pulls up from the "9" to the "12," we would not impact the passing of time even one second. So why do these books continue to multiply and be read so eagerly by people? It must be more complicated than one thinks or more difficult than the books make it.

> *It's not so much a matter of managing a clock as it is managing one's self.*

Self-management is really the issue here. The reason we don't call it by its real name is that we want to shift the emphasis away from ourselves and thus escape the self-incrimination, which is too condemning. Involved in this concept is self-control. This may sound like we are personalizing it too much, but that in reality is the problem or challenge.

Self-management begins with applying the same planning principles we use for businesses to our personal lives. First of all, we need to determine our personal mission statement then follow with the fundamental step of setting goals to realize our personal mission. However, we cannot stop there because these can easily seem daunting and impossible to us. Therefore, we must take the next step in determining the specific objectives to reach our goals. These objectives might be better understood as "bite-sized" activities that we can more easily understand and attempt to accomplish. These should have the following characteristics: attainable, challenging and, most of all, measurable.

> *The guiding management principle here is, "If a goal is worth doing, it must be measureable."*

There are several reasons they need to be measurable. The main reason is this will contribute greatly to our self-management. This goes a long way in managing what we do. In business, we do this to maximize our corporate resources. This takes some effort on our parts, but we can do the same with our personal resources of time, knowledge, skills and interests.

So, instead of deflecting our efforts at time management, let's see if we can look to ourselves and see if we can become better self-managers and thereby accomplish those high priority responsibilities we face in business, community and home.

REFERENCES
Chapter 15 – "Time"

Adams, S. (2013). *Time management secrets anyone can use.* Retrieved from http://www.forbes.com/sites/susanadams/2013/04/11/time-management-secrets-anyone-can-use-2/

Drucker, P. (1966). *The effective executive.* New York: Harper & Row.

Fairweather, K. (2013). *Fairweather: Does time management really exist?* Retrieved from http://www.news-journal.com/business/local_business/fairweather-does-time-management-really-exist/article_3b8bbeaa-51e8-508d-be9d-d748b894a0f8.html

Forsyth, P. (2013). *Successful time management.* London, UK: Kogan Page.

Lakein, A. (1974). *How to get control of your time and your life.* New York: Signet.

Manktelow, J., & Carlson, A. (n.d.). *Beating procrastination – Managing your time. Get it all done.* Retrieved from http://www.mindtools.com/pages/article/newHTE_96.htm

Mason, J. L. (1993). *You're born an original, don't die a copy.* Tulsa, OK: Insight International.

Mayo Clinic staff. (n.d.). *Time management tips to reduce stress and improve productivity.* Retrieved from http://www.mayoclinic.com/health/time-management/WL00048

McGee-Cooper, A. (1983). *Time management for unmanageable people.* Dallas, TX: Ann McGee-Cooper & Associates.

Pareto, V. (n.d.). *Thirteen timely tips for more effective time management.* Retrieved from http://www.ianrpubs.unl.edu/epublic/live/g1772/build/

Prochaska-Cue, K. M., Mahar, C. J., & Preston, S. D. (2007). *Thirteen timely tips for more effective time management.* University of Nebraska at Lincoln's NebGuide. Retrieved from http://www.ianrpubs.unl.edu/pages/publicationD.jsp?publicationId=860

Shellenbarger, S. (2009). No time to read this? Read this. *Wall Street Journal.* Retrieved from http://online.wsj.com/news/articles/SB10001424052748704538404574541590534797908

Ward, S. (n.d.). *11 time management tips.* Retrieved from http://sbinfocanada.about.com/cs/timemanagement/a/timemgttips.htm

Ward, S. (n.d.). *5 ways to get more time.* Retrieved from http://sbinfocanada.about.com/od/timemanagement/a/getmoretime.htm

Chapter 16
Excellence

Doing Your Best

The best; the highest level of performance; it doesn't get much better than excellent.

When I think of excellence, I think of quality, lots of effort was extended, thoughtful consideration and care was given to the task. A person who has done an excellent job is one who has provided quality. When I strive for excellence, I challenge myself to go that extra step, to not settle for good, but to try for better or even best. Excellence can (and maybe should) be personal. I'm not sure I go for excellence in everything. I would not consider myself a "perfectionist." However, there are some things in which I strive for excellence. Vince Lombardi is quoted as saying: "Perfection is not attainable, but if we chase perfection we can catch excellence."

Early research on excellence can be traced back to the study of the acquisition of expert performance. Ericsson, Krampe, and Tesch-Romer (1993) wrote an article titled "The Role of Deliberate Practice in the Acquisition of Expert Performance" that shed some light on the history of how excellence was seen.

> *Our civilization has always recognized exceptional individuals, whose performance in sports, the arts, and science is vastly superior to that of the rest of the population.*

Speculations on the causes of these individuals' extraordinary abilities and performance are as old as the first records of their achievements. Early accounts commonly attribute these individuals' outstanding performance to divine intervention, such as the influence of the stars or organs in their bodies or to special gifts (Murray, 1989). As science progressed, these explanations became less acceptable.

Chapter 16 – Excellence

Research on expert performance and expertise (Chi, Glaser, & Farr, 1988; Ericsson & Smith, 1991a) has shown that important characteristics of experts' superior performance are acquired through experience and that the effect of practice on performance is larger than earlier believed possible. For this reason, the account must specify the environmental circumstances, such as the duration and structure of activities, and necessary minimal biological attributes that lead to the acquisition of such characteristics and a corresponding level of performance. Sir Francis Galton (1869/1979) was the first scientist to investigate the possibility that excellence in diverse fields and domains has a common set of causes.

People believe that because expert performance is qualitatively different from normal performance, the expert performer must be endowed with characteristics qualitatively different from those of normal adults. This view has discouraged scientists from systematically examining expert performers and accounting for their performance in terms of the laws and principles of general psychology. We agree that expert performance is qualitatively different from normal performance and even that expert performers have characteristics and abilities that are qualitatively different from or at least outside the range of those of normal adults. However, we deny that these differences are immutable, that is, due to innate talent…Instead, we argue that the differences between expert performers and normal adults reflect a lifelong period of deliberate effort to improve performance in a specific domain.

Is It Important To You?

Things that matter include the work I do, the clothing I choose to purchase, the choices I make in places to go for a meal when I want to celebrate or choosing a major purchase. For some things that do not matter that much (to me), I strive for good, but not necessarily excellence. For example, I try to make my lawn look good, but I am not that particular about it looking excellent. Or my choice in choosing a place for a meal on non-special occasions or when I am cleaning my house on non-special occasions. In most cases, I strive for "good" but not excellence.

> *Excellence can be considered an attitude, a state of mind, and a position you take about what you do.*

When I think of things that I want to be excellent, those things represent me, they are important to me, they matter. Excellence is also a choice. It is something I have given importance to, something I am willing to make a priority. If I do something that is just okay or just good, then I have not put a high level of importance on it. Excellence to me is special. To some people, excellence is very, very special and to them good is special while okay is probably the norm. To the person who might be considered the "perfectionist," good is only okay. A benchmark is a standard of excellence or achievement against which similar things can be measured or judged.

Chapter 16 – Excellence

Everyone has to make up their own mind about the level of quality for which they will strive on a continuum of from very bad to excellent (very bad, bad, poor, okay, good, excellent). To define terms, very bad is harmful, bad is useless, poor is not very good, okay is acceptable, good is above average and excellent is the best. Everyone has their own definition of this continuum, including their own reasons for striving for one or the other.

Achieving excellence should be everyone's goal. But, it may be easier said than done. In the first place, excellence is relative. A soufflé made by your Aunt Mae that you consider excellent, might be considered mediocre in the restaurant world.

Better Than Good

To be excellent at something is to be very good at it—better than most people are. No one is excellent at everything. Most people are excellent at a few things. Excellence is usually acquired through practice. Generally speaking, the more we practice something, the more likely we are to be excellent at it. Very few things come naturally. And, even those things that come naturally, we can usually improve upon by practice. There are also some things that no matter how hard we try, we will never be excellent at it.

Above and beyond the "call of duty;" work that has been checked and double-checked;

> *something that is done with meticulous care and concern with quality in mind;*
> *something that is held to a higher than normal/average standard;*
> *All these are examples of EXCELLENCE.*

When a person starts out thinking that they want something to be excellent, they try to think creatively and comprehensively. When the goal is excellence, you think about how something can be unique, different, better, more full, more complete, more universally acceptable. Things that take on the characteristic of excellent, are special, often time consuming, sometimes tedious, laborious and "costly" (meaning more than just financially).

It's a funny thing about life; if you refuse to accept anything but the best, you very often get it. **(Somerset Maugham)**

Excellence is Subjective

Set apart, well done and something of which to be proud all describe excellence. Excellence is a judgment call by someone else, usually one with knowledge of the thing being judged. Excellence can also be a standard that is at the high end of a continuum or rating criteria. Some people strive for excellence in most things they do. Excellence can be a way of seeing things, qualitatively. Being focused and having a clear picture of the task before you improve your ability to do any excellent job.

Chapter 16 – Excellence

> ## *Unless you do something beyond what you have already done, you will never grow.*

That's a definition of "mediocrity:" best of the worst and worst of the best. "Potential" means you have not done your best yet. Its been said that the biggest enemy of great is good. Don't accept good as good enough. Tolerating mediocrity in others makes me more mediocre.

> ## *Only an average person is always at his best.*

> ## *The average man doesn't want much and usually gets even less.* ("You were Born an Original, Don't Die a Copy," by John L. Mason, 1993)

Excellence Among Teachers

Manuela Brusoni, Radu Damian, Josep Sauri and others (2014) wrote an article titled "The Concept of Excellence in Higher Education" that highlighted qualities of excellent teachers that I thought was worth sharing. They say excellence in teaching is determined by factors such as the inspirational nature of individual lecturers, the organization of presentations, the interaction with students as participants and how well the information provided meets the learning objectives of the course. Excellence can be identified both in terms of student satisfaction and also in terms of the performance of students in assessment. There are differences between deep and surface learning. Excellent teaching may be seen as the efficient presentation of information, which maximizes the students' opportunities to gain the highest marks in the course. Alternatively, excellence could be recognized as the stimulus for students to engage with the subject and to enhance their understanding and knowledge.

Excellence vs. Personal Excellence

Mrityunjay Kumar posted an article on the careermanagement.wordpress website titled "Personal Excellence" that exemplifies the difference between excellence and personal excellence. He opens the article with two interesting questions. Why do some individuals always try to do their best in a situation, while others don't? At work, why do some people bemoan their work, and still do an outstanding job, while others seem happy with their work, yet produce mediocre results? In my experience, this can be traced to one of the important traits of an individual: desire to seek excellence in whatever they do.

The writer goes on to say that everyone wants to be best at what they do, but it is not always easy to do so. Those with a healthy dose of this trait will continue to pursue excellence even when given a boring assignment or challenging environment, while others will give up and settle for mediocrity. So why do some people pursue excellence? Vince Lombardi (great football coach) suggests the quality of a person's life is in direct proportion to their commitment to excellence, regardless of their chosen field of endeavor. For Indian movie fans, Amir Khan's character in 3 Idiots says, "seek excellence, success will follow."

Chapter 16 – Excellence

To make sure we are talking about the same thing, let me state the dictionary definition of excellence:

Excel: *To surpass others or be superior in some respect or area; do extremely well.*
Excellence: *The state or quality of excelling or being exceptionally good; extreme merit; superiority.*

Note that excellence is in comparison with others. This means that my excellence is somehow also determined by how others perform. This can lead to a sense of hopelessness—"if my peers are better than me, I am worthless" kind of thoughts may arise. This may be relevant for skills-based excellence where "you can be excellent at anything" may be true. However, it is not true everywhere—otherwise college dropouts could never be billionaires, and Harvard toppers would be ruling the world.

> ### *Strive to be better than last time, every time*

There is another kind of definition of excellence, which does not depend on comparison with others for its definition. To disambiguate it, let's call it "personal excellence."
Personal Excellence: *Producing your best in any given situation, within or without a conducive environment to do so.*

This definition of excellence only compares with self, and, hence, is in my control. Given this definition, it is easy to answer the questions I posed at the beginning. People who believe in personal excellence always compete against themselves and their own performance last time. They don't let environment come in the way of their performance. When they believe they have given their best, they are happy and satisfied and see no reason to give up even when their best hasn't been good enough to achieve desired results.

Such people always strive to be better next time. And they succeed. As great all-time basketball coach John Wooden said so well: ***Success is peace of mind which is a direct result of self-satisfaction in knowing you made the effort to do the best of which you are capable.***

If we believe the above statement, success becomes a controlled process and is no longer dependent on whims of my manager or my organization or my competitors. Practicing this with no visible signs of success is a hard thing to do since we crave success so much. However, sustained success can come from following this principle as the coach's team has shown (nicknamed the "Wizard of Westwood," he won ten NCAA national championships in a 12-year period—seven in a row (http://en.wikipedia.org/wiki/John_Wooden)—as head coach at UCLA, an unprecedented feat (http://en.wikipedia.org/wiki/John_Wooden). Within this period, his teams won a record 88 consecutive games (http://en.wikipedia.org/wiki/John_Wooden). He was named national coach of the year six times.

How do we achieve this excellence? Here are a few relevant quotes:
If you are going to achieve excellence in big things, you develop the habit in little matters. Excellence is not an exception, it is a prevailing attitude. — **Colin Powell**

We are what we repeatedly do. Excellence, then, is not an act, but a habit. –**Aristotle**

> *A man can't make a place for himself in the sun if he keeps taking refuge under the family tree.*

Excellence is not about knowing what is excellent, it is about pursuing excellence all the time, in every little thing we do. I firmly believe that our work is our signature, it is our resume. We are what we do. Therefore, it is critical that we are excellent in whatever we do. We are remembered and known by what we created and how we created them, long after we have moved on. Excellence is a habit, mediocrity is a habit too. There are many reasons to do mediocre work ("I hate my work," "I hate my boss/salary," "I am bored"), but once mediocrity becomes a habit, it becomes you.

Here are a few examples in which it is easy to do mediocre work, but then it is easy to be excellent too, and the habit gets formed either way:

- You need to ask yourself what value you provide in an interaction—if you don't provide value, don't have that interaction. When you do, provide value. For example, it is easy to become an email forwarder (receive emails from one set of people, send it to another set of people without adding value) rather than figuring out a way to provide value (read and summarize the issue, talk instead of email, provide solutions without asking others, etc.).
- Push back on uninteresting work, but if you still get assigned to it, give your 100%. If you need to create a presentation as part of your work, people will remember the quality of the presentation for a long time, longer than they will remember the fact that you had a reason to produce mediocre work (if they remember at all). A PowerPoint deck lives forever!

> - *Do not compare with others, compare with yourself.*

- Can you do better than this? If so, do it. If you can create a better spec than last time, do so. Others not producing a good quality spec should not be a reason to create a poor spec.
- Success comes from personal excellence, personal excellence comes from true passion, true passion comes from deep interest; so work on what deeply interests you and you will achieve long-term success.

Chapter 16 – Excellence

In the literature, there are numerous suggestions on how to achieve excellence and how others have addressed the issue of excellence. In the next several pages, I will share such suggestions as how to guide your child to excellence; personal excellence tips; excellence in business; characteristics of excellence among anesthetists and steps to achieve excellence in anything.

4 Ways to Guide Your Child to Excellence

There was an article on the website of "Babble" (http://www.babble.com/kid/4-ways-child-education-development) that caught my attention. The article titled "4 Ways to Guide Your Child to Excellence" was an excerpt from David Shenk's book *The Genius in All of Us* (2010). The author prefaced their comments by first indicating that parents don't have anything close to complete control and in most cases, should not shoulder all the blame when things don't turn out well. But parenting does matter. And to the extent that parents can have a serious impact on the goals, strategies, and personal philosophies of their children, here are four key guideposts to excellence:

1. Believe

The author tells a story about a young Japanese violinist and instructor named Shinichi Suzuki who discovered through his experiences with his students that gifts and talents were not exclusive to the privileged few; with the right training and persistence, anyone could achieve remarkable success. It begins, Suzuki is convinced, with a simple faith that each child has enormous potential and that it is up to us to muster whatever resources we can to exploit that potential. Without that parental faith, it is highly unlikely that significant achievement will occur.

> *Rather than wonder if their child is among the "gifted" chosen few, parents should believe deeply in the extraordinary potential of their children.*

2. Support, Don't Smother

Columbia University psychiatrist Peter Freed talks about the Britney Spears Syndrome. He says it's a clear model for how the narcissistic parent injures a child's sense of self by attaching high achievement to love.

It all begins, explains Freed, with a parent who has grown up believing that, in order to be liked, he must be exceptional in some way. The parent subsequently showers his own children with affection after each accomplishment and shuns them after failure. According to Peter Freed, the parent beams when the child performs well, and then withdraws love when he's underperforming. In early adulthood, Freed explains, the child will inevitably struggle with social and emotional challenges (as everyone does) and find that he doesn't have a deep emotional reservoir to fall back on. The foundations of love and trust are corrupted by what he experienced as a child. The child victim of a narcissistic parent frequently has a difficult time forming stable life partnerships.

Chapter 16 – Excellence

The flip side, says Freed, is a parent who offers unconditional and unshifting love that is decidedly not connected to achievement. Non-narcissistic parents follow the child's lead. They're very good at limit-setting and setting high expectations, but they will wait to see what the kid wants to do and not become anxious if he isn't high-achieving early on. Their attitude is that the most important thing you're doing in childhood is making friends and being an active part of the community. If the team wins, they'll be happy, but if the team has trouble, they'll have them over and watch a movie. New science shows genes and environment are deeply intertwined. There is, in other words, a right way and a wrong way to direct your kids toward achievement. Early exposure to resources is wonderful, as is setting high expectations and demonstrating persistence and resilience when it comes to life challenges. But a parent must not use affection as a reward for success or a punishment for failure.

> ***Albert Einstein once said, it's not that I'm so smart, it's just that I stay with problems longer.***

3. Pace and Persist

Einstein's simple statement is a clarion call for all who seek greatness, for themselves or their children. In the end, persistence is the difference between mediocrity and enormous success. The big question is, can it be taught? Can persistence be nurtured by parents and mentors?

Robert Cloninger, a Washington University biologist, said the key is intermittent reinforcement.

> ***A person who grows up getting too frequent rewards will not have persistence, because they'll quit when the rewards disappear.***

This jives well with Anders Ericsson's finding about deliberate practice and with the ascetic philosophy of Kenyan runners: an emphasis on instant gratification makes for bad habits and no effective long-term plan. The ability to delay gratification opens up a whole new vista for anyone looking to better herself.

Any parent can adopt basic strategies to encourage self-discipline and delayed gratification. Here are two:
- Model self-control. Behave as you'd want your child to behave, now and in the future. Don't buy, eat, or grab whatever you want whenever you want it. The more self-control you demonstrate, the more your child will absorb.
- Give kids practice. Don't immediately respond to their every plea. Let them learn to deal with frustration and want. Let them learn how to soothe themselves and discover that things will be all right if they wait for what they want.

380

4. Embrace Failure

> *In the sometimes counterintuitive world of success and achievement, weaknesses are opportunities; failures are open doors.*

The only true failure is to give up or sell your children short. Developmental biologists stress that all of human development is set up to be a response to problems and failures. In other words, parents are not supposed to make things easier for kids. Instead, they are supposed to present, monitor, and modulate challenges. The great success stories in our world come about when parents and their children learn to turn straight into the wind and gain satisfaction from marching against its ever-increasing force.

Personal Excellence Tips

The website of Litemind.com (Exploring ways to use our minds efficiently) had a number of their readers give advice on what makes the most positive impact on their lives. Among the "66 best personal excellence tips," were 13, which I thought were worth sharing:

- **Make personal excellence... personal.** Bring a part of yourself into everything you do. The more your work reflects your individuality, the more it will stand out from the crowd, the more people will relate to it (and you) and the more "real" your achievements will seem to be. And when your efforts involve other people, involve them on a personal level as well, so the project becomes a relationship that brings out the best in everyone involved (by Tori Deaux).

- **Health, the neglected point.** There will be tons of people writing about how to be more productive or how to excel in time management, etc. Yet the first thing we must remember when we are talking about (excelling in) personal development is taking care of our health. You can have all the fancy techniques to get more done, but neglecting your health does not help to increase productivity in the long term. Exercise regularly and make the conscious effort to eat healthier food (by Vincent).

- **Learn to develop a "productive mindset."**

> *A productive mindset is one that makes the best use of your resources — your time, your energy and your effort.*

It's making the most and best of what you have while enjoying the process. It is a mindset that encompasses curiosity, open-mindedness, desire, critical thinking and a positive outlook among other qualities (by ZHereford).

- **Don't presume... ask!** How many times in life have we missed an opportunity, created a misunderstanding or just plain got it wrong because we presumed we knew what someone meant, was thinking or their motivation? Don't presume—just ask! Ask questions that connect: "What's going on for you around that?", "What's important to you in this?" Ask questions that clarify: "What is it you need me to understand?", "What did you take from that?" Ask questions that go to the next level, that is, beyond their current strategy: "Is x, y, z really important to you in this situation?" (by Leona Dawson)

- **Make your mind your playground.** Your mind is your ultimate tool (if everything else fails, you still have it). Making it fit, alert and ready to play is the best approach to make it your greatest asset. So make your brain healthy by providing it healthy food and plenty of sleep, and make it happy providing themes for it to play with. Give your mind a workout (e.g., play chess!) and you'll see the results immediately! (by Luciano S. Fier)

- **A chronometer by my side.** For me, tasks are challenges. My motivation is to think of them as competitions in which I always want to win. So, for example, if I need to learn something, I set a clock by my side to 1 hour. I concentrate as hard as I can in that hour— no Internet connection allowed, as it's totally distracting. If someone asks for a quick task, I do it as fast as I can and then I note down how long it took. That's a great way to give more excitement to my routine work (by Tiare Rivera).

- **Tomorrow is another day.** All too often, when trying to establish a new habit—or break an old one—I don't manage to keep on the straight and narrow! When on a diet, I occasionally forget about it and eat something I shouldn't. But then I remind myself that just because I forgot once, doesn't mean I have failed—and that I should just get back to the diet tomorrow. I apply this to every project I start and, gradually over time, the number of times I fail reduces to a well-established (excellent) level (by John Mullarkey).

- **Optimize your life with the SWOT matrix.** The SWOT matrix is a framework for analyzing your life and finding creative ways to optimize it. The acronym SWOT stands for Strengths, Weaknesses, Opportunities, and Threats. This matrix enables you to focus on your strengths, to minimize weaknesses, and to take advantage of every opportunity (by Mary Jaksch).

- **As you think, so you are.** July 10, 2000. A car accident took me to the hospital with an arm, leg and hip crushed. During the months of recovery (one of them motionless), my wife was diagnosed with an incurable illness and my mother died. I was sent back home in a wheelchair. By chance I came to read, "As a Man Thinketh" by James Allen. It led me to take charge of myself. In the months ahead, I never gave up until I could walk again. I took an examination to become a high-school counselor and passed it, although I was in my fifties. "Take charge of yourself" is the motto I always say to myself and the students I am counseling (by Joel Cardigan).

> *Rather than trying to figure out what someone else wants in a friend, partner, colleague, lover, boss, employee, then contorting yourself to fit what you believe they're looking for... just be you.*

- **Be real!** In all your glory. If you're a dork, be a glorious dork. If you're a geek, parade around in your geeky radiance. Quiet, outgoing, artistic, analytic, whoever you are, honor that essence and build out your world with people and experiences who support your authentic self (by Jonathan Fields).

- **Set aside a specific time each week for personal reflection.** Having a consistent weekly review is one of the most powerful ways to better focus your attention, realign your priorities, and make sure you're making progress toward your goals. Block off 30-45 minutes at the end of each week, ask questions, and write down your answers in your system of choice: What did I learn this week? What did I accomplish? What do I still need to focus on for next week? Have I made progress toward my long-term goals? What new ideas do I have? What did I learn this week that inspires me? (by Eric Blue)

- **Full Speed Ahead vs. Kickback & Wait.** Perseverance is two things, and you must befriend them both to get where you are going. I constantly ask myself whether it is time to persist in my efforts (toward excellence) or to be patient and wait for better circumstances. Always ask this question because the persistent rush can destroy, the patient wait can stagnate, and only the wise application of both can deliver you to your destination.

- **Happiness is a choice.** Happy people know that their happiness depends on their state of mind and that they have the power to choose their response to external events.

> *They avoid 'if only' fantasies, are grateful for simple pleasures, figure out their strengths and direct them toward achieving meaningful goals.*

They're engaged in their work, look for ways to get more pleasure out of life and are kind toward others. In the words of Aristotle: Happiness depends upon ourselves (by Marelisa Fabrega).

These 13 best personal excellence tips were retrieved from:
https://litemind.com/best-personal-excellence-tips

Fundamental Concepts of Excellence in Business

The EFQM (European Foundation for Quality Management) (n.d.) has put together an excellence model for business that I thought was worth of sharing. According to EFQM, the Fundamental Concepts of Excellence outline the foundation for achieving sustainable excellence in any organization. They can be used as the basis to describe the attributes of an excellent organizational culture. They also serve as a common language for top management.

The organization states that these eight Concepts have been identified through a rigorous process that included benchmarking globally, searching extensively for emerging management trends and, last but not least, conducting a series of interviews with senior executives from a cross-section of industries operating across Europe. Each of the Concepts is important in its own right but maximum benefit is achieved when an organization can integrate them all into its culture.

Chapter 16 – Excellence

Following are the eight concepts:

ADDING VALUE FOR CUSTOMERS
Excellent organisations consistently add value for customers by understanding, anticipating and fulfilling needs, expectations and opportunities.

CREATING A SUSTAINABLE FUTURE
Excellent organisations have a positive impact on the world around them by enhancing their performance whilst simultaneously advancing the economic, environmental and social conditions within the communities they touch.

DEVELOPING ORGANISATIONAL CAPABILITY
Excellent organisations enhance their capabilities by effectively managing change within and beyond the organisational boundaries.

HARNESSING CREATIVITY & INNOVATION
Excellent organisations generate increased value and levels of performance through continual improvement and systematic innovation by harnessing the creativity of their stakeholders.

LEADING WITH VISION, INSPIRATION & INTEGRITY
Excellent organisations have leaders who shape the future and make it happen, acting as role models for its values and ethics.

MANAGING WITH AGILITY

> *Excellent organisations are widely recognized for their ability to identify and respond effectively and efficiently to opportunities and threats.*

SUCCEEDING THROUGH THE TALENT OF PEOPLE
Excellent organisations value their people and create a culture of empowerment for the achievement of both organisational and personal goals.

SUSTAINING OUTSTANDING RESULTS
Excellent organisations achieve sustained outstanding results that meet both the short and long-term needs of all their stakeholders within the context of their operating environment.
This information was retrieved from: http://www.efqm.org/efqm-model/fundamental-concepts

Excellence is Excellence (especially among anesthetist)
Excellence is excellence no matter where you find it. Calls for reform to postgraduate medical training structures in the UK have included suggestions that training should foster excellence and not simply ensure competence. Smith, Glavin, and Greaves (2011) conducted a modified Delphi-type survey starting with an e-mail request to specialist anesthetists

involved in education, asking them to identify the attributes of an excellent anesthetist. Following are the results showing examples of characteristics of excellence in anesthesia.

Categories	Number of Responses	Example Responses
Strives for excellence	27	Critically appraises own practice and that of others. "Strive for perfection in what they do" is conscientious. Meticulous attention to detail. High professional standards. Motivated to improve themselves. A positive direction to problem solving, rather than diverting issues away from themselves.
Teacher	25	The ability to educate and inspire peers, trainees, medical students, and other clinical staff. Taking the time to teach. Enthusiasm to teach all comers. A talent for teaching. Inspirational to others. Able to express ideas and concepts clearly, both to individuals and groups.
Clinical skills	22	Demonstrates professional artistry in giving a good anesthetic. The capability to administer an anesthetic smoothly, safely, and slickly in both complex and routine circumstances. Manual dexterity and technical competence.
"Pull their weight"	21	Willing to "go the extra mile." Pulls his/her weight in the department, not necessarily head of department, but a reliable and hard-working member who can be called upon to help when needed.

Reliability—those who habitually offer to help out in times of crisis—that is, short-term notice of sickness for on-call cover.

Innovative/original	21	Flexibility of thought and actions. Unafraid to challenge established ideas. A willingness to innovate, provided that the value and safety of the changes can be proven. Creativity (setting up new services, changing from weak to strong service provision, thinking of new ways to provide excellent service for patients).

Categories	Number of Responses	Example Responses
Knowledge	20	Contemporaneous in general and specialist area of practice. Intellectual capacity and ability to integrate knowledge with skills. Relevant background knowledge and ability to apply it. Being up-to-date with current practice, drugs, techniques, literature, and adhering to current recommended standards of practice.

> ***A team player who is able to step up as team leader in a difficult situation.***

Leadership	17	Can interact with, or lead, a team. Enjoying good professional relationships within the various teams that one works with.
Good communicator	16	Has "the common touch," can communicate easily and clearly with all colleagues and patients. The ability to communicate clearly, politely, and effectively with both patients and staff. A collaborative mentality: able to communicate effectively with patients, relatives, and colleagues and to include others when making decisions.
Relationship with patients	15	Inspires patients' confidence. Protecting the patient and acting in the patient's best interest. Empathy toward patients and relatives. Impeccable bedside manner. Ability to form effective rapport with patients.
Liked and respected	15	They inspire trust and are trustable. They easily become the recipient of confidences. Ability to get on with colleagues and the theatre team. Above all is the person a senior anesthetist turns to for help and asks to anaesthetize their spouse.
"Nice person"	13	Approachable. Affable. Patience in even the most stressful situations. Kindness. Considerate of others. A reliable and supportive colleague.
Well organized	12	The ability to choreograph an operating list so that all aspects run smoothly. Forward planner. On time and prepared. Organized/efficient. They have a method/system.

Categories	Number of Responses	Example Responses
Calm	12	In control. Calm under pressure. Emotional stability, calm in emergency, clear and quick thought processes, no panic, non-aggression but able to convey urgency when necessary.
Organizational efficiency	12	Makes efficient use of team. Timeliness—starting on time, efficient work practices, finishing on time, business awareness.
Experience	12	Can interact with, or lead, a team. Enjoying good professional relationships within the various teams that one works with.
Flexible	11	"Out of programme" experience. Broad background of specialties. Wide knowledge of anesthetic practice, wide variety of techniques at one's fingertips, wide exposure to different surgical specialties.
Enthusiastic/keen	11	Enjoys the job. Passion. Having a particular "glow"—being someone people like having around.
Alert	10	Global awareness of working place and process. Observant/perceptive/situationally aware/sees "the big picture."

"10 steps to achieve excellence in anything"

Celestine Chua (2009) wrote a blog on which she shares key principles of personal excellence titled "10 Steps to Achieve Excellence in Anything."

1. Have the hunger for excellence

You need to want to achieve excellence.

> **The emphasis here is on what "you" want, not what others want.**

Make sure the goal is something you set for yourself, because unless it is, chances are you don't really want it.

2. Benchmark against the best

What is it you are working on? Who are the people who are the best in this area? What are the results they have achieved? Set your targets to the same level as their best results, or even higher if you are feeling up to it.

3. Believe that you can do it

Self-belief is paramount to every success. You need to first believe in yourself to get somewhere. If you don't have self-confidence, who is going to believe in you?

4. Build a concrete strategy & plans

Every goal needs a proper strategy and plan for it to come to life. Setting a goal and not following through with proper planning is like getting into your car to drive to your destination without knowing how to get there or even having a driving license. Many people fail in their goals because they fail to follow-through with planning. The bigger your goals, the more important that you invest proper time in building your plan.

5. Learn from the best

Hook up with people who are the best in the field and learn from them. They have the best practices, insights and tips, which will be extremely valuable in your pursuit of excellence. Rather than trying to learn everything from scratch, it's easier to leverage on the learnings from others and build on from there. This will jumpstart your learning curve by a huge degree.

6. Do not limit yourself

Don't be afraid to try every single thing that might take you to your goal. In fact, be more concerned about the potential opportunities you might be missing out on when you don't try something.

> *Opening yourself up to possibilities will enable you to pick up on things which might be fundamental to your success.*

7. Go all out; Work really hard

With every success, comes hard work. Without hard work, you cannot achieve results. People who try to find the easy way out are kidding themselves if they think they can achieve excellence without putting in hard work. If you observe around you, the people who seek out "get-rich-quick" methods are also the very people who don't achieve much in their lives. Hard work is the universal quality that will pay off in the long term. Once you invest the due time and effort, the results will start coming in.

8. Focus your efforts

Once you have finished trying out every single thing that you can see, focus your efforts in the areas that bring you the most results. I subscribe to the 80-20 principle, where 20% of causes lead to 80% of effects you see in a situation. Focus your energy on the few key drivers of success that will lead you to the results you want. This way, you will utilize your efforts more effectively, which can be subsequently channeled into more value-added activities.

9. Be adaptable.

Adaptability is one of the essential pillars of excellence. As you may already know,

> *change is inevitable—You can either cower in the face of change, learn to deal with it or even turn it into your favor.*

Be ready for change at all times and develop a friendly relationship with change. This also applies to changing your plans. Don't be overly attached to your plans and be prepared to alter them where needed. If there are certain things you are doing that are not very effective, be prepared to improvise them or drop them totally.

10. Never give up.
There is no failure except in no longer trying. (Elbert Hubbard)
Don't ever give up. Remember that defeat never occurs unless you accept it as defeat. If a certain problem is too big for you to handle, break it down into smaller pieces so it's easier for you to tackle them. As long as you keep trying, you will eventually achieve your goal.
This article "10 Steps to Achieve Excellence in Anything" was retrieved from:
http://www.lifeoptimizer.org/2009/09/04/steps-to-achieve-excellence/

Perfectionism vs. Healthy Pursuit of Excellence
I thought the comparison of perfectionism vs. healthy pursuit of excellence was shown nicely by Dr. Miriam Adderholdt (January 3, 2013) in the excerpt from *Perfectionism: What's Bad About Being Too Good?*

Perfectionists reach for impossible goals.
Pursuers of Excellence enjoy meeting high standards that are within reach.

Perfectionists value themselves by what they do.
Pursuers of Excellence value themselves by who they are.

Perfectionists get depressed and give up.
Pursuers of Excellence may experience disappointment, but keep going.

Perfectionists are devastated by failure
Pursuers of Excellence learn from failure.

> *Perfectionists remember mistakes and dwell on them.*
> *Pursuers of Excellence correct mistakes, then learn from them.*

Perfectionists can only live with being number one.
Pursuers of Excellence are happy with being number two if they know they have tried their hardest.

Chapter 16 – Excellence

Perfectionists hate criticism.
Pursuers of Excellence welcome criticism.

Perfectionists have to win to keep high self-esteem.
Pursuers of Excellence finish second and will still have a good self-image.

This information was retrieved from: http://janebluestein.com/2013/prefectionism-vs-healthy-pursuit-of-excellence/

REFERENCES
Chapter 16 – "Excellence"

Babble.com. (2010). *4 ways to guide your child to excellence.* Retrieved from http://www.babble.com/kid/4-ways-child-education-development

Brainyquote.com. (n.d.). *Definition of excellence.* Retrieved from http://www.brainyquote.com/words/ex/excellence162353.html

Brusoni, M., Damian, R., Grifoll, J. et al (2014). *The concept of excellence in higher education.* Retrieved from http://www.enqa.eu/indirme/ENQA%20Excellence%20WG%20Report_The%20Concept%20of%20Excellence%20in%20Higher%20Education.pdf

Chi, M. T. H., Glaser, R., & Farr, M. J. (Eds.) (1988). *The nature of expertise.* Hillsdale, NJ: Erlbaum.

Chi, M. T. H., Glaser, R., & Rees, E. (1982). Expertise in problem solving. In R. S. Sternberg (Ed.), *Advances in the psychology of human intelligence* (Vol. 1, pp. 1-75). Hillsdale, NJ: Erlbaum.

Chua, C. (2009). *10 steps to achieve excellence in anything.* Retrieved from http://www.lifeoptimizer.org/2009/09/04/steps-to-achieve-excellence/

Cruess, S. R., Cruess, R. L., & Steinert, Y. (2008). Role modelling—making the most of a powerful teaching strategy. *British Medical Journal, 336,* 718–721.

Ericsson K. A., Krampe R. T., & Tesch-Romer C. (1993). The role of deliberate practice in the acquisition of expert performance. *Psychology Review, 100,* 363–406. Retrieved from http://projects.ict.usc.edu/itw/gel/EricssonDeliberatePracticePR93.pdf

Ericsson, K. A., & Smith, J. (Eds.). (1991). *Toward a general theory of expertise: Prospects and limits.* New York: Cambridge University Press.

Gladwell, M. (2000). *Outliers: The Story of Success.* London: Penguin.

Janebluestein.com. (2013). *Perfectionism vs. healthy pursuit of excellence.* Retrieved from http://janebluestein.com/2013/prefectionism-vs-healthy-pursuit-of-excellence/

Kumar, M. (2011, December 25). Personal excellence. *Perspectives on Career Management.* [Web log]. Retrieved from https://careermanagement.wordpress.com/2011/12/25/personal-excellence/

Leman, K. (1985). *The birth order book.* Old Tappan, NJ: Fleming H. Revell Co.

Mason, J. L. (1993). *You're born an original, don't die a copy.* Tulsa, OK: Insight International.

Murray, P. (1989). Poetic genius and its classical origin. In P. Murray (Ed.), *Genius: The history of an idea* (pp. 9-31). Oxford: Basil Blackwell.

quotationspage.com. (n.d.). *Quotation details.* Retrieved from http://www.quotationspage.com/quote/3113.html

Reference.com. (n.d.). *Achieving excellence.* Retrieved from http://www.reference.com/motif/Education/achieving-excellence

Shenk, D. (2010). *The genius in all of us: Why everything you've been told about genetics, talent and IQ is wrong.* Doubletree: New York.

Skelton, A. (2007). Understanding teacher excellence in higher education. *British Journal of Educational Technology, 38*(1), 171-183.

Smith, A. F., & Greaves, J. D. (2010). Beyond competence: Defining and promoting excellence in anaesthesia. *Anaesthesia, 65,* 184–191.

Smith, A. F., Glavin, R. & Greaves, J. D. (2011). Defining excellence in anaesthesia: The role of personal qualities and practice environment. *British Journal of Anaesthesia, 106*(1), 38–43 .

Wright, S. M., Kern, D. E., Kolodner, K., Howard, M., & Brancati, F. L. (1988). Attributes of excellent attending physician role models. *New England Journal of Medicine, 339,* 1986–1993.

Chapter 17
Self Assessment

Choose an area in life to self assess and ask, Where am I? Where do I stand?

> *Before you talk about dealing with change, you need to have a clue about not only what needs to be changed but where things are currently.*

Consequently, starting with a self-assessment might be a first step in the process of self improvement.

Be for real!!
We are each obligated to take responsibility for our own reality. One way to keep in touch with what is really going on in our own lives is to do periodic self-assessments that are based on the "here-and-now" and that are brutally honest and as truthful and as straight forward as we can possibly make it. It is a good idea for you to make a written assessment of where you think you stand in all areas of your life at a particular (dated) time. This activity might take place over a period of several days, weeks, or maybe even months. The important thing is to begin to document as complete and as accurate an assessment of where you stand in each area of your life. Some people have gone so far as to get feedback from friends, relatives, colleagues and others who are knowledgeable about certain areas in your life. Their opinions are often helpful to either confirm or refute our own assessment.

Why do others sometimes know things about us that we don't know about ourselves?
That's a question Simine Vazire (2010) asked in an article published in the *Journal of Personality and Social Psychology*. We are far from perfectly accurate about ourselves, and, as Santayana (1905/1980) observed, outsiders are often at least as good as the self at describing what a person is like (Kolar, Funder, & Colvin, 1996; Vazire & Mehl, 2008). These findings violate the common sense conviction that nobody knows you better than you

do (Pronin, Kruger, Savitsky, & Ross, 2001; Vazire & Mehl, 2008). Regularly checking to make certain that your best effort is being made is recommended.

> *Self-assessment is a continuous activity. You should consider assessing and reassessing yourself periodically throughout life.*

Initially, you might do an assessment quarterly or twice a year and then maybe once a year on your birthday, the first or last part of the year or on some other significant day that will trigger the need to make the assessment.

Making an Honest, Current, and Personal Observation of Yourself

Self-assessments are only as good as you are honest, objective and as open as you can be. Self-assessments serve as barometers for later assessments or comparisons. When we make a self-assessment, we are looking at a certain aspect of our lives, as we see it, at this point in time. Self-assessments can help us see if we are on the right "track" toward achieving our goals in life or if we have deviated from our mission in life. Self-assessment can mean taking a look at where you are in the various areas in your life in relation to where you want to be, in relation to the proportioned balance in your life and in relation to having a current gestalt or total picture of where you are at this point in time.

Taking an Objective Look at Areas in Your Life That Matter to YOU

Self-assessments are made in an effort to stay true to your mission in life, to stay balanced, to make certain you are staying "in tune" with the times. The initial self-assessment can serve as baseline data that can be compared with later self-assessments. Self-assessments are useful reminders to keep us on target with decisions, goals or other such situations that we might have made for the sake of others or for our own benefit.

> *Self-assessments are only as good as our own objectivity and (sometimes brutal) honesty.*

Sometimes self-assessments need validation from people who are around us, who know us and who can confirm or correct our own assessment. You must remember that self-assessments are simply a snapshot of your life or situation at a given time. Consequently, the results of such an assessment must be accepted in light of that. Questions might be asked: "Is this assessment likely to have been the same days ago, weeks or months ago? Is it likely to be different tomorrow, next week or next month? Take time to examine your priorities and values to see if your lifestyle habits and routines are supporting your idea of a good life.

Why Self-Assessment?

For those of us who have been doing self-assessments for years, they are usually done for a reason. Oftentimes, someone has brought it to your attention or, somehow you have become aware that you need to self-assess.

Chapter 17 – Self Assessment

> *Whatever the reason, self-assessment involves looking at how you spend your time. It involves looking at your lifestyle and sometimes it involves reassessing your priorities.*

For example, I had to reassess how I was spending my time. I realized that if I wanted to complete this book, I would have to devote more time to writing and doing research. The reassessment caused me to set aside several days a month to do nothing but write or to write and do research. Self-assessments can result in planning to make big changes or in the consideration to make simpler, smaller changes. Sometimes self-assessments result in confirmation that you are right on track and do not need to make any changes. No matter the reason, self-assessment is a valuable tool to use.

One reason for self-assessment might be to ask yourself:
- how content am I with certain aspects of my life or with life in general?
- What things are going on in my life that I think I need to change?

> - *Am I relatively happy with the way things are going at work? At home? In life?*

- What about my financial security, or family life, or spiritual life?
- If I looked at my daily schedule, would I be happy with how I spend my time?
- What about short- and long-term goals? Am I moving in the right direction on those?
- Is life fun, boring, more boring than fun?
- How much stress do I have in my life?

Questions like those might be useful to ask yourself. Are you in a rut routine and need to consider making changes? Your routine is your life. Gradually change the routine and start a new one so the new one becomes routine. Reassessments help to answer some of these questions.

Personal Interest or Other Reasons for Assessment
Other reasons for self-assessments could be to assess your skills, abilities or the career for which you might be best suited. In that case Teri Fritsma (2009) offers 10 reasons why you should take a self-assessment, retrieved from http://iseekinteractive.org/blog/2009/10/21/top-10-reasons-why-you-yes-you-should-take-a-self-assessment/. Fritsma explains that assessments let you rate yourself on different characteristics (your skills, abilities, values, or interests, for example) and then see a list of occupations that could be a good match for you. But did you know that the *process* of taking an assessment might be just as valuable as the results you get? Read on to learn more about what an assessment can do for you.

Chapter 17 – Self Assessment

1. There is an assessment out there for you.

There are lots of different types of assessments out there; one of them is bound to give you new insights about yourself. Here are just a few: ISEEK's skills assessment (http://www.iseek.org/careers/skillsAssessment) lets you rate your skills—like writing, social skills, or technical skills. O*NET's ability profiler (http://www.onetcenter.org/AP.html) is a paper and pencil tool that lets you rate yourself on nine different abilities (such as verbal ability and manual dexterity). The MnCareers interest assessment, (http://www.iseek.org/careers/interestassessment.html) a paper and pencil tool, is great for career explorers without a lot of work experience who want to see what might be a good match for them (here's New York's interest profiler – an online version that's similar – found at: https://www.nycareerzone.org/graphic/assessment/index.jsp). O*NET's Work Importance Profiler (http://www.onetcenter.org/WIP.html) lets you see which occupations are a good match for the things you value in your job (like autonomy, pay, recognition, and other features). And these are just a few; find more here: http://www.iseek.org/careers/assessyourself.html

2. This is not a test.

> *A lot of people think of assessments as some sort of binding evaluation with right and wrong answers. Not true—the only "wrong" answers are the ones that don't truly reflect you.*

Not only that, but you can expect your answers to change as you change and your career evolves.

3. Assessments require as little or as much time as you want to spend.

The New York interest profiler (www.careerzone.ny.gov) takes about one minute to complete. ISEEK's skills assessment (http://www.iseek.org/careers/skillsAssessment) takes 5-10 minutes. Others may take a little longer. The point is, you don't have to spend half a day filling in bubbles. (Of course, the more time and effort you put into it, the more you're likely to get out of it.)

4. Assessments can help at any stage of your life.

Years ago, you might have spent most or all of your career working for the same company. There was little need to assess yourself once you got your foot in the door. Those days are gone. Today, if you're like most people, you'll work for lots of different companies or organizations over the course of your life.

> *This means YOU are in charge of deciding what's important to you, where to develop your skills, and when and why it's time to seek new opportunities.*

Whether you're 14, 44, 64 or 84, a self-assessment can help you do this.

5. Assessments help you recognize your transferable assets.

When exploring your options, you need not be limited to thinking only about your current and previous job duties. A good assessment will encourage you to think more about the qualities that you bring to any job. It won't ask you if you've ever written memos or handled customer phone calls; it'll ask you about your writing abilities or social skills. This is great if you want to explore the range of possibilities open to you.

6. Assessments help you identify your weaknesses.

No one is perfect at everything, and no one likes everything equally. If you really want to get the most out of your assessment, you MUST rate yourself honestly. It's probably more important to name the things you *don't* like or *aren't* good at than it is to identify your strengths. The more truthful and discriminating you are, the better your results will match the real you.

7. Assessments can help you make life decisions with a strong awareness of who you are and what you want.

> *Once you've identified your weaknesses honestly, the next questions is: what do you want to do about them?*

Again, there's no wrong answer here—it's just important to explore the question. Are you at a place in your life when you want to challenge yourself to grow in some of your weaker areas? Or are you satisfied with the opportunities that are open to you even if you never change a thing?

8. Assessments are objective.

The great thing about assessments is that they're totally impartial. Unlike your friends or relatives, they don't know you personally and they don't have preconceived ideas about what you can or should be based on your personality, your gender, your race, or anything else. Because of this, assessments can sometimes give you unexpected results. Before dismissing results that don't immediately make sense to you, ask yourself: is there anything about life that interests you?

9. (Many) assessments are free.

Hint: any assessment you find on ISEEK (http://www.iseek.org/) or O*NET (http://www.onetcenter.org/tools.html) will be free. In general, assessments at ".com" websites will probably have a price tag attached, whereas ".org" or ".edu" sites will probably provide free resources. And in the world of assessments, it isn't true that you get what you pay for. The free resources are typically just as good as the ones you pay for.

10. Assessments can help you with resume writing and "personal branding"

Personal branding (http://iseekinteractive.org/blog/2009/09/11/how-personal-brand-can-help-or-hurt-your-job-search/) is all the rage now. The phrase simply means knowing who you are and what makes you unique, especially to an employer. Taking the time to do an assessment could help you find the right words to describe yourself in a resume or cover letter. It could also give you insights about your unique "brand."

The Riley Guide website at http://www.rileyguide.com/assess.html provides information about how to assess your personality type and specifically what that means.

Personality and Type Indicators of Assessment

Many people talk about their "type" or how they have taken personality tests, but not all of these people understand the information they've been given, or how it applies to their careers (or their life in general).

According to the **Myers & Briggs Foundation**, the psychological types measured by their tests can describe the following:

- The ways in which a person prefers to take in information
- The ways in which he or she prefers to make decisions
- Whether a person derives energy from the outside world or the inner world
- Whether he or she prefers to keep things open or to move toward closure.

In the Myers & Briggs Foundation's form of testing, these four preferences are used to assemble a person's psychological "type," sometimes called his or her "personality type" — although different personality tests measure different aspects of a person's personality, and classify people into different categories based on these differences. In general, though, any theory of psychological type claims that people with different preferences naturally have different interests, perspectives, behaviors and motivations—and that awareness of these preferences helps people better understand themselves and others in terms of career goals and various other aspects of life.

Mentoring and Personal Self-growth

The organization "Thrive" (growth resources for thriving missionaries) offered a self-assessment questionnaire titled Mentoring and Personal Growth that I thought would be appropriate for this chapter of self-assessment. Their website is located at www.thrive.sim.org

Chapter 17 – Self Assessment

Mentoring and Personal Growth

Self-Assessment Questionnaire

> *Mentoring is defined as a relationship with a deliberate purpose of fostering growth. A mentor could be a friend or colleague, a more experienced person, or someone with specialist skills.*

This questionnaire is a self-evaluation tool provided by Thrive to help you:
- Discover areas where mentoring may be helpful for you;
- Consider the different types of mentor that could be available for you;
- Get you started in a mentoring relationship to stimulate personal growth.

This questionnaire is for your own use (you will not be asked to submit it to anyone). However, it is helpful for you to talk with someone about what you have learned and how you intend to respond.

> ### 1. How satisfied are you with the following areas of your life?

Satisfied?	Not at all									Fully
Physical strength and stamina	1	2	3	4	5	6	7	8	9	10
Intellectual	1	2	3	4	5	6	7	8	9	10
Relationships and family	1	2	3	4	5	6	7	8	9	10
Spiritual	1	2	3	4	5	6	7	8	9	10
Main work/ministry	1	2	3	4	5	6	7	8	9	10
Other ministry(s)	1	2	3	4	5	6	7	8	9	10
Life overall	1	2	3	4	5	6	7	8	9	10

2. The table below lists various aspects of life. Put a tick beside the ones for which you would like to have some guidance, training and or encouragement.

Like Help	Aspects of Life	Category of Life
	Management of time, finances, etc.	Life planning
	Handling major transitions	
	Life focus and priorities	
	Devotional life & spiritual disciplines	Spiritual
	Finding God's leading and will	
	Victory over temptations	
	Healthy lifestyle	Physical
	Physical exercise	
	Body weight	
	Reading and personal study	Intellectual
	Knowledge for work/ministry	
	Language and cultural competence	
	Handling stress	Emotional
	Freedom from anxieties	
	Personal identity	
	Relating well with others	Relationships and family
	Marriage and parenting	
	Singleness	
	Skills for work/ministry	Ministry and/or profession
	Professional advancement	
	Coping with life in a new context	Cultural adaptation
	Relating meaningfully with local people	
	Understanding and adapting to a culture	

If you have a lot of ticks in one category of life (see right hand column) this would indicate the need for a mentor who is competent in that area.

3. In what way would you like someone to help you? Place a tick beside the ones that apply:

A		B		C
Listen to you and understand you		Help build self-confidence		Offer challenging ideas
Offer friendship and care		Offer wise counsel		Guide professional development
Offer encouragement		Confront negative attitudes		Teach you some specific skills
Pray with you and for you		Provide growth opportunities		Help you analyze your situation
Provide accountability		Inspire to excellence		Help you to find direction in a specific area of life

There are three general kinds of mentors, which are each best suited to provide for the items listed in one of the columns in the table above:

A	B	C
Friend or peer mentor	General mentor	Specialist mentor
Someone at the same level as you, where normally you are mentoring each other.	Someone with more experience and maturity than you who can help you in a wide range of areas.	Someone with special knowledge of an aspect of life or ministry, or with special skills such as coaching or counseling.

If you have more ticks in one column than the others, this may indicate a priority to find that sort of mentor, although, most of us need people in all three categories.

4. The table below describes some types of specialist mentors. Many of these kinds of mentors have received formal training leading to certification, although others have learned through personal study and practical experience. Use of a specialist mentor tends to be short-term and many will require that you pay for their services.
Which of the following people could be helpful to you?

Chapter 17 – Self Assessment

Tick the ones you think could benefit you:

Category of Life	Types of Specialist Mentors	Description of particular approach and skills
Life planning	Life coach	Uses a questioning approach to help you think through a goal or issue and decide on an action plan.
Spiritual	Spiritual director	Discusses how God has been at work in your life with the aim of discerning his will and leading you into a closer relationship with God.
Physical	Medical doctor	Diagnoses health problems, prescribes treatment and advises on lifestyle issues.
	Personal trainer	Provides a physical exercise program suitable for you including training, motivation & monitoring.
Intellectual	Tutor	Answers questions and guides your learning in a subject area they are knowledgeable about.
Emotional	Counselor or psychologist	Explores your experiences and feelings so as to help you resolve emotional issues. Some counselors specialize in family and relational issues.
Relational		
Ministry/-Professional	Supervisor or trainer	Demonstrates skills and evaluates your performance for the purpose of ministry/professional competence.
	Professional coach	Uses a questioning approach to help you think through professional development and career planning.
Cultural	Orientation mentor	Encourages cultural reflection and adaptation by discussing your experiences and helping to give deeper understanding of these.

Chapter 17 – Self Assessment

This questionnaire was retrieved from:
http://www.thrive.sim.org/index.php?option=com_phocadownload&view=category&download=4:personal-growth-mentoring-questionnaire&id=6:mentoring

A Different Perspective on Self-Assessment
Self-Assessment in the Health Professions: A Reformulation and Research Agenda

Kevin Eva and Glenn Regehr (2005) wrote a research article on self-assessment that gives a completely different perspective than the one most of us are familiar with. Their article, published in the *Academic Medicine Journal,* sheds light on the complications involved in self-assessment that most of us do not pay attention to. The two authors noted that many researchers and educators have identified self-assessment as a vital aspect of professional self-regulation (Willoughby, Gordon, & Boud). This rationale has been the expressed motivation for a large number of studies of self-assessment ability in medical education, health professional education, and professions in education generally. Self-assessment has been defined broadly as the involvement of learners in judging whether or not learner-identified standards have been met. (Boud)

While attractive due to their concise and encompassing nature, we fear that such simple definitions risk being misleading as they can cause under-appreciation of the complexities of the construct.

> *Self-assessment functions both as a mechanism for identifying one's weaknesses and as a mechanism for identifying one's strengths.*

Each of these mechanisms can be considered to have distinct, albeit complementary, functions.

To fulfill these various functions, it seems that self-assessment must be effectively enacted in three forms: summatively, predictively, and concurrently. In enacting self-assessment summatively, a professional must reflect on completed performances both for the purposes of assessing the specific performance and for the purposes of assessing his abilities generally. When evaluating performance on a particular task, the professional can often assess the overall quality of the completed job as a question that may come in various forms.

That is, the individual might ask how good this performance was relative to what she could have done, relative to what her peers might typically do, relative to the best that could have been done (a gold standard) or relative to some minimally acceptable standard. Alternatively, there are some situations in which the mechanisms for objectively assessing the outcome are not immediately available, in which case the professional might ask herself how confident she is in the conclusion or outcome generated (is it right? will it stand up? could there have been a better solution given the situation?).

The professional might then use her assessment of the specific task to draw summative conclusions about herself or her abilities in this domain generally. Again, such conclusions may be in absolute terms (am I good enough in this domain? am I minimally competent?) or in relative terms (am I average, above average, or below average, and against whom should I be comparing myself?). In drawing general conclusions about her abilities from a particular performance, the professional must also make determinations about whether this particular episode should be taken as an appropriate reflection of her general skills: were there extenuating circumstances that led to a particularly high or low performance?

In addition to these summative functions, self-assessment must be used predictively. Professionals are constantly required to assess their likely ability to manage newly arising situations and challenges. In this predictive role, self-assessment leads to questions such as: Am I up to this challenge? Should I be starting this task (now, alone, in this way)? What are realistic goals for accomplishment in this context (what would I consider to be a good or acceptable outcome for me)? How much better might I imagine performing with some additional preparation, and is the increased preparation worth the anticipated increase in performance? What additional resources should I recruit (either internally or from the outside) to complement my strengths and shore up my weaknesses?

Finally, self-assessment plays a vital role in its concurrent mode of functioning. In this concurrent mode, self-assessment acts as an ongoing monitoring process during the performance of a task. It is self-assessment in its concurrent mode that leads to questions such as:

> *Is this coming out the way I expected? Am I still on the right track? Am I in trouble? Should I be doing anything differently?*

Should I persist in the face of negative feedback from the situation (that things are not going the way I thought they would or as easily as I thought they would)? Do I need to recruit additional resources (internal resources such as attention or external resources such as advice/assistance)? Do I need to reassess my original goal or my original plan?

<u>REFERENCES</u>
Chapter 17 – "Self-Assessment"

Arnold, L., & Willoughby, T. L. (1985). Self-evaluation in undergraduate medical education: A longitudinal perspective. *Journal of Medical Education, 60*, 21–28.

Bargh, J. A., & Chartrand, T. L. (1999). The unbearable automaticity of being. *American Psychologist, 54*, 462–479.

Bargh, J. A., & Williams, E. L. (2006). The automaticity of social life. *Current Directions in Psychological Science, 15*, 1– 4.

Boud, D. (1995). *Enhancing learning through self assessment*. London: Kogan Page.

Boud, D. (1999). Avoiding the traps: Seeking good practice in the use of self assessment and reflection in professional courses. *Social Work in Education, 18*, 121–132.

Dunning, D. (2005). *Self-insight: Roadblocks and detours on the path to knowing thyself*. New York: Psychology Press.

Epley, N., & Dunning, D. (2006). The mixed blessings of self-knowledge in behavioral prediction: Enhanced discrimination but exacerbated bias. *Personality and Social Psychology Bulletin, 32*, 641–655.

Eva, K. W., Cunnington, J. P. W., Reiter, H. I., Keane, D. R., & Norman, G. R. (2004). How can I know what I don't know? Poor self-assessment in a well defined domain. *Advances in Health Sciences Education, 9*, 211–224.

Eva, K., & Regehr, G. (2005). Self-Assessment in the health professions: A reformulation and research agenda. *Academic Medicine, 80*(10).

Fritsma, T. (2009). *Top 10 reasons why you (yes you) should take a self-assessment*. Retrieved from http://iseekinteractive.org/blog/2009/10/21/top-10-reasons-why-you-yes-you-should-take-a-self-assessment/

Gordon, M. J. (1991). A review of the validity and accuracy of self-assessments in health professions training. *Academic Medicine, 66*, 762–769.

Gosling, S. D., John, O. P., Craik, K. H., & Robins, R. W. (1998). Do people know how they behave? Self-reported act frequencies compared with online codings by observers. *Journal of Personality and Social Psychology, 74*, 1337–1349.

John, O. P., & Robins, R. W. (1993). Determinants of interjudge agreement on personality traits: The big five domains, observability, evaluativeness, and the unique perspective of the self. *Journal of Personality, 61*, 521–551.

John, O. P., & Robins, R. W. (1994). Accuracy and bias in self-perception: Individual differences in self-enhancement and the role of narcissism. *Journal of Personality and Social Psychology, 66*, 206–219.

Kolar, D. W., Funder, D. C., & Colvin, C. R. (1996). Comparing the accuracy of personality judgments by the self and knowledgeable others. *Journal of Personality, 64*, 311–337. More resource on assessing yourself: http://www.iseek.org/careers/assessyourself.html

Paulhus, D. L., & John, O. P. (1998). Egoistic and moralistic bias in self-perceptions: The interplay of self-deceptive styles with basic traits and motives. *Journal of Personality, 66*, 2024 –2060.

Paulhus, D. L., & Vazire, S. (2007). The self-report method. In R. W. Robins, R. C. Fraley, and R. Krueger (Eds.), *Handbook of research methods in personality psychology* (pp. 224–239). New York: Guilford Press.

Chapter 17 – Self Assessment

Personal assessment web sites for careers, skills and abilities from Fritsma's article: (1) ISEEK's skills assessment (http://www.iseek.org/careers/skillsAssessment) (2) O*NET's ability profiler (http://www.onetcenter.org/AP.html) (3) MnCareers interest assessment, (http://www.iseek.org/careers/interestassessment.html) (4) O*NET's Work Importance Profiler (http://www.onetcenter.org/WIP.html) (5) The New York interest profiler (https://www.nycareerzone.org/graphic/assessment/index.jsp) (6) Personal branding (http://iseekinteractive.org/blog/2009/09/11/how-personal-brand-can-help-or-hurt-your-job-search/)

Pronin, E., & Kugler, M. B. (2007). Valuing thoughts, ignoring behavior: The introspection illusion as a source of bias blind spot. *Journal of Experimental Social Psychology, 43*, 565–578.

Pronin, E., Kruger, J., Savitsky, K., & Ross, L. (2001). You don't know me, but I know you: The illusion of asymmetric insight. *Journal of Personality and Social Psychology, 81*, 639–656.

Riley Guide. (n.d.). *Self-assessment resources*. Retrieved from http://www.rileyguide.com/assess.html

Robins, R. W., & John, O. P. (1997a). Effects of visual perspective and narcissism on self-perception: Is seeing believing? *Psychological Science, 8*, 37–42.

Robins, R. W., & John, O. P. (1997b). The quest for self-insight: Theory and research on accuracy and bias in self-perception. In R. T. Hogan, J. A. Johnson, & S. R. Briggs (Eds.), *Handbook of personality psychology* (pp. 649 – 679). New York: Academic.

Santayana, G. (1980). *Reason in common sense: The life of reason* (Vol. 1). New York: Dover. (Original work published 1905).

Sedikides, C., & Strube, M. J. (1997). Self-evaluation: To thine own self be good, to thine own self be sure, to thine own self be true, and to thine own self be better. In M. P. Zanna (Ed.), *Advances in experimental social psychology* (Vol. 29, pp. 209–269). San Diego, CA: Academic Press.

Vazire, S. (2006). Informant reports: A cheap, fast, and easy method for personality assessment. *Journal of Research in Personality, 40*, 472–481.

Vazire, S. (2006a). Informant reports: A cheap, fast, and easy method for personality assessment. *Journal of Research in Personality, 40*, 472–481.

Vazire, S. (2006b). *The person from the inside and outside* (Unpublished doctoral dissertation). The University of Texas at Austin.

Vazire, S. (2010). Who knows what about a person? The Self–Other Knowledge Asymmetry (SOKA) Model. *Journal of Personality and Social Psychology, 98*(2), 281–300.

Vazire, S., & Doris, J. M. (2009). Personality and personal control. *Journal of Research in Personality, 43*, 274–275.

Vazire, S., & Gosling, S. D. (2004). e-Perceptions: Personality impressions based on personal websites. *Journal of Personality and Social Psychology, 87*, 123–132.

Vazire, S., & Mehl, M. R. (2008). Knowing me, knowing you: The accuracy and unique predictive validity of self-ratings and other-ratings of daily behavior. *Journal of Personality and Social Psychology, 95*, 1202–1216.

Vazire, S., Gosling, S. D., Dickey, A. S., & Schapiro, S. J. (2007). Measuring personality in nonhuman animals. In R. W. Robins, R. C. Fraley, & R. Krueger (Eds.), *Handbook of research methods in personality psychology* (pp. 190–206). New York: Guilford Press.

Vazire, S., Naumann, L. P., Rentfrow, P. J., & Gosling, S. D. (2008). Portrait of a narcissist: Manifestations of narcissism in physical appearance. *Journal of Research in Personality, 42*, 1439–1447.

Vazire, S., Rentfrow, P. J., Mehl, M. R., & Gosling, S. D. (2005, January). *The multiple faces of reputation*. Paper presented at the meeting of the Society for Personality and Social Psychology, New Orleans, LA.

Ward, M., & Gruppen, L. (2002). Regehr G. Research in self-assessment: Current state of the art. *Advances in Health Science Education, 7*, 63–80.

Wilson, T. D. (2002). *Strangers to ourselves: Discovering the adaptive unconscious*. Cambridge, MA: Belknap Press/Harvard University Press.

Wilson, T. D., & Dunn, E. W. (2004). Self-knowledge: Its limits, value, and potential for improvement. *Annual Review of Psychology, 55*, 493–518.

Wilson, T. D., & Gilbert, D. T. (2003). Affective forecasting. In M. P. Zanna (Ed.), *Advances in experimental social psychology* (Vol. 35, pp. 345–411). San Diego: Academic Press.

406

Chapter 18
Change

Change happens.
Change is difficult.
Change is strange.

> *Change happens because nothing stays the same; it's inevitable; change is difficult because it takes us out of our comfort zone; change is strange because it is both difficult and inevitable. Change requires you to go in a different direction.*

Even though change is inevitable, it is also unnatural to make change happen. The human body and psyche are designed to maintain its current state of being. Consequently, extraordinary conditions are usually required to make change happen. The human body and psyche are controlled by homeostasis. Homeostasis is defined in *Webster's Dictionary* as the tendency to maintain, or the maintenance of, normal, internal stability in an organism by coordinated resources of the organ systems that automatically compensate for environmental changes. In other words, our natural system has a tendency to stay the same. To make change happen, you must "override" your natural tendency to maintain the current status quo.

The *American Heritage Dictionary* (updated in 2009) defines change as: To cause to be different; to give a completely different form or appearance to; to put a fresh covering on; a transformation or transition from one state, condition, or phase to another. The act, process, or result of altering or modifying. The replacing of one thing for another; substitution. Change tends to be less difficult when it is less stressful. It is less stressful when it is done in smaller increments. It tends to be easier to start a reading assignment with one chapter a week and gradually moving up to five chapters a week over a period of six months rather than starting the reading assignment out with five chapters a week.

Chapter 18 – Change

Best Times for Change

> *Change is also easier when we are clearest about why change is necessary, how change will take place and specifically when we need to make adjustments.*

It also helps if we know for how long the change must continue or if it is a permanent change needing to take place and, in that case, when the change is likely to become a routine part of things. Change is also less difficult when we can "fit it in" with our normal routine or when it can become a part of something we normally do, relatively easily.

> *There must be a readiness to change. You have to be ready to take on the challenges of change.*

You need to be ready to take the risks of leaving the familiar to venture into the unknown. You have to take the initiative to move forward, away from your comfort zone. This often entails learning to learn which can be critical for the ultimate and lasting change that is desired.

Change What?

First, however, to make a change, you must focus on what is being changed, what behavior is being changed, how that change will affect my feelings and how it will affect the people around me. How will the change impact things that I don't want to change? Change often has unintended consequences or things that you don't want impacted. It has to be considered in the big scheme of things. Sometimes the thing that made you initiate the thought or decision changes or your interest changes or is no longer a top priority for you at this time.

Some of the challenging changes I have made within the past few years include health-related things such as cutting down my cholesterol intake. I did this by changing my choice of salad dressing from ranch to vinaigrette and lowering my daily coffee consumption from an average of three cups a day to one. The decaffeinated coffee I drank was never the problem, it was the amount of half-and-half cream I put in it and, to some extent, I also slowed down or just about stopped eating fried foods, muffins, potato chips and other high-fat foods.

Another challenge for me was joining a gym which I had tried before but never stuck with it. For years, I had been jogging around the neighborhood. The big change was when I decided to get off the streets of the neighborhood and join the gym. I'm much happier now because not only am I out of the sometimes inclement weather of Sacramento, but I am also surrounded by other people going through their workout regiment along with me which is an incentive for me to continue working out.

Chapter 18 – Change

> **Some changes we cannot make on our own and some change is not supposed to happen.**

As we try to make changes and are unsuccessful, we need to acknowledge that we have tried several times on our own and can't seem to do it on our own. This might give us some indication that we need help. Or, it might mean that we need to reassess whether we need to make that change or not.

Change Starts in Your Mind

Change is more psychological than anything else and it has a lot to do with control. When you are at a crossroad of choosing to continue doing something that you usually do or changing that behavior, which do you choose? Why do you make the choices you make and what choice will you make the next time? When you are trying to change a certain set of behaviors, you have to always be alert to the fact that you do not want to continue with your previous "automatic," habitual, and usual behavior. You might ask the question, "What's different this time?" My motivation? Am I ready now? I see more clearly now? My schedule is more flexible? What?

> **Change often occurs when the current situation is no longer tolerable or when you are simply "ready" to make that choice.**

Minor changes can come about as a matter of course or whim or thought at the time. Major changes are generally brought about as a result of much thought and effort or dissatisfaction with a current situation. Change over time seems to be preferred to abrupt, unplanned, spur-of-the-moment or whimsical change.

What's not working that there is a need to change? Change requires acquiring a new set of habits, a new set of rituals and quite a bit more energy. Most people are used to doing things a certain way, but when you have to change, it requires thought and sometimes focus on the "new way." Change can often take place, temporarily, but to make change more permanent requires discipline and "stick-to-it-ness" until you have made it a natural part of your routine.

Stages of Change When Seen as Loss

Change can sometimes be seen as loss (of the status quo or of an existing familiar structure) and can be compared to a bereavement process. Just as in a bereavement process one goes through the following "stages," so too, that person would go through a similar process with change:

Bereavement ("Models for change-toward sustainability")
Denial: "It can't be true!" or "I don't believe it!"

Blaming others: "They should not have done that" or simply, "It's their fault."

Blaming self: "I should have known" or "It's my fault"

Accepting the new situation: "It's happened and I/we must go on from here."

Commitment to change: "I'm going to do something about this."
Creative problem solving: "What can I/we do about this?" or "what are our/my options?"
Perseverance: "overcoming obstacles through persistence and more creative problem solving."

Change

Strong objection: "It can't be done!" "We don't really need to do this!"
The opposition: "So and so is always causing problems;" or, "So and so started this or it is their idea."
Hindsight: "I should have seen this coming;" or "we should have acted earlier."
Accepting change: "It's a done deal now, we might as well make the Change."
Commitment to change: "I'm committed to doing my part."
Developing plan/strategizing: "budget resources/seek support."
Perseverance: "monitor our progress and evaluate results and continue follow through."

Idea from: http://www.biothinking.com/applysd/models.htm

Sometimes people (or organizations) get stuck at one or more of these "stages" and have to work through them.

What's Your Attitude About Change?
As you look at how you are currently handling change, you are probably realizing that it is the attitude you have about making the change that is the driving force around the issue. The change that you have to make is likely not one you have embraced. Consequently, you are making it just that much more difficult because of your attitude about making it. Use your creative mind. We get so caught up in what we are used to doing that to have to change becomes a nuisance that we would prefer to not have to deal with.

> ***Change takes time. It requires us to think differently than we are used to thinking about a thing. It is work! For most people, change is not effortless or without some frustration.***

Unless there is some good reason for making the change, most of us prefer to keep things the way they are. However, on the things we are comfortable changing, we still have to overcome habit, including accepting some inconvenience and sometimes frustration. Change has an initial stage, which involves those first steps in making the change. Then there is the maintenance stage when you have to become used to the "new" way of doing things until it becomes a part of your regular habit pattern. In both cases, you have to remain alert, continue to be patient and keep a positive attitude.

Is there a difference in results when you REALLY want to make a change as opposed to when you just want to make a change? Or, when you are forced or coerced to make the change? What kind of circumstance would have to be presented for a person to promise themselves or someone else that they will make a (big) change and to have them actually follow through with it? Under such a situation, would it be considered irresponsible of that person if they did not then keep their word to themselves or to the other person?

Is it possible to predict before hand what the odds will be that you will follow through with it?

Personal Views on Change

> *What kind of change agent are you (on big changes)? Can you say with some degree of certainty that you are going to change something and you actually make it happen? What proof do you have, based on past experience?*

Have you tried different strategies, visualization, prayer, telling a friend, writing out a plan?

Does it matter if money is involved? Your honor? Your integrity?

Easier Said Than Done

What would happen if you checked your progress every day?

How realistic is it to say that after a week of sticking to a change that was promised and the interest to continue is still strong that there was a good chance it will be continued? What about two weeks? Surely after three weeks, one can say that they are home free?

How realistic are you with what you can and cannot do? Is it possible that you could be in denial about what you are capable of changing?

> *Is it even conceivable for anyone to leave a conference or some other gathering and immediately begin implementing some of the good ideas they heard?*

Most of us, when we leave these kinds of gatherings, we have to "go back to our lives" and usually don't have time (or don't make the time) to even try to make changes that might be good for us. Many people simply don't have that kind of flexibility in their lives.

As much as you might want something to change and as important and as significant as it might be, you cannot simply will it to happen. Some change is easy to talk about and discuss, but not so easy to do. Change for some people is relatively easy to do, while others struggle to make it happen. Researchers have identified reasons for such differences. In many cases, it all boils down to a person's motivation to change.

Classical Theorists and Therapist Weigh in on Motivation for Change
Abraham Maslow, known for establishing the theory of a hierarchy of needs, believed human beings are motivated by unsatisfied needs and that certain lower needs need to be satisfied before higher-order needs can be satisfied. Following that line of thinking, one would surmise that one's motivation to change might be determined by the level of need that will be satisfied by the proposed change.

> *For example, if one is motivated to change to meet some physiological need, then the change has a better chance of success than if the change is motivated by a less significant need such as self-improvement.*

The first four needs (physiological, safety, belongingness and love, and esteem) are often referred to as deficiency needs because they motivate people to act only when they are unmet to some degree. Self-actualization, by contrast, is often called a growth need because people constantly strive to satisfy it. Basically, self-actualization refers to the need for self-fulfillment—the need to develop all of one's potential talents and capabilities (Snowman, McCown, & Biehler, 2009).

This hierarchy is most often displayed as a pyramid. The lowest levels of the pyramid are made up of the most basic needs, while the more complex needs are located at the top of the pyramid. Needs at the bottom of the pyramid are basic physical requirements including the need for food, water, sleep, and warmth. Once these lower-level needs have been met, people can move on to the next level of needs, which are for safety and security.

As people progress up the pyramid, needs become increasingly psychological and social. Soon, the need for love, friendship, and intimacy become important. Further up the pyramid, the need for personal esteem and feelings of accomplishment take priority. Like Carl Rogers, Maslow emphasized the importance of self-actualization, which is a process of growing and developing as a person in order to achieve individual potential.

Here's a quick summary of needs:
Physiological Need
These are your most basic needs for human survival such as food, air, water, sex (reproduction) and temperature range fit for humans (homeostasis).
Safety Need
When your physiological needs have been met, the next one is the need to feel secure. This just means people yearn to create a steady, predictable environment. This can mean a number

of things such as financial security (job, savings), health (doctors, supplements), insurance against catastrophe, and overall personal security (protection from government intrusion).

Need of Love, Affection and Belongingness

The next hierarchy of needs is about establishing a sense of belonging by receiving and giving love. Maslow states that we seek relationships to avoid feelings of loneliness. There are three primary types: friendship, family and intimate relationships.

Need for Esteem

The fourth class is the need for respect and self-esteem.

Maslow states there are two types of esteem. The lower one is the need for fame, status recognition, and respect from others. The higher order esteem is about self-respect, and the need for mastery, confidence and independence.

If the esteem need isn't met, a person can feel inferior, helpless and weak. The latter need is a higher one because it doesn't rely on outside factors, rather on inner strength.

Need for Self-Actualization

When all four of Maslow's lower-level needs have been met, then a person can focus on doing what he/she is "born to do." At this stage, a person can direct their focus on living their potential. At this stage, the person is looking to develop themselves and/or looking for a challenge.

Self-Actualization Characteristics

It's people who are

- Aware of their surroundings
- Comfortable with solitude, content with themselves
- Display compassion, wanting to help others
- Accept and embraces the differences of others
- True to themselves, don't distort the truth
- Act on their own convictions, not peer pressure
- Curious, always asking questions to learn
- Open to new ideas, willing to try, create and do new things
- Relaxed with clean sense of humor
- Interdependent – person who is independent but realize a team can do more

---

B.F. Skinner, a noted psychologist whose motivational models are based on simple reward and punishment, might suggest one is more likely to change depending upon the balance between the reward associated with the change or its connection to punishment.

Chapter 18 – Change

Retrieved from "Operant Conditioning" (B.F. Skinner)
(http://www.simplypsychology.org/operant-conditioning.html)

Alfred Adler, a noted psychiatrist states that a single "drive" or motivating force is behind all our behavior and experience (Boeree, 2006). He called that motivating force the "striving for perfection." It is the desire people have to fulfill our potentials, to come closer and closer to our ideal. Another word Adler used to refer to basic motivation was "compensation," or striving to overcome. Consequently, Adler might suggest that our motives for change could come from our desire to compensate for some shortcoming or our striving to improve a certain aspect of life. Adler would certainly agree that if we had a burning desire to make a change, our chances of success would be greater than if the desire were less important to us.

According to **Sigmund Freud** (Boeree, 2009), another noted psychiatrist, the unconscious is the source of our motivation. Consequently, change oftentimes begins in the mind. Sometimes we are unaware of something that we have seen or heard that later enters our consciousness and becomes a motivating force for us to change. For example, people see a style of clothing over and over again until finally, they change from their old style of dress to the new.

Circumstances Under Which People Make Change Happen

(1) Inspired by someone or something (speech, movie, book, song, article in magazine, newspaper, see or hear (about) someone else doing it and believe that you can do it, too). Something you have been wanting to do for a long time.
(2) Take advantage of forced change – (e.g., on the job having to change computer systems from Mac to PC)
(3) Take advantage of a death or some other mishap or bad news. Certain difficult-to-take situations can oftentimes provide the necessary motivation to get one to act.
(4) Just tired of putting it off
(5) Just do it!
(6) Plan it
(7) Pay someone to help you
(8) Find yourself doing it (by accident)–decide to continue (e.g., run 5 miles instead of usual 4)
(9) Circumstances change making it easier, more necessary (e.g., sick-lost weight)
    Force yourself into changing by setting up circumstances where you have to do it.
(10) Visualize it such that you "Will it" to happen.

Personal Change Attributes

Change—learn the process that works best for you—doing research on yourself.
  – How do you deal with change?

  – *What has been your experience (past successes and past failures) and especially why and how did you succeed when you did and why and how did you fail?*

Chapter 18 – Change

- We all have a few basic tenets that we will probably never change, nor do we want to change (i.e., many of my current religious beliefs are strong and solid and are tied to my basic foundation as a person)
- There are, however, some things we have always wanted to change, but never did (or even tried to do). For me, a fear of snakes is one that I still have and will probably never change.

Then there are little things we think we want to change, but just have not really gotten serious about it. We even think we could make the change, but just have not gotten around to doing it.

- Sometimes we get "caught up" with everyday routines and challenges of life that we don't make time to deal with trying to change some things.
- How do you keep the change started in the forefront? Keeping it as a top priority? Keep from losing interest, losing that initial passion?
- However, every now and then, life throws us a curve and forces us to change—a new job assignment, death of a loved one or that dreaded bad news from our doctor.

> - ***Forced change needs to be embraced and taken in stride or it can become more of a challenge than it needs to be. Most forced changes can become blessings in disguise, if we let them.***

- Change over time seems to be preferred to abrupt, unplanned, spur-of-the-moment or whimsical change.
- If it's not broken, don't (try to) fix it!

Important Areas of Your Life to Be Assessed for Potential Change
A lifelong challenge – never ending

1. Spiritual
2. Mental Health
3. Physical Health
4. Family
5. Purpose/passion/vision
6. Financial
7. Work/school
8. Civic (public service)
9. Social
10. Personal initiatives, challenges and aspirations i.e., esthetic, personal appearance, hobby wise (fun/pleasure), other such as, attitude, something concerning your house, feelings about something or someone, something really personal (such as a secret habit), whatever "you" feel is personal.

Chapter 18 – Change

Change From Idea to Practice
One example of a process by which ideas become a habit or routine
(1) <u>Idea</u> enters into your repertoire of thought – maybe even before you become aware of it.
(2) <u>conscious</u> awareness level
(3) <u>Interest</u>, with <u>possibilities</u>
(4) You <u>ARE interested</u>
(5) You <u>see</u> it in writing. You <u>hear</u> about it
(6) You see it <u>demonstrated</u>; see <u>examples</u> being done
(7) You try it out <u>experimentally</u> – experience it
(8) You <u>do it</u> as something that you <u>hope to be continued</u>.
(9) You <u>maintain</u> level of activity with it and work out a <u>regular schedule</u> for it, work out "bugs," levels of discomfort, set the ideal pace, intensity and tolerance level.
(10) It <u>becomes a permanent</u> part of your life.

Sustainability and Maintenance

> *Once change has come about, one of the most difficult aspects of this issue is sustaining the change long enough for it to catch on or for it to become a habit or a part of your regular routine.*

In an article titled "How Long Does It Take to Form a Habit?" by Luc Reid (2009), he mentions an often-repeated piece of information that it takes 28 days to form a habit. He goes on to say I've heard this more than once, but never heard that it was based on any reliable research. My guess is that it's meant to be inspirational guesswork, and since people like round figures so much, it caught on. I've also heard 21 days cited; don't believe that one either. In any case, the comment drove me to find research that gives something more like a real answer to the question, which led me to Lally et al.'s study that was first published online on July 16, 2009, and then again in 2010 in the *European Journal of Social Psychology*.

Don't get too attached to a number. We'll want to try not to get too wrapped up in a specific number of days, like the Lally et al. article where they seize on that 66-day average and proclaim it as a universal truth. However much we human beings like a simple, unchanging answer, 66 days is just an average: your average is extremely likely to vary.

Why it doesn't always matter. And it may help to act as though habit formation won't be happening at all, to simply use feedback loops to keep up good practices and make good choices, and to take habit formation a wonderful accident. As with any other positive development that results from being motivated, habit formation causes problems if it's thought of as the end goal: it's essential to find things to enjoy about the steps along the way in order to keep up anything important long enough for it to matter.

416

Chapter 18 – Change

Roger Dobson first picked up on this study July 18, 2009, in an article titled: "It Takes 66 Days to Form a Habit," in *The Telegraph*, a United Kingdom publication. Retrieved from: http://www.telegraph.co.uk/health/healthnews/5857845/It-takes-66-days-to-form-a-habit.html

---

<u>How Long Does It Take to Form a Habit?</u>
What was found was that it takes 66 days on average for people in our study to acquire a habit, according to Professor Jane Wardle of University College London, who carried out the study with Dr. Phillippa Lally.

It varied between individuals, but the finding is that if you do something everyday in the same situation, it will become an automatic reaction in response to those situational cues, a habit. It is the first time this has been established.

Performing an action for the first time requires planning, even if plans are formed only moments before the action is performed, and attention.

As behaviours are repeated in consistent settings they then begin to proceed more efficiently and with less thought as control of the behaviour transfers to cues in the environment that activate an automatic response—a habit.

In the research, being reported in the *European Journal of Social Psychology*, the researchers set out to investigate how long it took for the repetition of behaviour to reach a stage of "automacity," where it is performed whenever the situation is encountered without thinking, awareness or intention.

The volunteers who took part in the study were asked to choose a healthy eating, drinking or exercise behaviour that they would like to make into a habit. It had to be done in response to a particular cue, such as eating a piece of fruit with lunch, drinking a bottle of water with lunch, or running for 15 minutes before dinner. Participants were asked to try to carry out the behaviour every day.

Each day they also completed a test designed to measure features of habits that are central to automaticity, including lack of awareness and lack of control. Results showed that whilst the average time to form a habit was 66 days, more complex behaviours took longer; an exercise habit took longer to form than a healthy eating or drinking habit.

Phillippa Lally was involved in two subsequent studies on the topic of habit. In the first study, published in the *Psychology, Health & Medicine* and titled "Experiences of habit formation: A qualitative study" by Lally, Wardle, and Gardner (2011), he explains that habit formation is an important goal for behavior change interventions because habitual behaviors are elicited automatically and are therefore likely to be maintained. This study documented experiences of habit development in 10 participants enrolled on a weight loss intervention

417

explicitly based on habit-formation principles. Thematic analysis revealed three themes: Strategies used to support initial engagement in a novel behavior; development of behavioral automaticity; and selecting effective cues to support repeated behavior. Results showed that behavior change was initially experienced as cognitively effortful but as automaticity increased, enactment became easier. Habits were typically formed in work-based contexts. Weekends and vacations temporarily disrupted performance due to absence of associated cues, but habits were reinstated upon return to work.

In the second study in which Lally was involved titled "Promoting Habit Formation," by Lally, and Gardner (2013) in the *Health Psychology Review,* they explain that habits are automatic behavioral responses to environmental cues, thought to develop through repetition of behavior in consistent contexts.

> *When habit is strong, deliberate intentions have been shown to have a reduced influence on behavior.*

The habit concept may provide a mechanism for establishing new behaviors, and so healthy habit formation is a desired outcome for many interventions. Habits also, however, represent a potential challenge for changing ingrained unhealthy behaviors, which may be resistant to motivational shifts.

What to Do When You Want to Build Better Habits (But Can't Get Started)

James Clear published an article on September 9, 2013 with the above title that emphasized, if you're serious about making change, then you can't sit around and hope to magically become aware of the important things. Instead, you need to make an active effort to measure and track what you're doing and how you're doing it. This is much simpler than you might think and it's also one of the best ways to kick start new behaviors.

Here are a few examples…(from James Clear)

Exercise—I have a good streak going with weightlifting right now. It all started when I began tracking my pushup workouts. That simple action prompted me to track the rest of my training with a more watchful eye. It sounds so simple, but writing down how many days I was training each week helped me get my butt in the gym more consistently. (And along the way, I doubled the amount of pushups I could do.)

Writing—Before November 2012, I *thought* I was writing consistently, but I wasn't. Eventually, I decided to measure my writing output and realized that I was unpredictable and erratic. I wrote when I felt motivated or inspired, which turned out to be about once every three weeks. After becoming aware of how inconsistent I was, I decided to set up a Monday and Thursday publishing schedule. It's been 10 months now and I haven't missed a week.

Chapter 18 – Change

Money and Business—Recently, I read about John Rockefeller's life and learned that he was known for tracking every single penny across his massive empire. After reading about Rockefeller's strategies, I was inspired to track my own finances even more closely. What happened? I quickly became more aware of my finances and discovered a handful of places where I could cut costs and increase earnings. Furthermore, my increased tracking and measurement has helped me learn about things like tax efficiency and asset allocation, which I had previously thought very little about.

Notice that in each example above, I didn't start by worrying about all the improvements I needed to make. I simply started by becoming more aware of my behavior. I tracked and measured. And by paying attention to what I was doing and how I was spending my time, ideas for improving my habits naturally presented themselves.

Your Challenge

Nothing happens before awareness. If you aren't aware of your decisions, then you can't do anything to improve them—no matter how smart you are.

With that in mind, I'd like to challenge you to measure something in your life for the next week.

Pick something that is important to you and make an effort to be more aware of the things that drive your decisions and actions. Don't worry about changing your whole life. Don't judge yourself for not being as good as you want to be. Just pick one thing that's important to you and measure it. Take stock of it. Be aware of it.

> *Your awareness and your habits go hand-in-hand. The simple act of noticing what you do is the first step for improving how you do it. If you recognize how you're spending your time, then the next step will often reveal itself.*

This article was retrieved from: http://jamesclear.com/awareness-start-better-habits

Lots and lots of questions come up when you think about change. A few questions to ponder:

- Why change? Change for change sake, or change to make a difference, a positive difference?
- What is the motivation? What initiated the need for change? (Oftentimes, change starts in the mind and in the attitude, oftentimes days, maybe even weeks or months before you start to act on the thought.)
- Do you NEED to change or do you just WANT to change?
- How bad do you want or need to change? The more serious you want the change, the more passionate you are about making the change, the more committed you are to doing it, the more likely it will happen. Is it in your heart? Or, is it just surface, for "show?" The less passionate you are about making the change, the more likely you

are to start renegotiating the necessity for it or reconsidering the need, especially when things start getting rough or when it becomes more difficult to continue. Oftentimes, people have a tendency to start longing for the way it used to be; how simple it used to be and how much more "natural" it is to go back to the way things were.

– A few examples of wanting (or needing) to do something: I want to write a book (which might necessitate that I make some changes in my daily schedule to make that happen). I want to improve the quality of my life (by choosing more healthy food to eat, more consistently). I need to stop eating so much salt. I have to change computers at my job from a Mac to a PC. I want to earn more money so to make that happen, I will have to make time to figure out how I am going to do that (i.e., start a business, change jobs, get a second job, start looking for consulting opportunities.)

> – *If you really want to make change happen, have a burning desire to do it. Be excited about it and however you can maintain that passionate and positive attitude about it, the better, especially when things start getting inconvenient or just down right rough.*

– Who benefits from making change happen? You or someone else or maybe both?
– How much will the benefit likely be?
– What is the balance or ratio of benefit over difficulty – what you get versus what you have to give or go through.
– How certain are you about either the benefit or the challenge? Sometimes you simply don't know how big the benefit will be or even if there will be a benefit at the end at all. And we often miscalculate how difficult changing something might be, especially if it's a long-held habit.
– Do you have the capacity to carry it out? More simply put, can you do it?
– Are you going to be dependent on someone else to help you make it happen? Or, are you completely in control?
– When's the last time you made a significant change in your behavior, your schedule, your life?

> – *How do YOU deal with change, based on your previous experiences with it?*

– What was it and why did you do it?
– Is it over or are you still going through it?
– Can you identify other instances?
– How much are you willing to "give" to this change effort?
– Do you know what it will or should look like, what it will be like when you've made the change?
– Will it be temporary or permanent?
– Have you considered whether you can try it first and if you don't like it, change back?

- Is it personal or business?
- Lots of people involved or affected or just you and/or a few others?
- Nervous or excited about the thought of changing or are you nonchalant about it, it's no big deal?
- Been needing or wanting to do it for a long time, or just something that has recently come up?
- Was this change thing your idea or someone else's?
- Did you or do you embrace it (right away) or is it something you have to think about and decide later?
- There is a (slight) difference between change and wanting to do something. "Change" usually comes after you've decided what it is that you want or need "to do."
- When do you start?

Making Preparation for Change

Ideally, some people want to make change happen so that it is as positive, painless and as less disruptive as possible. You might need to prepare for change psychologically, physically and emotionally, depending upon the nature and extent of the change being contemplated.

> *Just as change is unnatural, it is also the one thing you know for certain will happen. It is inevitable.*

The question, however, is do you let it happen and get what you get or deal with it when it happens (and most likely when you are less prepared to deal with it) or do you direct it, plan for it, structure it, make it happen on your terms?

<u>REFERENCES</u>
Chapter 18 – "Change"

Abouteducation. (n.d.). *Carl Rogers biography (1902-1987)*. Retrieved from http://psychology.about.com/od/profilesofmajorthinkers/p/bio_rogers.htm

The American Heritage® Dictionary of the English Language, Fourth Edition (2009). New York: Houghton Mifflin Company.

Biothinking.com. (n.d.). *Models for change-towards sustainability*. Retrieved from http://www.biothinking.com/applysd/models.htm

Boreree, C. G. (2006). *Alfred Adler 1870–1937*. Retrieved from http://webspace.ship.edu/cgboer/adler.html/

Boreree, C. G. (2009). *Sigmund Freud 1856–1939*. Retrieved from http://webspace.ship.edu/cgboer/freud.html

Clear, J. (2013). *What to do when you want to build better habits (but can't get started)*. Retrieved from http://jamesclear.com/awareness-start-better-habits

Instructionaldesign.org. (n.d.). *Operant conditioning*. (B.F. Skinner). Retrieved from http://www.instructionaldesign.org/theories/operant-conditioning.html

Lally, P., & Gardner, B. (2013). Promoting habit formation. *Health Psychology Review, 7*(Supplement 1), S137–S158.

Lally, P., van Jaarsveld, C. H. M., Potts, H. W. W., & Wardle, J. (2010). How are habits formed: Modelling habit formation in the real world. *European Journal of Social Psychology, 40*(6), 998–1009.

Lally, P., Wardle, J., & Gardner, B. (2011). Experiences of habit formation: A qualitative study. *Psychology, Health & Medicine, 16*(4), 484-489.

Managing-change.net. (n.d.). *Making Maslows hierarchy of needs work for you*. Retrieved from http://www.managing-change.net/maslows-hierarchy-of-needs.html

Reid, L. (2009, September 14). *How long does it take to form a habit*. Retrieved from http://www.lucreid.com/?p=645

Ruskin-brownassociates.com. (n.d.). *Maslow's hierarchy of needs*. Retrieved from http://www.ruskin-brownassociates.com/pdfs/maslow.pdf

Snowman, J., McCown, R. R., & Biehler, R. F. (2009). *Psychology applied to teaching*. Boston, MA: Houghton Mufflin.

Chapter 19
Commitment

Yes I will means yes, I will!

Commitment is almost like a promise. If I'm committed to something, I will very likely follow through on it. I will find a way to do it. If I'm committed to it, it's a priority; I will try to write it down in a place where I will not forget it.

There are certain levels of commitment. A low level of commitment is to be made to follow through if … and there are a large number of possible conditions that follow, such as "if I feel like it," "if it is convenient," "if I have time," and so on. A higher level of commitment is to be made to follow through if … and there are fewer and usually more pressing "ifs."

> *Among the highest levels of commitment is to be committed to follow through if at all possible, regardless of the inconvenience or cost of discomfort. You are invested!*

Different Forms of Commitment

Some forms of commitment are obviously long-term and some are short-term. For example, short-term commitment is like being committed to saving enough money to purchase a car or to buy a camera. A long-term commitment is like being committed to a spouse, having children, and being committed to your spiritual choice of worship. These commitments are for life. Other forms of commitment, however, are not time bound. One example might be your commitment to work for the State of California before retiring in five years. Your commitment to that agency/organization after that will be for as long as you are happy working there. It could be for one more year or for 20 more years.

Most contractual arrangements are forms of commitment that can be legally binding. The level or form or kind of commitment that you make is largely determined by the

423

circumstances surrounding the commitment itself. Some people are committed to trying to stay healthy, and in that regard, they live up to that commitment by exercising regularly and by trying to maintain a healthy diet among other things.

Problems with Some Commitments

One of the key elements in commitment is to not over-commit. Sometimes a commitment to one thing can cause other things to "suffer." If you commit to working with boys at your church on Wednesday nights, you might have to skip some other important activity if it takes place on Wednesday night at the same time you are working with the boys. There might come a time when one commitment is in competition with another commitment. In those cases, you would have to choose which is the most important at the time. In other words, there might be times when some problems might have to go unsolved, for a while at least.

Synonymous Names

Commitment has been described in many ways. A few that come to mind are:

A promise to follow through

A contract

Almost guarantee

> *It becomes a priority. Resources are made available, time, money, and energy.*

Mentally prepared to take it on.

It's pretty much a done deal; you only now have to simply follow through with the activities.

It's my duty to follow through

It's like a pledge that I give or a vow I have taken

You have my word on it

I'm good for it

You have a good idea of what the end result looks like.

You are able to "think" in terms that the thing committed to "is done."

Inactivity is not an option.

Positive planning and thinking takes place

You're prepared to make it happen;

Roadblocks and other challenges are taken on; they are met head on.

Almost unconditional resolve

Ready to take the initiative, be on the offensive to move forward.

Commitments can be to yourself or to another person or to a certain practice, activity or way of life. If you are committed to something, you are likely to follow through with what needs to be done to maintain its status or existence. Being committed to your girlfriend means that you will not see other women, one will work at making her happy, trying to meet her needs and spending time with her. Commitment to a diet is to follow that diet and to not deviate too far from it.

Chapter 19 – Commitment

> *Commitment to a certain lifestyle is to work at trying to maintain that particular way of life.*

Jim Selman (n.d.) wrote an article titled "Commitment and Change," in which he talked about the characteristics of commitment. In it, he emphasizes that first and foremost, commitment is an action. To commit is to bring something into existence that wasn't there before. At the moment of its coming into existence, a commitment is a creative act, distinct from whatever reasons or rationale we might have for making the commitment. This action is being taken by and between human beings all the time. Whether we are committing to meeting a friend or paying a bill or going to school, we are always moving within a fabric of conscious and unconscious commitments.

The action of committing is also always connected to the future—to another action, event or result. When we commit, we are saying, "I will be responsible for something happening in the future which would not occur in the absence of my commitment." Commitment defines the relationship between a future that is entirely determined by historical circumstances and one that can be influenced, changed or created by human beings. When we don't consciously commit or commit conditionally, we are in effect committed anyway—to the status quo.

A second important aspect of commitments is that they are not just personal. When we commit, we are also creating expectations on the part of others and, in some cases, our commitments have a direct and important impact on the choices others have and how they perceive their future. Commitments have the characteristic of both opening particular futures and closing other futures simultaneously.

When a parent commits to send a child to a private school, he or she is doing more than just providing an educational opportunity: the child is also being placed into a particular situation that will allow for choices or commitments that would not otherwise present themselves. Likewise, the commitments of our forefathers are passed to us as "reality" which we must either accept as our own or change by means of new commitments. In this sense, commitment is as much a social phenomenon as it is an expression of individual choices.

A third characteristic of commitments is that they exist only in our speaking and listening—in language. A commitment occurs in conversation as a "speech action" which brings into existence some desired future condition as a possibility which, when fulfilled, becomes a new "reality." The power of commitment is that it is the only action of which human beings are capable for which the future and the present appear in the same moment.

> *When I promise to meet you, I am evoking the future time and circumstances of our meeting in the same moment as I speak the promise.*

Chapter 19 – Commitment

In making the promise, I am committing to be at the meeting at the time and place we've agreed to. Likewise, if you requested the meeting or accept my offer, you've committed to be there also. In this sense, BOTH promising and requesting are commitments to participate in creating particular futures together. If I am not serious about my promises and requests, you will stop listening to them as commitments and will not coordinate your actions with mine. The result will be chaotic, produce distrust or annoyance, and eventually we will either not communicate at all or, more likely (as is the common case), will implicitly agree to cope with whatever our circumstances allow and avoid the question of responsibility for our actions altogether.

In his article, Selman adds an appropriate comment from Shearson Lehman:
Commitment is what transforms a promise into reality. It is the words that speak boldly of your intentions. And the actions which speak louder than the words. It is making the time when there is none. Coming through time after time after time, year after year after year. Commitment is the stuff character is made of: the power to change the face of things. It is the daily triumph of integrity over skepticism.

Excuses Not Allowed

A real commitment will not include excuses or rationalizations as to why a commitment is not met. Commitments can be conditional or unconditional. Conditional commitments mean that one is committed to something as long as certain conditions are met. For example, a person is committed to a relationship as long as it is interesting or fun or satisfying. Or, a person is committed to their job when they are at work, but not to the point of bringing work home (condition: must be at work). Or, a person is committed to following a certain diet as long as the diet is convenient to follow through and things don't get too difficult. Unconditional commitment means that the person will do everything within their power to follow through with their commitment.

A good start isn't good enough

In Gary McGuire's book *Learning to Laugh* (2009), he has a chapter (24) titled "Making a Commitment." The subtitle of this chapter is "A good start isn't good enough." In addition to sharing a few things that prevent us from experiencing the joy we were meant to have when we make commitments, he also describes commitment as a determination that does not allow for excuses or rationalizations.

> *Great ideas often lead to good starts and bright beginnings. But good starts are not good enough, for brilliant ideas are no better than poor ones, unless we follow through.*

The author says that we all have flashes of insight and bright ideas. But of the countless number of inspirational moments we've had and already acted upon, how many of them have we pursued to the end? How many of them have we realized? Ideas are seeds. Locked within them is great potential. Yet, what good are seeds unless we plough, harrow, and fertilize the soil, and follow that by planting, watering, and looking after the seeds until they bloom?

A good idea and follow-through is an explosive combination. It is the material that is used to transform lives and change the world. The detonator of this highly charged package is COMMITMENT. It is also called DETERMINATION. Commitment means NO MATTER WHAT! And determination is a refusal to allow obstacles to stop us.

Anything is possible for the determined because they reject the very notion of "trying" and insist on doing. Despite the jeers and skepticism of their friends, young people move to Hollywood with the dream of becoming a star. Even for those who are committed, however, not everyone will make it. You see, it is not ALWAYS true that "Where there is a will there is a way," but one thing is certain: where there is no will, there is no way.

Let's look at a few things that may prevent us from making a commitment and experiencing the joy we were meant to have.

1. Disappointment. A certain amount of negative feelings are inevitable, even necessary. But don't repress them or get bogged down in them. Instead, experience them, work through them, and learn from them. For example, don't allow disappointment to halt your progress. Disappointment is just a message or feedback telling you that things are not going according to plan. So, instead of quitting, find out what went wrong and what changes need to be made.

> *2. Lack of confidence or low self-esteem. Your experiences in early childhood may have caused you to lose confidence in yourself. If so, that is a FACT, not an EXCUSE. It's time to let go of the past, acknowledge you are an adult, and accept responsibility for your own actions.*

Stop chasing after self-esteem because it is not a goal, but a result. It is something you win each time you reach a goal. So, stop refusing to act just because you may fail. Who cares if you fail? You don't have to win every battle, you just have to win the war. And you do so by remaining determined and plodding ahead, no matter what.

3. Rebellion. Stop rebelling. Stop getting in your own way. Stop fighting yourself. Many of us are stuck in the "resistance syndrome." That is, when we were forced as children to yield to the will of an adult, we expressed our autonomy by rebelling. Each time you tell yourself you SHOULD be doing something, you remember the commands you received as a child and automatically resist. You need to change your self-talk. Rather than saying, "I SHOULD go to night school to complete my degree," say "I WANT to go to night school to complete my degree BECAUSE I will be learning new things, making new friends, feeling great about my accomplishments, and improving my chances for future advancement." Recapping,

Chapter 19 – Commitment

SHOULDs create resistance while WANTs dissolve resistance. Don't forget to give power to your WANTs by adding BECAUSE plus the reasons for your choice.

4. Here is another point for us to think about: follow the path of wisdom. Your life is too short to experience and learn everything by yourself. So, learn from the wisdom passed down to us. For example, consider the words of Marcus Tullius Cicero (c. 106 ~ 43 BC), which says that what one has, one ought to use: and whatever he does he should do with all his might. Are you using what you have, your talents, and using them with all your might? To bring this point home, let's add the comments of Orison Swett Marden (1850 ~ 1924) that says the greatest trouble with most of us is that our demands upon ourselves are so feeble, the call upon the great within us so weak and intermittent that it makes no impression upon the creative energies; it lacks the force that transmutes desires into realities. If we make only half-hearted efforts, why are we surprised by half-hearted results? Are we determined to be great men and women? Are we DETERMINED? Are we COMMITTED?

Issues That Come Up with Commitments

Commitment often means different things to different people. Some people take commitment more seriously than do others. For some people, when they say they are committed to something, they simply mean that their plan (for that moment) is to do whatever they are committing to do, but if something else (more interesting) comes along, then they might not follow through with the original commitment. Or, sometimes people make commitments without putting into place the necessary mechanisms to ensure that they will more likely be able to follow through with that commitment.

One example of that is when a person makes a commitment to do something and does not write it down so they do not forget, or does not make arrangements to ensure they will be able to follow through (e.g., check with their spouse to see if there might be a conflict). I can be committed to do a certain thing as long as certain conditions are met. In some cases, the conditions are extensive, in other cases, the conditions are few and simple. For example, I am committed to going to the gym at least three times a week (as long as my work schedule remains reasonably flexible). On the other hand, I am more committed to reading my Bible everyday, even when it is not convenient for me to do so. Consequently, my commitment to do one is stronger than it is to do the other.

Your Will to Act

Most people are not willing to make the necessary commitment to make a <u>real</u> difference; it is hard work. Our biggest obstacle is our lack of will to act. Once we have overcome that problem, the actual event is nothing. In many cases, the difference is motivation.

> *If you are motivated to do something, you are much more likely to do it and thus follow through on your commitment.*

Chapter 19 – Commitment

Moral Commitment in Intimate Relationships

Craig Cashwell and Amber Pope wrote an article about moral commitment in intimate relationships. In the *Family Journal* article, they talk about Johnson's Tripartite Model of Commitment.

Ongoing debate abounds in the scholarly literature about which theories of relationship commitment best explain the processes of commitment in interpersonal relationships (Ramirez, 2008). One of the most prominent theories of commitment that is gathering increasing empirical support is Johnson's (1991, 1999) Tripartite Model of Commitment. Johnson (1991, 1999) developed a commitment framework in which he contends there are three distinct types of commitment (personal, moral, and structural) that are experienced in a unique manner, with each having distinct causes and different behavioral, cognitive and emotional consequences (Johnson, 1999; Johnson, Caughlin, & Huston, 1999).

In addition to the three types of commitment, Johnson (1991, 1999) further theorized commitment as including two dichotomous dimensions of the commitment experience: (a) the components of attractions and constraints and (b) the internal and external processes that influence one's decision and behaviors to maintain a relationship. The attractions force of commitment captures the idea that partners want to maintain their relationships based on personal dedication and love. The constraints force of commitment refers to the extent that partners remain in their relationships to avoid the consequences of relationship dissolution (Adams & Jones, 1997; Johnson, 1999).

The internal processes that influence relationship commitment refer to occurrences within an individual, such as attitudes, identity, and values. Processes external to the relationship that impact one's decisions and behaviors to maintain a relationship refer to those forces that exist outside of an individual. These include social pressures, difficulty of terminating the relationship, availability and quality of relationship alternatives, and irretrievable investments into the relationship (Johnson, 1991, 1999).

Types of Commitment

The three types of commitment identified by Johnson (1991, 1999) are personal, moral and structural. Personal commitment refers to the extent to which a partner wants to maintain their relationship and encompasses the attractions dimension of commitment. Moral commitment is the feeling that one ought to or should remain in their relationship and is a part of the constraints dimension. Johnson (1999) defines the components of moral commitment as relationship-type values, person specific obligation, and general valuing of consistency.

Both personal and moral commitment are a result of internal experiences, such as one's general and relationship-specific attitudes and values (Johnson, 1999). Finally, structural commitment is part of the constraints dimension and refers to the degree to which a partner feels they must stay in their relationship. Structural commitment is a result of external

429

experiences that makes one perceive the dissolution of the relationship as costly (Adams & Jones, 1997; Johnson, 1991, 1999; Johnson et al., 1999; Ramirez, 2008).

> *Lokhorst et al. (2013) did an extensive study on commitment and behavior change in which they point out the theoretical underpinnings of what processes underlie commitment effects.*

Theoretical underpinnings: What processes underlie commitment effects?

Current views on commitment processes are strongly influenced by the work of Cialdini (2001). His seminal book on social influence devotes a chapter to explaining commitment processes and emphasizes that for commitment interventions to be successful, the act of committing needs to lead to fundamental changes in the individual. The individual needs to change his or her self-concept to be in line with the new behavior and/or the individual needs to change cognitions, values, and attitudes, to be more favorable toward the new behavior. It is these internalized changes that sustain the behavior over the long term. Others have suggested that social norms guide people to adhere to their commitments (Abrahamse et al., 2005), whereas a different line of research examined the idea that commitment can lead the individual to develop a personal norm that would support engaging in the behavior (Kerr, Garst, Lewandoski, & Harris, 1997). Although these processes—self-concept, attitudes, and social and personal norms—possibly overlap or may complement each other, each operates a little differently, and we review each in turn.

Self-concept and consistency

One theme in Cialdini's (2001) explanations for commitment's effectiveness is that in many societies, people have been socialized to be consistent, so when people commit and follow-through on a behavior, they bring their self-concept in line with the behavior. Consistent with Bem's (1972) work on self-perception theory, this means that if people freely choose to perform a behavior, they believe they must have wanted to: They must believe in the cause or expect to enjoy the behavior.

When people view their behaviors as voluntary and not coerced, they conclude that they have come to these decisions by themselves and that their behaviors reflect their true motivations, their internal self, or self-concept. One can think of this as a change in self-concept or as a change in the salience of some aspect of the self (e.g., see Rhodewalt & Agustsdottir, 1986, on salience and the malleable self). Either way, this belief should cause the behavior to continue in the future. It is important to note that such a process does not imply mindless compliance to whatever previously made commitment but rather a change in how people think about themselves due to what they have committed to.

Chapter 19 – Commitment

> *This process has been studied in a technique that closely resembles commitment making, called Foot In The Door (FITD).*

In this technique, participants are first asked to commit to a small request and then within a few weeks are asked to commit to a much larger request (the actual target request); a great deal of evidence has been found for changes in self-perception as a mediator for this phenomenon (Burger, 1999).

Direct evidence for commitment leading to a changed self-concept comes from a study that induced commitment and then collected related personality measures (Burger & Caldwell, 2003). Compared with a control group, those who had complied with a small request to support the homeless (signed a petition and wrote a brief essay) described themselves as (a) more compassionate and (b) more willing to provide support for the homeless, and, shortly thereafter, (c) were more likely to comply with a request to volunteer for a food drive. Mediation analysis showed that the change in self-concept mediated the relationship between commitment and follow-through. Similar changes in self-concept were obtained in another study (Burger & Guadagno, 2003), and both add weight to claims that making a commitment can actually change one's self-concept.

> *The importance of a need for consistency in these processes is underscored by research showing that people who favor consistency are more likely, whereas people who favor inconsistency and spontaneity are less likely to confirm commitment hypotheses, especially when their initial behaviors are made salient (Burger & Guadagno, 2003; Cialdini, Trost, & Newsom, 1995).*

This personality-based qualifier also suggests that commitment effects will not be universal and depend on participants' needs for consistency.

Attitudinal approach

A related approach to understanding the effect of commitment on behavior change is offered by a cognitive attitudinal approach. Cialdini (2003) alluded to these processes without giving details, but there is an extensive literature on how attitudes are changed through self-persuasion and cognitive elaboration (i.e., people generating reasons for embracing a new attitude; e.g., Chaiken's Heuristic Systematic Model or HSM, 1987; Greenwald's Cognitive Elaboration, 1968; Petty & Cacioppo's Elaboration Likelihood Model or ELM, 1986). There is considerable evidence that people bring their attitudes in line with their behavior, whether because of self-perception (Bem, 1972) or dissonance (Aronson, 1999) processes. Both of these processes require that people feel they made their commitment voluntarily.

> *The cognitive elaboration literature complements these processes by suggesting a mechanism by which people transform short-term commitment into long-term self-directed behavior, that is, that people persuade themselves the commitment and new behavior are worthwhile.*

In this model, attitude change takes time, as people think about the issue and their commitment and generate reasons and favorable attitudes. In theory, over time, the net effect is to integrate multiple favorable cognitions into a single attitude, thereby strengthening and solidifying their commitment to the new behavior.

A consequence of elaboration is that people create "strong," accessible attitudes that guide behavior (Fazio, 1990, 1995; Holland, Verplanken, & Van Knippenberg, 2002). "Attitude strength" is a multifaceted construct that emphasizes that the attitude is accessible, durable, resists efforts to change it and predicts behavior (Petty, Haugtvedt, & Smith, 1995). If making a commitment keeps the issue at hand salient and activates cognitive elaboration, the process of this elaboration enables the individual to develop a strong and accessible attitude that serves both to remind and motivate the individual to engage in the behavior. As Pardini and Katzev (1983-1984) argued, making a commitment to recycle may lead participants to "find their own reasons for recycling, to begin to even like doing so, and, as a result, to continue to perform these behaviors on their own" (p. 253).

Although the commitment-elaboration-attitude change model is appealing, Werner et al. (1995) reviewed a number of studies showing that commitment did not lead to attitude change, although it did lead to behavioral maintenance. Werner et al. suggested that previous research had not allowed sufficient time for attitudes to change. They used a 4-month period with weekly observations and found that although participants began their study with similar recycling behaviors (and presumably similar recycling attitudes), those who recycled for the 4 months had final attitudes significantly more favorable than those who did not recycle. These results did not support the idea that commitment is better than other interventions at leading to attitude change, because all conditions, not just commitment, showed this increase. Thus, although cognitive elaboration provides a potential mechanism for connecting an initial commitment to long-term behaviors, further research is needed to determine how elaboration might be encouraged in relation to commitment.

Norms
Another explanation that could account for commitment effects is based on a normative approach or concerns about what others do and think. Cialdini (2001) provided extensive examples of social pressures (ridicule, criticism) brought to bear on those who renege on their commitments as well as examples of people who explained their behavioral consistency by pointing to their fear of others' scorn.

Chapter 19 – Commitment

> *Thus, a commitment made in public leads to adherence because of the possible negative social sanctions that would follow for breaking it (Abrahamse et al., 2005).*

This view emphasizes the importance of others' opinions and suggests that a commitment is primarily effective if others witness or might learn about the commitment and could possibly enforce it, even if only through social sanctions.

Although the impact of public surveillance (or fears about others' reactions) on adherence seems plausible, this process has not been demonstrated in commitment literature. However, it has been complemented by research on commitment and internalized norms. This is particularly important because social pressure is an external motivator, and durable behavior change is more likely if the pressure is internal and self-directed. Theory and research on values and norms suggests that when people perceive a problem, a need for action can be activated by their moral values, which produces feelings of moral obligation to perform or refrain from certain behaviors (Schwartz & Howard, 1984).

These feelings of moral obligation are personal, internalized norms. In their research on commitment, Kerr et al. (1997) specifically pitted the social norm explanation against the alternative explanation of a personal norm. In two experiments, Kerr and his colleagues showed that even when no one would know whether participants adhered to their commitments, they still kept the promises they made to their groups. Kerr et al. concluded that their studies offered support for the personal norm explanation (see also Kerr & Kaufman- Gililand, 1994).

Summary

In sum, there is considerable evidence that making a commitment can activate psychological processes related to self-concepts, attitudes, and norms and that these processes motivate the individual to maintain the new behavior. Although the processes have been studied independently, it is possible they can be seen as mutually supportive. Changes in self-concept, attitudes/cognitions, and in personal or social norms all reflect the idea that making a voluntary commitment makes salient one's personal desire for consistency or one's concerns for appearing consistent to others; cognitions can be activated to support attitude–behavior consistency, to strengthen moral norms, and to support a positive view of one's self. Ultimately, internalization can occur, yielding behaviors that are motivated by personal, durable feelings, and beliefs.

REFERENCES
Chapter 19 – "Commitment"

Abrahamse, W., Steg, L., Vlek, C., & Rothengatter, T. (2005). A review of intervention studies aimed at household energy conservation. *Journal of Environmental Psychology, 25*, 273–291.

Adams, J. M., & Jones, W. H. (1997). The conceptualization of marital commitment: An integrative analysis. *Journal of Personality and Social Psychology, 72*, 1177–1196.

Adams, J. M., & Jones, W. H. (1999). Interpersonal commitment in historical perspective. In J. M. Adams & W. H. Jones (Eds.), *Handbook of interpersonal commitment and relationship stability* (pp. 3–36). New York: Kluwer Academic/Plenum Publishers.

Aronson, E. (1999). The power of self-persuasion. *American Psychologist, 54*, 875–884.

Bem, D. (1972). Self-perception theory. In L. Berkowitz (Ed.), *Advances in experimental social psychology* (Vol. 6, pp. 1–62). San Diego, CA: Academic Press.

Burger, J. M. (1999). The foot-in-the-door compliance procedure: A multiple-process analysis and review. *Personality and Social Psychology Review, 3*, 303–325.

Burger, J. M., & Caldwell, D. F. (2003). The effects of monetary incentives and labeling on the foot-in-the-door effect: Evidence for a self-perception process. *Basic and Applied Social Psychology, 25*, 235–241.

Burger, J. M., & Guadagno, R. E. (2003). Self-concept clarity and the foot-in-the-door procedure. *Basic and Applied Social Psychology, 25*, 79–86.

Cashwell, C., & Pope, A. (2013). Moral commitment in intimate committed relationships: A conceptualization from cohabiting same-sex and opposite-sex partners. *The Family Journal: Counseling and Therapy for Couples and Families, 21*(1), 5–14.

Chaiken, S. (1987). The heuristic model of persuasion. In M. P. Zanna, J. M. Olson, & C. P. Herman (Eds.), *Social influence: The Ontario symposium* (Vol. 5, pp. 3–39). Hillsdale, NJ: Lawrence Erlbaum.

Cialdini, R. B. (2001). *Influence: Science and practice*. Boston, MA: Allyn & Bacon.

Cialdini, R. B. (2003). Crafting normative messages to protect the environment. *Current Directions in Psychological Science, 12*, 105–109.

Cialdini, R. B., Eisenberg, N., Green, B. L., Rhoads, K., & Bator, R. (1998). Undermining the undermining effect of reward on sustained interest. *Journal of Applied Social Psychology, 28*, 249–263.

Cialdini, R. B., Trost, M. R., & Newsom, J. T. (1995). Preference for consistency—The development of a valid measure and the discovery of surprising behavioral implications. *Journal of Personality and Social Psychology, 69*, 318–328.

Fazio, R. H. (1990). Multiple processes by which attitudes guide behavior: The MODE model as an integrative framework. In M. P. Zanna (Ed.), *Advances in experimental social psychology* (Vol. 23, pp. 75–109). New York: Academic Press.

Fazio, R. H. (1995). Attitudes as object-evaluation associations: Determinants, consequences, and correlates of attitude accessibility. In R. E. Petty & J. A. Krosnick (Eds.), *Attitude strength: Antecedents and consequences* (pp. 247–282). Hillsdale, NJ: Lawrence Erlbaum.

Greenwald, A. G. (1968). Cognitive learning, cognitive response to persuasion, and attitude change. In A. Greenwald, T. Brock, & T. Ostrom (Eds.), *Psychological foundations of attitudes* (pp. 147–170). New York: Academic Press.

Holland, R. W., Verplanken, B., & Van Knippenberg, A. (2002). On the nature of attitude-behavior relations: The strong guide, the weak follow. *European Journal of Social Psychology, 32*, 869–876.

Johnson, M. P. (1991). Commitment to personal relationships. In W. H. Jones and D. Perlman (Eds.), *Advances in personal relationships* (Vol. 3, pp. 117–143). London, England: Cambridge University Press.

Chapter 19 – Commitment

Johnson, M. P., Caughlin, J. P., & Horton, T. L. (1999). The tripartite nature of marital commitment: Personal, moral, and structural reasons to stay married. *Journal of Marriage and the Family, 61*, 160–177.

Kerr, N. L., & Kaufman-Gililand, C. M. (1994). Communication, commitment, and cooperation in social dilemmas. *Journal of Personality and Social Psychology, 66*, 513–529.

Kerr, N. L., Garst, J., Lewandowski, D. A., & Harris, S. E. (1997). That still, small voice: Commitment to cooperate as an internalized vs. a social norm. *Personality and Social Psychology Bulletin, 23*, 1300–1311.

Kingsley, J., & Johnson, M. P. (1999). Personal, moral, and structural commitment to relationships: Experiences of choice and constraint. In J. M. Adams & W. H. Jones (Eds.), *Handbook of interpersonal commitment and relationship stability* (pp. 73–90). New York: Kluwer Academic/Plenum Publishers.

Lokhorst, A. M., Werner, C., Staats, H., van Dijk, E., & Gale, J. L. (2013). Commitment and behavior change : A meta-analysis and critical review of commitment-making strategies in environmental research. *Environment and Behavior, 45*, 3. (Several other references included in this article)

McGuire, G. (2009). *Learning to laugh* (Chapter 24). New Delhi: Epitome Books.

Pardini, A., & Katzev, R. (1984). The effect of strength of commitment on newspaper recycling. *Journal of Environmental Systems, 13*, 245–254.

Petty, R. E., & Cacioppo, J. T. (1986). *Communication and persuasion: Central and peripheral routes to attitude change.* New York: Springer-Verlag.

Petty, R. E., Haugtvedt, C. P., & Smith, S. M. (1995). Elaboration as a determinant of attitude strength: Creating attitudes that are persistent, resistant, and predictive of behavior. In R. E. Petty & J. A. Krosnick (Eds.), *Attitude strength: Antecedents and consequences* (pp. 93–130). Hillsdale, NJ: Lawrence Erlbaum.

Ramirez, A., Jr. (2008). An examination of the tripartite approach to commitment: An actor-partner interdependence model analysis of the effect of relational maintenance behavior. *Journal of Social and Personal Relationships, 25*, 943–965.

Rhodewalt, F., & Agustsdottir, S. (1986). The effects of self-presentation on the phenomenal self. *Journal of Personality and Social Psychology, 50*, 47–55.

Schwartz, S. H., & Howard, J. A. (1984). Internalised values as motivators of altruism. In E. Staub, D. Bar-Tal, J. Karylowski, & J. Reykowski (Eds.), *Development and maintenance of prosocial behavior* (pp. 229–256). New York: Plenum Press.

Selman, J. (n.d.). *Commitment and change.* Retrieved from http://www.paracomm.com/commitment-and-change/

Werner, C. M. (2003). Changing homeowners' use of toxic household products: Transactional approach. *Journal of Environmental Psychology, 23*, 33–45.

Werner, C. M., & Makela, E. (1998). Motivations and behaviors that support recycling. *Journal of Environmental Psychology, 18*, 373–386.

Werner, C. M., Turner, J., Shipman, K., Twitchell, S. F., Dickson, B. R., Bruschke, G. V., & von Bismarck, W. B. (1995). Commitment, behavior, and attitude change: An analysis of voluntary recycling. *Journal of Environmental Psychology, 15*, 197–208.

Young, S. (2007). *How to make commitments you will actually keep.* Retrieved from http://www.scottyoung.com/blog/2007/01/24/how-to-make-commitments-you-will-actually-keep/

Chapter 20
Motivation

Ready To Act

You are ready to move forward; maybe even hungry; excited about it. Motivation brings about an "Aha moment" to follow through.

People are motivated for different reasons. When I think of motivation, I think of encouragement, enticement to action or being pushed to DO something. When I am motivated to do something, I am usually excited about doing it. I'm looking forward to it. If my motivation is low, it's a lot more difficult for me to move into action. The things that seem to motivate me are the potential loss of money, timelines, deadlines, promise keeping, love, strong interest or caring.

It's been said that one person cannot motivate another. What might be possible, however, could be that a person could hold another in such high esteem that they are "motivated" to act. In that case, one does it for that person or the relationship between the two people is such that the one is "motivated" to action by the other (possibly because they do not want to let that person down).

As I think of motivation speakers, I think of people who are exciting, interesting and uplifting. They make common, everyday situations, problems and concerns seem easy, simple and not difficult. After listening to a motivational speaker, I'm often left with ideas that I might try. I'm often excited and left in a positive mood.

> *To be motivated is to be ready for action, needing little encouragement. How do you get a person to be motivated? Sometimes incentives help, encouragement, enticements.*

Try identifying why they are not motivated about this particular thing. Identify some things that they are motivated about or interested in. Maybe try role reversing. Identify someone they respect or think highly of and see if that can help. Ask yourself, what motivates you and why?

Examples of Motivation

I see friends and colleagues who are motivated to exercise regularly because they want to stay healthy. Some of them are motivated to follow through on their promises because they value promise keeping. Colleagues at work are motivated to seek office in our professional organization because it provides opportunities for them to exercise leadership and to have a say in the future direction of their chosen profession. It also provides privileges and prestige that they value. Some people are motivated to try dressing well because they feel good (or better) when they think they look good in their clothing. They also appreciate the compliments they receive from others.

Motivation by a different name

Other words that come to mind concerning motivation are:

Moving into a mode of action.

Somewhat excited about doing something.

Being motivated is being ready.

Committed to take on the challenge.

Having a positive frame of mind toward a certain activity or project.

> *Having the desire and/or wanting something to happen and being ready to start.*

Having a rationale (that works for you and that you can identify with) to move forward. Encouragement, and having the desire to follow through with something.

Action Oriented

Being motivated is having the desire to do something, or having a reason to do it or having a motive to do it. The necessary elements of a decision are sufficiently present or put together that a motivated person is willing and desirous to move forward on a certain task. The conditions are such that they are willing to follow through.

> *They are sufficiently inspired or "ready" to act. Having the mental state of mind to do something is also motivation.*

Some questions that come to mind concerning motivation are such things as:

What is the impetus, what is the carrot, the stick, the situation, circumstance, the thing that causes the motivated person to act? What condition needs to precede the motivation? Why are some people motivated and others are not? Why now? What is the reason for the change of heart? What is the motive for acting? Who benefits from this action? Is the thing that caused the motivation capable of being duplicated? Or, is it just a temporary thing? If a similar situation or condition occurred, would the person be similarly motivated? Can this motivating factor be generalized to others beyond this person? Are there certain "types" of people for whom this would work?

Personal Experience

Some people are motivated by personal experiences. We often see movie stars, athletes and other well-to-do people supporting certain causes because of a personal experience they have with that cause. Examples are cancer victims supporting cancer research and victims of drunk driving accidents supporting MADD (Mothers Against Drunk Drivers).

I know people who are motivated when they can see a clear benefit for others or for themselves.

Motivation is sometimes helped by planning and setting aside time to do certain things. Motivation is also sometimes helped by encouragement from others or even expectation from others. One of the best motivators is to have the task or activity built into your regular routine. If you are used to doing it, you are likely to be motivated to continue doing it.

It's About Staying the Course

The Ultimate Guide to Motivation—How to Achieve Any Goal (Editor-in-chief of Pickthebrain.com (2007) One of the biggest challenges in meeting any goal, whether it be related to productivity, waking early, changing a habit, exercising, or just becoming happier, is finding the motivation to stick with it.

If you can stick with a goal for long enough, you'll almost always get there eventually. It just takes patience, and motivation. This site http://zenhabits.net/the-ultimate-guide-to-motivation-how-to-achieve-any-goal/ offered 20 Ways to Sustain Motivation When You're Struggling, including just start, stay accountable, find like-minded friends and build on your successes.

Self Motivation

The same author also wrote "How To Motivate Yourself—Self Motivation" that gave three primary reasons we lose motivation. Staying motivated is a struggle, our drive is constantly assaulted by negative thoughts and anxiety about the future. The author of this article goes on to say that what separates the highly successful is the ability to keep moving forward. Even after beating it, the problem reappears at the first sign of failure. The key is understanding your thoughts and how they drive your emotions. For me, sometimes reading or seeing someone else's success story is motivating.

Chapter 20 – Motivation

> *By learning how to nurture motivating thoughts, neutralize negative ones, and focus on the task at hand, you can pull yourself out of a slump before it gains momentum.*

Reasons We Lose Motivation

The author mentions that the three primary reasons we lose motivation are

- lack of confidence
- lack of focus and
- lack of direction.

Retrieved from: http://www.pickthebrain.com/blog/how-to-motivate-yourself/

According to Morsella, Bargh, and Gollwitzer (2009), motivations are closely related to emotions. A motivation is a driving force that initiates and directs behavior. Some motivations are biological, such as the motivation for food, water and sex. But there are a variety of other personal and social motivations that can influence behavior, including the motivations for social approval and acceptance, the motivation to achieve, and the motivation to take, or to avoid taking, risks.

> *Jonathan Steele (2010) on Speechmastery.com defines motivation as communicating to an internal force that actuates a behavioral pattern, thought process, action or reaction.*

Negative forces or positive forces can act as actuators. These forces can be either intrinsic or extrinsic. Intrinsic is when the force comes from within oneself. Extrinsic is when the external forces, positive or negative, produce a behavioral change.

According to Steele, extrinsic motivation would include circumstances, situations, rewards or punishment, both tangible and intangible that participation in results in an external benefit. Tangible benefits could include monetary reward or a prize. Intangible could include things like adoration, recognition and praise.

Intrinsic motivation would include involvement in behavioral pattern, thought process, action, activity or reaction for its own sake and without an obvious external incentive for doing so. A hobby is an example. If you are desirous of mastering public speaking for the sake of mastery and not any reward, you have experienced intrinsic motivation.

Differing Viewpoints on Motivation

From the scientific viewpoint, by most accounts, (according to inspirational-sayings-in-action.com) motivation is defined as an inner state of need or desire. That state of desire creates a movement or activity toward satisfying that desire.

Chapter 20 – Motivation

In my never-ending quest to spread the word about turning ideas into action, I view inspiration as the state of mind that primes us to come up with great ideas and motivation as the state of mind that spurs us to action.

From a practical standpoint, we can dig into our motives to get better results and move ourselves from point A to point B. For example, if you know what motivates you, you can use those motives to get yourself to do things that you wouldn't do otherwise. These same principles can be applied to motivating others as well.

Motivational techniques, therefore, are useful to (counselors) teachers, leaders, parents, employers, and really, almost anyone.

> *The key is in understanding that you are not motivating someone else. Instead, you are simply helping to provide a circumstance that triggers that person to be motivated.*

Getting Started and Keeping it Going are Critical Points to Remember!

Shaun Rosenberg commented that one of the hardest parts of accomplishing your goals in life, whether they be losing more weight, saving money, or lowering your cholesterol, has to be finding the motivation to start it up and to keep it going every day. He wrote an article titled "10 Motivational Strategies that Work," and he reported that once you have the momentum going, everything else can just fall in place, but getting that momentum going can be a challenge.

In his article, found at: http://www.shaunrosenberg.com/motivational-strategies-that-work, he goes on to explain that to an extent

> *it really depends on how badly you want to achieve your goal.*

You can listen to as many motivational strategies as you want, but if you don't want to achieve your dreams bad enough, it is still going to be hard to get out of bed and run a mile every morning, start writing your own book, or accomplish whatever it is you set out to accomplish.

You need to desire it because you love doing it and you know the benefits it can give you. If you have that desire, here are some motivational strategies to help pull you along when you feel like dragging your feet and guide you on the path to success.

Chapter 20 – Motivation

1. Stay Active

> *Our bodies adapt to what we do and how we live our lives. If we don't put any effort into life, our body wants to keep not putting any effort into life.*

If we are active and put in a lot of effort into our life then our body wants to keep pushing the limits and keep on doing and achieving more. Getting results is motivating.

2. Hang Around with Motivated People

You may have heard the statement, "your income is the average of the five people you spend the most time with." This brings up a powerful point which can be applied to nearly every aspect of life. In addition to your income, I like to say that your motivation is the average of the five people you spend the most time with. Call it peer pressure if you like, but motivated people help other motivated people stay motivated. Couch potatoes only hold you back and keep you lazy.

3. Have a Goal

Sometimes it can be hard to do things that seem boring or complicated. It is so easy to just put them off until tomorrow instead of dealing with them now (even if we secretly know that tomorrow never comes). One way to deal with this is to start creating your life plan and have a goal.

4. Let Others Know Your Goal

When you create your goal, the next thing you can do is to let others know about it. Tell everyone that is close to you what you plan on doing and how you plan on doing it. Ideally you want to tell someone who will understand and support your goal.

> *By letting others know your intentions, you know that other people are watching you and are holding you accountable for your goals.*

This way you are more likely to stay motivated to prove to others that you are not a failure and you are a person of your word.

5. Get a Role Model

Find someone to look up to who has already achieved what it is you aspire to achieve. When you have a role model, you have a standard to compare yourself with. It helps you grow and it gives you hope because you know what the light at the end of the tunnel looks like.

6. Realize That We All Have Bumps in the Road

Everybody hits bumps in the road. The greater your goals, the bigger those bumps will be. But these bumps do not have to defeat you. To be successful you have to realize that bumps in the road are just that. They will not stop you from your goal as long as you are motivated enough to keep pushing forward and doing what you can to achieve your goal.

7. Read Motivational Quotes

Another thing you can do is to read motivational quotes about life. There are billions of people who have gone through this thing called life before you, many of which have left us with some great wisdom about how to achieve success and find yourself. Reading motivational quotes can inspire you and get you ready to take action. I would even go so far as to recommend you get yourself a favorite quote you can look at every time you need to feel motivated to get up and take action. (This author's favorite source for motivational quotes is the Bible.) My personal favorite motivational quote is "The whole idea of motivation is a trap. Forget motivation. Just do it" (John C. Maxwell).

8. Take Bite-Sized Pieces

If you try to do too much too fast then you will burn yourself out or you will make so much work for yourself that it will be hard to even get started. It is much better to simply take bite-sized pieces and go after your goals little by little than it is to try and do everything at once.

9. Do The Hardest Thing First

> *Sometimes we procrastinate simply because we do not want to do the hardest thing on our list. When you have something you don't want to do, it is exactly what you need to do first.*

Instead of postponing it all day, think of how much more you will accomplish if you get rid of it first and then go after all of the easier tasks.

10. Make It Fun

No matter what you have to do, you should be able to make it fun. After all, if we enjoy what we are doing it is a whole lot easier to keep doing it.

The Reason for Action

A definition taken from motivation-for-dreamers.com states that motivation is simply the reason for an action – that which gives purpose and direction to behavior. Motivation is "WHAT drives you" to behave in a certain way or to take a particular action. It is your WHY. Your WHY is the strong reason for you to desire something. It is not what you desire, but the strong reason you desire it. If your reason for wanting something is strong enough, even if at the time you don't know how to achieve it, pursue it.

Chapter 20 – Motivation

> *It has often been said that when you desire something strongly enough the whole universe conspires to bring about the circumstances, people and resources you will need to achieve that purpose. (For me, that means the Holy Spirit is talking to you.)*

Other motivation-for-dreamers.com comments worthy of repeating come from their "Define Motivation for Yourself." I am in complete agreement with their position that it is important that you define motivation in a personal manner in order to fully understand its power and apply it to your own situation. Only by doing this can you be empowered to take action.

In its simplest form, motivation is what causes or stimulates a person to act.

> *Motivation is only motivation if it gets you to take action.*

Taking action is what separates the losers from the winners. Taking action is the difference between wishing and doing.

Motivation is Personal

What gets one person motivated may not work for someone else. Having a luxury car may work for one, but for another making a difference in other people's lives may be their biggest desire.

You must define motivation for yourself. You must know what your own values and principles are. What really gets you excited? What makes you feel good about yourself? What are your spiritual guidelines? What is it you want?

If you define motivation in a personal manner that is relevant to you, it will compel you to take action. If it does not then you haven't found the right motivation. Keep searching. Look deep within yourself.

What motivates you? According to Captain Bob Webb in "Elements of Motivation" (Webb, 2006), (Some) dreamers have a sense of purpose and meaning to their lives. Total freedom is not possible or desirable, but the struggle to achieve that ideal is the basis for motivation. It is said that to change our lifestyle, we must change our thinking habits. We change our thinking habits by focusing on desired goals. Achievement requires developing attitudes/habits that keep you on track – perseverance. To grow and change, we must be discontent with our current comfort zone. Analyze your comfort zone. Comfort zone is our living, work, and social environments that we have grown accustomed to. Some people can adjust to changing comfort zones with ease, others cannot. As we age, there is a tendency to lose the ability to adapt to wide-ranging comfort zones. Social prejudice narrows the range.

Chapter 20 – Motivation

Elements of Motivation

(1) creative freedom; motivation starts with a need, vision, dream or desire to achieve. Creativity is associated with ideas, projects and goals, which can be considered a path to freedom.

(2) love to learn; developing and maintaining a love-to-learn lifestyle, and/or continually seek new opportunities to learn what works and what does not work; and

> **(3) *learning from failure; failure is a learning tool. It is a temporary by-product of creativity.***

It is challenging the learning process, developing and maintaining a desire to overcome barriers and to bounce back from discouragement or failure. Individuals learn to tolerate the agony that failure brings. Bouncing back requires creative thinking, as it is a learning process. Most ideas don't work but with each try, people learn from their failures and get closer to their goal.

It is experiential education at work. Success is achieved by those who are willing to take risk and lose. If everything you do works, you are not trying hard enough. Our first reaction to failure is to blame. If we perceive others are to blame, then there is nothing we can do to correct the problem. If we assume responsibility, then we can analyze what went wrong and take corrective action. Failure separates those who think they want success from those who are determined to win. Failure narrows the playing field.

> ***People around us play a big role in our being motivated to follow through on a project, either positively or negatively; directly or indirectly; openly or undercover in subtle ways or out in the open.***

Emotional Hype Can Become a Trap (Webb, 2006)

The passive follower becomes hooked and has changed his primary goal. The new goal, "seek and maintain an emotional high." An addict becomes dependent on motivational material to maintain this illusion and, in time, can't live without them.

> ***Some people replace action with emotional hype. There is no creativity in emotional hype other than ideas sound good.***

Some people like to listen to good ideas, ways to get things done, how to's and other motivational ideas, but seldom or even never get around to "doing" anything themselves, or never get around to making needed changes they have heard about or have learned from listening to the motivation speaker or seeing the video. Most of us can enjoy a good motivational speech or see an exciting video that touches an emotional nerve that gets us excited. The question that might be asked is:

Chapter 20 – Motivation

> ***Are you excited enough or touched to the point of acting on the good ideas brought out by the motivational speaker or the exciting video?***

In many cases, the answer is "no." We oftentimes leave a workshop session or a conference all excited, upbeat and thinking positive about what we heard or saw just to be faced with the reality of our already busy life the following day. Every now and then, I can make a decision to follow through with what I heard at a conference if I can fit what I heard into my life at the time and not let other things in my life throw me off track from following through.

The art of positive thinking will not replace required knowledge or the ability to make right decisions. Positive attitudes can provide persistence until knowledge and quality decision skills are acquired. When you are ready to make a decision, it helps to have a process in mind, a process that fits what's going on in your life at that time and one that is complete and comprehensive enough to be effective, efficient and long lasting.

For example, if you just heard an exciting speaker explain how easy it can be to lose 20 pounds in one month, that sounds reasonable enough and you might be determined to make a decision to try that for yourself. However, important issues in making that decision might be whether you can fit what is required of the process into the next 30 days, after consulting with your doctor, family member and others and whether you can maintain that behavior for an extended period after you have lost the weight. These and other questions and considerations need to be a part of the decision-making process.

Motivation Through Goal Setting

In 1968, the American Pulpwood Association became concerned about how to increase its loggers' productivity as mechanization alone was not increasing the productivity of its logging crews. Two industrial organization psychologists—Edwin A. Locke and Gary P. Latham—assured the firm's managers that they had found a way to increase productivity at no financial expense to anyone. The policy seemed too easy; it merely involved setting specific production goals for the loggers. The novelty was that these goals were wage irrelevant, in contrast with classical wage relevant goals such as bonuses. The psychologists argued that introducing a goal that was difficult but attainable would increase the challenge of the job while making it clear to the workers what was expected from them. Although the managers were quite skeptical at the beginning, the results were surprising: the performance of logging crews increased 18% and the firm's profits rose as well (Latham & Locke, 1979).

That story is how Joaquín Gómez-Miñambres introduced the article titled "Motivation Through Goal Setting" that was published in the *Journal of Economic Psychology*.

The author went on to say how psychologists and experts in management have long documented the importance of goal setting in workers' motivation. In particular, they have found that when workers are committed to challenging but attainable goals, their performance increases even if those goals are not directly linked to wages.

> *Agents care about goal setting because achieving those goals creates a sense of achievement and accomplishment that modifies their intrinsic motivation to work.*

We have shown that, in an optimal contract, more challenging objectives increase agents' performance and that the goals set by the principal increase with the agent's standard. Therefore, goals that are payoff irrelevant, since they do not directly affect agents' extrinsic incentives, increase the principal's profits. We have also shown that a mid-ranged standard gives the highest satisfaction to an agent and that a mid-ranged agent type could be the most satisfied among all the agent types. Therefore, being very demanding can be detrimental.

Initial stage or advanced stage of goal pursuit, which provides the most motivation?

Conventional wisdom suggests that the more means available for people to attain a goal, the more likely they will be to adopt the goal. More generally, Szu-chi Huang and Ying Zhang (2013) ask the question of how the presence of multiple means for goal attainment influences people's motivation in pursuing the goal, and whether these impacts remain the same at different stages of goal pursuit.

This is explained in an article based on their research titled "All Roads Lead to Rome: The Impact of Multiple Attainment Means on Motivation." We propose that because people focus on different aspects of goal pursuit at the initial versus advanced stages of the pursuit, the presence of multiple attainment means may either increase or decrease their motivation.

> *Specifically, when people are at the initial stage of goal pursuit (e.g., just started to train for marathon), they focus primarily on whether the goal is attainable and derive motivation from the perceived attainability.*

Compared with having a single attainment means, the presence of multiple complementary means makes the goal seem more easily attainable and, hence, induces greater motivation for the pursuit.

> *However, when people have made substantial progress on a goal and its attainability is relatively secured, they focus more on how they can finally attain the goal and complete the pursuit.*

Compared with multiple means, a single means provides a more straightforward roadmap for people to "race to the end," making the goal seem more easily attainable, which in turn leads to greater motivation.

Combining these two propositions, we hypothesize that while the presence of multiple attainment means to a goal increases people's motivation at the initial stages, it may lower their motivation at more advanced stages of the pursuit. In addition, such distinctive motivational consequences are caused by the differences in people's dominant concerns at a given moment.

Contrary to the popular belief that offering more options for people to pursue a goal always increases their motivation, we suggest that while it induces more effort investment at the initial stages of the pursuit, the presence of multiple means may in fact undermine people's motivation when they are at more advanced stages of goal pursuit.

We attribute this change to the shift in people's primary concerns as they progress toward the endpoint of a goal and suggest that while the presence of multiple attainment means makes the goal seem more easily attainable initially, it complicates the pursuit and makes the attainment seem more difficult when people focus on how to reach the endpoint at the advanced stages of goal pursuit.

Results from five studies supported the hypothesis

While the present research focuses mainly on the two extremes of goal pursuit (the initiation versus completion of a goal), Huang and Zhang's (2013) findings have further implications for understanding the difference between initiating versus maintaining the pursuit of a goal.

The initiation of a goal pursuit signals one's establishment of commitment and changes a person's behavioral pattern (from not pursuing a goal to pursuing a goal).

By comparison, one's maintenance of goal pursuit signals the extension of this commitment and requires only the continuation of a person's existing behavioral pattern. On the basis of our current discussion, people infer goal difficulty at these two stages differently because they focus on different aspects of goal pursuit. It would therefore be possible that

> *people might prefer the presence of multiple means when they are initiating a new goal because it reduces the uncertainty in the pursuit, but would conversely prefer the simplicity of a proven means when maintaining a goal that they know how to accomplish.*

In our studies, we found that the presence of multiple means not only enhances motivation when people are deliberating which goal to pursue, it also facilitates motivation in actual goal pursuit until people are relatively certain about the goal's attainability.

However, their findings sound a cautionary bell to organizations by suggesting that while this practice may indeed be effective in eliciting greater motivation when the goal's attainability is in question, it may be counterproductive when the attainability is not a primary concern.

The findings further add to the thriving literature that suggests that choices may not always be desirable (Iyengar & Lepper, 2000; Shafir, Simonson, & Tversky, 1993; Shafir & Tversky, 1992).

> *In the context of goal pursuit, we found that offering choices among available attainment means is productive when people are concerned about goal attainability, but it becomes counterproductive when people focus on reducing the discrepancy.*

This notion is consistent with the distinction between experiential and instrumental choices (Choi & Fishbach, 2011), which separates choices that one has to make from those one does not have to make. It was found that when people deliberate among options without any particular goal in mind, choices are more enjoyable and thus desired, which closely resembles our findings at the initial stage of goal pursuit—it is good to know that there are plenty of options to choose from in the pursuit but there is little urgency in making a decision.

Now to shift gears from motivation to help oneself to helping someone else, the question becomes where does the motivation to help someone else come from?

What Motivates People to Help Other People?

A question that is sometimes asked, but often misunderstood is the question, "What motivates people to help others? Netta Weinstein and Richard Ryan (2010) wrote an article based on their research that helps answer that question. The title of the article in the *Journal of Personality and Social Psychology* is: "When Helping Helps: Autonomous Motivation for Prosocial Behavior and Its Influence on Well-Being for the Helper and Recipient."

The two authors explain that several theoretical approaches have highlighted the role of motivation in prosocial behaviors. For example, the functional approach (Clary & Snyder, 1991) states that individuals will engage in prosocial behaviors to the extent that they have certain motives for these behaviors (these include the expression of values, developing understanding, social responsibility, and career enhancement).

Prosocial behavior is an umbrella term used to describe acts undertaken to protect or enhance the welfare of others (Schwartz & Bilsky, 1990) and includes helpful interventions (e.g., Batson, 1987; Cialdini et al., 1987), volunteer work (e.g., Foster, Mourato, Pearce, & Ozdemiroglu, 2001; Freeman, 1997), and donating money (Frey & Meier, 2004) or blood (Piliavin & Callero, 1991), among other examples.

These behaviors each have unique characteristics, but they all involve intentional actions that help or benefit others. Such helping behaviors are prevalent in our society (Thoits & Hewitt, 2001); in fact, a recent report estimated that 26.4% of Americans over age 16 volunteered in

2007–2008 (Bureau of Labor Statistics, U.S. Department of Labor, 2009), and past prevalence estimates have been similarly high (e.g., Wilson, 2000).

Given the frequency of prosocial behaviors, it appears clear that many people are motivated to help others. Yet past research has suggested that the motives leading people to help others can affect the experience and outcomes of helping (e.g., Batson & Oleson, 1991; Clary & Snyder, 1991; Reykowski, 1982). In the present studies, we attempt to extend the research on the motives of helping by considering the degree of volition or autonomy behind the actor's behavior as it impacts both the experience of the helper and that of the recipient of help.

Prosocial behaviors and wellbeing

It has long been thought that prosocial behaviors affect the wellbeing of the helper as well as the help recipient.

For example, Aristotle (350 BC/1985, p. 1159) claimed that true human happiness, which he described as eudaimonia (Ryan & Deci, 2001), was furthered more "by loving rather than in being loved." More recently, Mother Teresa stated, "Nothing makes you happier than when you reach out in mercy to someone who is badly hurt" (Myers, 1992, p. 194).

Research has lent empirical support to such claims. For example, studies demonstrate that volunteers are less prone to depression and experience greater personal happiness, life satisfaction, and self-esteem.

(Brown, Gary, Greene, & Milburn, 1992; Rietschlin, 1998; Wilson & Musick, 1999) and experience greater personal happiness (Ellison, 1991), life satisfaction (Wheeler, Gorey, & Greenblatt, 1998), and self-esteem (Gecas & Burke, 1995; Newman, Vasudev, & Onawola, 1986). Studies also demonstrate that giving help is correlated with higher levels of mental health (Schwartz, Meisenhelder, Yusheng, & Reed, 2003), life adjustment (Crandall & Lehman, 1977), and lower feelings of hopelessness (Miller, Denton, & Tobacyk, 1986) and depression (Crandall, 1975).

Notably, this important body of work has largely focused on volunteering behavior, which offers different rewards and incentives than those afforded by other forms of prosocial behaviors, especially those that occur spontaneously in day-to-day life (Snyder, Clary, & Stukas, 2000; Wilson, 2000).

Research on prosocial behavior and wellbeing suggests that helping others can yield wellbeing benefits for the helper. These benefits depend on the motivation for helping and the satisfaction of basic psychological needs that helping acts potentiate.

Specifically, we proposed that autonomous motivations (i.e., those with an internal perceived locus of causality) in the helper yield greater wellbeing benefits to both helper and recipients of help than controlled motivations (i.e., those that have an external perceived locus of causality).

This hypothesis, drawn from self-determination theory (SDT), has not been previously examined. To test this we conducted four studies assessing helping behavior under various conditions (natural and experimental) and contrasting motivational states (autonomous and controlled). Across varied methods, results largely supported our hypotheses.

The capacity of helping others to satisfy psychological needs has been described in the context of other theoretical approaches. The functional approach, for example, states that individuals continue engagement in prosocial behaviors to the extent that those activities satisfy needs (Clary et al., 1998). For the functional approach, needs vary among people, and as such, individuals are differently motivated as a function of their particular needs. Self-determination theory suggests, instead, that particular needs, namely those for relatedness, competence, and autonomy, will be universally advantageous for the wellbeing of helpers.

Together, these results support self-determination theory expectations for the importance of autonomous versus controlled motivation. We emphasize in this article that not all motivations have the same consequences, and we stress that it is essential for motivation to be experienced as self-initiated and/or self-endorsed for helpers to gain from their prosocial engagement and for their recipients to most reliably benefit from being helped.

Altruism/Egoism Literature

The current studies may also have relevance to the classic discussions of altruism and egoistic motives for prosocial behaviors. In this discussion (e.g., Batson, 1987; Batson, Van Lange, Ahmad, & Lishner, 2003; Cialdini et al., 1987; Post, 2005), theorists have debated the relevance and impact of egoistic and altruistic motives in helping behaviors.

That is, do people help because they enjoy helping or care about others (altruism) or is their helping instrumental to some other goal (egoism)?

Wilson and Musick (1997) similarly have argued that helping is ultimately motivated by moral incentives (see also Schervish, 2005), though more selfish reasons may also encourage helping behavior. For instance, helping might be propelled by compassion or a value for a good cause, or alternatively, a desire to advance one's career, reduce ego conflicts, or even learn a new skill.

451

Relatedness

Helping is inherently interpersonal and thus impacts relatedness by directly promoting closeness to others, positive responses from others, and cohesiveness or intimacy. This argument is similar to one made by Caprara and Steca (2005)

> **Caprara and Steca (2005) claimed that the human capacity to help is essential to the maintenance of mutually rewarding relationships.**

They proposed that humans are evolutionarily wired to experience relatedness through helping others. Initial support of this claim was demonstrated in a longitudinal study of volunteers, which showed that the subjective experience of mattering, including feeling recognized, important, and relied upon, mediated effects of helping others on wellbeing (Piliavin & Siegl, 2007).

Autonomy

Prosocial actions that are freely done and are expressions of well-internalized values also provide opportunities to experience autonomy need satisfaction and the positive states that follow from it. The experience of autonomy need satisfaction has been strongly linked with happiness and wellbeing across cultures (e.g., Chirkov, Ryan, & Willnes, 2005; Deci & Ryan, 2000). Although autonomy need satisfaction and autonomous motivation both involve the experience of autonomy, the two are conceptually and operationally distinct. Autonomy as a motivational state refers to the perceived source of behavioral regulation, or one's perceived locus of causality for a particular behavior (PLOC; deCharms, 1968). It is assessed by asking the person the reasons for acting, anchored by external pressures on the one end (e.g., "because others would get mad at me if I didn't") and personal values and interests on the other ("because I valued doing so"). Autonomy need satisfaction refers to the notion that individuals experience themselves as having been generally free and self-congruent over time and is assessed with items such as "Today, I felt free to be who I am."

Motivational Quotes and Citations

Proverbs 19:17 "If you help the poor, you are lending to the Lord – and He will repay you!"

Proverbs 21:5 "Good planning and hard work leads to prosperity, but hasty shortcuts lead to poverty."

I hated every minute of training, but I said, "Don't quit. Suffer now and live the rest of your life as a champion."
–Muhammad Ali

"The quality of a person's life is in direct proportion to their commitment to excellence, regardless of their chosen field of endeavor." –**Vince Lombardi**

Chapter 20 – Motivation

> *"The best way to predict the future is to create it."*
> *–Dr. Forrest C. Shaklee*

"Failure is the opportunity to begin again more intelligently." –**Henry Ford**

"Destiny is not a matter of chance; it's a matter of choice." –**Anonymous**

> *"It takes courage to grow up and turn out to be who you really are."* *–E.E.*
> *Cummings*

"It is never too late to be what you might have been." –**George Eliot**

Mostly Retrieved from "25 Of the Most Inspiring Quotes Ever Spoken" at:
http://www.pickthebrain.com/blog/25-of-the-most-inspiring-quotes-ever-spoken/#more-3577

REFERENCES
Chapter 20 – "Motivation"

Batson, C. D. (1987). Prosocial motivation: Is it ever truly altruistic? In L. Berkowitz (Ed.), *Advances in experimental social psychology* (Vol. 20, pp. 65–122). New York: Academic Press.

Batson, C. D., & Oleson, K. C. (1991). Current status of the empathy–altruism hypothesis. In M. S. Clark (Ed.), *Review of personality and social psychology: Vol. 12. Prosocial behavior*. Newbury Park, CA: Sage.

Batson, C. D., Coke, J. S., Jasnoski, M. L., & Hanson, M. (1978). Buying kindness: Effects of an extrinsic incentive for helping on perceived altruism. *Personality and Social Psychology Bulletin, 4*, 86–91.

Batson, C. D., Van Lange, P. A. M., Ahmad, N., & Lishner, D. A. (2003). Altruism and helping behavior. In M. A. Hogg & J. Cooper (Eds.), *Sage handbook of social psychology* (pp. 279–295). London: Sage.

Brown, D. R., Gary, L. E., Greene, A. D., & Milburn, N. G. (1992). Patterns of social affiliation as predictors of depressive symptoms among urban Blacks. *Journal of Health and Social Behavior, 33*, 242–253.

Bureau of Labor Statistics, U.S. Department of Labor. (2009). *Volunteering in the United States, 2008* (USDL Report No. 09-0078). Retrieved from http://www.bls.gov/news.release/volun.nr0.htm

Caprara, G. V., & Steca, P. (2005). Self-efficacy beliefs as determinants of prosocial behavior conducive to life satisfaction across ages. *Journal of Social and Clinical Psychology, 24*, 191–217.

Chirkov, V. I., Ryan, R. M., & Willnes, C. (2005). Cultural context and psychological needs in Canada and Brazil: Testing a self-determination approach to the internalization of cultural practices, identity and well-being. *Journal of Cross-Cultural Psychology, 36*, 423–443.

Chirkov, V. I., Ryan, R. M., Kim, Y., & Kaplan, U. (2003). Differentiating autonomy from individualism and independence: A self-determination theory perspective on internalization of cultural orientations and well-being. *Journal of Personality and Social Psychology, 84*, 97–109.

Choi, J., & Fishbach, A. (2011). Choice is an end versus a means. *Journal of Marketing Research, 48*, 544–554. doi:10.1509/jmkr.48.3.544

Cialdini, R. B., Schaller, M., Houlihan, D., Arps, K., Fultz, J., & Beaman, A. L. (1987). Empathy-based helping: Is it selflessly or selfishly motivated? *Journal of Personality and Social Psychology, 52*, 749–758.

Clary, E. G., & Snyder, M. (1991). A functional analysis of altruism and prosocial behavior: The case of volunteerism. In M. Clark (Ed.), Review of personality and social psychology (Vol. 12, pp. 119–148). Newbury Park, CA: Sage.

Clary, E. G., Snyder, M., Ridge, R. D., Copeland, J., Stukas, A. A., Haugen, J., & Miene, P. (1998). Understanding and assessing the motivation of volunteers: A functional approach. *Journal of Personality and Social Psychology, 74*, 1516–1530.

Crandall, J. E. (1975). A scale for social interest. *Journal of Individualistic Psychology, 31*, 187–195.

Crandall, J. E., & Lehman, R. E. (1977). Relationship of stressful life events to social interest, locus of control and psychological adjustment. *Journal of Consulting and Clinical Psychology, 45*, 1208.

deCharms, R. (1968). *Personal causation*. New York: Academic Press.

Deci, E. L., & Ryan, R. M. (1985a). The general causality orientations scale: Self-determination in personality. *Journal of Research in Personality, 19*, 109–134.

Deci, E. L., & Ryan, R. M. (1985b). *Intrinsic motivation and self-determination in human behavior*. New York: Plenum Press.

Deci, E. L., & Ryan, R. M. (2000). The "what" and "why" of goal pursuits: Human needs and the self-determination of behavior. *Psychological Inquiry, 11*, 227–268.

Editor-in-chief of Pickthebrain.com. (2007). *How to motivate yourself – Self-motivation*. Retrieved from www.pickthebrain.com/blog/how-to-motivate-yourself/

Chapter 20 – Motivation

Foster, V., Mourato, S., Pearce, D., & Ozdemiroglu, E. (2001). *The price of virtue: The economic value of the charitable sector.* Cheltenham, England: Elgar.

Freeman, R. B. (1997). Working for nothing: The supply of volunteer labor. *Journal of Labor Economics, 15,* 140–166.

Frey, B. S. (1997). *Not just for the money: An economic theory of personal motivation.* Cheltenham, England: Elgar.

Frey, B. S., & Jegen, R. (2001). Motivation crowding theory. *Journal of Economic Surveys, 15,* 589–611.

Frey, B. S., & Meier, S. (2004). Pro-social behavior in a natural setting. *Journal of Economic Behavior & Organization, 54,* 65–88.

Gecas, V., & Burke, P. J. (1995). Self and identity. In K. S. Cook, G. Fine, & J. S. House (Eds.), *Sociological perspectives on social psychology* (pp. 41–67). Boston, MA: Allyn & Bacon.

Huang, S.-C., & Zhang, Y. (2013). All roads lead to Rome: The impact of multiple attainment means on motivation. *Journal of Personality and Social Psychology, 104,* 236–248.

inspirational-sayings-in-action.com. (n.d.). *Definition of motivation getting from A to B.* Retrieved from http://www.inspirational-sayings-in-action.com/definition-of-motivation.html

Iyengar, S. S., & Lepper, M. R. (2000). When choice is demotivating: Can one desire too much of a good thing? *Journal of Personality and Social Psychology, 79,* 995–1006. doi:10.1037/0022-3514.79.6.995

Miller, M. J., Denton, G. O., & Tobacyk, J. J. (1986). Social interest and feelings of hopelessness among elderly patients. *Psychological Reports, 58,* 410.

Morsella, E., Bargh, J. A., & Gollwitzer, P. M. (2009). *Oxford handbook of human action.* New York: Oxford University Press.

motivation-for-dreamers.com. (nd). *Definition of motivation.* Retrieved from http://www.motivation-for-dreamers.com/definition-of-motivation.html

Mr.SelfDevelopment. (2010). *25 of the most inspiring quotes ever spoken.* Retrieved from http://www.pickthebrain.com/blog/25-of-the-most-inspiring-quotes-ever spoken/#more-3577

Myers, D. C. (1992). *The pursuit of happiness.* New York: Morrow.

Nadler, A. (1991). Help-seeking behavior: Psychological costs and instrumental benefits. In M. S. Clark (Ed.), *Prosocial behavior: Review of personality and social psychology* (Vol. 12, pp. 290–311). Newbury Park, CA: Sage.

Newman, S., Vasudev, J., & Onawola, R. (1986). Older volunteers' perceptions of impacts of volunteering on their psychological well-being. *Journal of Applied Gerontology, 4,* 123–134.

Piliavin, J. A., & Callero, P. L. (1991). *Giving blood: The development of an altruistic identity.* Baltimore, MD: Johns Hopkins University Press.

Piliavin, J. A., & Siegl, E. (2007). Heath benefits of volunteering in the Wisconsin Longitudinal Study. *Journal of Health and Social Behavior, 48,* 450–464.

Piliavin, J. A., Grube, J. A., & Callero, P. L. (2002). Role as resource for action in public service. *Journal of Social Issues, 58,* 469–485.

Post, S. G. (2005). Altruism, happiness, and health: It's good to be good. *International Journal of Behavioral Medicine, 12,* 66–77.

Reykowski, J., & Smolenska, Z. (1980). Personality mechanisms of prosocial behavior. *Polish Psychological Bulletin, 11,* 219–230.

Rietschlin, J. (1998). Voluntary association membership and psychological distress. *Journal of Health and Social Behavior, 39,* 348–355.

Romando, R. (2007). *Define motivation.* Retrieved from http://ezinearticles.com/?Define-Motivation&id=410696

Rosenberg, S. (n.d.). *10 motivational strategies that work.* Retrieved from http://www.shaunrosenberg.com/motivational-strategies-that-work

Ryan, R. M. (1982). Control and information in the intrapersonal sphere: An extension of cognitive evaluation theory. *Journal of Personality and Social Psychology, 43,* 450–461.

Ryan, R. M., & Connell, J. P. (1989). Perceived locus of causality and internalization. *Journal of Personality and Social Psychology, 57,* 749–761.

Ryan, R. M., & Deci, E. L. (2000). Self-determination theory and the facilitation of intrinsic motivation, social development, and well-being. *American Psychologist, 55*, 68–78.

Ryan, R. M., & Deci, E. L. (2001). To be happy or to be self-fulfilled: A review of research on hedonic and eudaimonic well-being. *Annual Review of Psychology, 52*, 141–166.

Ryan, R. M., & Deci, E. L. (2008). From ego depletion to vitality: Theory and findings concerning the facilitation of energy available to the self. *Social and Personality Psychology Compass, 2*, 702–717.

Ryan, R. M., & Frederick, C. M. (1997). On energy, personality and health: Subjective vitality as a dynamic reflection of well-being. *Journal of Personality, 65*, 529–565.

Ryan, R. M., Rigby, S., & King, K. (1993). Two types of religious internalization and their relations to religious orientation and mental health. *Journal of Personality and Social Psychology, 65*, 586–596.

Schervish, P. (2005). Major donors, major motives: The people and purposes behind major gifts. *New Directions of Philanthropic Fundraising, 47*, 59–87.

Schwartz, C. E., & Sendor, R. M. (1999). Helping others helps oneself: Response shift effects in peer support. *Social Science and Medicine, 48*, 1563–1575.

Schwartz, C. E., Meisenhelder, J. B., Yusheng, A., & Reed, G. (2003). Altruistic social interest behaviors are associated with better mental health. *Psychosomatic Medicine, 65*, 778–785.

Schwartz, S. H. (1973). Normative explanations of helping behavior: A critique, proposal, and empirical test. *Journal of Experimental Social Psychology, 9*, 349–364.

Schwartz, S. H., & Bilsky, W. (1990). Toward a theory of the universal content and structure of values: Extensions and cross-cultural replications. *Journal of Personality and Social Psychology, 58*, 878–891.

Schwartz, S. H., & Fleishman, J. A. (1982). Effects of negative personal norms on helping behavior. *Personality and Social Psychology Bulletin, 8*, 81–86.

Shafir, E., & Tversky, A. (1992). Thinking through uncertainty: Non- consequential reasoning and choice. *Cognitive Psychology, 24*, 449–474. doi:10.1016/0010-0285(92)90015-T

Shafir, E., Simonson, I., & Tversky, A. (1993). Reason-based choice. *Cognition, 49*, 11–36.

Snyder, M., Clary, E., & Stukas, A. (2000). The functional approach to volunteerism. In G. Maio & J. Olson (Eds.), *Why we evaluate: Functions of attitudes* (pp. 365–393). Mahwah, NJ: Erlbaum.

Steele, J. (2010). *The definition of motivation*. Retrieved from http://www.speechmastery.com/definition-of-motivation.html

Thoits, P. A. (1992). Social support functions and network structures: A supplemental view. In H. O. F. Veiel & U. Baumann (Eds.), *The meaning and measurement of social support* (pp. 57–62). New York: Hemisphere.

Thoits, P. A. (1994). Stressors and problem-solving: The individual as psychological activist. *Journal of Health and Social Behavior, 35*, 143–159.

Thoits, P. A., & Hewitt, L. N. (2001). Volunteer work and well-being. *Journal of Health and Social Behavior, 42*, 115–131.

Webb, C. B. (2006). *Elements of motivation*. Retrieved from http://www.motivation-tools.com/downloads/motivation_booklet_elements.pdf

Weinstein, N., & Ryan, R. (2010). When helping helps: Autonomous motivation for prosocial behavior and its influence on well-being for the helper and recipient. *Journal of Personality and Social Psychology, 98*(2), 222–244. (Several other references included in this article)

Wheeler, J. A., Gorey, K. M., & Greenblatt, B. (1998). The beneficial effects of volunteering for older volunteers and the people they serve: A meta-analysis. *International Journal of Aging and Human Development, 47*, 69–79.

Wilson, J. (2000). Volunteering. *Annual Review of Sociology, 26*, 215–240.

Wilson, J., & Musick, M. (1997). Who cares? Toward an integrated theory of volunteer work. *American Sociological Review, 62*, 694–713.

Wilson, J., & Musick, M. (1999). The effects of volunteering on the volunteer. *Law and Contemporary Problems, 62*, 141–168.

Zenhabits.net. (2008). *The ultimate guide to motivation: How to achieve any goal*. Retrieved from http://zenhabits.net/the-ultimate-guide-to-motivation-how-to-achieve-any-goal/

Chapter 21
Decision Making

A Process Tool

Decision-making is a tool for meeting our goals.

Many decisions are also made based on desires, interests and curiosity.

I believe most major decisions are based on need—either real or perceived. Following that line of thinking, I think that people should pay more attention to Abraham Maslow's Hierarchy of Needs (i.e., the need for water and food, shelter, security, accomplishments, love/relationship and a sense of belonging, acceptance, attention, appreciation, etc.)

When I think of decision making, I think of outcome, results, or consequences. Making a decision ideally involves a process of deliberation, consideration and thought about the thing being decided.

Decision-Making Questions

A few questions I might have asked myself (or even a trusted friend, colleague or family member) is, "Did I have to make this decision now? Or later? What happens if I don't make it? Are there other alternatives or options? Will I benefit from this decision or is it more for someone else's benefit?"

> ***Will my following through with this cause anyone else harm?***

Am I being selfish by making this decision? Is this the right thing to do? WWJD: "What Would Jesus Do" in this or a similar situation? I could have asked the question, how could I be assured that I am following a process that would likely improve my chances of success?

Chapter 21 – Decision Making

Decision making is a process by which decisions are made from the time the thought is first created to the time it is carried out and everything in between. A decision is born from a need, a desire, a request, and/or a circumstance. Whatever its origin, having to make a decision is an active process. Decision-making is sometimes taking time out to consider rearranging priorities, deciding whether something deserves or warrants attention and or resources.

> *Considering the merits or benefits or advantage of a certain thing as to whether you should take it on, be involved or disregard; decision making often involves "brainstorming" the pros and cons of a thing, assessing its relative value or interest to you.*

Decision making is often bringing a thing forward, from darkness to light, from one stage to another from thought to reality. Assigning a certain level of relevance or importance to something.

The Process

> *Most decision making is deciding on a course of action, a process to follow, a set of activities.*

Decision making involves looking at options, pros and cons, potential outcomes and consequences. Decision making is a process of coming to a decision. Some decisions result from indecision, which happens when you fail to decide and are left with the result of that indecision. Decisions can be made in writing, verbally or mentally. Once made, they can be followed, ignored, partially followed and, in some cases, completely forgotten. Technically, decisions that are not followed are not really decisions; they are just thoughts about a decision.

Meaningful decisions should be specifically stated and in behavioral terms so they can be objectively assessed as to whether they were completed or not. If I decide to go to the movies and don't go, that means that I have made a subsequent decision to override my previous decision. The same is true when I make a decision to write a book. That decision requires a number of more specific decisions that will lead up to the ultimate decision to write the book.

Likewise, if I decide to make a good meal for Saturday's meeting, that decision is dependent upon my making "smaller" decisions about what is going to constitute a "good" meal and whether I can afford what I really want to get or whether I want to spend the time to make certain preparations, etc. Therefore, decisions need to be specific, they need to have steps leading up to the execution of each step and they need to be doable.

Chapter 21 – Decision Making

Decisions are often made long before they are verbalized or consciously expressed. In many cases, a person has been considering whether to make a certain decision in their mind and, in some cases, they are not consciously aware that it is happening. Once a decision has been made, the person's conscious mind begins to focus on things related to the decision. For example, when a friend decided to purchase a digital camera, all of a sudden television commercials and advertisements in newspapers and magazines caught his eye.

The University of Washington (n.d.), referencing another source, offered a number of approaches for you to assess how you generally make decisions.

Put an X next to the statement(s) below that best describe how you typically make decisions, based on past experience. Be honest with yourself. You will be the only person who sees this questionnaire.

_____	I approach decision-making in a systematic, step-by-step manner. I set a goal, identify alternatives, collect information, identify the best option, and take action.
_____	I attempt to make decisions in a systematic, step-by-step manner but I tend to think too much, get stuck, and fail to reach a decision.
_____	I am usually able to select one alternative over another, with good outcomes, without too much thinking. I typically listen to my feelings.
_____	I like to decide quickly, without spending time thinking about or feeling out various alternatives.
_____	I typically seek input from everybody I know and rely heavily on their opinions. I sometimes even allow others to make decisions for me.
_____	I don't believe I have control over the events of my life. I believe my life circumstances are largely determined by external forces.
_____	I tend to recognize that a decision needs to be made but procrastinate (or avoid) making it because of fear, lack of information, or lack of motivation.

Niles, S. G., & Harris-Bowlsbey, J. (2005). *Career Development Interventions in the 21st Century* (2nd ed*.).* Upper Saddle River, NJ: Merrill Prentice Hall.

Kescia D. Gray (January 29, 2014) wrote a simple 5-step decision-making process that is worthy of sharing:

Chapter 21 – Decision Making

When decision making, there are many steps that can be taken; but when making good decisions there are really only five steps that need to be considered. These steps are as follows:

Step 1: Identify Your Goal

One of the most effective decision-making strategies is to keep an eye on your goal. This simply means identifying the purpose of your decision by asking yourself what exactly is the problem that needs to be solved? And why does this problem need to be solved? Figuring out what's most important to you will help you make good decisions. When you know the reason why you are making a particular decision, it will better serve you in staying with it and defending it.

Step 2: Gather Information for Weighing Your Options

When making good decisions, it is best to gather necessary information that is directly related to the problem. Doing this will help you to better understand what needs to be done in solving the problem and will also help to generate ideas for a possible solution.

When gathering information, it is best to make a list of every possible alternative, even ones that may initially sound silly or seem unrealistic. Always seek the opinions of people that you trust or speak to experts and professionals because it will help you come up with a variety of solutions when weighing all your options for a final decision. You will want to gather as many resources as possible in order to make the best decision.

Step 3: Consider the Consequences

This step can be just as important as step one because it will help you determine how your final decision will impact yourself and/or others involved. In this step, you will be asking yourself what is likely to be the results of your decision. How will it affect you now? And how will it affect your future? This is an essential step because it allows you to review the pros and cons of the different options you listed in the previous step. It is also important because you want to feel comfortable with all your options and the possible outcome of whichever one you choose.

Step 4: Make Your Decision

Now that you have identified your goal, gathered all necessary information, and weighed the consequences, it is time to make a choice and actually execute your final decision. Understanding that this step can cause some people a lot of anxiety is important because this is where you have to trust your instincts. Although you may still be slightly indecisive about your final decision, you have to take into account how this makes you feel. Ask yourself, does it feel right? And does this decision work best for you now, and in the future? When you answer those questions, you should feel good about the result.

Step 5: Evaluate Your Decision

Once you have made your final decision and put it into action, it is necessary to evaluate the decision and the steps you have taken to ensure that it works. This final step is probably just as important as step one, if not more important, because it will help you to further develop your decision making skills for future problems. This step is also fundamental because it may require you to seek out new information and make some changes along the way. Remember, this step requires some patience and it can also encourage perseverance. Why? Because it may take some time to see the final outcome. Recognize that if the first decision is not working, you may have to go back to step two and choose another option. Always looking for and anticipating unexpected problems will help alleviate undue stress, if and when a problem occurs.

This was retrieved from:

http://www.corporatewellnessmagazine.com/focused/5-steps-to-good-decision-making/

The Many Facets of Decisions

Even though there are some similarities among the various processes people follow, individuals tend to have their own process they usually follow.

> *And then there are the different kinds of decisions: little one, big ones, long-term and short-term decisions that will affect only you as opposed to those decisions that affect others, long-lasting and not-so-long-lasting decisions.*

In many cases, the processes followed are similar: deliberating on the merits of the decision, the consequences or impact, the level of difficulty to carry it out and the benefits, among other factors to be considered. "Focus!" Decision making is a process that should begin with "focus." To maximize your efforts, you need to focus on the process and make certain you have a clear vision of how to proceed.

Developing a decision making process is a good idea for anyone. Also being aware of your own decision-making process is helpful. Some decisions are made without much thought. Some decisions, however, require some thought as well as planning. Decisions that are made without some kind of plan to carry them out are little more than words of little consequence. Most decisions, especially big decisions, require careful planning, continuous assessment and follow through.

Continuous assessment is needed to make certain you are on track with your original decision or if you need to make any adjustments and follow through is necessary to ensure the decision is being carried out. Some people make decisions and never follow through. Unless the decision is very simple and can be made on the spot, many decisions require thoughtful and deliberate planning.

Chapter 21 – Decision Making

<u>5 Smart Decision-Making Strategies</u>

Anna Davies (2012) wrote an article that posted on the <u>womenshealthmag.com</u> blog on Christmas Day 2012 titled "5 Smart Decision-Making Strategies."

She cautioned that unless you're deciding between, say, Team Edward or Team Jacob, you know that any choice you make has a potential downside. That's why it's so easy to get caught up in indecision when you're facing bigger choices, like two job offers, or figuring out what new neighborhood to live in.

> *And, not to make the decision-making process more stressful or anything, but research shows that the closer a decision looms, the more likely you are to make choices based on emotions, rather than objective facts.*

In a study published by the *Journal of Consumer Research*, nearly 100 college students were asked to imagine they were about to graduate, had landed a good job, and needed to pick a one-bedroom apartment. Half imagined it would happen in the next month, and half imagined it would happen the next year. The students imagining that this would happen sooner chose the apartment that appealed more to their feelings (prettier, smaller) than the larger, more convenient one that was objectively "better."

Art Markman, PhD, professor of psychology and marketing at the University of Texas at Austin and the author of *Smart Thinking* says that It's not a bad thing to let your emotions play a factor in your decision making strategy. After all, if home is important to you and you're going to spend a lot of time there, you very well might be happier in an apartment you love, even though it means a farther commute than if you'd chosen the one that's just okay. But it's also important to know why you're making the decision you are.

Following are his five top decision-making strategies:

> *1. Limit your options. Studies show that people are happier when they have fewer choices, according to Art Markman.*

So while it may seem like you're doing due diligence by, say, test-driving 10 types of cars or spending an entire weekend looking at apartments in every single neighborhood, giving yourself three potential options is ideal. Three will allow you to compare and contrast different features without getting overwhelmed.

2. But don't go pro/con list crazy. While pro and con lists can be helpful, they also make you ignore clues from your subconscious. For example, maybe a job offer sounds good on paper, but the potential boss gave you a bad feeling. It's easy to overlook your uneasiness when faced with an overwhelming "pro" column, but when you're actually at the job, dealing with a monster of a supervisor will end up being a huge negative in real life. If you feel very strongly one way or another, you should pay attention to that.

3. Test drive your choice. You do it for cars, but Markman says this is also a smart strategy when weighing other options. Considering applying to grad school? Spend a day at the university in your town, sitting in on a lecture, browsing the bookstore, or sipping coffee in a campus café.

> *By imagining yourself living the option, you'll get more cues into whether or not it's a smart choice for you.*

4. Look to the past. The past can be a good indicator of how future events will work. Trying to decide whether it's worth it to pack up and move cross country for a job offer? Think back to another time—when you started college, when you joined a running group—when you were the new person in a community. If that worked out well, chances are this will too.

5. Always have a routine. Heading to the gym every AM, always having the same salad for lunch, hitting happy hour with the crew on Monday nights … the more same-old your day-to-day is, the easier it will be to figure out big choices with a clear head. Having to always make choices leads to what's called decision fatigue. When you're making fewer decisions a day, you have more mental reserve to tackle the ones that matter.

This article was retrieved from:
http://blog.womenshealthmag.com/scoop/5-smart-decision-making-strategies/

The Timing of Decisions
Decisions made should have a beginning time and date, regular checking intervals, specific (clearly identified) milestones or partial completion points and (at least) tentative completion dates. It sometimes helps if other people (friends or relatives or colleagues) know of your decision and can periodically ask you how things are going (what progress you are making) with the decision.

Some decisions that are difficult to follow through on might need some unique or special strategy to implement. My unique way of dealing with certain difficult decisions is to go into what I call my "no think" mode of operation. An example is with my (physical) workout schedule. I get up at 7:30 in the morning and without thinking, or considering whether I "feel" like going or considering other options, I roll out of bed, put on my workout clothes and go to the gym. I have to do that sometimes when I am around chocolates. I cannot think about whether I should or should not start eating them. I must pass it up and immediately start thinking about something else. My motto is to stay focused, keep it simple, listen to my conscience and try to remember the difference between reality decision making and fantasy decision making.

Chapter 21 – Decision Making

Decisions for Life

> *Among the most difficult decisions to make are often about finding purpose in your work and life.*

In his book, *The Power of Purpose: Creating Meaning in Your Life and Work*, author and counselor Richard Leider (1997) believes that each individual is born with a reason for being and that life is a quest to discover that purpose. He emphasizes that people are overwhelmed at times by the decisions they get to make—and have to make—about their jobs, their families, their businesses, their futures. If you don't have a way to sort it all out, he states, you can become paralyzed.

Leider advises people to make decisions the way senior citizens wish they had. For nearly 25 years, he states, he has done interviews with senior citizens, asking them to look back over their lives and talk about what they've learned. He conducted more than 1,000 interviews with people who were successful in their jobs, who retired from leading companies after distinguished careers.

Almost without exception, first they say that if they could live over again, they would be more reflective. They got caught up in the doing, they say, that they often lost sight of the meaning. Usually it took a crisis for them to look at their lives in perspective and try to reestablish the context. Looking back, they wish they had stopped at regular intervals to look at the big picture.

Second, if they could live their lives over again, they would decide to take more risks. In relationships, they would have been more courageous. And in expressing their creative side, they would have taken more chances.

> *Third, if they could live their lives over again, they would understand what really gave them fulfillment. (What senior citizens in a study said they would do).*

Leider calls that the power of purpose: doing something that contributes to life, adding value to life beyond yourself. Purpose is always outside yourself, beyond your ego or your financial self-interest. We all want both success and fulfillment. Success is often measured in external ways, but there is an internal measure of success, and it is called fulfillment. Consequently, make sure your life decisions take fulfillment into account.

Can't decide what action to take? Six steps to making an effective decision are offered by James Manktelow and Amy Carlson on mindtool.com: "A Systematic Approach to Decision Making."
Retrieved from: http://www.mindtools.com/pages/article/newTED_00.htm
For me, the author, I usually rely on WWJD – What Would Jesus Do?

Chapter 21 – Decision Making

Create a constructive environment.
Generate good alternatives.
Explore these alternatives.
Choose the best alternative.
Check your decision.
Communicate your decision, and take action.

Great Life Decision Strategies

Making great decisions can be tricky, according to Luciano Passuello (2010), author of an article titled: "How to Make Great Decisions in Life: Top 5 Practical Insights."
He says there are many hidden traps and potential roadblocks you need to be aware of. Here are 5 practical, actionable insights to help you make the best possible decisions to improve your life.

1. Value is in the eye of the beholder

How much is a gallon of water worth? Well, if you're reading this, you can probably get a gallon of water for pennies from your kitchen tap. Yet, if you were dying of thirst in a desert, you'd happily pay a hundred bucks for it, right? On the other hand, you'd pay a hundred bucks an hour for a plumber to avoid the water being there in the first place (in your flooded basement, that is).

Many people believe value is intrinsic to an object. Sure, water is water is water, but its value varies enormously depending on what you need it for.

Decision making is a very personal business—it's about assessing what's valuable to **you**. There's no absolute best job, best car or best life to be lived: value is in the eye of the decision maker.

Always decide on your own. Sure, factor in other people's opinions, but bear in mind that they may value things (very) differently. Blindly following other people's advice may lead to disastrous decisions—even if they are based on "sound" advice from people with the best intentions of helping you.

2. Know your goals before choosing

As we've seen in insight #1 above, no decision outcomes are intrinsically "good" or "bad"—the outcome depends on who you ask, and there are never absolute answers. How do you make sure you're making the best decision for your life, then? (Once again, I rely on the Holy Spirit.)

It may sound obvious at first, but it all boils down to your goals—knowing what you want out of the decision.

But establishing a clear picture of your goals for decision making is not always trivial, and I don't think people invest enough time to do it properly.

3. Your decision outcome can be no better than your best alternative

Many people see decision making as an analytical process that, if done right, is guaranteed to lead to nice outcomes. They believe that if they just think long and hard enough, great outcomes will result from their decisions.

The truth is: no matter how much effort you put in, no decision outcome can be better than the best alternative you considered. And no amount of analysis or systematic thinking will change that.

> *Having a good amount of alternatives to explore and choose from, then, is essential for making great decisions.*

If you're having a hard time deciding, it doesn't mean you're a poor decision maker: most likely you're just out of decent alternatives.

– Generate many alternatives. Before jumping in and deciding among just two or three options that first come to mind, spend time generating plenty of new alternatives. Don't be shy about flexing your brainstorming muscles.

4. Make effort proportional to importance

> *The more important a decision is, the more time you should spend on it (unless urgency is an issue).*

"Duh, that's just common sense," you say. Well, just like with many other things in life, common sense does not equal common practice.

Here's what often happens: we spend time on decisions not based on how important they are, but on how difficult they are. These are two very different concepts. Let me illustrate.

Suppose you're buying a car, and you're torn between two very similar models: One has slightly better transmission, but the other has a slightly better engine. One is slightly cheaper, but the other is slightly more reliable. You see, it's a decision that is hard to analyze, with many complex tradeoffs!

Yes, it sure is a hard decision… but that doesn't mean it's an important one! After all, you're probably going to be fine with either car as the differences are minimal.

The closest your alternatives are, the harder it is to decide and, perversely, the less relevant your decision will be one way or another!

As a wise decision maker, you will realize that if alternatives are very close to each other in value, it matters less which one you pick. You should save your energy for more important decisions—those with very different payoffs.

- Pay attention to "hard" decisions.

> – *When you can't make up your mind between two choices, chances are they're so similar that it doesn't matter which one you pick. See if the tradeoffs you're considering match your decision objectives (see insight #2 above).*

- **Agree on a decision deadline.** If you still find yourself bogged down on a decision of borderline importance, set a fixed block of time aside and agree to have the decision made at the end of it no matter what. Can't really make up your mind for such a minimal difference? Toss a coin at the last second if necessary.

5. Taking a structured approach makes a big difference

Making great decisions is a process that involves many unique and diametrically opposed "thinking modes." For instance, to generate good alternatives, you must be creative and non-judgmental. But to ultimately make up your mind, you need to be judgmental. Knowing when to switch thinking modes is important, and it's too easy to get it wrong.

In that context, I strongly advise that you see the decision-making process as a chain of separate steps. Isolate each step, going into different thinking modes in turn in order to make the best possible decision.

This article was retrieved from: http://litemind.com/decision-insights/

<u>REFERENCES</u>
Chapter 21 – "Decision Making"

Chapman, A. (n.d.). *A simple 5-step decision making process*. Retrieved from http://myedison.tesc.edu/tescdocs/Web_Courses/EDL530/documents/DecisionMaking_Proc.htm

Davies, A. (2012). *5 smart decision-making strategies*. Retrieved from http://blog.womenshealthmag.com/scoop/5-smart-decision-making-strategies/

Leider, L. (1997). *The power of purpose: Creating meaning in your life and work*. San Francisco: Berrett-Koehler.

Manktelow, J., & Carlson, A. (n.d.). *A systematic approach to decision making*. Retrieved from http://www.mindtools.com/pages/article/newTED_00.htm

Maslow, A. (1954). *Motivation and personality*. New York: Harper and Row.

Maslow, A. H. (1943). A theory of human motivation. *Psychological Review, 50*, 370–396. Retrieved from http://psychclassics.yorku.ca/Maslow/motivation.htm

Mason, J. L. (1993). *You're born an original, don't die a copy*. Tulsa, OK: Insight International.

Niles, S. G., & Harris-Bowlsbey, J. (2005). *Career development interventions in the 21st century* (2nd ed.). Upper Saddle River, NJ: Merrill Prentice Hall.

Passuello, L. (2010). *How to make great decisions in life: Top 5 practical insights*. Retrieved from http://litemind.com/decision-insights/

University of Washington. (n.d.). *Crash course in decision-making*. Retrieved from http://careers.washington.edu/ifiles/all/files/docs/gradstudents/pdfs/Personal_Development-CrashCourseinDecisionMaking-08-08.pdf

Chapter 22
Resilience

For me, one of the most useful descriptions and benefits of resilience was described in a list of factors that promote resilience provided by the American Psychological Association in the form of "10 Ways to Build Resilience" (APA, n.d.):

(1) maintain good relationships with close family members, friends and others;
(2) avoid seeing crises or stressful events as unbearable problems;
(3) accept circumstances that cannot be changed;
(4) develop realistic goals and move toward them;
(5) take decisive actions in adverse situations;
(6) look for opportunities of self-discovery after a struggle with loss;
(7) develop self-confidence;
(8) keep a long-term perspective and consider the stressful event in a broader context;
(9) maintain a hopeful outlook, expect good things and visualize what is wished;
(10) take care of your mind and body and exercise regularly, paying attention to your own needs and feelings and engaging in relaxing activities that you enjoy. Learning from the past and maintaining flexibility and balance in life.

> *Risk factors verses protective factors; resilience provides insurance against permenant damage because of bounce-back factor.*

Resilience is the process of adapting well in the face of adversity, trauma, tragedy, threats, or even significant sources of stress—such as family and relationship problems, serious health problems, or workplace and financial stressors. It means "bouncing back" from difficult experiences. "Resilience" is the positive capacity of people to cope with stress and adversity. This coping may result in the individual bouncing back to a previous state of normal functioning, or using the experience of exposure to adversity to produce a "steeling effect"

469

and function better than expected (much like an inoculation gives one the capacity to cope well with future exposure to disease) (Masten, 2009).

In the executive summary of their book titled "Building Resiliency: How to Thrive in Times of Change," Mary Pulley and Michael Wakefield (2003) talk about resilience and change. Resiliency allows you to recover quickly from change, hardship, or misfortune. Resilient people demonstrate flexibility, durability, an attitude of optimism, and openness to learning.

> *A lack of resilience is signaled by burnout, fatigue, malaise, depression, defensiveness, and cynicism.*

Resiliency not only gives you the tools to handle hardship and disappointment, but it allows you to develop new skills and perspectives that lead to continued success at work and away from the job.

Psychosocial Factors & Possible Neurobiological Underpinnings Associated with Resilience

Feder, Nestler, and Charney (2009) defined human resiliency as consisting of five capacities:

> *(1) the capacity to circumscribe fear responsiveness so that one can continue to be effective through active coping strategies despite fear. That's resilience.*

Facing fears promotes active coping strategies such as planning and problem solving. The ability to face one's fears might be facilitated by stress inoculation (exposure to tolerable levels of stress) during development and might be linked to the optimal functioning of fear extinction mechanisms. Physical exercise, which can be viewed as a form of active coping, has positive effects on mood, attenuates stress responses and is thought to promote neurogenesis (Masten & Coatsworth, 1998; Southwick, Vythilingam, & Charney, 2005).

(2) the capacity to use adaptive social behaviors to secure support through bonding and teamwork and to provide support through altruism. Social competence and openness to social support promote resilience in children and adults (Masten & Coatsworth, 1998; Southwick et al., 2005). Mutual cooperation is associated with activation of brain reward circuits. Oxytocin enhances the reward value of social attachments and reduces fear responses. Future research might identify potential differences in these measures in resilient individuals.

> *(3) the ability to use cognitive skills to reinterpret the meaning of negative stimuli in a more positive light. That's resilience, too.*

Cognitive reappraisal involves reinterpreting the meaning of negative stimuli, with a resulting reduction in emotional responses. Resilient individuals might be better at reappraisal or might use reappraisal more frequently. Neurobiological mechanisms that underlie some of these processes include memory suppression, memory consolidation and cognitive control of emotion (Goldin, McRae, & Gross, 2008; Ochsner et al., 2004).

(4) the capacity to experience reward and motivation nested in dispositional optimism and high positive emotionality. Positive emotions might contribute to healthier cognitive responses (Folkman & Moskowitz, 2000; Fredrickson, 2001) and decreased autonomic arousal (Folkman & Moskowitz, 2000). Mesolimbic dopamine pathways might be more reward responsive and/or stress resistant in individuals who remain optimistic when faced with trauma (Charney, 2004). Accordingly, resilience in animals has been related to specific molecular adaptations in the mesolimbic dopamine system (Krishnan et al., 2007).

> *(5) the integration of a sense of purpose in life along with a moral compass, meaning and spiritual connectedness: resilience (Caspi et al., 2003; Duman & Monteggi,a 2006).*

A sense of purpose and an internal framework of beliefs about right and wrong are characteristic of resilient individuals (Alim et al., 2008; Southwick et al., 2005). Religious and spiritual beliefs and practices might also facilitate recovery and finding meaning after trauma (Southwick et al., 2005). Brain imaging studies are beginning to identify the neural correlates of human morality (Raine & Yang, 2006).

In an article on the website of the Center for Creative Leadership, the two lead contributors of the article made interesting comments about resiliency. Contrary to popular belief, Mary Lynn Pulley and Michael Wakefield (2003) noted that people often view resilient people as characteristically unflappable, strong, or unaffected. But being resilient isn't the same as being tough, even though dogged determination—especially the determination to learn from mistakes and successes—plays a key role. A resilient person gets that way by broadening his or her perspective, by being open to change, and by being willing to learn.

The two writers also felt that resiliency can be developed. It's possible to change your views, habits, and responses by modifying your thoughts and actions in nine areas: acceptance of change
continuous learning
self-empowerment
sense of purpose
personal identity
personal and professional networks
reflection
skill shifting
and your relationship to money.

By becoming resilient you can absorb and learn from personal and career changes, making them key components of your leadership development.

Chapter 22 – Resilience

Most research now shows that resilience is the result of individuals interacting with their environments and the processes that either promote wellbeing or protect them against the overwhelming influence of risk factors (Zautra, Hall, & Murray, 2010). These processes can be individual coping strategies, or may be helped along by good families, schools, communities, and social policies that make resilience more likely to occur (Leadbeater, Dodgen, & Solarz, 2005). In this sense, resilience occurs when there are cumulative protective factors. These factors are likely to play a more and more important role the greater the individual's exposure to cumulative risk factors.

There is also controversy about the indicators of good psychological and social development when resilience is studied across different cultures and contexts (Boyden, & Mann, 2005; Castro & Murray, 2010; Dawes & Donald, 2000). The American Psychological Association's Task Force on Resilience and Strength in Black Children and Adolescents (APA, 2008) for example, notes that there may be special skills that these young people and families have that help them cope, including the ability to resist racial prejudice. People who cope may also show "hidden resilience" (Ungar, 2004b) when they don't conform with society's expectations for how someone is supposed to behave (in some contexts, aggression may be required to cope, or less emotional engagement may be protective in situations of abuse) (Obradović, Bush, Stamperdahl, Adler, & Boyce, 2010).

The Mayo Clinic staff wrote an article titled "Resilience: Building Skills to Endure Hardship" that I thought was worth sharing.

When something goes wrong, do you tend to bounce back or fall apart?
When you have resilience, you harness inner strength that helps you rebound from a setback or challenge, such as a job loss, an illness, a disaster or the death of a loved one. If you lack resilience, you might dwell on problems, feel victimized, become overwhelmed or turn to unhealthy coping mechanisms, such as substance abuse.

> *Resilience won't make your problems go away — but resilience can give you the ability to see past them, find enjoyment in life and better handle stress.*

If you aren't as resilient as you'd like to be, you can develop skills to become more resilient. (I like the saying I saw recently on a church sign: "Faith makes things possible, not easy.")

Adapting to Adversity

Resilience is the ability to roll with the punches. When stress, adversity or trauma strikes, you still experience anger, grief and pain, but you're able to keep functioning—both physically and psychologically. However, resilience isn't about toughing it out, being stoic or going it alone. In fact, being able to reach out to others for support is a key component of being resilient.

472

Chapter 22 – Resilience

Resilience and Mental Health

Resilience can help protect you from various mental health conditions, such as depression and anxiety. Resilience can also help offset factors that increase the risk of mental health conditions, such as being bullied or previous trauma. If you have an existing mental health condition, being resilient can improve your ability to cope.

Tips to Improve Your Resilience

If you'd like to become more resilient, consider these tips:

> • *Get connected. Building strong, positive relationships with loved ones and friends can provide you with needed support and acceptance in both good times and bad.*

- Establish other important connections by volunteering or joining a faith or spiritual community.
- **Make every day meaningful.** Do something that gives you a sense of accomplishment and purpose every day. Set goals to help you look toward the future with meaning.
- **Learn from experience.** Think of how you've coped with hardships in the past. Consider the skills and strategies that helped you through rough times. You might even write about past experiences in a journal to help you identify positive and negative behavior patterns—and guide your future behavior.

> • *Remain hopeful. You can't change the past, but you can always look toward the future.*

- Accepting and even anticipating change makes it easier to adapt and view new challenges with less anxiety.
- **Take care of yourself.** Tend to your own needs and feelings. Participate in activities and hobbies you enjoy. Include physical activity in your daily routine. Get plenty of sleep. Eat a healthy diet. Practice stress management and relaxation techniques, such as yoga, meditation, guided imagery, deep breathing or prayer.

> • *Be proactive. Don't ignore your problems. Instead, figure out what needs to be done, make a plan and take action.*

- Although it can take time to recover from a major setback, traumatic event or loss, know that your situation can improve if you work at it.

When to Seek Professional Advice

Becoming more resilient takes time and practice. If you don't feel you're making progress — or you don't know where to start — consider talking to a mental health provider. With guidance, you can improve your resiliency and mental wellbeing.

This article was retrieved from: http://www.mayoclinic.org/tests-procedures/resilience-training/in-depth/resilience/art-20046311

Focus on Building Strengths – Attending To Challenges

When all is said and done at the end of the day the bottom line becomes, "are you better off today than you were before you started doing stuff mentioned in this book?" If the answer is no, then, I apologize for wasting your time. However, if the answer is yes, then one of the big questions might be, "What made the difference?" This author thinks a lot of your success has come from your ability to focus and adapt. Focus on building strengths needed to overcome life's barriers; adapt to difficult situations or more specifically problem solving; identify and make good use of support systems to be empowered to get the job done of meeting your goals.

Focus

Focus means to "give attention to," or spend time with, adjusting, magnifying, making more clear, striving toward, consider or reconsider. So to "focus" on building strengths, means to make building strengths a priority.

> *Learning to focus has a lot to do with being successful.*

To be focused is to concentrate your attention to a narrow area of interest. To focus on building strength implies that there exists some level of competence or strength and that you are not starting from zero—not starting from scratch.

> *Ultimately, building strengths means doing more, risking more, accepting more challenges, being taken from your "comfort zone" more often and to some extent, changing your priorities or at least making some priority adjustments.*

When I think of focusing on building strengths, I think of making it through challenges, taking on challenges and developing sufficiently to meet that challenge. Building strengths in certain areas of your life requires courage. For example, strengthening your **social life** requires taking risks of being rejected when meeting new people or changing your relationship with the people you already know. Strengthening your **financial life** requires seeking a promotion, changing jobs, adding jobs, changing investment strategies, saving more and spending less or some combination of these and other efforts. Strengthening your **spiritual life** requires more praying, reading, meditation, reflection, attending religious activities, more soul searching, fellowshipping more with like-minded people and focus on

Christ. Strengthening your **work and/or school** standing might require taking on more leadership roles which might involve separating your feelings from objective decision-making, doing research, writing, reading more, spending more time with other professionals and accepting more speaking engagements.

You do not usually build strengths by continuing the status quo. Building strengths is moving from your present position to a stronger one. Building strengths in character is something that you might be trying to do all the time, whereas building strength in your social life might be more time specific. We might not want our social life any stronger, whereas we are always striving to strengthen our character.

Building character, to me, is always striving to do the right thing, being helpful, humble, less pretentious, giving of yourself, being kind, considerate, sensitive to the needs and concerns of others, for some it's even being willing to put others ahead of yourself.

> ***Think positive. How can what is already a plus be made to be even stronger?***

How can good be made to be excellent or moving mediocre up the chain toward excellence. Or, how can a skill in one area be transferred to another? After identifying areas of strength, it's a matter of building or further developing those areas. Diversification is a position of strength. Variety is something called "the spice of life." You want to avoid burnout, if at all possible. And, the way that's done is through "relief." Build "relief" into your schedule with fun and rewards.

Accentuate the Positive

> ***Accentuating the positive rather than focusing on the negative is a better way to look at a situation.***

Opposite from focusing on a problem, focusing on the negative, looking at risk factors, looking at the disease or the medical model or the psychosis/neurosis, this focus is on the positive, the protective factors, or looking at the healthy aspects, the prevention (from getting any worse) model. Plus, starting out on the positive allows you to build momentum, build encouragement, and strengthen the positive side that might be used to do battle with the negative side. Spend time reinforcing the positive rather than focusing on the negative or giving the negative most of the attention. Focusing on the positive builds self-esteem and allows the person to see that there is hope and that they have not done "all" bad. Sometimes focusing on building strength is more difficult than focusing on the negative, especially if the negative is perceived as being predominant.

Chapter 22 – Resilience

When you are focusing on building strengths, you are looking at assets rather than liabilities, looking at what's working, what's positive about a situation and how the good can be made better.

One of the by-products of building strengths is addressing weaknesses. For example, if I am wanting to complete this book rather than focusing on the things that are keeping me from completing the job, I am focusing on the fact that now that I am retired, I have the freedom to devote time for the task, I can look back at my success of previous writings and I can draw on my possibly being able to submit for publication articles that will eventually turn into chapters in my book.

> *Opposite the deficit model (which focuses on what's wrong) of looking at improving a situation, focusing on the strengths of the situation is more productive.*

Sometimes creative uses of humor can make a difference for the better. The resiliency model of addressing problems focuses on the positive or the strengths of the situation.

Ready for a Change?

Sometimes our focus on building strengths requires us to look at our present situation to see to what extent we are content or stress free because stress weakens us and takes away those resources that could be used for other purposes other than to fight off stressful situations. On the other hand, however, we cannot be too content either. When we are content, we tend to have our efforts in neutral rather than in full force. It can sometimes keep us from decisive risk taking, which is sometimes necessary to get ahead. A little uneasiness keeps us on our toes and closer to our peek performing level. People need to be a little hungry.

Control over your fate helps you focus on building strengths. People who are mentally healthy can often conjure up the strength to talk about their past in a healthy way and yet not dwell on it or become anxious thinking about it. This frees them up from subconscious worrying. They can sometimes use thoughts about a bad experience and turn it into something good. This can happen with school-age children who develop social skills and other new skills and are called "at promise" rather than "at risk." Positive responses from others as well as their positive expectations can be helpful. The productive climate that is conducive to constructive discussion builds strength in both individuals as well as organizations and institutions. Sometimes the development of healthy relationships can bring about optimism and hopefulness.

Research on the Subject of Resilience

According to Timothy Smith (2006), research on the association between personality characteristics and subsequent physical health has produced several consistent findings and identified other tentative relationships.

476

Chapter 22 – Resilience

> **Chronic anger/hostility and neuroticism/negative affectivity are the best established personality risk factors for poor health.**

Optimism, social dominance, and other traits also appear to influence risk. Smith's article was titled, "Personality as Risk and Resilience in Physical Health."

TRAITS LINKED TO HEALTH
Dozens of purportedly distinct personality characteristics have been studied as influences on health. The following review summarizes the most compelling evidence.

Beyond Type A: Hostility and Dominance
The groundbreaking work of Friedman and Rosenman (1959) on Type A behavior and coronary heart disease (CHD) is perhaps the most well-known example of the personality–health hypothesis. Two decades of research following their description of the Type A behavior pattern (i.e., competitiveness, achievement striving, impatience, hostility, excessive job involvement, and emphatic speech) generally supported its role as a risk factor. Several failures to replicate later challenged this conclusion, even though the literature as a whole demonstrated an association.

The failures to replicate led researchers to examine individual elements within the multifaceted Type A construct, as inconsistent associations between the pattern and coronary heart disease might indicate that only some components influenced health. Hostility soon emerged as the most unhealthy Type A characteristic. Although negative findings have also appeared in this literature, many subsequent studies have supported an association of individual differences in the tendency to experience anger, cynical or suspicious beliefs, and antagonistic interpersonal behavior with asymptomatic atherosclerosis, the incidence of Coronary Heart Disease (CHD), and mortality from cardiovascular and other causes (Smith, Glazer, Ruiz, & Gallo, 2004).

Other studies indicate another unhealthy aspect of the Type A pattern. A socially dominant style including loud, rapid, and emphatic speech and a tendency to "cut off" and "talk over" others during social interaction is associated with CHD risk (Houston, Chesney, Black, Cates, & Hecker, 1992). Other prospective studies have supported an association between dominance and subsequent health (cf. Smith, Gallo, & Ruiz, 2003), as do the results of nonhuman primate models of atherosclerosis (Kaplan & Manuck, 1998).

Negative Affectivity, Neuroticism, and Risk
Individual differences in the experience of negative emotions (e.g., anxiety, sadness) have long been suspected as contributing to poor health. This trait is represented in major personality taxonomies, commonly labeled neuroticism or negative affectivity. An early and

influential review concluded that this broad dimension conferred vulnerability to disease (Friedman & Booth-Kewley, 1987).

However, critical responses to the review's conclusions suggested that this effect may have been overestimated through the inclusion of studies relying on health-outcome measures that combined illness behavior (e.g., somatic complaints) and actual illness (e.g., diagnosed diseases or mortality). As a result, the apparent association between neuroticism and subsequent disease might have reflected—at least in part—an association between this trait and somatic complaints rather than objectively defined disease. However, subsequent well-designed prospective studies have consistently supported the prior conclusion (Suls & Bunde, 2005); neuroticism and negative affectivity are associated with reduced longevity and increased incidence of objectively diagnosed serious illness.

Personality as Resilience: Optimism and Conscientiousness

> *The tendency to hold optimistic—as opposed to pessimistic or even hopeless—beliefs about the future has been found to be associated with better health in several prospective studies.*

These effects include lower incidence of CHD (Kubzanky, Sparrow, Vokonas, & Kawachi, 200 better prognosis following heart surgery (Scheier et al., 1999), and greater longevity (Gilt Kamphuis, Kalmijin, Zitman, & Kromhout, 2006). Previous research suggested that some of apparent association between optimism and health could actually involve shared variance w neuroticism and the related tendency toward excessive somatic complaints.

However, recent studies support a prospective association with objective health outcomes. In so studies, these effects have been independent of measures of negative affectivity or neuroticis although in others it is unclear if the possible overlap between these traits and optimism co contribute to observed associations with objective health outcomes. Conscientiousness has be found to predict longevity, even when this trait is measured during childhood (Friedman et 1995). Among patients with chronic medical illness, conscientiousness is associated with lon survival (Christensen et al., 2002).

Resilience and Vulnerability to Daily Stressors Assessed via Diary Methods

> *According to David Almeida (2005), stressors encountered in daily life, such as family arguments or work deadlines, may play an important role in individual health and wellbeing.*

He wrote an article that presents a framework for understanding how characteristics of individuals and their environments limit or increase exposure and reactivity to daily stressors. His article is titled "Resilience and Vulnerability to Daily Stressors Assessed via Diary

Methods." He states that research on daily stressors has benefited from diary methods that obtain repeated measurements from individuals during their daily lives. These methods improve ecological validity, reduce memory distortions, and permit the assessment of within-person processes. Findings from the National Study of Daily Experiences, which used a telephone-diary design, highlight how people's age, gender, and education and the presence or absence of chronic stressors in their lives predict their exposure and reactivity to daily stressors.

Major life events, however, are relatively rare, and thus their cumulative effect on health and wellbeing may not be as great as that of minor yet frequent stressors, such as work deadlines and family arguments (Lazarus, 1999; Zautra, 2003). Daily stressors are defined as routine challenges of day-to-day living, such as the everyday concerns of work, caring for other people, and commuting between work and home. They may also refer to more unexpected small occurrences—such as arguments with children, unexpected work deadlines, and malfunctioning computers—that disrupt daily life.

Tangible, albeit minor, interruptions like these may have a more immediate effect on wellbeing than major life events. Major life events may be associated with prolonged physiological arousal, whereas daily hassles may be associated with spikes in arousal or psychological distress confined to a single day. Yet minor daily stressors affect wellbeing not only by having separate, immediate, and direct effects on emotional and physical functioning, but also by piling up over a series of days to create persistent irritations, frustrations, and overloads that may result in more serious stress reactions such as anxiety and depression (Lazarus, 1999; Zautra, 2003).

Vulnerability and Resilience to Daily Stressors

> *Some stressors are unhealthier than other stressors, and some individuals are more prone to the effects of stressors than other individuals.*

Recent improvements in the measurement of daily stressors and in study design have allowed researchers to address (a) how different types of stressors and personal meanings attached to these stressors affect well-being and (b) how sociodemographic factors and personal characteristics account for group and individual differences in daily-stress processes.

The Role of Resilience in Adjustment and Coping with Chronic Pain

Resilience has been studied extensively in relation to stress and adversity. One consistent finding in this research is that not everyone who faces adversity suffers negative psychological outcomes (Fitzpatrick, 2010). Certain people appear to have the ability to adapt and move forward in a positive way, despite negative life events (Fitzpatrick, 2010).

Chapter 22 – Resilience

Researchers have posited, however, that resilience and recovery are two distinct processes (Bonanno, Papa, Lalande, Westphal, & Coifman, 2004; Zautra, 2009). It is proposed that whereas "recovery" refers to facing temporary negative psychological states after experiencing an acute stressor, "resilience" is a more complicated process whereby an individual is able to maintain "stable equilibrium" over the long term in spite of facing some continuing adversity. In relation to the experience of a long-term pain condition, resilience is not so much the ability to bounce back after the initial injury, but rather the ability to continue to function when repeated setbacks occur, such as pain flare-ups (Sturgeon & Zautra, 2010).

It has been suggested that, among a number of dispositional and situational factors involved in resilience, self-reliance and social support are key characteristics (Reich, Zautra, & Hall, 2010). Self-reliance is the ability to utilize one's own resources instead of relying on the help of others. In the case of illness, this would include developing strategies of self-care rather than depending on health professionals, medications, and the health system (Zautra, 2009). This is pertinent to the investigation of pain-related disability because it is consistently reported that sufferers of chronic pain can be major consumers of health care and develop reliance upon passive treatment interventions (e.g., Blyth et al., 2005; Tan, Teo, Anderson, & Jensen, 2011).

The contribution of social supports in developing resilience has also received considerable interest (Charney, 2004; Ozbay et al., 2008; Southwick et al., 2005). Studies report a mutually reinforcing relationship between social support and resilience, such that people with high social supports tend to have better mental health and superior levels of resilience and, in turn, these factors and the associated positive emotions tend to make it easier to create and maintain strong social supports (Berkman, 1995; Ozbay, Fitterling, Charnet, & Southwick, 2008; Southwick et al., 2005).

Studies of resilience have encompassed a number of clinical presentations, but there have been relatively few that have investigated the relationship between resilience and persistent pain (Sturgeon & Zautra, 2010). Studies to date have indicated that higher resilience is associated with the use of more active pain coping strategies (López-Martínez, Ríos-Velasco, Ruiz-Párraga, Esteve-Zarazaga, & Sánchez-Reina, 2009), better long-term functional recovery, more positive mood and higher activity levels in the pain sufferers (Peters, 2011). Research findings suggest a close relationship between resilience and other forms of positive functioning, such as active coping styles, attitudes and beliefs about pain, social and occupational functioning, and decreased reliance on medication and the health-care system (Karoly & Ruehlman, 2006; Sturgeon & Zautra, 2010).

Please note, the article titled, "The Role of Resilience in Adjustment and Coping with Chronic Pain" (above) was written by Toby R. O. Newton-John, Christie Mason, and Mick Hunter and published in the *Rehabilitation Psychology*.

Chapter 22 – Resilience

Empirical Findings from The National Study of Daily Experiences

A 2005 project called the National Study of Daily Experiences (NSDE) was aimed to investigate the sources of vulnerability and resilience to daily stressors. The NSDE is a telephone-diary study of a U.S. national sample of 1,483 adults ranging in age from 25 to 74 years. Interviews occurred over eight consecutive nights, resulting in 11,578 days of information.

Prevalence of Daily Stressors

Respondents reported experiencing on average at least one stressor on 40% of the study days and multiple stressors on 10% of the study days (Almeida, Wethington, & Kessler, 2002).

> **The most common stressors for both men and women were interpersonal arguments and tensions, which accounted for half of all the stressors.**

Gender differences were also evident. Women were more likely than men to report network stressors—stressors involving their network of relatives or close friends—whereas men were more likely than women to report stressors at work or at school. On average, the respondents subjectively rated stressors as having medium severity, whereas objective coders rated the stressors as having low severity.

Forgiveness Can Reduce Health Risks and Promote Health Resilience

According to Worthington and Scherer (2004), experimental evidence suggests that when people are transgressed against interpersonally, they often react by experiencing unforgiveness, which is conceptualized as a stress reaction. Forgiveness is conceptualized as an emotional juxtaposition of positive emotions (i.e., empathy, sympathy, compassion, or love) against the negative emotions of unforgiveness.

> **Forgiveness can thus be used as an emotion-focused coping strategy to reduce a stressful reaction to a transgression.**

Direct empirical research suggests that forgiveness is related to health outcomes and to mediating physiological processes in such a way as to support the conceptualization that forgiveness is an emotion-focused coping strategy. Indirect mechanisms might also affect the forgiveness-health relationship. Namely, forgiveness might affect health by working through social support, relationship quality, and religion.

The researchers found that in 1997, research on forgiveness consisted of only 58 empirical studies (McCullough et al., 1998). Since then, that number of studies has more than quadrupled.

Within this stress-and-emotion-focused coping framework, we suggest four principal theoretical propositions that relate unforgiveness, emotional forgiveness, and health.

Chapter 22 – Resilience

1. Unforgiveness is stressful.
2. Coping mechanisms besides forgiveness can reduce unforgiveness.
3. Forgiveness reduces the stress of unforgiveness.
4. Forgiveness as a coping strategy is related to health.

Building Resilience

In a *Harvard Business Review* article titled "Building Resilience," Martin Seligman makes his point in a story about two people who lost their jobs:

Douglas and Walter, two University of Pennsylvania MBA graduates, were laid off by their Wall Street companies 18 months ago. Both went into a tailspin: They were sad, listless, indecisive, and anxious about the future. For Douglas, the mood was transient. After two weeks he told himself, It's not you; it's the economy going through a bad patch. I'm good at what I do, and there will be a market for my skills. He updated his résumé and sent it to a dozen New York firms, all of which rejected him. He then tried six companies in his Ohio hometown and eventually landed a position. Walter, by contrast, spiraled into hopelessness by saying he got fired because he could not perform under pressure. He was not cut out for finance. The economy will take years to recover. Even as the market improved, he didn't look for another job; he ended up moving back in with his parents.

Douglas and Walter (actually composites based on interviewees) stand at opposite ends of the continuum of reactions to failure. The Douglases of the world bounce back after a brief period of malaise; within a year, they've grown because of the experience. The Walters go from sadness to depression to a paralyzing fear of the future. Yet failure is a nearly inevitable part of work, and along with dashed romance, it is one of life's most common traumas. People like Walter are almost certain to find their careers stymied, and companies full of such employees are doomed in hard times. It is people like Douglas who rise to the top, and whom organizations must recruit and retain in order to succeed. But how can you tell who is a Walter and who is a Douglas? And can Walters become Douglases? Can resilience be measured and taught?

> *Thirty years of scientific research has put the answers to these questions within our reach. We have learned not only how to distinguish those who will grow after failure from those who will collapse, but also how to build the skills of people in the latter category.*

Seligman say that he has worked with colleagues from around the world to develop a program for teaching resilience. It is now being tested in an organization of 1.1 million people where trauma is more common and more severe than in any corporate setting: the U.S. Army. Its members may struggle with depression and post-traumatic stress disorder (PTSD), but thousands of them also experience post-traumatic growth. Our goal is to employ resilience training to reduce the number of those who struggle and increase the number of those who grow. We believe that businesspeople can draw lessons from this approach, particularly in times of failure and stagnation. Working with both individual soldiers (employees) and drill sergeants (managers), we are helping to create an army of Douglases who can turn their most difficult experiences into catalysts for improved performance.

Optimism Is the Key

Although I'm now called the father of positive psychology, I came to it the long, hard way, through many years of research on failure and helplessness. In the late 1960s, I was part of the team that discovered "learned helplessness."

> *We found that dogs, rats, mice, and even cockroaches that experienced mildly painful shock over which they had no control would eventually just accept it, with no attempt to escape. It was next shown that human beings do the same thing.*

In an experiment published in 1975 by Donald Hiroto and me [Seligman] and replicated many times since, subjects are randomly divided into three groups.

Those in the first were exposed to an annoying loud noise that they could stop by pushing a button in front of them. Those in the second heard the same noise but couldn't turn it off, though they tried hard. Those in the third, the control group, heard nothing at all. Later, typically the following day, the subjects were faced with a brand-new situation that again involved noise. To turn the noise off, all they had to do was move their hands about 12 inches. The people in the first and third groups figured this out and readily learned to avoid the noise. But those in the second group typically did nothing. In phase one they failed, realized they had no control, and became passive. In phase two, expecting more failure, they didn't even try to escape. They learned helplessness.

Strangely, however, about a third of the animals and people who experience inescapable shocks or noise never become helpless. What is it about them that makes this so? Over 15 years of study, my colleagues and I discovered that the answer is optimism. We developed questionnaires and analyzed the content of verbatim speech and writing to assess 'explanatory style' as optimistic or pessimistic.

> *We discovered that people who don't give up have a habit of interpreting setbacks as temporary, local, and changeable.*

(They say such things as, It's going away quickly; it's just this one situation, and I can do something about it.) That suggested how we might immunize people against learned helplessness, against depression and anxiety, and against giving up after failure: by teaching them to think like optimists.

Chapter 22 – Resilience

In November 2008, when the legendary General George W. Casey, Jr., the army chief of staff and former commander of the multinational force in Iraq, asked me what positive psychology had to say about soldiers' problems, I offered a simple answer: How human beings react to extreme adversity is normally distributed. On one end are the people who fall apart into PTSD, depression, and even suicide. In the middle are most people, who at first react with symptoms of depression and anxiety but within a month or so are, by physical and psychological measures, back where they were before the trauma. That is resilience. On the other end are people who show post-traumatic growth. They, too, first experience depression and anxiety, often exhibiting full-blown PTSD, but within a year they are better off than they were before the trauma. These are the people of whom Friedrich Nietzsche says *That which does not kill us makes us stronger.*

I told General Casey that the army could shift its distribution toward the growth end by teaching psychological skills to stop the downward spiral that often follows failure. He ordered the organization to measure resilience and teach positive psychology to create a force as fit psychologically as it is physically. This $145 million initiative, under the direction of Brigadier General Rhonda Cornum, is called Comprehensive Soldier Fitness (CSF) and consists of three components: a test for psychological fitness, self-improvement courses available following the test, and "master resilience training" (MRT) for drill sergeants. These are based on PERMA: positive emotion, engagement, relationships, meaning, and accomplishment—the building blocks of resilience and growth.

Post-Traumatic Growth

The module interactively teaches soldiers about five elements known to contribute to post-traumatic growth:

1. Understanding the response to trauma (read "failure"), which includes shattered beliefs about the self, others, and the future. This is a normal response, not a symptom of PTSD or a character defect.
2. Reducing anxiety through techniques for controlling intrusive thoughts and images.
3. Engaging in constructive self-disclosure. Bottling up trauma can lead to a worsening of physical and psychological symptoms, so soldiers are encouraged to tell their stories.

> *4. Creating a narrative in which the trauma is seen as a fork in the road that enhances the appreciation of paradox—loss and gain, grief and gratitude, vulnerability and strength.*

A manager might compare this to what the leadership studies pioneer Warren Bennis called "crucibles of leadership." The narrative specifies what personal strengths were called upon, how some relationships improved, how spiritual life strengthened, how life itself was better appreciated, or what new doors opened.

5. Articulating life principles. These encompass new ways to be altruistic, crafting a new identity, and taking seriously the idea of the Greek hero who returns from Hades to tell the world an important truth about how to live.

REFERENCES
Chapter 22 – "Resilience"

Alim, T. N., Feder, A., Graves, R. E., Wang, Y., Weaver, J. et al. (2008). Trauma, resilience, and recovery in a high-risk African-American population. *American Journal of Psychiatry, 165*, 1566–1575.

Almeida, D. M. (2005). Resilience and vulnerability to daily stressors assessed via diary methods. *Current Directions in Psychological Science, 14*, 64.

American Psychological Association (APA). (2008). Resilience in African American children and adolescents: A vision for optimal development. Task Force on Resilience and Strength in Black Children and Adolescents. Washington, DC: Author. *Annals of Innovation & Entrepreneurship, 2*, 7986. doi: 10.3402/aie.v2i1.7986

American Psychological Association (APA). (n.d.). *10 ways to build resilience.* Retrieved from http://www.appleseeds.org/10-Ways-Build-Resilience_APA.htm

American Psychological Association (APA). (n.d.). *The road to resilience: What is resilience?* Retrieved from http://www.apa.org/helpcenter/road-resilience.aspx

Berkman, L. F. (1995). The role of social relations in health promotion. *Psychosomatic Medicine, 57*, 245–254.

Blyth, F. M., March, L. M., Nicholas, M. K., & Cousins, M. J. (2005). Self-management of chronic pain: A population-based study. *Pain, 113*, 285–292.

Bonanno, G. A., Papa, A., Lalande, K., Westphal, M., & Coifman, K. (2004). The importance of being flexible: The ability to both enhance and suppress emotional expression predicts long-term adjustment. *Psychological Science, 15*, 482–487. doi: 10.1111/j.0956-7976.2004.00705.x

Boyden, J., & Mann, G. (2005). Children's risk, resilience, and coping in extreme situations. In M. Ungar (Ed.), *Handbook for working with children and youth: Pathways to resilience across cultures and contexts* (pp. 3–26). Thousand Oaks, CA: Sage.

Caspi, A., Sugden, K., Moffitt, T. E., Taylor, A., Craig, I. W. et al. (2003). Influence of life stress on depression: moderation by a polymorphism in the 5-HTT gene. *Science, 301*, 386–389.

Castro, F. G., & Murray, K. E. (2010). Cultural adaptation and resilience: Controversies, issues, and emerging models. In J. W. Reich, A. J. Zautra, & J. S. Hall (Eds.), *Handbook of adult resilience* (pp. 375–403). New York: Guilford Press.

Charney, D. S. (2004). Psychobiological mechanism of resilience and vulnerability: Implications for successful adaptation to extreme stress. *The American Journal of Psychiatry, 161*, 195–216. doi: 10.1176/appi.ajp.161.2.195

Christensen, A. J., Ehlers, S. L., Wiebe, J. S., Moran, P. J., Baichle, K. et al. (2002). Patient personality and mortality: A 4-year prospective examination of chronic renal insufficiency. *Health Psychology, 21*, 315–320.

Dawes, A., & Donald, D. (2000). Improving children's chances: Developmental theory and effective interventions in community contexts. In D. Donald, A. Dawes, & J. Louw (Eds.), *Addressing childhood adversity* (pp. 1–25). Cape Town, South Africa: David Philip.

Duman, R. S., & Monteggia, L. M. (2006). A neurotrophic model for stress-related mood disorders. *Biological Psychiatry, 59*, 1116–1127.

Feder, A., Nestler, E. J., & Charney, D. S. (2009). Psychosocial factors & possible neurobiological underpinnings associated with resilience. *Nature Reviews Neuroscience, 10*, 446-451.

Fitzpatrick, M. (2010). The power of wishful thinking. *British Journal of General Practice, 60*, 301. doi: 10.3399/bjgp10X484057

Folkman, S., & Moskowitz, J. T. (2000). Positive affect and the other side of coping. *American Psychology, 55*, 647–654.

Chapter 22 – Resilience

Fredrickson, B. L. (2001). The role of positive emotions in positive psychology. The broaden-and-build theory of positive emotions. *American Psychology, 56*, 218–226.

Friedman, H. S., & Booth-Kewley, S. (1987). The "disease-prone personality": A meta-analytic view of the construct. *American Psychology, 42*, 539–555.

Friedman, H. S., Tucker, J. S., Schwartz, J. E., Martin, L. R., Tomlinson-Keasey, C. et al. (1995). Childhood conscientiousness and longevity: Health behaviors and cause of death. *Journal of Personality and Social Psychology, 68*, 696–703.

Friedman, M., & Rosenman, R. H. (1959). Association of specific overt behavior pattern with blood and cardiovascular findings; blood cholesterol level, blood clotting time, incidence of arcus senilis, and clinical coronary artery disease. *Journal of American Medical Association, 169*(12), 1286–1296.

Goldin, P. R., McRae, K., Ramel, W., & Gross, J. J. (2008). The neural bases of emotion regulation: Reappraisal and suppression of negative emotion. *Biological Psychiatry, 63*, 577–586.

Houston, B. K., Chesney, M. A., Black, G. W., Cates, D. S., & Hecker, M. L. (1992). Behavioral clusters and coronary heart disease risk. *Psychosomatic Medicine, 54*, 447–461.

Kaplan, J. R., & Manuck, S. B. (1998). Monkeys, aggression, and the pathobiology of atherosclerosis. *Aggressive Behavior, 24*, 323–334.

Karoly, P., & Ruehlman, L. (2006). Psychological "resilience" and its correlates in chronic pain: Findings from a national community sample. *Pain, 123*, 90–97. doi: 10.1016/j.pain.2006.02.014

Krishnan, V., Han, M.-Hu, Graham, D. L., Berton, O., Renthal, W. et al. (2007). Molecular adaptations underlying susceptibility and resistance to social defeat in brain reward regions. *Cell (Journal), 131*, 391–404.

Kubzansky, L. D., Sparrow, D., Vokonas, P., & Kawachi, I. (2001). Is the glass half empty or half full? A prospective study of optimism and coronary heart disease in the normative aging study. *Psychosomatic Medicine, 63*, 910–916.

Lazarus, R. S. (1999). *Stress and emotion: A new synthesis*. New York: Springer.

Leadbeater, B., Dodgen, D., & Solarz, A. (2005). The resilience revolution: A paradigm shift for research and policy. In R. D. Peters, B. Leadbeater, & R. J. McMahon (Eds.), *Resilience in children, families, and communities: Linking context to practice and policy* (pp. 47–63). New York: Kluwer.

López-Martínez, A., Ríos-Velasco, L., Ruiz-Párraga, G., Esteve-Zarazaga, R., & Sánchez-Reina, A. (2009). The role of resilience and acceptance versus catastrophizing and pain related fear in chronic-pain adjustment. *European Journal of Pain, 13*, S273–S285. doi: 10.1016/S1090-3801(09)60973-3

Masten, A. S. (1994). Resilience in individual development: Successful adaptation despite risk and adversity. In M. Wang & E. Gordon (Eds.), *Risk and resilience in inner city America: Challenges and prospects* (pp. 3-25). Hillsdale, NJ: Erlbaum.

Masten, A. S. (2009). Ordinary magic: Lessons from research on resilience in human development. *Education Canada, 49*(3), 28-32.

Masten, A. S., & Coatsworth, J. D. (1998), The development of competence in favorable and unfavorable environments. Lessons from research on successful children. *American Psychology, 53*, 205–220.

Mayo Clinic Staff. (n.d.). *Resilience: Building skills to endure hardship*. Retrieved from http://www.mayoclinic.org/tests-procedures/resilience-training/in-depth/resilience/art-20046311

McCullough, M. E., Exline, J. J., & Baumeister, R. F. (1998). An annotated bibliography of research on forgiveness and related topics. In E. L. Worthington, Jr. (Ed.), *Dimensions of forgiveness: Psychological research and theological speculations* (pp. 193-317). Philadelphia: Templeton Foundation Press.

McCullough, M. E., Rachal, K. C., Sandage, S. J., Worthington, E. L., Jr., Brown, S. W., & Hight, T. L. (1998). Interpersonal forgiveness in close relationships II: Theoretical elaboration and measurement. *Journal of Personality and Social Psychology, 75*, 1586–1603.

Newton-John, T., Mason, C., & Hunter, M. (2014). The role of resilience in adjustment and coping with chronic pain. *Rehabilitation Psychology, 59*, 360–365.

Obradović, J., Bush, N. R., Stamperdahl, J., Adler, N. E., Boyce, W. T. (2010). Bilogical sensitivity to context: The interactive effects of stress reactivity and family adversity on socioemotional behavior and school readiness. *Child Development, 81*(1), 270–289.

486

Chapter 22 – Resilience

Ochsner, K. N., Ray, R. D., Cooper, J. C., Robertson, E. R., Chopra, S., Gabrieli, J. D., & Gross, J. J. (2004). For better or for worse: Neural systems supporting the cognitive down- and up-regulation of negative emotion. *Neuroimage, 23*, 483–499.

Ozbay, F., Fitterling, H., Charnet, D., & Southwick, S. (2008). Social support and resilience to stress across the life span: A neurobiological framework. *Current Psychiatry Reports, 10*, 304–310. doi: 10.1007/ s11920-008-0049-7

Peters, M. (2011). Resilience and pain: Mechanisms and clinical implications. *European Journal of Pain Supplements, 5*, 2–3. doi: 10.1016/ S1754-3207(11)70008-6

Pulley, M., & Wakefield, M. (2003). *Building resiliency: How to thrive in times of change.* Greensboro, NC: Center for Creative Leadership.

Raine, A., & Yang, Y. (2006), Neural foundations to moral reasoning and antisocial behavior. *Social Cognitive and Affective Neuroscience, 1*, 203–213.

Reich, J. W., Zautra, A. J., & Hall, J. S. (Eds.). (2010). *Handbook of adult resilience.* New York: Guilford Press.

Scheier, M. F., Matthews, K. A., Owens, J. F., Schulz, R., Bridges, M. W. et al. (1999). Optimism and rehospitalization after coronary artery bypass graft surgery. *Archives of Internal Medicine, 159*, 829–835.

Seligman, M. (2011). Building resilience. *Harvard Business Review.* Retrieved from https://hbr.org/2011/04/building-resilience/ar/1 And https://hbr.org/2011/04/building-resilience

Smith, T. (2006). Personality as risk and resilience in physical health. *Current Directions in Psychological Science, 15*, 227.

Smith, T. W., Gallo, L. C., & Ruiz, J. M. (2003). Toward a social psychophysiology of cardiovascular reactivity: Interpersonal concepts and methods in the study of stress and coronary disease. In J. Suls & K. Wallston (Eds.), *Social psychological foundations of health and illness* (pp. 335–366). Oxford, UK: Blackwell.

Smith, T. W., Glazer, K., Ruiz, J. M., & Gallo, L. C. (2004). Hostility, anger, aggressiveness, and coronary heart disease: An interpersonal perspective on personality, emotion, and health. *Journal of Personality, 72*, 1217–1270.

Southwick, S. M., Vythilingam, M., & Charney, D. S. (2005). The psychobiology of depression and resilience to stress: Implications for prevention and treatment. *Annual Review of Clinical Psychology, 1*, 255–291.

Sturgeon, J. A., & Zautra, A. J. (2010). Resilience: A new paradigm for adaptation to chronic pain. *Current Pain and Headache Reports, 14*, 105–112. doi: 10.1007/s11916-010-0095-9

Suls, J., & Bunde, J. (2005). Anger, anxiety, and depression as risk factors for cardiovascular disease: The problems and implications of overlapping affective dispositions. *Psychology Bulletin, 131*, 260–300.

Tan, G., Teo, I., Anderson, K. O., & Jensen, M. P. (2011). Adaptive versus maladaptive coping and beliefs and their relation to chronic-pain adjustment. *The Clinical Journal of Pain, 27*, 769–774. doi: 10.1097/AJP.0b013e31821d8f5a

Tull, M. (2014). *Preventing the development of PTSD.* Retrieved from http://ptsd.about.com/od/causesanddevelopment/a/resiliency.htm

Ungar, M. (2004). *Nurturing hidden resilience in troubled youth.* Toronto: University of Toronto Press.

Worthington, E. L., & Scherer, M. (2004). Forgiveness is an emotion-focused coping strategy that can reduce health risks and promote health resilience: Theory, review, and hypotheses. *Psychology & Health, 19*, 385–405.

Zautra, A. J. (2003). *Emotions, stress, and health.* New York: Oxford University Press.

Zautra, A. J. (2009). Resilience: One part recovery, two parts sustainability. *Journal of Personality, 77*, 1935–1943. doi: 10.1111/j.1467-6494 .2009.00605.x

Chapter 23
Problem Solving

> *Option generation, strategy consultation, solution focused on getting the problem solved.*

The Basics

Certainly one of the first orders of business in this process is to understand the nature of the problem—big problem, little problem? Simple or complex? My problem or someone else's problem? A real problem or just a relatively minor "situation?" High priority or low priority? Once it has been determined that this is a problem that I am going to deal with, then I start thinking about the resources I currently have and other resources I might need in order to address the problem. Even though it is not something I think about while dealing with problems,

> *in reality problems and barriers are opportunities to grow. Problems and obstacles are hurdles that strengthen us (and our self-esteem) each time we overcome. Our response to adversity is critical to our own continuous growth.*

Problem solving, to me, is taking on a challenge, finding answers or options, and identifying potential solutions to a situation or circumstance. When I think of problem solving, one of the first things I think of is what life experiences can I draw upon that might be helpful in this current situation. I think of alternatives, consequences, causes and compromise. What caused the problem? What alternatives exist to alleviate or eradicate the problem? What consequences might there be as a result of trying to address the problem? What compromises might be necessary to resolve the problem?

Other questions that come up about problem solving include such things as who's affected by the problem? How long has it been a problem? What will "problem-solved" look like? How many possible ways might the problem be solved? Did someone or something cause the problem? Is it a systemic problem like racism or is it a problem that can be readily "fixed?"

Considerations

Problem solving usually requires some form of (sometimes hard) work, cooperation, coordination, compromise and reasonable and rational consideration, for example, a school counselor has a problem trying to help a young person get into college who has been turned down at several places already. This problem might take putting a lot more effort (hard work) into looking at other colleges, re-evaluating the young person's applications or making compromises on a four-year or two-year college.

On the other hand, that same school counselor has a problem being assigned to twice as many students because the other counselor was let go because of budget cuts is another matter. In this case, the counselor will have to come up with a different strategy to address the problem. Here, the counselor will have to work harder, seek cooperation of other school personnel, coordinate his workload differently and possibly make some compromises on level of service provided to students in the school. Whatever the situation, problem solving often involves an assessment of the situation, the development of a plan of action, the recruitment of support from others and persistence and perseverance.

> *Problem solving can be seen as a way of life, because life can be seen as a series of "problems" or challenges or situations that need to be addressed.*

Problem solving can also be seen as a series of choices that need to be made. Your basic belief system has a lot to do with how you will solve problems that arise. Problems that arise are likely to receive a better solution if they are addressed (almost) immediately. The longer a problem is allowed to linger, the more likely the person will get "used to" the problem, thereby lessening its significance or urgency. Consequently, problems are best handled soon after they are discovered. Problem solving can take on a number of different aspects, such as the size of the problem. Big problems are more likely to get immediate attention whereas smaller problems might receive lesser attention. Some "problems" are simply seen as minor setbacks or inconveniences.

The word "problem" might need to be defined. Something can be called a problem if solving it is going to take you out of your normal course of routine or behavior. The size of the problem might correlate to the degree of digression from one's normal routine or behavior. Problems that are likely to grow into progressively worse situations are best handled immediately. It has been said that most people have or know the answers to most of the problems they encounter, or they know how and where to obtain the answer. "Solutions" can be seen as permanent (or long range) or temporary (or short term). Permanent, long-range solutions are usually best.

Chapter 23 – Problem Solving

Causes

Sometimes looking for what caused the problem can be a good place to start, especially if you want to get at the root of the problem and not just address symptoms of the problem. Problems that have been around for a long time sometimes require a different strategy than do problems that are more recent. Some problems are not as obvious as they might first seem. Some people will talk around a problem and the person listening has to read between the lines to get to the real, underlying problem. Plus, some people have "their head in the sand" and let problems get so bad that it is much more difficult to address the problem. Then again, some problems don't have solutions that can be seen right away.

> *Some problems have to be tolerated for a while or even endured.*

A good example of that is when Paul in the Bible (2 Corinthians 12:9) had a thorn in his side that he couldn't get rid of and God's response to his cry for help was: "My grace is sufficient."

When addressing a problem, you want to try to the best of your ability to not make the problem any worse. It helps to have a positive attitude when solving a problem. Some problems turn out to be positive situations rather than the challenge they were originally thought to be. All problems are not automatically bad.

Personal Observation

> *When I am faced with a problem, I oftentimes seek God's advice to see if He is trying to tell me something or trying to teach me something.*

Some problems make you think in ways you would not otherwise think, which turns out to not be so bad after all. As was said earlier, I think most people have answers to their own problems. They often just don't want to follow through or don't want to be inconvenienced or are simply afraid to follow through with the solution. Problems can be seen as challenges that can make you stronger. All you have to do is to face the problem with a positive, optimistic attitude and have confidence that God will not give you more than you can handle.

Solving problems is almost always a challenge. It can be exciting and especially rewarding in the end. Problems are challenges that can be overcome. Problem solving forces you to think differently, creatively, and sometimes even adventurously. The more you are able to solve problems the more confident you become to solve the next problem. Problems are put before us, I believe, in order to keep us strong. If there were no problems to solve, life would be less interesting, less challenging and probably less fulfilling. Problem solving keeps the creative juices moving in your life. It keeps you sharp, alert and on task. When a person has made a commitment to accomplish a certain thing or has made a decision to do something, then it is up to the "problem solving department" to take over the challenge and make it happen.

Chapter 23 – Problem Solving

Problem solving forces you to focus your thoughts on potential scenarios that are possible. Problem solving can be fun if you take time and energy to follow through with the process.

In most cases, we have the answers to our own problems if only we focus on our strengths and how we might go about solving our problems in a systematic, logical and constructive manner.

> *Problem solving is best accomplished in the preventative mode. Stop the problem before it starts or at least catch it as early as possible before it gets worse.*

Combining Resources

Rather than sharing six different problem-solving strategies that had a number of overlapping components, I have consolidated the six into a single strategy that I thought provide a complete and comprehensive strategy worth sharing. These different components were taken from the following sources:

- The Global Development Research Center (n.d.)
- J. Dan Rothwell's book *In Mixed Company* (2013) explains "The effective problem-solving process"
- Zoe, B. (2013). *Simple life strategy: A Simple 5-step Problem Solving Strategy*. Retrieved at:
  http://simplelifestrategies.com/5-step-problem-solving-strategy/?COLLCC=2155933833
- Matthew Tull (2012). Retrieved from:
  http://ptsd.about.com/od/selfhelp/a/Successful-Problem-Solving.htm
- Lorain County Community College. (n.d.). *Problem Solving Strategies*. Retrieved from:
  http://www.loraincc.edu/current+students/advising+and+counseling/counseling/problem+solving.htm
- Cottrell, S. (n.d.). *The Study Skills Handbook*. Also wrote an article on Palgrave study skills website titled "Problem-Solving Skills."

One Potential Strategy for Problem Solving

Problem-solving is a tool, a skill, and a process. As a tool it helps you solve a problem or achieve a goal. As a skill you can use it repeatedly throughout your life. And, as a process it involves a number of steps.

It is not unusual for problems to arise when you are working toward a goal and encounter obstacles along the way. Students usually have many and varied goals, both related to school and to other areas of their lives, and it is likely you will encounter barriers to your success at times. As these barriers are encountered, problem-solving strategies can be utilized to help you overcome the obstacle and achieve your goal. With each use of problem-solving strategies, these skills become more refined and integrated so that eventually their use becomes second nature.

Chapter 23 – Problem Solving

Define the Problem

Before you are ready to take any steps to solve the problem, you first have to be sure that you are clear about what the problem really is.

> **It can be easy to get distracted by solving a different problem than what is actually causing distress if it is easier than dealing with the real problem.**

This step involves thinking about the following questions:

- How is the current situation different from what I actually want it to be?

- What do I actually want, or how do I actually want things to be?

- What is preventing me from achieving my goals, or from things being the way I want them to be?

It can be very helpful to write down the answers to these questions so you are forced to clarify that the problem you are defining is the actual one you want to solve. Just thinking about things in your head can cause confusion and end up distracting you from the actual problem at hand.

> **If you are dealing with more than one problem at a time, it may be helpful to prioritize them.**

That way you can focus on each one individually, and give them all the attention they require.

Become aware. What are you focused on? Are you getting caught up in the problem itself?

Write this thing, whatever it is, in very specific objective terms using the month of (this month) as the time frame within which you will: (1) have achieved it, (2) gotten a really good, solid start on it because it is too much to actually achieve by the end of the month, or (3) honestly and truly changed your mind about it being a high priority item in your life (Caution on rationalizations). Don't focus on the potential consequences or implications of the problem. This can give you a better sense of what you are specifically dealing with.

Problem Analysis

The next step in the process is often to check where you are, what the current situation is and what is involved in making it a priority. This section of the problem solving process ensures that time is spent in stepping back and assessing the current situation and what actually needs to be changed.

You need to think about it from different perspectives to insure that you understand all the dimensions of the problem and the urgency of addressing the problem.

The following questions can be useful to help you analyze the problem.
- How is this problem affecting me?
- How is this problem affecting other people?
- Who else is experiencing this problem?
- How do other people deal with this problem?

After you have completed this step, check to make sure your definition of the problem still fits. It is not unusual at this point to find that the problem you really want to solve is different than the one you initially identified.

> *Once you have looked at the problem from different perspectives, you can decide what you want to achieve and establish your goals.*

Establish Your Goals
You need to answer the very specific question— "What is my immediate goal?"

Generate Possible Solutions
During this stage, the goal is to generate as many possible solutions as you can. It can be very helpful to ask yourself what you have done in the past when faced with similar problems and how other people you know have dealt with similar situations. In addition, you can also approach friends, family, a counselor, teachers, books, or the Internet, etc. to obtain ideas for solutions. Be sure to write down all the possibilities you generate so you can approach this task systematically.

Brainstorming
You want to brainstorm and come up with as many solutions as you possibly can for the problem. This process of generating solutions can also help you look at the problem from multiple perspectives. Keep in mind that it may be impossible to address all areas of a problem. When this is the case, break the problem down and try to generate solutions for parts of the problem (as opposed to the problem as a whole). It may be necessary to seek out help with this part of solving a problem.

> *Brainstorming is the creative problem-solving technique that promotes plentiful, even zany, ideas in an atmosphere free from criticism and with enthusiastic participation.*

There are several guidelines for using this technique (Kelley & Littman, 2001; Nussbaum, 2004):
- encourage wild ideas – what appears to be a dumb idea initially can provoke a really good solution to a problem.
- don't evaluate ideas while brainstorming.
- don't clarify or seek clarification of an idea. This will slow down the process.

– do not engage in task-irrelevant discussion. Idea generation is significantly diminished when conversation is permitted during brainstorming sessions (Dugosh et al., 2000).

– stay focused on the topic. You want all suggestions to be related to the topic. Wild ideas that are not related to the topic are not helpful.

– expand on the ideas of other group members (if you are in a group).

– record all ideas without reference to who contributed the idea. Do not censor any ideas, no matter how silly they may seem, as long as they are focused on the problem.

– evaluate ideas generated once the brainstorming phase is completed.

Framing/Reframing

One other point brought out by the textbook author J. Dan Rothwell concerns framing/reframing. Our frame of reference can lock us unto a mindset, making solutions to problems difficult if not impossible to discover. This mental gridlock can block the free flow of creative ideas. Postman (1976) provides an example. You have the number VI. By the addition of a single line, make it into a seven. The answer is simple: VII. Now consider the problem: You have the number IX. By the addition of a single line, make it into a six. The answer is not so obvious because of your frame of reference, which identifies the number as a Roman numeral and all lines as straight. Not until you break away from this frame of reference by reframing the problem—by no longer assuming that the answer must be in terms of a Roman numeral and that all lines are straight—will you solve the problem. Have you found the answer? How about SIX? Frames determine whether people notice problems, how they understand and remember problems, and how they evaluate and act on them (Fairhurst & Sarr, 1996).

> *Reframing is the creative process of breaking a mindset by describing the problem from a different frame of reference.*

For example, a service station proprietor put an out-of-order sign on a soda machine. Customers paid no attention to the sign, lost their money, then complained to the station owner. Frustrated and annoyed, the owner changed the sign to read "$5.00" for a soda. No one made the mistake of putting money in the dispenser.

Search for Workable Solutions

Come at the problem with solutions instead of getting stuck on what is wrong or missing.

During this stage, you will examine each alternative and write down both the advantages and disadvantages to each. Some considerations to keep in mind include:
1. Is it relevant to my situation?
2. Is it realistic?
3. Is it manageable?
4. What are the consequences – both good and bad?
5. What is the likelihood that it is going to help me reach my goal?

Selecting the Best Solution(s)

This is the section where you look through the various influencing factors for each possible solution and decide which solutions to keep and which to disregard. You look at the solution as a whole and use your judgment as to whether to use the solution or not. Weigh the short- and long-term pros and cons of each solution.

Implementation

> *This step involves identification of all the steps necessary to implement it, and also ongoing monitoring of the effectiveness of the solution to make sure it actually solved the problem.*

What roadblocks would keep you from implementing some of these potential solutions?

- What things do you have going for you that you have total control of that can be used to eliminate some of these road blocks?
- What kind of support do you think you need?
- Where can this person get the needed support?
- Put time lines on specific activities together—who will do what? When?
- Is it worth all the work/trouble?
- Are you willing to commit?
- What will the reward be? How will you celebrate when you have achieved it?

Evaluation

During this stage of the process, ask yourself the following questions:
- How effective is the solution?
- Did it achieve what I wanted?
- What consequences (good and bad) did it have for my situation?

A Scientific Perspective on Problem Solving

William Huitt (1992) wrote an article that relates a model of the problem-solving process to Jung's theory of personality types (as measured by the MBTI – Myers-Briggs Type Indicator) and identifies specific techniques to support individual differences. The article that follows was published in the *Journal of Psychological Types* and is titled "Problem Solving and Decision Making: Consideration of Individual Differences Using the Myers-Briggs Type Indicator."

There is concurrent and parallel research on personality and cognitive styles that describes individuals' preferred patterns for approaching problems and decisions and their utilization of specific skills required by these processes (e.g., encoding, storage, retrieval, etc.).

496

One conclusion that may be drawn from these investigations is that individual differences in problem solving and decision making must be considered to adequately understand the dynamics of these processes (Stice, 1987). Attention must be paid to both the problem-solving process and the specific techniques associated with important personal characteristics. That is, individuals and organizations must have a problem-solving process as well as specific techniques congruent with individual styles if they are to capitalize on these areas of current research.

The purpose of this paper was to relate a model of the problem-solving process to a theory of personality type and temperaments in order to facilitate problem solving by focusing on important individual differences. Specific techniques that can be used in the problem-solving/decision-making process to take advantage of these differences are also identified. The integrated process is applicable to a variety of individual and group situations.

Problem-Solving and Decision-Making Process

> *Problem solving is a process in which we perceive and resolve a gap between a present situation and a desired goal, with the path to the goal blocked by known or unknown obstacles.*

In general, the situation is one not previously encountered, or where at least a specific solution from past experiences is not known. In contrast, decision making is a selection process where one of two or more possible solutions is chosen to reach a desired goal. The steps in both problem solving and decision making are quite similar. In fact, the terms are sometimes used interchangeably.

Most models of problem solving and decision making include at least four phases (e.g., Bransford & Stein, 1984; Dewey, 1933; Polya, 1971): (a) an Input phase in which a problem is perceived and an attempt is made to understand the situation or problem, (b) a Processing phase in which alternatives are generated and evaluated and a solution is selected, (c) an Output phase which includes planning for and implementing the solution, and (d) a Review phase in which the solution is evaluated and modifications are made, if necessary. Most researchers describe the problem-solving/decision-making process as beginning with the perception of a gap and ending with the implementation and evaluation of a solution to fill that gap.

Each phase of the process includes specific steps to be completed before moving to the next phase. These steps are discussed in greater detail in the paper.

Consideration of Individual Differences

Although there are a variety of ways to consider individual differences relative to problem solving and decision making, this paper focused on personality type and temperament as measured by the MBTI–Myers-Briggs Type Indicator (Huitt, 1992).

497

Chapter 23 – Problem Solving

Personality type and problem solving

Researchers have investigated the relationship of Jung's theory of individuals' preferences and their approach to problem solving and decision making (e.g., Lawrence, 1982, 1984; McCaulley, 1987; Myers & McCaulley, 1985). The following is a summary of their findings.

> *When solving problems, individuals preferring introversion will want to take time to think and clarify their ideas before they begin talking, while those preferring extraversion will want to talk through their ideas in order to clarify them.*

In addition, I's will more likely be concerned with their own understanding of important concepts and ideas, while E's will continually seek feedback from the environment about the viability of their ideas.

Sensing individuals will be more likely to pay attention to facts, details, and reality. They will also tend to select standard solutions that have worked in the past. Persons with intuition preferences, on the other hand, will more likely attend to the meaningfulness of the facts, the relationships among the facts, and the possibilities of future events that can be imagined from these facts. They will exhibit a tendency to develop new, original solutions rather than to use what has worked previously.

> *Individuals with a thinking preference will tend to use logic and analysis during problem solving.*

They are also likely to value objectivity and to be impersonal in drawing conclusions. They will want solutions to make sense in terms of the facts, models, and/or principles under consideration. By contrast, individuals with a feeling preference are more likely to consider values and feelings in the problem-solving process. They will tend to be subjective in their decision making and to consider how their decisions could affect other people.

The final dimension to be considered describes an individual's preference for either judging (using T [true] or F [false]) or perceiving (using S [sometime] or N [never]). J's (judging) are more likely to prefer structure and organization and will want the problem-solving process to demonstrate closure. P's (perceiving) are more likely to prefer flexibility and adaptability. They will be more concerned that the problem-solving process considers a variety of techniques and provides for unforeseen change.

The following narrative will provide an example of how these techniques can be used at specific points in the problem-solving process to address important individual differences. The techniques are presented within the context of a group problem-solving situation but are equally applicable to an individual situation. The terms in parentheses refer to personality dimensions to which the technique would appeal.

498

Chapter 23 – Problem Solving

The Input Phase

> **The goal of the Input phase is to gain a clearer understanding of the problem or situation.**

The first step is to identify the problem(s) and state it (them) clearly and concisely. Identifying the problem means describing as precisely as possible the gap between one's perception of present circumstances and what one would like to happen. Problem identification is vital to communicate to oneself and others the focus of the problem-solving/decision-making process. Arnold (1978) identified four types of gaps: (a) something is wrong and needs to be corrected, (b) something is threatening and needs to be prevented, (c) something is inviting and needs to be accepted, and (d) something is missing and needs to be provided. Tunnel vision (stating the problem too narrowly) represents the major difficulty in problem identification, as it leads to artificially restricting the search for alternatives.

Brainstorming is an excellent technique to begin the problem-solving process. Individually, participants quickly write possible solutions (introversion, perception), share these alternatives as a group in a non-judgmental fashion, and continue to brainstorm (extraversion, perception). Participants then classify, categorize, and prioritize problems, forming a hierarchy of the most important to the least important (intuition, thinking).

The second step of the Input phase is to state the criteria that will be used to evaluate possible alternatives to the problem as well as the effectiveness of selected solutions. During this step, it is important to state any identified boundaries of acceptable alternatives, important values or feelings to be considered or results that should be avoided. In addition, criteria should be categorized as either essential for a successful solution or merely desired. Brainstorming can also be used during this second step.

The third step is to gather information or facts relevant to solving the problem or making a decision. This step is critical for understanding the initial conditions and for further clarification of the perceived gap. Most researchers believe that the quality of facts is more important than the quantity. In fact, Beinstock (1984) noted that collecting too much information can actually confuse the situation rather than clarify it. The brainstorming technique could again be used in this step.

The Processing Phase

> **In the Processing phase, the task is to develop, evaluate, and select alternatives and solutions that can solve the problem. The first step in this phase is to develop alternatives or possible solutions.**

Chapter 23 – Problem Solving

Most researchers focus on the need to create alternatives over the entire range of acceptable options as identified in the previous phase (Schnelle, 1967). This generation should be free, open, and unconcerned about feasibility. Enough time should be spent on this activity to ensure that non-standard and creative alternatives are generated.

Again, brainstorming is a technique that can be used first.

The next step is to evaluate the generated alternatives vis-a-vis the stated criteria. Advantages, disadvantages, and interesting aspects for each alternative (using the PMI technique – Plus-Minus-Interesting, considering the positive, negative, and interesting or thought-provoking aspects of an idea or alternative).

The third step of the processing phase is to develop a solution that will successfully solve the problem. For relatively simple problems, one alternative may be obviously superior. However, in complex situations, several alternatives may likely be combined to form a more effective solution. A major advantage of this process is that if previous steps have been done well then choosing a solution is less complicated (Simon, 1969).

Before leaving this phase it is important to diagnose possible problems with the solution and implications of these problems (what could go wrong—sensing, judging; implications—intuition, perceiving). When developing a solution, it is important to consider the worst that can happen if the solution is implemented. In addition, the solution should be evaluated in terms of overall "feelings." That is, does the alternative match important values as previously stated (feeling).

The Output Phase

> *During the Output phase a plan is developed and the solution actually implemented.*

The plan must be sufficiently detailed to allow for successful implementation, and methods of evaluation must be considered and developed. When developing a plan, the major phases of implementation are first considered (intuition), and then steps necessary for each phase are generated. It is often helpful to construct a timeline and make a diagram of the most important steps in the implementation using a technique such as network analysis (sensing, judging). Backwards planning and task analysis are also useful techniques at this point. The plan is then implemented as carefully and as completely as possible, following the steps as they have been developed and making minor modifications as appropriate (sensing, judging).

The Review Phase

The next step, evaluating implementation of the solution, should be an ongoing process. Some determination as to completeness of implementation needs to be considered prior to evaluating effectiveness. This step is often omitted and is one reason the problem-solving/decision-making process sometimes fails: the solution that has been selected is simply not implemented effectively. However, if the solution is not implemented then evaluation of effectiveness is not likely to be valid.

The second step of this phase is evaluating the effectiveness of the solution. It is particularly important to evaluate outcomes in light of the problem statement generated at the beginning of the process. Affective, cognitive, and behavioral outcomes should be considered, especially if they have been identified as important criteria. The solution should be judged as to its efficiency (thinking, judging), its impact on the people involved (feeling, judging), and the extent to which it is valued by the participants (feeling, judging).

The final step in the process is modifying the solution in ways suggested by the evaluation process. Evaluation of the solution implementation and outcomes generally presents additional problems to be considered and addressed. Issues identified in terms of both efficiency and effectiveness of implementation should be addressed.

Summary and conclusions

> *In general, there is a need to develop and use a problem-solving/decision-making process that is both scientific and considerate of individual differences and viewpoints.*

While the scientific process has provided a method used successfully in a wide variety of situations, researchers have described individual differences that can influence perspectives and goals related to problem solving. These differences can be used to identify appropriate problem-solving techniques used in each step of the problem-solving process.

The process described in the Huitt (1992) paper allows individuals to use a standard method in a variety of situations and to adapt it to meet personal preferences. The same process can be used in group situations to satisfy the unique perspectives of individual members. Decisions made in this manner are more likely to be effective since individuals can consciously attend to both personal strengths and weaknesses, while groups are more likely to select solutions that will both solve the problem and be acceptable to individual group members.

Individual. One of the primary benefits to individuals in using this process is that the strengths and weaknesses of the individual can be identified and used or compensated for when making a decision. Everyone has strong and weak points that result from preferences in how a problem is viewed or considered. Careful selection and application of techniques reviewed in Huitt's (1992) paper (or similar techniques) increase the likelihood that individuals will enhance their strengths and attend to issues they would otherwise omit or attend to less well.

REFERENCES
Chapter 23 – "Problem Solving"

Arnold, J. (1978). *The seven building blocks to better decisions*. New York: AMACON.

Beinstock, E. (1984). *Creative problem solving* (Cassette Recording). Stamford, CT: Waldentapes.

Bloom, B., Englehart, M., Furst, E., Hill, W., & Krathwohl, D. (1956). *Taxonomy of educational objectives: The classification of educational goals* (Handbook I). New York: Longmans Green.

Bransford, J., & Stein, B. (1984). *The IDEAL problem solver*. New York: W. H. Freeman.

Cottrell, S. (2008). *The study skills handbook*. New York: Palgrave Macmillan.

Cottrell, S. (n.d.). *Problem-solving skills*. Retrieved from http://www.palgrave.com/skills4study/studyskills/thinking/problem.asp

Dewey, J. (1933). *How we think*. New York: Heath. (Originally published in 1910).

Dugosh, K. L., Paulus, P. B., Roldan, E. J., & Yang, H. (2000). Cognitive stimulation in brainstorming. *Journal of Personality and Social Psychology, 79,* 722–735.

Fairhurst, G., & Sarr, R. (1996). *The art of framing: Managing the language of leadership*. San Francisco: Jossey-Bass.

Global Development Research Center. (n.d.). *The problem solving process*. Retrieved from http://www.gdrc.org/decision/problem-solve.html

Huitt, W. (1992). Problem solving and decision making: Consideration of individual differences using the Myers-Briggs Type Indicator. *Journal of Psychological Type, 24,* 33–44.

Jung, K. (1971). *Psychological types*. Princeton, NJ: Princeton University Press. (Originally published in 1921).

Kelleiy, T., & Littman, J. (2001). *The art of innovation*. New York: Doubleday.

Kiersey, D., & Bates, M. (1978). *Please understand me: Character and temperament types*. Del Mar, CA: Prometheus Nemesis Book Co.

Lawrence, G. (1982). *People types and tiger stripes: A practical guide to learning styles* (2nd ed.). Gainesville, FL: Center for Applications of Psychological Type, Inc.

Lawrence, G. (1984). A synthesis of learning style research involving the MBTI. *Journal of Psychological Type, 8,* 2-15.

Lewis, K. (1947). Frontiers in group dynamics. *Human Relations, 1,* 5-42.

Lorain County Community College. (n.d.). *Problem solving strategies*. Retrieved from http://www.lorainccc.edu/current+students/advising+and+counseling/counseling/problem+solving.htm

McCaulley, M. (1987). The Myers-Briggs Type Indicator: A Jungian model for problem solving. In J. Stice (Ed.), *Developing critical thinking and problem-solving abilities* (pp. 37–54). San Francisco: Jossey-Bass.

Myers, I. (1980). *Gifts differing*. Palo Alto, CA: Consulting Psychologists Press.

Myers, I., & McCaulley, M. (1985). *Manual: A guide to the development and use of the Myers-Briggs Type Indicator*. Palo Alto, CA: Consulting Psychologists Press.

Nussbaum, B. (2004 May 17). The power of design. *Business Week,* 86–94.

Polya, G. (1971). *How to solve it*. Princeton, NJ: Princeton University Press. (Originally published in 1957).

Rothwell, J. D. (2013). *In mixed company: Communicating in small groups and teams*. Boston, MA: Wadsworth.

Schnelle, K. (1967). *Case analysis and business problem solving*. New York: McGraw-Hill.

Simon, H. (1969). *The sciences of the artificial*. Cambridge: M. I. T. Press.

Skinner, B. (1954). The science of learning and the art of teaching. *Harvard Educational Review, 24,* 86–97.

Stice, J. (Ed.). (1987). *Developing critical thinking and problem-solving abilities*. San Francisco: Jossey-Bass.

Tull, M. (2012). *Five easy steps for successful problem-solving: A way to effectively cope with problems when you have PTSD*. Retrieved from http://ptsd.about.com/od/selfhelp/a/Successful-Problem-Solving.htm

Chapter 23 – Problem Solving

Woods, D. (1987). How might I teach problem solving. In J. Stice (Ed.), *Developing critical thinking and problem-solving abilities* (pp. 55-72). San Francisco: Jossey-Bass.

Zoe, B. (2013). *Simple life strategy: A simple 5 step problem solving strategy*. Retrieved from http://simplelifestrategies.com/5-step-problem-solving-strategy/?COLLCC=2155933833

Chapter 24
Support

> *Two heads are better than one; help from another person is often useful and sometimes we just need to see or hear a different perspective.*

It Can Be Powerful

When support is given proper respect, it can be a very powerful tool of success.
With the right support, a person's chances of success has just doubled. Following are a few suggestions to keep in mind about support.

Thoughtful Process Helps

Selectivity of supporter – one has to be very selective about the person chosen to provide support. You do not want to waste your time nor do you want to waste the time of the person providing support. One of the most important things to keep in mind is very clearly and specifically, what the supporter is providing. Get agreement, understanding, clarity of goal and specifics on enforcement powers given to supporter (i.e., "if I...then you...") Get an understanding of availability of support, willingness of supporter to support and an idea of the potential outcome after the support is no longer needed.

There are certain pros and cons on multiple supporters vs. one or two supporters. It is this author's opinion that the number of people providing support should be appropriate for the situation. If I am seeking support on losing weight, I will need support from key people who are in my life as it relates to my diet, exercise schedule and other areas that might relate to weight loss. If, however, I am seeking support on deciding a career choice, more than one or two supporters can cause confusion. Consequently, one should think about what the support is needed for and act accordingly. Supporters hold a special relationship with the person they are supporting. When you are asking a person to help you, it is imperative that you be super considerate in as many ways as possible, especially with not wasting that person's time. Plus,

505

> *it is up to you to build in stronger tolerance to this person "getting on your nerves."*

If you want the supporter to do his or her job, you have to allow them certain privileges such as divulging "secrets," tips and other hints you know are give-aways on your rationalizations, excuses and other "anti" behaviors that often keep you from reaching your goal. "Anti" behaviors are obvious violations of what you are being supported on (i.e., "anti" behavior is breaking diet, breaking promise, not following through, and disregarding an agreed upon plan.

Personal Example

For example, if I know I have a problem staying away from fried foods and I know that certain friends of mine love fried food, I might need to ask for help staying away from those friends during lunch or dinner time. Another example might be if I'm trying to save money for, say, a car and I know I can make extra money spending half my regular lunch hour from work consulting as a computer repairman, then those kinds of ideas are among the things that should be a part of the brainstorm that you and a person who is trying to support you in your efforts should know about. Likewise,

> *if you have a problem procrastinating, then your support person should be told to look out for your bad habits of procrastination.*

And, you should be committed to not getting upset when your support person calls you on some of your bad habits and suggest ways to overcome them.

It is important to set up specific communication options with your supporter. If they cannot reach you at work or at home, you should provide them your cell phone number and maybe a preferred time to make contact.

There comes a time when it becomes necessary for the two of you to go your separate ways. That time is when there is no movement on your goal, when the two of you are not connecting the way you said you would or when it simply is not working. Sometimes people get the advice of other supporters or significant others who might agree with your strong feelings that it's time to fire a supporter.

Chapter 24 – Support

How to Be a Better Supporter:

Be sure you understand <u>CLEARLY</u> what you are supporting the person on and you know you can do your part.

Do not become an enabler and know the difference:

<u>enabling</u>	<u>supporting</u>
giving in	standing firm
feeding bad habits	saying <u>no</u> to bad habits
giving money because "they need it"	helping person to get done what needs to be done without direct money transaction

<u>Remember your commitment to the person</u>

- be sensitive to their need to do "it" their way
- <u>consider</u> – what would you want someone else to do for you relative to doing it your way?

Because the position of supporter is so special, the "supporter" should be cautious to not take advantage of their special position (i.e., be "supportive" not "critical;" don't "use" your position to get special favors from the person you are supporting; don't abuse influence of special position; be supportive unless there is some exceptional reason not to be).

Nothing takes the place of person-to-person communication between you and your support – more support, more communication (generally)

The support process

Each time we meet:

- Acknowledge each other's presence – good, bad, etc.
- If it is possible to take accurate notes or make an assessment of where the person is with their goal; the progress they have made, stumbling blocks and other problems, etc.
- Summarize everything we have covered
- Identify specific next steps for each of us
- What we will <u>do</u> at the next meeting
- Set dates for all-day (or at least an extended time period) encounter
- <u>Deal</u> with each other

Sometimes we ask for support for something that we don't really want support for.

> **Sometimes it's not support we want or need, it is motivation for us to do "our" part.**

We sometimes want other people to do everything and we do nothing.

Sometimes role models can play a role in support. Most role models are people doing something that I want to do or someone who is in a certain role I admire or hold in high esteem, someone who could possibly support me in something I am pursuing.

Family and friends provide the best support

Kathy Bosch from the University of Nebraska wrote a brief article asking the question: When times are tough–how can family and friends support me? In it, she indicated that for whatever reason, when times are tough it is easy to become isolated from family and friends.

> *Some people simply don't want to talk about difficulties they experience.*

Maybe it's because they feel it is no one else's business; maybe it's because they are embarrassed. But when times are tough, a supportive network is needed to help you process through the difficulties, problems, concerns and struggles.

Research shows that family and friends, the informal support network, are those most often approached when support is needed. When you talk with someone you trust, the burdens seem lighter and the problems seem less of a concern. Your family and friends cannot help fix the problems, nor should they even if they could. But they can offer support to you in various ways such as emotionally, informationally and physically.

They can let you know you are loved and cared for, that you can rely on them for information and advice, and that they'll be there when you're in a pinch for a few extra dollars, or help with chores, a meal or childcare. A big part of the solution when times are tough is allowing others to help you when they can. You need to be willing to allow others to help you in a variety of ways. Of course, with primary relationships with family and friends, there will be reciprocal behavior and exchange of helping most of the time. However, if you are "down and out" or simply need a helping hand, accept the help when needed.

This article was retrieved from: http://lancaster.unl.edu/family/trouble5.shtml

Peer Support

Peer support occurs when people provide knowledge, experience, emotional, social or practical help to each other (Mead, Hilton, & Curtis, 2001).

> *A peer has "been there, done that" and can relate to others who are now in a similar situation.*

The effectiveness of peer support is believed to derive from a variety of psychosocial processes described best by Phyllis Solomon (2004): social support, experiential knowledge, social learning theory, social comparison theory and the helper-therapy principle.

Chapter 24 – Support

Social support is the existence of positive psychosocial interactions with others with whom there is mutual trust and concern (Sarason, Levine, Basham, & Sarason, 1983). Positive relationships contribute to positive adjustment and buffer against stressors and adversities by offering emotional support (esteem, attachment, and reassurance), instrumental support (material goods and services), and information support (advice, guidance, and feedback) (Solomon, 2004).

Experiential knowledge is specialized information and perspectives that people obtain from living through a particular experience such as substance abuse, a physical disability, chronic physical or mental illness, or a traumatic event such as military combat, a natural disaster, domestic violence, sexual abuse, or imprisonment. Experiential knowledge tends to be unique and pragmatic and when shared contributes to solving problems and improving quality of life (Shubert & Borkman, 1994).

Social learning theory postulates that peers, because they have undergone and survived relevant experiences, are more credible role models for others. Interactions with peers who are successfully coping with their experiences or illness are more likely to result in positive behavior change (Salzer & Shear, 2002).

Social comparison means that individuals are more comfortable interacting with others who share common characteristics with themselves, such as a psychiatric illness, in order to establish a sense of normalcy. By interacting with others who are perceived to be better than them, peers are given a sense of optimism and something to strive toward (Festinger, 1954).

The **helper-therapy principle** proposes that there are four significant benefits to those who provide peer support (Riessman, 1965; Skovholt, 1974): (a) increased sense of interpersonal competence as a result of making an impact on another person's life, (b) development of a sense of equality in giving and taking between himself or herself and others, (c) helper gains new personally relevant knowledge while helping, and (d) the helper receives social approval from the person they help and others (Salzer & Shear, 2002).

Providing Support to Others is a Win-Win Proposition
There is a part of the concept of support that is predicated on the old saying,

> *"you scratch my back and I'll scratch your back."*

This is brought out very clearly in an article published on *The Joy of Giving* blog titled "Updating the Helper Therapy Principle" by Stephen G. Post (2008). In it, they confirm that the therapeutic benefits of helping others have long been recognized by everyday people.

This concept was first formalized in a highly cited and often reprinted article by Frank Riessman that appeared in 1965 in *Social Work*.

> *Frank Riessman (1965) defined the "helper therapy" principle on the basis of his observations of various self-help groups, where helping others is deemed absolutely essential to helping oneself.*

These are grassroots groups that nowadays involve tens of millions of Americans. As the saying goes, "If you help someone up the hill, you get closer yourself."

Riessman observed that the act of helping another heals the helper more than the person helped. In the early 1970s, the helper therapy principle was noted in a few premier psychiatry journals as professional researchers found that helping others was beneficial in a variety of contexts, including among teens doing tutoring for younger children (Rogeness & Badner, 1973).

Whether the group is focused on weight loss, smoking cessation, substance abuse, alcoholism, mental illness and recovery, or countless other needs, a defining feature of the group is that people are deeply engaged in helping one another, and are in part motivated by an explicit interest in their own healing. These groups adhere to the view that people who have experienced a problem can help each other in ways that professionals cannot, i.e., with greater empathy and more self-disclosure. The members of these groups are replacing negative emotional states with the positive state called the "helper's high," a pleasurable and euphoric emotional sensation of energy and warmth. The "helper's high" was first carefully described by Allen Luks (1988). Luks, in a survey of thousands of volunteers across the United States, found that people who helped other people consistently reported better health than peers in their age group, and many stated that this health improvement began when they started to volunteer.

The Ultimate Support Group

The oldest and largest self-help group in the United States is, of course, Alcoholics Anonymous (Alcoholics Anonymous, 1952). Researchers at Brown University Medical School (Pagano et al., 2004) examined the relationship between helping other alcoholics to recover (the famous 12th step) and relapse in the year following treatment. The data were derived from a prospective study called Project MATCH, which examined different treatment options for alcoholics and evaluated their efficacy in preventing relapse. Two measures of helping other alcoholics in Alcoholics Anonymous (being a sponsor and having completed the 12th step) were isolated from the data, and proportional hazards regressions were used to separate these variables from the number of AA meetings attended during the period.

> *The authors found that those who were helping were significantly less likely to relapse in the year following treatment. (results from an Alcoholics Anonymous study)*

Among those who helped other alcoholics (8% of the study population), 40% avoided taking a drink in the year following treatment; only 22% of those not helping had the same outcome.

These findings around AA are especially significant because AA is a prototype organization, with offshoot organizations such as Al-Anon (for spouses of AA members), Alateen (for their children), and Narcotics Anonymous. It is widely estimated that close to 350 anonymous 12-step self-help programs exist in United States, including Overeaters Anonymous, and they help people with innumerable forms of suffering. Thus, many millions of Americans know about the 12th step through a self-help organization, but too few realize its importance to them. The pattern of one person helping another with the same problem was so central to Bill W., founder of AA, that he summed up the entire 12 steps in terms of surrender to a higher power and service to others (Bill W., 1988). Bill W. died in 1971, prominent in Life's list of the 100 greatest Americans of the 20th century as the originator of the entire self-help movement in America and worldwide (Life, 1990).

Altruistic activities are associated with better care of the self. Adolescent generativity (as present in the lives of a subset of adolescents decades ago) predicted reports of feeling satisfied with life, being peaceful and happy, having good mental health, and not being depressed as older adults. The researchers indicate that one important mechanism involved is adolescent prosocial competence, which results in a lifetime of sound judgments, choices and habits. The generative adolescents tended not to be smokers or excessive drinkers (Wink & Dillon, 2007).

Ralph Waldo Emerson, in his famous essay on the topic of compensation, wrote:

> *It is one of the most beautiful compensations of this life that no man can sincerely try to help another without helping himself.*

The 16th-century Hindu poet Tulsidas, as translated by Mohandas K. Gandhi, wrote that this and this alone is true religion – to serve others. This is sin above all other sin – to harm others. In service to others is happiness. In selfishness is misery and pain. The 9th-century sage Shantideva wrote that all the joy the world contains has come through wishing the happiness of others.

Building A Personal Support System

Essentiallifeskills.net (n.d.) has an article titled "Build A Personal Support System" that I thought was worthy of being shared. The article that can be found at
http://www.essentiallifeskills.net/supportsystem.html
gives a few tips and strategies on how to develop a support system.

When things aren't going well or we're just not feeling that great, we all need support and encouragement.

Chapter 24 – Support

For those who try to tough it alone, it can be a difficult uphill battle. On the other hand, much wisdom, experience and insight can be gained from friends, family or colleagues who have been there and have learned what it takes to prevail.

Before we get to the point of great difficulty, or in anticipation of life's little setbacks, we should implement strategies or have a support system in place to help us through some of those rough spots.

Here are some tips and strategies to develop a support system:

- **Turn to family and friends.**

There is no substitute for family and good friends to support and encourage you when the chips are down.

> *Sometimes just talking to someone can lift your spirits and help take the weight off your shoulders.*

Having someone listen to your concerns helps make you feel supported and understood, which in turn encourages you to look at things differently.

- **Cultivate a variety of interests.**

Read more, go to the movies or a play, listen to great music, enjoy beautiful art, learn to dance. Engaging in healthy and mind-expanding activities can preoccupy you when you need a healthy distraction. Not only do they preoccupy you, they help you grow and develop, therefore leaving less time to brood or stay down for too long.

- **Exercise and play sports.**

Have an assortment of exercises or fun sports you can draw upon to work out and let off some pent up energy and steam. There is nothing like a good workout to stimulate your happy hormones (endorphins). The after-effects can last up to three hours and put you in a positive frame of mind.

- **Take a short, affordable trip.**

We all have someplace we've always wanted to visit, but just never got around to. Travel to a big city such as New York City, Montreal, Boston or Toronto and partake of the cultural treasures it has to offer. It can expand your horizons and give you that change of scenery you need. If you happen to live in one of these bustling big cities, take a trip to the countryside and enjoy the bucolic surroundings.

- **Create a quiet place or sanctuary for yourself.**

> *Find a quiet place in your home, a corner in your local library, or a park where you can go to meditate, contemplate or rejuvenate yourself.*

In your home, it could be a nice bubble bath with candles and soft music playing. In the library you could find a secluded corner where you can curl up with a book and be lost to the world. You can go for a stroll in the park and enjoy the flowers, trees and birds and connect with the surroundings.

- **Volunteer at a hospital or a home for the handicapped.**

Take a day and volunteer your services to someone who needs your help. Giving support is as important as receiving it. It would put things in perspective. Life is short. Learn to appreciate and make the best of it.

What Research Says About the Benefits of Support

> *Peggy Thoits (2011) did a study making note that substantial evidence has accumulated over the past few decades showing that social ties and social support are positively and causally related to mental health, physical health, and longevity*

(Berkman, 1995; Cohen & Janicki-Deverts, 2009; Cohen & Wills, 1985; Ertel, Glymour, & Berkman, 2009; House, Umberson, & Landis, 1988; Hughes & Gove, 1981; Kessler & McLeod, 1985; Kessler, Price, & Wortman, 1985; Seeman, 1996; Taylor, 2007; Stroebe & Stroebe, 1996; Thoits, 1995; Turner & Turner, 1999; Uchino, 2004; Umberson & Montez, 2010).

Evidence also documents that social support buffers the harmful physical and mental health impacts of stress exposure, although these buffering effects are less dramatic and consistent than the direct effects of social ties on health (Cassel, 1976; Cobb, 1976; Cohen & Wills, 1985; House, 1981; Kessler et al., 1985; Kessler & McLeod, 1985; Thoits, 1995; Uchino, 2004)

The author made note that emotional support may be rebuffed or prevented by distressed persons who wish to shield significant others from upset on their behalf. This is accomplished by withholding information about the problematic situation or the depth and range of one's emotions and concerns. Such withholding may be typical of men who adhere to traditional masculine gender roles and parents who wish to protect their children. Emotional sustenance should be proffered by significant others and to have stress-alleviating effects only when the distressed person has signaled his or her willingness to talk about the stressor.

Active coping assistance: Primary group/significant others

In addition to emotional sustenance, family, relatives, and friends also offer active coping assistance in a variety of forms: instrumental aid, information and advice, and coping encouragement. I posit that among these various types of help, instrumental support (i.e., financial aid or help with practical tasks) from primary group members will be the most effective in alleviating the harmful effects of stress.

> ***Receiving instrumental support from people in one's primary circle of ties is normatively more appropriate than from secondary group members;***

family and friends are traditionally expected to lend a hand (Messeri, Silverstein, & Litwak 1993), so this type of coping assistance should be more frequent from significant others.

Material and practical aid may be especially important to the distressed person on two counts: First, it can reduce situational demands directly, lessening physiological arousal and upset. Second, it symbolically conveys that significant others care for and value the distressed person (Cohen & McKay, 1984), bolstering his or her sense of mattering and self-esteem. Hence, instrumental coping assistance from primary group members is likely to be an efficacious stress buffer, both directly in its problem-solving effects and indirectly through the message that one matters to others and is esteemed in their eyes.

Significant others also are very likely to offer information, advice, and coping encouragement. Although family and friends intend these acts to be helpful, they can be ineffective for two broad reasons. First, primary group members are typically upset about the individual's situation themselves, even more so if it creates serious disruptions in their own lives. They are invested in the problem being resolved as quickly as possible to alleviate their own and their loved one's distress. Invested supporters therefore may minimize the threatening aspects of the problem, insist on maintaining a positive outlook, or pressure the person to recover or problem solve before he or she is ready. These attempts at problem-focused coping assistance can create resentment and resistance in the distressed individual, negating supporters' intended benefits (Coates & Winston, 1983; Dakof & Taylor, 1990; Dunkel-Schetter, 1984; Martin et al., 1994; Peters-Golden, 1982).

Secondly, and perhaps more importantly, primary group members often have little or no direct experience with the person's stressor themselves (Taylor, 2007). Because of experiential dissimilarity, the information or advice they offer will seem too generic, inappropriate, or even misguided to the distressed individual, and their encouraging faith in his or her ability to handle the problem may seem naïve or unrealistic. A sense of alienation or social isolation may follow, again canceling the intended benefits of these forms of coping assistance.

In short, because primary group members are often emotionally invested in the person's recovery and because they frequently are unfamiliar with the specific demands of the stressor, their information, advice, appraisals, and encouragement are likely to be relatively ineffective at softening its health and mental health consequences. More effective coping assistance should come instead from experientially similar others in the secondary network, to whom we now turn.

514

Summing up.

In general, significant others' emotional support (concern and caring, valuing, companionate presence) and instrumental coping assistance should sustain the individual's sense of mattering, self-esteem, and belonging, which in turn should reduce his or her physiological arousal and emotional distress.

Their instrumental support can also lessen the burdens or demands of the problematic situation directly, decreasing the degree of perceived threat and, thus, the stressor's physiological and emotional impacts. Similar others' emotional sustenance consists of empathic understanding and accepting and validating feelings/concerns, acts that alleviate tension directly as well as shore up wavering self-esteem.

Their experientially grounded coping assistance (information, advice, appraisal and encouragement) directly protects physical and psychological wellbeing and indirectly fosters a sense of control, which in turn should promote further problem- and emotion-focused coping efforts that diminish the harmful physical and psychological consequences of stress (Taylor & Stanton, 2007). Similar others additionally serve as role models to emulate, influencing by example the individual's coping strategies and sense of personal control.

There are likely important variations in social integration and in supportive processes by social status and culture (Kawachi & Berkman, 2001; Taylor, 2007). The number of ties and the levels and types of support individuals possess depend on their age, gender, race/ethnicity, marital status, and socioeconomic status (e.g., Ertel et al., 2009; Haines, Beggs, & Hurlbert, 2008; Kawachi & Berkman, 2001; Schnittker 2007; Turner & Marino, 1994; Turner & Turner, 1999).

Studies also suggest that social integration and supportive dynamics may be contingent on cultural context. Persons socialized in interdependent cultures avoid seeking support in order to maintain harmony, save face and maintain norms that personal problems should be solved on one's own; in contrast, individuals raised in Western independent cultures see support networks as resources that can be used to meet personal needs (Badr et al., 2001; Taylor, 2007). The theoretical processes outlined here may be specific to Western cultures in general and to subcultures within the United States that most highly value independence over interdependence in social relationships, an important condition that deserves further investigation.

A New Look at Social Support Including the Concept of Thriving

Brooke Feeney and Nancy Collins (2014) wrote an article in *Personality and Social Psychology Review* that takes a new look at social support. They noted that in recent years, there has been a dramatic increase in the scientific study of wellbeing and positive aspects of mental health (e.g., Deci & Ryan, 2000; Diener, Lucas, & Scollon, 2006; Keyes, 2005, 2007; Lyubomirsky, Sheldon, & Schkade, 2005; Ryff & Singer, 1998, 2008; Seligman, 2002,

2008), and although theoretical models differ in how they define optimal wellbeing, they all agree that deep and meaningful close relationships play a vital role in human flourishing.

> *A large body of empirical work supports this view, showing that people who are more socially integrated and who experience more supportive and rewarding relationships with others have better mental health, higher levels of subjective wellbeing, and lower rates of morbidity and mortality*

(e.g., Cohen, 2004; Cohen & Syme, 1985; Collins, Dunkel-Schetter, Lobel, & Scrimshaw, 1993; Kawachi & Berkman, 2001; Lakey & Cronin, 2008; Miller et al., 2011; Sarason, Sarason, & Gurung, 1997; Seeman, 2000; Uchino, 2009; Uchino, Cacioppo, & Kiecolt-Glaser, 1996; Vaux, 1988). Especially notable, a meta-analysis (Holt-Lunstad & Smith, 2012) shows that being socially integrated in a network of meaningful relationships predicts mortality more strongly than many lifestyle behaviors (e.g., smoking, physical activity) that have been the focus of national health care campaigns.

Speaking more specifically about their writings, the two authors state that they present an integrative model of thriving through relationships in which they conceptualize social support as an interpersonal process that functions to promote thriving in two life contexts—experiences of adversity and opportunities for growth in the absence of adversity. They began by identifying core components of thriving and highlighting two life contexts in which individuals can thrive. Next, they specify two corresponding relational support functions that contribute to thriving in each life context, followed by a discussion of potential mechanisms linking these support functions to long-term thriving outcomes.

Components of Thriving

Although thriving has been conceptualized in a variety of ways, all perspectives agree that it includes flourishing both personally and relationally (e.g., Benson & Scales, 2009; Bundick et al., 2010; Diener et al., 2010; Keyes, 2003, 2007; Lerner et al., 2010; Ryff & Singer, 1998, 2000, 2008; Seligman, Steen, Park, & Peterson, 2005; Theokas et al., 2005).

Integrating these perspectives, thriving is conceptualized in terms of five broad components of wellbeing and their respective indicators: (a) **hedonic well-being** (happiness and life satisfaction—the perceived quality of one's life), (b) **eudaimonic well-being** (having purpose and meaning in life, having and pursuing passions and meaningful goals, personal growth, self-discovery, autonomy/self-determination, mastery/efficacy, development of skills/talents, accumulation of life wisdom, movement toward one's full potential), (c) **psychological well-being** (positive self-regard, self-acceptance, resilience/hardiness, a positive belief system, the absence of mental health symptoms or disorders), (d) **social well-being** (deep and meaningful human connections, positive interpersonal expectations, a prosocial orientation toward others, faith in others/humanity), and (e) **physical well-being** (physical fitness, the absence of illness or disease, health status above expected baselines, longevity).

This definition incorporates Ryff and Singer's (1998, 2008) specification of "criterial goods" that embody lives well lived, and other specifications of psychological flourishing (e.g., Henderson & Knight, 2012; Keyes, 2003, 2007; Seligman et al., 2005) and positive health (e.g., Seligman, 2008).

Relational Support Functions as Predictors of Thriving

What enables people to thrive through adversity and through life opportunities for growth? That is, how do people "flower into the kinds of persons who don't simply avoid problems and pathologies, but who embrace life and make full use of their special gifts in ways that benefit themselves and others" (Benson & Scales, 2009, p. 90)?

> ***Our ultimate goal is to make a case for how responsive social support within the context of one's close relationships promotes thriving.***

In making this case, a model is presented of thriving through relationships that puts relationships at the forefront in facilitating or hindering thriving. This perspective requires us to take a new look at social support and to re-conceptualize it in terms of the promotion of positive wellbeing instead of only buffering stress—and to view it as an interpersonal process that unfolds over time instead of an attitude or expectation (e.g., perceived available support).

A key proposition of this perspective is that well-functioning close relationships (with family, friends, and intimate partners) are fundamental to thriving because they serve two important support functions that correspond to the two life contexts through which people may potentially thrive—coping successfully with adversity and participating in opportunities for growth and fulfillment in the absence of adversity.

These support functions are rooted in attachment theory (Bowlby, 1973, 1982, 1988; Mikulincer & Shaver, 2007), which proposes that all individuals enter the world with propensities to seek proximity to close others in times of stress (an attachment behavioral system), to explore the environment (an exploration system), and to support the attachment and exploration behavior of close others (a caregiving behavioral system). The perspective advanced here extends attachment theory in its focus on thriving and in its detailed articulation of ways in which supportive relationships contribute to thriving outcomes.

Bad Support

Just as there is positive support, there is also negative support. The two authors suggest that unresponsive and insensitive support behaviors will undermine thriving because they promote either overdependence or underdependence: Overdependence (an over-reliance on others to do what can be done oneself) represents a means of clinging to significant others whose availability and acceptance is perceived to be uncertain or to others who provide support when it is not needed.

Underdependence (defensive self-reliance) represents a means of coping with a support environment in which significant others have been insensitive to or rejecting of one's needs. Optimal dependence (a healthy dependence on others in response to genuine need), optimal independence (a healthy degree of autonomy), and optimal interdependence (relationships characterized by mutual dependence) are made possible when significant others support thriving by providing sensitive and responsive source of support (SOS) and relational catalyst (RC) support.

> *Thus, it is important to recognize that close relationships can be a source of strain as well as support.*

(Brooks & Dunkel Schetter, 2011; Newsom, Mahan, Rook, & Krause, 2008; Rook, 1984; Rook, Mavandadi, Sorkin, & Zettel, 2007). The presence of poor-quality support can have a negative impact on thriving, and the mere existence of a relationship (e.g., a marriage) is not enough to confer thriving benefits. Poor quality source of (SOS) support (or lack thereof) can exacerbate stress, prolong recovery, reduce resilience and hinder growth from adversity. Likewise, poor-quality relational catalyst (RC) support can thwart goal striving, reduce intrinsic motivation, and hinder the development of new talents and capacities. Thus, individuals may fail to thrive either because they are socially isolated and lack access to a reliable relational support system or because they are embedded in central relationships (e.g., a marriage or parent–child relationship) that offer poor-quality support.

REFERENCES
Chapter 24 – "Support"

Alcoholics Anonymous. (1952). *Twelve steps and twelve traditions.* New York: Alcoholics Anonymous World Services.

Benson, P. L., & Scales, P. C. (2009). The definition and preliminary measurement of thriving in adolescence. *The Journal of Positive Psychology, 4*, 85-104.

Berkman, L. F. (1995). The role of social relations in health promotion. *Psychosomatic Medicine 57*, 245–254.

Bill, W. (1988). *The language of the heart.* New York: Cornwall Press.

Bosch, K. (n.d.). *When times are tough–How can family and friends support me?* University of Nebraska Panhandle Research & Extension Center. Retrieved from http://lancaster.unl.edu/family/trouble5.shtml

Bowlby, J. (1973). *Attachment and loss: Separation, anxiety and anger.* New York: Basic Books.

Bowlby, J. (1982). *Attachment and loss: Vol. 1. Attachment.* New York: Basic Books.

Bowlby, J. (1988). *A secure base.* New York: Basic Books.

Brooks, K., & Dunkel Schetter, C. (2011). Social negativity and health. *Social & Personality Psychology Compass, 5*, 904–918.

Bundick, M. J., Yeager, D. S., King, P. E., & Damon, W. (2010). Thriving across the life span. In W. F. Overton & R. M. Lerner (Eds.), *The handbook of life-span development* (Vol. 1, pp. 882-923). Hoboken, NJ: John Wiley.

Cassel, J. (1976). The contribution of the social environment to host resistance. *American Journal of Epidemiology, 104*, 107–123.

Coates, D., & Winston, T. (1983). Counteracting the deviance of depression: Peer support groups for victims. *Journal of Social Issues, 39*, 169–194.

Cobb, A. (1976). Social support as a moderator of life stress. *Psychosomatic Medicine, 38*, 300–314.

Cohen, S. (1988). Psychosocial models of the role of social support in the etiology of physical disease. *Health Psychology, 7*, 265–297.

Cohen, S. (2004). Social relationships and health. *American Psychologist, 59*(Special Issue), 676–684.

Cohen, S., & Janicki-Deverts, D. (2009). Can we improve our physical health by altering our social networks? *Perspectives on Psychological Science, 4*(Special Issue), 375–378.

Cohen, S., & McKay, G. (1984). Social support, stress and the buffering hypothesis: A theoretical analysis. In A. Baum, S. E. Taylor, & J. E. Singer (Eds.), *Handbook of psychology and health* (pp. 253–267). Hillsdale, NJ: Lawrence Erlbaum.

Cohen, S., & Syme, S. L. (1985). *Social support and health.* San Diego, CA: Academic Press.

Cohen, S., & Wills, T. A. (1985). Stress, social support, and the buffering hypothesis. *Psychological Bulletin, 98*, 310–357.

Cohen, S., Gottlieb, B. H., & Underwood, L. G. (2000). Social relationships and health. In S. Cohen, L. G. Underwood, & B. H. Gottlieb (Eds.), *Social support measurement and intervention: A guide for health and social scientists* (pp. 3–25). New York: Oxford University Press.

Collins, N. L., Dunkel-Schetter, C., Lobel, M., & Scrimshaw, S. C. M. (1993). Social support in pregnancy: Psychosocial correlates of birth outcomes and postpartum depression. *Journal of Personality and Social Psychology, 65*, 1243–1258

Dakof, G. A., & Taylor. S. E. (1990). Victim's perceptions of social support: What is helpful from whom?" *Journal of Personality and Social Psychology, 58*, 80–89.

Deci, E. L., & Ryan, R. M. (2000). The "what" and "why" of goal pursuits: Human needs and the self-determination of behavior. *Psychological Inquiry, 11*, 227–268.

Chapter 24 – Support

Diener, E., Lucas, R., & Scollon, C. N. (2006). Beyond the hedonic treadmill: Revising the adaptation theory of well-being. *American Psychologist, 61*, 305–314.

Diener, E., Wirtz, D., Tov, W., Kim-Prieto, C., Choi, D., Oishi, S., & Biswas-Diener, R. (2010). New well-being measures: Short scales to assess flourishing and positive and negative feelings. *Social Indicators Research, 97*, 143–156.

Dunkel-Schetter, C. (1984). Social support and cancer: Findings based on patient interviews and their implications. *Journal of Social Issues, 40*, 77–98.

Ertel, K. A., & Glymour, M. M., & Berkman, L. F. (2009). Social networks and health: A life course perspective integrating observational and experimental evidence. *Journal of Social and Personal Relationships, 26*, 73–92.

Essentiallifeskills.net. (n.d.). *Build a personal support system.* Retrieved from http://www.essentiallifeskills.net/supportsystem.html

Festinger, L. (1954). A theory of social comparison processes. *Human Relations, 7*, 117–140.

Haines, V. A., Beggs, J. J., & Hurlbert, J. S. (2008). Contextualizing health outcomes: Do effects of network structure differ for women and men? *Sex Roles, 59*, 164–175.

Henderson, L. W., & Knight, T. (2012). Integrating the hedonic and eudaimonic perspectives to more comprehensively understand wellbeing and pathways to wellbeing. *International Journal of Wellbeing, 2*(3), 196-221. doi:10.5502/ijw.v2i3.3

Hoda, B., Acitelli, L., Duck, S., & Carl, W. J. (2001). Weaving social support and relationships together. In *Personal relationships: Implications for clinical and community psychology* (pp. 1–14). New York: John Wiley.

Holt-Lunstad, J., & Smith, T. B. (2012). Social relationships and mortality. *Social & Personality Psychology Compass, 6*, 41-53.

House, J. S. (1981). *Work stress and social support.* Reading, MA: Addison-Wesley.

House, J. S., & Kahn, R. L. (1985). Measures and concepts of social support In S. Cohen & S. L. Syme (Eds.), *Social support and health* (pp. 83–108). San Diego, CA: Academic Press.

House, J. S., Umberson, D., & Landis, K. R. (1988). Structures and processes of social support. *Annual Review of Sociology, 14*, 293–318.

Hughes, M., & Gove, W. R. (1981). Living alone, social isolation, and mental health. *American Journal of Sociology, 87*, 48–74.

Kawachi, I., & Berkman, L. F. (2001). Social ties and mental health. *Journal of Urban Health: Bulletin of the New York Academy of Medicine, 78*, 458–467.

Kessler, R. C., & McLeod, J. D. (1985). Social support and mental health in community samples. In S. Cohen & L. S. Syme (Eds.), *Social support and health* (pp. 219–240). San Diego, CA: Academic Press.

Kessler, R. C., Price, R. H., & Wortman, C. B. (1985). Social factors in psychopathology: Stress, social support, and coping processes. *Annual Review of Psychology, 36*, 531–572.

Keyes, C. L. M. (2003). Complete mental health: An agenda for the 21st century. In C. L. M. Keyes & J. Haidt (Eds.), *Flourishing: Positive psychology and the life well-lived* (pp. 293–312). Washington, DC: American Psychological Association.

Keyes, C. L. M. (2005). Mental illness and/or mental health? Investigating axioms of the complete state model of health. *Journal of Consulting and Clinical Psychology, 73*, 539–548.

Keyes, C. L. M. (2007). Promoting and protecting mental health as flourishing: A complementary strategy for improving national mental health. *American Psychologist, 62*, 95–108.

Lakey, B., & Cronin, A. (2008). Low social support and major depression: Research, theory and methodological issues. In K. S. Dobson & D. J. A. Dozois (Eds.), *Risk factors in depression* (pp. 385–408). San Diego, CA: Elsevier/Academic Press.

Lerner, R. M., von Eye, A., Lerner, J. V., Lewin-Bizan, S., & Bowers, E. P. (2010). Special issue introduction: The meaning and measurement of thriving: A view of the issues. *Journal of Youth and Adolescence, 39*, 707–719.

Luks, A. (1988, October). Helper's high: Volunteering makes people feel good, physically and emotionally. *Psychology Today, 22*(10), 34–42.

Chapter 24 – Support

Lyubomirsky, S., Sheldon, K. M., & Schkade, D. (2005). Pursuing happiness: The architecture of sustainable change. *Review of General Psychology, 9*, 111–131.

Martin, R., Davis, G. M., Baron, R. S., Suls, J., & Blanchard, E. B. (1994). Specificity in social support: Perceptions of helpful and unhelpful provider behaviors among irritable bowel syndrome, headache, and cancer patients. *Health Psychology, 13*, 432–439.

Mead, S., Hilton, D., & Curtis, L. (2001). Peer support: A theoretical perspective. *Psychiatric Rehabilitation Journal, 25*(2), 134–141.

Messeri, P., Silverstein, M., & Litwak, E. (1993). Choosing optimal support groups: A review and reformulation. *Journal of Health and Social Behavior, 34*, 122–137.

Mikulincer, M., & Shaver, P. R. (2007). *Attachment in adulthood: Structure, dynamics, and change.* New York: Guilford Press.

Miller, G. E., Lachman, M. E., Chen, E., Gruenewald, T. L., Karlamangla, A. S., & Seeman, T. E. (2011). Pathways to resilience: Maternal nurturance as a buffer against the effects of childhood poverty on metabolic syndrome at midlife. *Psychological Science, 22*, 1591–1599.

Newsom, J. T., Mahan, T. L., Rook, K. S., & Krause, N. (2008). Stable negative social exchanges and health. *Health Psychology, 27*, 78–86.

Pagano, M. E., Friend, K. B., Tonigan, J. S., & Stout, R. L. (2004). Helping other alcoholics in Alcoholics Anonymous and drinking outcomes: Findings from Project MATCH. *Journal of Studies on Alcohol, 65*, 766–773.

Peters-Golden, H. (1982). Breast cancer: Varied perceptions of social support in the illness experience. *Social Science & Medicine, 16*, 483–491.

Post, S. (2008). Updating the helper therapy principle. *The joy of giving.* [Web log]. Retrieved from http://www.psychologytoday.com/blog/the-joy-giving/200809/updating-the-helper-therapy-principle

Riessman, F. (1965). The helper-therapy principle. *Social Work, 10*(2), 27–32.

Rodin, J., & Langer, E. (1976). The effect of choice and enhanced personal responsibility for the aged: A field experiment in an institutional setting. *Journal of Personality and Social Psychology, 34*(2), 191–198.

Rogeness, G. A., & Badner, R. A. (1973). Teenage helper: A role in community mental health. *American Journal of Psychiatry, 130*, 933–936.

Rook, K. S. (1984). The negative side of social interaction: Impact on psychological well-being. *Journal of Personality and Social Psychology, 45*, 1097–1108.

Rook, K. S., Mavandadi, S., Sorkin, D. H., & Zettel, L. A. (2007). Optimizing social relationships as a resource for health and well-being in later life. In C. M. Aldwin & C. L. Park (Eds.), *Handbook of health psychology and aging* (pp. 267–285). New York: Guilford Press.

Ryff, C. D., & Singer, B. H. (1998). The contours of positive human health. *Psychological Inquiry, 9*, 1–28.

Ryff, C. D., & Singer, B. H. (2000). Interpersonal flourishing: A positive health agenda for the new millennium. *Personality and Social Psychology Review, 4*, 30–44.

Ryff, C. D., & Singer, B. H. (2008). Know thyself and become what you are: A eudaimonic approach to psychological well-being. *Journal of Happiness Studies, 9*, 13–39.

Salzer, M., & Shear, S. L. (2002). Identifying consumer-provider benefits in evaluations of consumer-delivered services. *Psychiatric Rehabilitation Journal, 25*, 281–288.

Sarason, B. R., Sarason, I. G., & Gurung, R. A. R. (1997). Close personal relationships and health outcomes: A key to the role of social support. In S. Duck (Ed.), *Handbook of personal relationships* (pp. 547–573). New York: Plenum Press.

Sarason, I., Levine, H., Basham, R., & Sarason, B. (1983). Assessing social support: The social support questionnaire. *Journal of Personality and Social Psychology, 44*, 127–139.

Schnittker, J. (2007). Look (closely) at all the lonely people: Age and the social psychology of social support. *Journal of Aging and Health, 19*, 659–682.

Seeman, T. E. (1996). Social ties and health: The benefits of social integration. *Annals of Epidemiology, 6*, 442–451.

Seeman, T. E. (2000). Health promoting effects of friends and family on health outcomes in older adults. *American Journal of Health Promotions, 14*, 362–370.

Chapter 24 – Support

Seligman, M. E. P. (2002). *Authentic happiness: Using the new positive psychology to realize your potential for lasting fulfillment*. New York: Free Press.

Seligman, M. E. P. (2008). Positive health. *Applied Psychology, 57*(s1), 3–18.

Seligman, M. E. P., Steen, T. A., Park, N., & Peterson, C. (2005). Positive psychology progress: Empirical validation of interventions. *American Psychologist, 60,* 410–421.

Shubert, M., & Borkman, T. (1994). Identifying the experiential knowledge developed within a self-help group. In T. Powell (Ed.), *Understanding the self-help organization*. Thousand Oaks, CA: Sage.

Skovholt, T. M. (1974). The client as helper: A means to promote psychological growth. *Counseling Psychologist, 43,* 58–64.

Sober, E. & Wilson, D. S. (1998). *Unto others: The evolution of unselfish behavior*. Cambridge, MA: Harvard University Press.

Solomon, P. (2004). Peer support/peer provided services underlying processes, benefits, and critical ingredients. *Psychiatric Rehabilitation Journal, 27,* 392–401.

Stroebe, W., & Stroebe, M. (1996). The social psychology of social support. In E. T. Higgins & A. W. Kruglanski (Eds.), *Social psychology: Handbook of basic principles* (pp. 597–621). New York: Guilford.

Taylor, S. E., & Stanton, A. L. (2007). Coping resources, coping processes, and mental health. *Annual Review of Clinical Psychology, 3,* 377–401.

Theokas, C., Almerigi, J. B., Lerner, R. M., Dowling, E. M., Benson, P. L., Scales, P. C., & von Eye, A. (2005). Conceptualizing and modeling individual and ecological asset components of thriving in early adolescence. *Journal of Early Adolescence, 25,* 113–143.

Thoits, P. A. (1995). Stress, coping and social support processes: Where are we? What next?" *Journal of Health and Social Behavior (Extra Issue),* 53–79.

Thoits, P. A. (2011). Mechanisms linking social ties and support to physical and mental health. *Journal of Health and Social Behavior, 52,* 145.

Thoits, P. A. (2011). Perceived social support and voluntary, mixed, or pressured use of mental health services. *Society and Mental Health 1,* 4–19.

Turner, R. J., & Marino, F. (1994). Social support and social structure: A descriptive epidemiology. *Journal of Health and Social Behavior, 35,* 193–212.

Turner, R. J., & Turner, J. B. (1999). Social integration and support. In C. S. Aneshensel & J. C. Phelan (Eds.), *Handbook of the sociology of mental health* (pp. 301–319). New York: Kluwer Academic/Plenum.

Uchino, B. N. (2004). *Social support and physical health: Understanding the health consequences of relationships*. New Haven, CT: Yale University Press.

Uchino, B. N. (2009). Understanding the links between social support and physical health: A lifespan perspective with emphasis on the separability of perceived and received support. *Perspectives on Psychological Science, 4,* 236–255.

Uchino, B. N., Bowen, K., Carlisle, M., & Birmingham, W. (2012). Psychological pathways linking social support to health outcomes: A visit with "ghosts" of research past, present, and future. *Social Science & Medicine, 74, 949–957.*

Uchino, B. N., Cacioppo, J. T., & Kiecolt-Glaser, J. K. (1996). The relationship between social support and physiological processes: A review with emphasis on underlying mechanisms and implications for health. *Psychological Bulletin, 119,* 488–531.

Umberson, D., & Montez, J. K. (2010). Social relationships and health: A flashpoint for health policy. *Journal of Health and Social Behavior, 51*(Special Issue), S54–66.

Vaux, A. (1988). *Social support*. New York: Praeger.

Wink, P., & Dillon, M. (2007). Do generative adolescents become healthy older adults? In S. G. Post (Ed.), *Altruism and health: Perspectives from empirical research* (pp. 43–54). Oxford, United Kingdom: Oxford University Press.

Chapter 25
Empowerment

Self Help Development

> *Providing someone with the tools to be or become self-sufficient.*

A person who is empowered can act independently. As the old saying goes (in the author's words), give me a fish and I can eat today, teach me to fish and I can eat forever. To empower a person is to help them control their own lives. The World Bank (n.d.) defines empowerment as the process of increasing the capacity of individuals or groups to make choices and to transform those choices into desired actions and outcomes. They say central to this process are actions that both build individual and collective assets, and improve the efficiency and fairness of the organizational and institutional context which govern use of these assets.

The Blanchard, Carlos, and Randolph (1996/2001) book *Empowerment Takes More Than a Minute* says the process of empowerment enables individuals/groups to fully access personal/collective power, authority and influence, and to employ that strength when engaging with other people, institutions or society. In other words, Empowerment is not giving people power, people already have plenty of power, in the wealth of their knowledge and motivation, to do their jobs magnificently. We define empowerment as letting this power out. It encourages people to gain the skills and knowledge that will allow them to overcome obstacles in life or work environment and ultimately, help them develop within themselves or in the society.

They go on to say that empowerment includes the following, or similar, capabilities:
- The ability to make decisions about personal/collective circumstances
- The ability to access information and resources for decision-making

- Ability to consider a range of options from which to choose (not just yes/no, either/or)

- Ability to exercise assertiveness in collective decision making

- Having positive thinking about the ability to make change

- Ability to learn and access skills for improving personal/collective circumstance

- Ability to inform others' perceptions through exchange, education and engagement

- Involving in the growth process and changes that is never ending and self-initiated

- Increasing one's positive self-image and overcoming stigma

- Increasing one's ability in discreet thinking to sort out right and wrong

- Coping skills can be developed

> *Invest in the success of others because when you help someone up a mountain, you'll find yourself close to the summit too. (Taken from "You're Born an Original, Don't Die a Copy" by John L. Mason, 1993)*

Personal Empowerment

Skillsyouneed.com (n.d.) provided a comprehensive look at personal empowerment by giving a definition, providing dimensions and language of personal empowerment. The following points were retrieved from:
http://www.skillsyouneed.com/ps/personal-empowerment.html

- Personal empowerment is about looking at who you are and becoming more aware of yourself as a unique individual.

- Personal empowerment involves developing the confidence and strength to set realistic goals and fulfill your potential. Everyone has strengths and weaknesses and a range of skills that are used in everyday situations, but all too often, people remain unaware of, or undervalue, their true abilities.

- A person aiming for empowerment is able to take control of their life by making positive choices and setting goals. Developing self-awareness, an understanding of your strengths and weaknesses—knowing your own limitations—is key to personal empowerment.

- Taking steps to set and achieve goals—both short and longer-term and developing new skills—acts to increase confidence, which, in itself, is essential to self-empowerment.

What is Personal Empowerment?

At a basic level, the term *empowerment* simply means *becoming powerful*. Building personal empowerment involves reflecting on our personal values, skills and goals and being prepared to adjust our behavior in order to achieve our goals. Personal empowerment also means being aware that other people have their own set of values and goals, which may be different from ours.

Many other, more detailed, definitions exist. These usually center on the idea that personal empowerment gives an individual the ability to:

- Take control of their circumstances and achieve their own goals in their personal and working life.
- Become more aware of their strengths and weaknesses and, therefore, be better equipped to deal with problems and achieve goals.
- Enhance the contribution they make both as an individual and as a member of a team.
- Take opportunities to enhance personal growth and a sense of fulfillment.

Developing personal empowerment usually involves making some fundamental changes in life, which is not always an easy process. The degree of change required will differ from person to person, depending on the individual starting point.

Dimensions of Personal Empowerment

The following dimensions of personal empowerment are based on the belief that the greater the range of coping responses an individual develops, the greater their chance of coping effectively with diverse life situations. These dimensions are:

Self-Awareness

> *Self-awareness involves understanding our individual character and how we are likely to respond to situations.*

This enables us to build on our positive qualities and be aware of any negative traits that may reduce our effectiveness. Self-aware people make conscious decisions to enhance their lives whenever possible, learning from past experiences.

Values

Values are opinions or beliefs that are important to us but of which we are not always aware. They can be any kind of belief or perceived obligation, anything we prefer and for any reason. The reasons we may prefer one thing over another, or choose one course of action over another, may not always be obvious or known; there may be no apparent reason for our values. Nevertheless, our values are important to us as individuals. To be self-aware it is necessary to be aware of our values, to critically examine them and to accept that our values may be different from those of others.

Chapter 25 – Empowerment

Skills

An individual's skills are the main resource which enables them to achieve their desired goals. Skills can be gained through experience, practice, education and training. It is only by developing such skills that individual values can be translated into action.

Information

Knowledge or information is necessary in the development of self-awareness and skills. It is an essential skill in itself to know where to find appropriate information. Without information, the choices open to people are limited, both in their personal and working lives. The Internet has provided an easy way for everybody to access huge amounts of information very quickly and easily. The problem is then centered around the quality of the information found, and the skillset is concerned with finding accurate and reliable information.

Goals

Setting goals is a means by which an individual can take charge of his/her life. The process of setting a goal involves people thinking about their values and the direction they would like their lives to follow. Choices are made through reflection followed by action. Goals should always be both specific and realistic. Setting personal goals gives us a sense of direction in life, this direction is essential to personal empowerment.

Language and Empowerment

Language is the main medium of human communication whether used in spoken or written form. The use of language, how individuals express themselves verbally and non-verbally to others, can be empowering to both themselves and the people with whom they are communicating. Looking at how language is used is important in terms of self-empowerment and when attempting to empower other people.

The use of language for personal empowerment

In terms of personal empowerment and communication, the following ideas are helpful and their use can be both self-affirming and positive:

- **Use Positive Language:** Research into language suggests that a person's self-image is reflected in the words they use. For example, people who say they *should* behave in a certain way implies passivity and can detract from them seeming to be in control and taking responsibility for their actions. Talking about yourself in a positive way, acknowledging strengths and weaknesses, can be empowering.

- **Use Active Language:** Use terms which imply positive action rather than making vague statements, particularly when talking about the future. For example, "I will..." and "I can...."

- **Use Words to Define Your Own Space and Identity:**

> *If you fail to use words to define your own space and identity then others will tend to define you and set standards by which you evaluate yourself.*

Furthermore, they will try to persuade you to conform to their demands. Be clear about who you are and what your values and goals are – do not let others define you.

The use of language for empowering others

To use language to help empower others:

- **Do not use jargon or complex terminology:** The use of jargon and complex terminology can be both alienating and dis-empowering. When working with clients the use of jargon can create feelings of intimidation and inferiority. Without shared understanding of the words you use, effective and empowering communication cannot take place. Choose words with care, which give clarity to what you are trying to express.

- **Focus on the words people use:** Mirror words people use. Using shared terminology appropriately can enable you to appear more "in tune" with the other person and what they are saying.

- **Choose positive words:** Choosing positive or active words such as *will* or *can* indicates that you have control in your life and is more likely to induce positive action in others. Compare the use of these words with others such as *might* or *maybe*, which suggest hesitancy. Using words and statements that carry responsibility are empowering as they suggest a determined rather than a passive approach.

- **Avoid criticism and negativity:** Criticism should always be given with extreme care and only when absolutely necessary.

> - *Once words have been spoken they cannot be easily taken back.*

If criticism is necessary then it can be given in a constructive way, through the use of positive and supporting words and phrases. Always attempt to cushion criticism with positive observations.

- **Use open questions when appropriate:** The use of closed questions will restrict responses to "yes" and "no" answers. This type of question can leave people feeling powerless because there is no opportunity to explain their response. On the other hand, open questions give the person being asked the chance to explore the reasons behind their answers. Open questions encourage a person to take responsibility for their thoughts and actions and can therefore aid empowerment. Open questions can also help people solve problems through their own devices and help them to set their own goals and work out an appropriate plan of action.

The same website, skillsyouneed.com, also expounds on developing self-empowerment through developing trust, understanding strengths, weakness and limits and developing confidence and self-esteem. http://www.skillsyouneed.com/ps/personal-empowerment.html

Developing Self-Empowerment

We all have opportunities to explore and develop new skills. To become more empowered, we should, in our interactions with others, aim to:

- Develop trust.
- Understand our strengths, weaknesses and limits.
- Develop confidence and self-esteem.

Developing Trust

Developing trust can be a difficult and lengthy process. To develop trust with others, one should aim to:
- **Be Open:** In the sharing of information, ideas and thoughts. When appropriate, also share emotions, feelings and reactions. Also aim to reciprocate appropriately, when somebody shares their emotions, thoughts or feelings with you.
- **Share and Cooperate:** Share resources and knowledge with others to help them achieve their goals. Work together toward mutual goals.
- **Be Trustworthy:** When other people place their trust in you, do your best to provide positive outcomes.
- **Be Accepting:** Hold the values and views of others in high regard.
- **Be Supportive:** Support others when necessary but also recognize their strengths, allowing them to work toward goals without your intervention, as appropriate.

In the workplace and in any professional working relationship, there are three basic components of trust:

> - *Trust in the integrity and goodwill between all workers, regardless of salary or status and whether paid or unpaid.*

- Trust that all workers within an organization share the same objectives and are open with each other about any conflicting objectives.
- Trust in each other's competence and do what you promise to undertake.

Trust can be broken very quickly and may never be restored to its former level; think about the points above and try to build and maintain trusting relationships in both your personal and professional life.

Chapter 25 – Empowerment

Avoid the following actions that may destroy trust and have a detrimental effect on personal empowerment:

Making a joke at another's expense.

Being judgmental about another's behavior, attitudes or beliefs.

Communicating rejection or non-acceptance, either verbally or non-verbally.

Understanding Your Strengths, Weaknesses and Limits

Becoming empowered includes knowing your own strengths and weaknesses, and identifying these will enable you to work on improving your weaknesses and build on your strengths.

It is not uncommon for other people to have misjudged your strengths and weaknesses, or for you to misjudge those of others. This can lead to opportunities being limited due to the misconception of abilities. It is important, therefore, to know your own strengths and weaknesses and to communicate them clearly to others, whilst encouraging others to communicate their strengths and weaknesses to you.

In some circumstances, you may feel that you face problems that are truly beyond your capabilities. In such cases you should seek help. Empowered people know their own limits and have no problems with asking for help or guidance. Self-knowledge, often referred to as self-awareness, is a strength that enables you to set personal improvement goals in order to make a more substantial contribution. The more empowered you become, the more you will be able to help others become empowered.

Developing Confidence

Confidence acts as one of the greatest motivators or most powerful limitations to anyone trying to change their behavior and become more empowered. Most people only undertake tasks that they feel capable of doing and it takes great effort to overcome a lack of confidence in one's capabilities. Self-empowerment involves people constantly challenging their own beliefs and what they are capable of undertaking.

> *Personal empowerment is not a static thing that you can do once in your life; you should view personal empowerment as ongoing personal development.*

As circumstances change and develop, and as we ourselves change and develop, so do our needs for development and empowerment.

All the above material with headings from "Personal Empowerment," "What is Personal Empowerment," and "Dimensions of Personal Empowerment" to "Understanding Your Strengths, Weaknesses and Limits" to "Developing Confidence" were taken from Skillsyouneed.com at http://www.skillsyouneed.com/ps/personal-empowerment.html

Chapter 25 – Empowerment

Attaining Real Personal Power

Guy Winch wrote an article called "The Squeaky Wheel" that was published in the January 11, 2011 edition of *Psychology Today* that talked about how to attain real personal empowerment. In addition to sharing how to deal with complaints, he gives six steps to increase your personal empowerment. He begins by commenting that psychologists have proposed a new model of personal empowerment that states that true empowerment cannot come from merely *feeling* empowered but must involve real-world evidence of our ability to have an impact on our relationships and social surroundings.

> *Popular culture often misrepresents the concept of personal empowerment by placing emphasis on attaining a subjective emotion in which one feels empowered. However, empowerment by its very definition requires increasing our actual influence within our social sphere, whether we do so within our intimate relationships our larger social context, as citizens or as consumers.*

A model that emphasizes having a real world impact

Lauren Cattaneo and Aliya Chapman of George Mason University proposed a model of personal empowerment that describes an interactive process, emphasizing the real-world actions we take and the impact these actions have on our social relations. Feeling empowered is great but it can only contribute to increases in actual personal empowerment if we then apply these feelings in the real world and get results.

For example, reading a self-help book might make us feel empowered to improve our relationship with our spouse, but unless we are able to initiate a productive dialogue with them and unless that dialogue leads to actual improvements in the relationship, we are no more empowered than we were when we started.

How to Increase Our Personal Empowerment

Cattaneo and Chapman define personal empowerment as "a process in which a person who lacks power sets a personally meaningful goal oriented toward increasing power, takes action toward that goal, and observes and reflects on the impact of this action, drawing on his or her evolving self-efficacy, knowledge, and competence related to the goal" (p. 647).

A crucial aspect of this new model is the dynamic feedback between our efforts and the results they yield. Successes and failures along the way can impact the process of empowerment in both positive and negative ways. Taking action is not sufficient in and of itself. Rather, doing so will only contribute to our sense of empowerment if our actions have the intended impact and we meet with success. Failures can hamper feelings of empowerment and set us back.

One of the most important takeaways from this new model is that identifying goals that promise a higher likelihood of success can be vitally important to any empowerment process.

Chapter 25 – Empowerment

In addition, being able to acquire the necessary skills to attain these goals can make a huge difference in how quickly and successfully the empowerment process proceeds. One of the easiest and most accessible ways we can apply these lessons and gain empowerment is by pursuing a meaningful complaint.

Why complaints are the perfect tools for achieving personal empowerment

We all encounter complaints on a regular basis, yet far more often than not we fail to pursue them effectively. Instead, we typically complain about them for the sole purpose of venting our frustrations. For example,

> *we feel so helpless and hopeless about resolving our consumer complaints that a staggering 95% of consumer dissatisfactions go unresolved because we fail to complain effectively about them. The same holds true for complaints in our personal lives.*

When we are frustrated or hurt by a friend or loved one, we discuss our complaint with a large number of *other* friends and loved ones and rarely with the original person.

We are convinced that bringing up our complaints with the people responsible, whether they are friends and loved ones or companies and businesses, will be more trouble than it's worth, will not lead to a satisfying resolution and might actually make the situation worse. However,

> *by pursuing a complaint successfully, we can demonstrate our influence in our relationships and/or our social context and feel more capable, competent and empowered.*

The 6 Steps to Personal Empowerment

Cattaneo and Chapman lay out 6 steps in the process of attaining personal empowerment. Let's illustrate these steps by applying them to the pursuit of a consumer complaint.

1. Identify a power-oriented goal: The idea is to increase our level of influence at any level of social interaction, either with another person, a group or a system. When pursuing a consumer complaint, we in essence are doing battle with a business, a company or a corporation. Winning the battle by attaining the result we want is a significant demonstration of our social influence. When we address a complaint to a friend or loved one and resolve it successfully, we are having an impact on a relationship that is both meaningful and highly significant to our lives.

2. Knowledge: To attain our goal, we need an understanding of the system involved, the power dynamics we might encounter, the resources we will require and a plan of action. The book *The Squeaky Wheel* has all the information one needs to pursue complaints effectively both with loved ones and as consumers. It lays out clear guidelines for complaining effectively to spouses, friends, and teenagers. It specifies what to know when calling customer service hotlines, how to manage our emotions in such situations and how to construct effective complaints that will elicit best efforts from the service representative. It also discusses how to escalate complaints to company executives.

3. Self-efficacy: To take action we must first believe we can accomplish our goal. Acquiring the knowledge and skill set necessary to pursue our complaints and having a variety of effective complaining tools at our disposal can make all the difference in the world to our confidence and feelings of self-efficacy.

4. Competence: The better our skills, the greater our competence. Putting our newly acquired complaining skillset into action will quickly give us information about where we are strongest and which skills or competencies need work. Pursuing complaints with loved ones requires delicacy and the right techniques, both of which can be improved through practice. Complaining to companies and business can take persistence and here too, the more efforts we make, the more we learn, the higher our level of competence becomes.

5. Action:

> *The process of empowerment is a dynamic one where we act, reflect, assess, and act. again.*

When complaining to a loved one, we should try out our skillset by addressing small and less meaningful complaints first (for example, a complaint about an incomplete house chore or a specific episode of lateness). We might have an exchange with a customer service representative that does not resolve our problem but gives us important information we can use when speaking to a supervisor later on or when escalating a complaint to company executives.

6. Impact: Personal empowerment can be hard earned and in a sense, it should be if we wish to change how we feel deep within. Not all our efforts will yield results right away. The process of empowerment is just that, a process and not an overnight metamorphosis. The more meaningful our social influence, the more empowered we will feel.

The process of empowerment is not a linear drive toward stronger internal feelings of efficacy, but rather a dynamic process in which we acquire knowledge, take action, assess our impact and refine our efforts. It is best to build slowly by pursuing simpler complaints before tackling more meaningful dissatisfactions.

> *Each small complaint we resolve along the way will create another building block upon which we can build a stable and lasting sense of personal empowerment, self-esteem and self efficiacy.*

Chapter 25 – Empowerment

http://www.psychologytoday.com/blog/the-squeaky-wheel/201101/how-attain-real-personal-empowerment

Strategies for Personal Empowerment in Difficult Situations

In an article from the website of lifehack.org by Debbie Bowie titled "5 Strategies for Personal Empowerment in Difficult Situations" (June 24, 2010), she gives several noteworthy suggestions on things, focusing on what you can do.

When you find yourself in situations in which you are exposed to negative energies over which you have no control, remember that you can control your own sources of positive energy if you so choose. Here are some ideas.

- Avoid reacting to others and taking their behaviors personally. Pia Mellody, author of *Facing Codependence*, once said that people's reactions have more to do with them and their history than they do with you, unless you've been offensive. So, observe others and wonder about their behaviors, but know that what you're getting from them could have absolutely nothing to do with you.

- Stay in your own power by remaining calm even when others are not. "Shut your mouth and breathe" is another of my favorite reminders from Pia Mellody. Doing that will help you stay grounded and avoid saying or doing anything you might regret later.

- Ask for what you need from people who are capable of giving it to you. If you don't ask, the answer is always no. Only you know what you need. And, it is empowering to respectfully make your needs known.

> - *Don't make requests of people who are incapable of responding appropriately to your requests. That's a setup for disappointment and will only fuel your anger. (Supervisors can make decisions that line-staff cannot.)*

Bonus: How to Stop Obsessing over Your Body Image and Beat Negative Thoughts:
Look for the good that does exist. Feel grateful for it. When you deliberately look for good, you will find it. When you focus on negatives, you'll find it. Wouldn't you rather have a steady diet of good energies? They will help you more effectively cope with the challenges.

Information from Debbie Bowie's article was retrieved from:
http://www.lifehack.org/articles/lifehack/5-strategies-for-personal-empowerment-in-difficult-situations.html

Empowerment and Disempowerment as Social Processes

In Elisheva Sadan's book *Empowerment and Community Planning* (1997), she talks about empowerment and disempowerment as social processes. Empowerment is a process of transition from a state of powerlessness to a state of relative control over one's life, destiny, and environment. This transition can manifest itself in an improvement in the perceived ability to control, as well as in an improvement in the actual ability to control.

> ***Disempowering social processes are responsible for creating a sense of powerlessness among people who belong to groups that suffer from stigma and discrimination.***

A sense of powerlessness leads to a lack of self-worth, self-blame, indifference toward and alienation from the environment, besides leading to the inability of acting for oneself and growing dependence on social services and specialists for the solution of problems in one's life.

Empowerment is a transition from this passive situation to a more active one of control. The need for it is part of the realization of one's very humanity, so much so that one could say that a person who is powerless with regard to his life and his environment is not realizing his innate human potential. Since the sources of powerlessness are rooted in social processes that disempower entire populations, the empowerment process aims to influence the oppressed human agency and the social structure within the limitations and possibilities in which this human agency exists and reacts.

The empowerment process in most cases begins from a sense of frustration: people's sense that there exists an unbridgeable gap between their aspirations and their possibilities of realizing them. People discover that the realization of their aspirations depends on abilities and resources that are beyond their reach (Kieffer, 1984).

For the empowerment process to be able to develop, this sense needs to be accompanied by a minimal level of ability and resources to enable organized activity, as well a minimum of social legitimation to permit such activity.

> ***Empowerment begins, then, with people's will to obtain resources and means to develop ability in order to achieve something in their lives. The mobilization of resolve and will is a first outcome in the process.***

Elisheva Sadan's book *Empowerment and Community Planning* (1997) was also translated from Hebrew by Richard Flantz in 2004.

5 Self-Empowerment Tips for Success

There are other articles with suggested strategies on how to become more empowered. Many of them share common concepts even though they use different words. Hopefully one of these strategies will work for you. This article was retrieved from:
http://operationmeditation.com/discover/5-self-empowerment-tips-for-success/

Chapter 25 – Empowerment

The article starts out with a few questions: Are you ready to take your life to the next level? Do you want to reach new heights in areas of your life that seem to be, well, lacking?

Here's the good news. You have everything you need to be successful. It's already in you. All you have to do is know how to harness and use it. Once you do, you'll be unstoppable! Ready? Good. Here's five tips to help you unleash the power of your inner self:

Take responsibility for yourself and your actions

If you want to do great things, then you need to take full responsibility for everything you do, and don't do, that gets you there. No more blaming others for putting hurdles in your way. No more creating excuses for why you've not met your goals before. If you truly want to succeed, you have to realize that you are 100% responsible for your success, and your failure.

Challenge your negative inner thoughts

When you start to feel like you can't achieve what you've set out to do, you have to challenge those thoughts. For instance, if you want to lose weight but keep telling yourself that you can't, you need to ask yourself whether that's true. Can you, in fact, lose weight? Yes, because you've done it before? Then you know that your thoughts are just thoughts and you don't have to listen to them because they're not correct. Let them go. Replace your can'ts with cans and won'ts with wills. You'll start to feel your inner strength immediately!

Set and enforce boundaries

Being successful means that you have to protect and value your time. If you don't, then don't expect anyone else to. When someone asks you to do something that you really don't want to do, ask yourself if it will get you closer to your goals. If not, then say no. Don't feel guilty about it either. You aren't responsible for making someone else's goals, dreams or ideas a reality. Just as they aren't responsible for yours. Besides, don't you respect someone a little bit more when they aren't a pushover?

Meditate

To achieve high levels of success, you have to know yourself inside and out. You have to be prepared to take on life when it throws things at you and tries to derail you from your path. Meditating allows both of these to happen. In the lightest state of meditation, you're more capable of learning and have an effortless creativity. A deeper state of meditation heightens your problem-solving skills and increases your inspiration and motivation. The deepest state that you can achieve helps your body rejuvenate and strengthens your immune system. Achieve all of these levels and you're on your way to success in any endeavor!

Find a mentor

If you want to succeed in something, find someone who has achieved before you and learn from them. Find out what worked and what didn't. Study their processes and patterns. Why reinvent the wheel and try everything on your own?

Chapter 25 – Empowerment

If you don't know someone personally who has achieved what you desire to achieve, find someone famous. Watch television programs that feature them. If they've published any books, read them and take in the valuable information. Research them on the internet. One word of caution with this one; make sure the information is from a reputable source before you put too much credibility in it.

Success is within your grasp

By taking responsibility for yourself, challenging your inner critic, being comfortable with boundaries, meditating and following the path of those who have succeeded before you, you can't lose. Now get out there and be successful! (Operationmediation.com, n.d.)

<u>REFERENCES</u>
Chapter 25 – "Empowerment"

Blanchard, K. H., Carlos, J. P., & Randolph, A. (1996/2001). *Empowerment takes more than a minute*. San Francisco: Berrett-Koehler.

Bowie, D. (2010). *5 strategies for personal empowerment in difficult situations*. Retrieved from http://www.lifehack.org/articles/lifehack/5-strategies-for-personal-empowerment-in-difficult-situations.html

Cattaneo, L. B., & Chapman, A. R. (2010). The process of empowerment: A model for use in research and practice. *American Psychologist, 65*, 646–659.

Kieffer, C. H. (1984). Citizen empowerment: A developmental perspective. *Prevention in Human Services, 1*, 9–36.

Mason, J. L. (1993). *You're born an original, don't die a copy*. Tulsa, OK: Insight International.

Mellody, P. (1989). *Facing codependence: What it is. Where it comes from. How it sabotages our lives*. San Francisco: Harper-Collins.

Operationmeditation.com. (n.d.). *5 Self-empowerment tips for success*. Retrieved from http://operationmeditation.com/discover/5-self-empowerment-tips-for-success/

Sadan, E. (1997). *Empowerment and community planning: Theory and practice of people-focused social solutions*. Tel Aviv: Hakibbutz Hameuchad Publishers [in Hebrew]. The book was translated from Hebrew by Richard Flantz in 2004.

Skillsyouneed.com. (n.d.). *Personal empowerment*. Retrieved from http://www.skillsyouneed.com/ps/personal-empowerment.html

Winch, G. (2011). *The squeaky wheel: Complaining the right way to get results, improve your relationships and enhance self-esteem*. Retrieved from http://www.psychologytoday.com/blog/the-squeaky-wheel/201101/how-attain-real-personal-empowerment

The World Bank. (n.d.). *Empowerment*. Retrieved from http://go.worldbank.org/S9B3DNEZ00

About the Author

Dr. Joseph Dear is a counselor educator who hopes to demystify or simplify the work of counselors for the general public as well as for counselors in training. He shares some of the "secrets" of counseling along with his forty years of professional experience so the reader can have a resource for how to live a healthy, balanced life and lifestyle based on the latest research and best practices on the subject.

Following are comments on how the author works in the ten primary areas of his own life.

Physically, he works hard at eating a nutritious diet daily and exercises at the gym at least three times a week. He is well known for his love of food. Fortunately, he has acquired a great taste for healthy food and fine dining.

Mentally, he works at staying sharp by learning new things, staying ahead of his students at the university and staying away from stress, worry and negative people. His 2-hour workout at the gym also helps with his mental stability.

Spiritually, he is a devoted Christian who lives his faith, follows the voice of the Holy Spirit and stays in prayer for direction to combat the challenges of this world.

Family life is a continuous challenge to keep family members' cares and concerns ahead of his own. If there were one area that proves to be his greatest challenge, it would be here where he has sought counseling and continues to strive to do better.

Professionally/educationally, he continues to teach in the counselor education department at the university in spite of his retiring several years ago from the California Credentialing Commission.

Following his **passion, purpose and vision** is the work he has been doing through his involvement with his profession, his church and community organizations and now, finally, through his writings.

Financially, he is comfortably solvent, living frugally and investing wisely.

Civically, he continues to be involved at all levels locally at his church and in his local community as well as nationally; he has served on numerous local, state and national boards of directors and his Christian and professional involvements keep him busy.

Socially, he has continued to be active with his men's group for decades; his professional organization has become a social and professional outlet for many activities, but mostly he socializes with his Christian brothers and sisters.

Personally, he is always finding something new to learn especially with the many new electronic gadgets that continue to capture his personal interest.